MATHEMATICAL METHODS FOR MATHEMATICIANS, PHYSICAL SCIENTISTS AND ENGINEERS

ELLIS HORWOOD SERIES IN
MATHEMATICS AND ITS APPLICATIONS

Series Editor: Professor G. M. BELL, Chelsea College, University of London

The works in this series will survey recent research, and introduce new areas and up-to-date mathematical methods. Undergraduate texts on established topics will stimulate student interest by including present-day applications, and the series can also include selected volumes of lecture notes on important topics which need quick and early publication.

In all three ways it is hoped to render a valuable service to those who learn, teach, develop and use mathematics.

MATHEMATICAL THEORY OF WAVE MOTION
G. R. BALDOCK and T. BRIDGEMAN, University of Liverpool.
MATHEMATICAL MODELS IN SOCIAL MANAGEMENT AND LIFE SCIENCES
D. N. BURGHES and A. D. WOOD, Cranfield Institute of Technology.
MODERN INTRODUCTION TO CLASSICAL MECHANICS AND CONTROL
D. N. BURGHES, Cranfield Institute of Technology and A. DOWNS, Sheffield University.
CONTROL AND OPTIMAL CONTROL
D. N. BURGHES, Cranfield Institute of Technology and A. GRAHAM, The Open University, Milton Keynes.
TEXTBOOK OF DYNAMICS
F. CHORLTON, University of Aston, Birmingham.
VECTOR AND TENSOR METHODS
F. CHORLTON, University of Aston, Birmingham.
TECHNIQUES IN OPERATIONAL RESEARCH
VOLUME 1: QUEUEING SYSTEMS
VOLUME 2: MODELS, SEARCH, RANDOMIZATION
B. CONNOLLY, Chelsea College, University of London
MATHEMATICS FOR THE BIOSCIENCES
G. EASON, C. W. COLES, G. GETTINBY, University of Strathclyde.
HANDBOOK OF HYPERGEOMETRIC INTEGRALS: Theory, Applications, Tables, Computer Programs
H. EXTON, The Polytechnic, Preston.
MULTIPLE HYPERGEOMETRIC FUNCTIONS
H. EXTON, The Polytechnic, Preston
COMPUTATIONAL GEOMETRY FOR DESIGN AND MANUFACTURE
I. D. FAUX and M. J. PRATT, Cranfield Institute of Technology.
APPLIED LINEAR ALGEBRA
R. J. GOULT, Cranfield Institute of Technology.
MATRIX THEORY AND APPLICATIONS FOR ENGINEERS AND MATHEMATICIANS
A. GRAHAM, The Open University, Milton Keynes.
APPLIED FUNCTIONAL ANALYSIS
D. H. GRIFFEL, University of Bristol.
GENERALISED FUNCTIONS: Theory, Applications
R. F. HOSKINS, Cranfield Institute of Technology.
MECHANICS OF CONTINUOUS MEDIA
S. C. HUNTER, University of Sheffield.
GAME THEORY: Mathematical Models of Conflict
A. J. JONES, Royal Holloway College, University of London.
USING COMPUTERS
B. L. MEEK and S. FAIRTHORNE, Queen Elizabeth College, University of London.
SPECTRAL THEORY OF ORDINARY DIFFERENTIAL OPERATORS
E. MULLER-PFEIFFER, Technical High School, Ergurt.
SIMULATION CONCEPTS IN MATHEMATICAL MODELLING
F. OLIVEIRA-PINTO, Chelsea College, University of London.
ENVIRONMENTAL AERODYNAMICS
R. S. SCORER, Imperial College of Science and Technology, University of London.
APPLIED STATISTICAL TECHNIQUES
K. D. C. STOODLEY, T. LEWIS and C. L. S. STAINTON, University of Bradford.
LIQUIDS AND THEIR PROPERTIES: A Molecular and Macroscopic Treatise with Applications
H. N. V. TEMPERLEY, University College of Swansea, University of Wales and D. H. TREVENA, University of Wales, Aberystwyth.
GRAPH THEORY AND APPLICATIONS
H. N. V. TEMPERLEY, University College of Swansea.

MATHEMATICAL METHODS FOR MATHEMATICIANS, PHYSICAL SCIENTISTS AND ENGINEERS

J. DUNNING-DAVIES, B.Sc., Ph.D.
Department of Applied Mathematics
University of Hull

ELLIS HORWOOD LIMITED
Publishers · Chichester

Halsted Press: a division of
JOHN WILEY & SONS
New York · Brisbane · Chichester · Toronto

First published in 1982 by

ELLIS HORWOOD LIMITED
Market Cross House, Cooper Street, Chichester, West Sussex, PO19 1EB, England

The publisher's colophon is reproduced from James Gillison's drawing of the ancient Market Cross, Chichester.

Distributors:

Australia, New Zealand, South-east Asia:
Jacaranda-Wiley Ltd., Jacaranda Press,
JOHN WILEY & SONS INC.,
G.P.O. Box 859, Brisbane, Queensland 40001, Australia

Canada:
JOHN WILEY & SONS CANADA LIMITED
22 Worcester Road, Rexdale, Ontario, Canada.

Europe, Africa:
JOHN WILEY & SONS LIMITED
Baffins Lane, Chichester, West Sussex, England.

North and South America and the rest of the world:
Halsted Press: a division of
JOHN WILEY & SONS
605 Third Avenue, New York, N.Y. 10016, U.S.A.

© 1982 J. Dunning-Davies/Ellis Horwood Limited

British Library Cataloguing in Publication Data
Dunning-Davies, J.
Mathematical methods for mathematicians, physical scientsts and engineers. —
(Ellis Horwood series in mathematics and its applications)
1. Mathematics
I. Title
510   QA8.4

Library of Congress Card No. 81-13510 AACR2

ISBN 0-85312-367-5 (Ellis Horwood Limited, Publishers — Library Edn.)
ISBN 0-85312-387-X (Ellis Horwood Limited, Publishers — Student Edn.)
ISBN 0-470-27322-4 (Halsted Press)

Printed in the USA by Eastern Graphics Inc., Old Saybrook, Conn.

Table of Contents

Chapter 9 Line, Surface and Volume Integrals

Chapter 10 Vector Analysis

Chapter 11 Fourier Series

Chapter 12 Partial Differential Equations

Author's Preface

As its title indicates, this book is a collection of mathematical methods which are of use to mathematicians, physical scientists, and engineers alike. With any text of this nature, there is bound to be some argument over the choice of material included. In the present work, the material incorporated is that included in the first two years of methods courses given to undergraduates in the above-mentioned categories at Hull University, together with the necessary pure mathematical background material. All that has been assumed is a knowledge of algebra, trigonometry, and geometry of the standard usually attained in the sixth form of a British high or secondary school.

It will be noticed that two topics—statistics and numerical methods—which are of use to many mathematicians, physical scientists, and engineers have been omitted. This is because, owing to their nature and size, these topics seem deserving of separate specialised texts—many of which are available.

For the topics that have been covered, the aim has been to give the reader a good working knowledge of some important mathematical techniques together with a brief glimpse of the rigorous framework underlying these methods. To obtain complete mastery of any mathematical technique, most people need to work through a number of examples for practice. Hence, the inclusion of exercises at the end of each chapter which will, it is hoped, help to consolidate what has been learnt from the text. This is true in particular of the chapter dealing with integration, at the end of which is a longish list of exercises. This is because the ability to integrate given functions is so important in so many fields. However, the exercises (problems) at the end of each chapter should be regarded as an integral part of the text.

On a personal note, I should like to thank all who have taught me and so contributed in many ways to this book. In particular, I wish to thank my parents who were my first teachers and have given me constant support, Mr E. G. Jones who taught me so much and Professor P. T. Landsberg who has helped and encouraged me for so many years. Finally, my thanks to Mrs L. Walker for typing the manuscript so quickly and so accurately and to Mr D. Waite for help with the diagrams.

J. DUNNING-DAVIES
University of Hull

Chapter 1
Functions of One Variable

1.1 THE CONCEPT OF A FUNCTION

In the study of any branch of mathematics, physical science, or engineering, the idea of a relation existing between the values of two variable physical quantities is met frequently. These quantities are able to take different real values normally, and usually they are called real variables or simply variables. In general, a variable y is said to be a **function** of another variable x if a rule is specified by which the value, or values, of y may be determined when the value of x is given. The same value of y may correspond to more than one value of x but, when to each value of x there corresponds one, and only one, value of y, the function is said to be single-valued. Mathematically, the fact that y is a function of x is expressed by writing, for example,

$$y = f(x)$$

where $f(x)$ is merely an abbreviation for 'function of x'.

If the two variables x and y satisfy the equation

$$x^2 + axy + y^2 = b,$$

then if x is given a specific value, the equation becomes a quadratic in y which may be solved. Therefore, in this example, y may be written as an explicit function of x. In general, if the equation linking x and y may be solved for y in terms of x, then y is said to be an **explicit** function of x. Similarly, any equation connecting x and y determines y as a function of x, but it is not possible to obtain the algebraic solution of the equation always. In such cases, y is said to be an **implicit** function of x. An example is provided by the equation.

$$\cos x + ay = b \sin y.$$

Now suppose that, in the equation $y = f(x)$, instead of being the independent variable subject to choice, x is dependent on another independent variable t and suppose x and t are related via $x = \phi(t)$. If values of t are assigned arbitrarily, the corresponding values for x are obtained from $x = \phi(t)$, when these values of x are substituted in $y = f(x)$, values of y are obtained which are dependent on the arbitrarily chosen values of t. Symbolically

$$y = f\{\phi(t)\}$$

and this denotes that y is a **function of a function** of t.

If y is given as a function of x by an equation $y = f(x)$, it is often possible to solve the equation for x in terms of y and so obtain x expressed as a function of y in the form $x = g(y)$. This function is said to be the **inverse function**. The value of the inverse function, where it exists, may be single valued or many valued.

Usually, in algebraic expressions, a real variable x may take any value in a certain range. If the lowest value of x is a and the highest value b and x may take any value between a and b, then x is said to be a continuous variable in the range $[a,b]$ and takes all values such that $a \leqslant x \leqslant b$. Since the end-points are included among the values of x which form this range, the interval is called a **closed** interval. The interval defined by the inequality $a < x < b$ is called an **open** interval and is denoted by (a,b). In this case, the end-points are not included among the admissible values of x. When speaking of the closed interval $[a,b]$, a and b are understood to be finite. If x may take indefinitely large positive values, b is replaced in the open interval (a,b) by ∞. If x may take any real value, then it is customary to write $-\infty < x < \infty$.

1.2 LIMITS OF FUNCTIONS

Suppose y is a function of the variable x. It is possible that such a function will approach a definite value, b say, when the variable x tends to some finite value, a say. The value b is said to be the **limit** of the function y as x approaches a. The definition of the existence of a limit for a function $y = f(x)$ as x approaches a finite value a is

$f(x)$ is said to have the limit b as x tends to a when, given ε, a positive number η, depending on ε, may be found such that whenever

$$|x - a| \leqslant \eta, \quad |f(x) - b| < \varepsilon.$$

If this criterion is satisfied, it is usual to write

$$\lim_{x \to a} f(x) = b$$

and $f(x)$ may be said to converge to the limit b as x tends to a.

For simple functions the limit, when it exists, is usually the same whether x approaches a from above (that is, through values of x greater than a) or from below (that is, through values of x less than a), but it is possible that the limit may be different in these two cases. If a limit exists as x approaches a from above, the limit is denoted by

$$\lim_{x \to a+0} f(x) \qquad \text{or} \qquad f(a + 0).$$

If a limit exists as x approaches a from below, the limit is denoted by

$$\lim_{x \to a-0} f(x) \quad \text{or} \quad f(a-0) .$$

The statement

$$\lim_{x \to a} f(x) = b$$

involves the equations

$$\lim_{x \to a-0} f(x) = b = \lim_{x \to a+0} f(x) .$$

The above definition of the limit of a function $f(x)$ as x approaches a finite value a is extended easily to the case of the limit of a function $f(x)$ as x increases indefinitely as follows:

The function $f(x)$ is said to approach the limit b as x tends to infinity if given ε, there exists a positive number X such that $|f(x) - b| < \varepsilon$ whenever $x \geqslant X$ If this condition is satisfied, it is usual to write

$$\lim_{x \to \infty} f(x) = b .$$

If $f(x)$ possesses a graph, this definition corresponds to the existence of an asymptote parallel to the x-axis; the asymptote is $y = b$.

1.3 PROPERTIES OF LIMITS
Suppose that as $x \to a$, $f(x) \to \alpha$ and $g(x) \to \beta$, then

$$\text{(i)} \quad f(x) + g(x) \to \alpha + \beta \tag{1.1}$$

$$\text{(ii)} \quad f(x)\, g(x) \to \alpha\beta \tag{1.2}$$

$$\text{(iii)} \quad 1/f(x) \to 1/\alpha \quad \text{provided } \alpha \neq 0 . \tag{1.3}$$

The proof of (ii) is as follows:
From the definition

$$|f(x) - \alpha| < \varepsilon \text{ for } |x - a| < \eta_1$$

$$|g(x) - \beta| < \varepsilon \text{ for } |x - a| < \eta_2$$

Let η_1 be the smaller of η_1 and η_2, then provided $|x - a| < \eta_1$

$$|f(x)\, g(x) - \alpha\beta| = |(f(x) - \alpha)(g(x) - \beta) + \alpha(g(x) - \beta) + \beta(f(x) - \alpha)|$$

$$\leqslant |f(x) - \alpha|\, |g(x) - \beta| + |\alpha|\, |g(x) - \beta| + |\beta|\, |f(x) - \alpha|$$

$$\leqslant \varepsilon^2 + \alpha\, \varepsilon + \beta\, \varepsilon .$$

If ε is chosen to be the positive root of

$$\varepsilon^2 + |\alpha|\, \varepsilon + |\beta|\, \varepsilon = \varepsilon_1$$

where ε_1, is any given small quantity, then the result may be written

$$|f(x)\,g(x) - \alpha\beta| < \varepsilon_1 \quad \text{whenever} \quad |x - a| < \eta_1 .$$

This concludes the proof.

Examples

(1) Find

$$\lim_{x \to 1} \frac{x^2 + x - 2}{2x - 2}$$

Suppose $x = 1 + h$, then as $x \to 1$, $h \to 0$ and

$$\frac{x^2 + x - 2}{2x - 2} = \frac{(1 + h)^2 + (1 + h) - 2}{2(1 + h) - 2} = \frac{h^2 + 3h}{2h} = \frac{h + 3}{2} .$$

Therefore,

$$\lim_{x \to 1} \frac{x^2 + x - 2}{2x - 2} = \lim_{h \to 0} \frac{h + 3}{2} = \frac{3}{2} .$$

(2) Find

$$\lim_{x \to \infty} \frac{x^2 + 3x + 4}{2x^2 + 5x + 6}$$

Now

$$\frac{x^2 + 3x + 4}{2x^2 + 5x + 6} = \frac{1 + 3/x + 4/x^2}{2 + 5/x + 6/x^2}$$

As $x \to \infty$, $1/x \to 0$ and $1/x^2 \to 0$ and so, as $x \to \infty$, $1 + 3/x + 4/x^2 \to 1$ and $2 + 5/x + 6/x^2 \to 2$.

Hence,

$$\lim_{x \to \infty} \frac{x^2 + 3x + 4}{2x^2 + 5x + 6} = \frac{1}{2} .$$

As a further example of a limit, consider

$$\lim_{x \to a} \frac{x^n - a^n}{x - a}$$

This limit will be evaluated when n is (i) a positive integer, (ii) a negative integer, (iii) a rational fraction.

(i) Let n be a positive integer, then

$$\frac{x^n - a^n}{x - a} = x^{n-1} + ax^{n-2} + \cdots + a^{n-1} .$$

Thus

$$\lim_{x \to a} \frac{x^n - a^n}{x - a} = na^{n-1} .$$

(ii) Let n be a negative integer, $-m$ say where m is a positive integer; then

$$\lim_{x \to a} \frac{x^n - a^n}{x - a} = \lim_{x \to a} \frac{x^{-m} - a^{-m}}{x - a}$$

$$= \lim_{x \to a} \left(- \frac{1}{x^m a^m} \right) \left(\frac{x^m - a^m}{x - a} \right)$$

$$= - \frac{1}{a^{2m}} m a^{m-1}$$

using the properties of limits and (i)
Therefore, in this case also,

$$\lim_{x \to a} \frac{x^n - a^n}{x - a} = na^{n-1} .$$

(iii) Let n be a rational fraction, p/q say, where p and q may be positive or negative integers; then put $x = y^q$ and $a = b^q$ so that

$$\lim_{x \to a} \frac{x^{p/q} - a^{p/q}}{x - a} = \lim_{y \to b} \frac{y^p - b^p}{y^q - b^q}$$

$$= \lim_{y \to b} \left\{ \left(\frac{y^p - b^p}{y - b} \right) \middle/ \left(\frac{y^q - b^q}{y - b} \right) \right\}$$

$$= \frac{pb^{p-1}}{qb^{q-1}} = \frac{p}{q} b^{p-q}$$

using the properties of limits together with (i) and (ii). But

$$\frac{p}{q} b^{p-q} = \frac{p}{q} (b^q)^{(p/q)-1} = na^{n-1}$$

and so, in this case,

$$\lim_{x \to a} \frac{x^n - a^n}{x - a} = na^{n-1} \tag{1.4}$$

1.4 CONTINUOUS FUNCTIONS

The idea of continuity is a direct consequence of the concept of a limit. For example, if the function $f(x) = \tan x$ is considered, it is found to possess two limits as $x \to \pi/2$:

$$\lim_{x \to \frac{1}{2}\pi + 0} f(x) = -\infty , \qquad \lim_{x \to \frac{1}{2}\pi - 0} f(x) = +\infty .$$

Consequently, the graph of this function is found to have a break at the point $x = \pi/2$ and so is said to be **discontinuous** at that point. A function is said to be **continuous** at a point if its graph has no break at that point.

It is important to note that continuity is essentially the property of a point, although the concept may be extended by saying that a function $f(x)$ is continuous in an interval if it is continuous at every point in that interval.

The formal definition of a continuous function is as follows:

The function $f(x)$ is said to be continuous when $x = x_0$ if $f(x)$ possesses a definite limit as x tends to x_0 from either side, and each of these limits equals $f(x_0)$:

$$\lim_{x \to x_0 - 0} f(x) = f(x_0) = \lim_{x \to x_0 + 0} f(x)$$

or alternatively

The function $f(x)$ is continuous when $x = x_0$ if given ε, a number $\eta(\varepsilon)$ may be found such that, whenever $|x - x_0| \leqslant \eta$,

$$|f(x) - f(x_0)| < \varepsilon \, .$$

The equivalence of these two definitions is obvious immediately if the second is compared with the definition of a limit given earlier.

From the properties of limits discussed earlier, it is straightforward to deduce that the sum, product, difference, or quotient of two functions which are continuous at a certain point are themselves continuous at that point, except that in the case of the quotient the denominator must not vanish at the point in question.

1.5 DERIVATIVE OF A FUNCTION

Suppose $y = f(x)$ denotes a single-valued function of x in a given interval (a,b) and let x be any point in this interval. If x is given a small positive or negative increment δx, then the corresponding increment of y, which will be denoted by δy, will be

$$\delta y = f(x + \delta x) - f(x) \, .$$

The ratio of these increments is

$$\frac{\delta y}{\delta x} = \frac{f(x + \delta x) - f(x)}{\delta x} \, . \tag{1.5}$$

If this ratio tends to a definite limit as $\delta x \to 0$, this limit is called the **derivative** of $f(x)$ at the point x and is denoted by $f'(x)$.

If δx is restricted to have positive values only, and if a definite limit exists when δx approaches zero via positive values only, this limit may be called the **right-hand** derivative of $f(x)$ at the point x. Similarly, if δx approaches zero via negative values only, the **left-hand** derivative may be defined. The function $f(x)$ possesses a unique derivative $f'(x)$ only if the right and left-hand derivatives are equal.

Three simple but important results will be proved now.

(1) Every function $f(x)$ which possesses a finite derivative for a given value of x must be a continuous function of x at this point.

Since $f(x)$ possesses a finite derivative at the point x, say a,

$$\lim_{\delta x \to 0} \frac{f(x + \delta x) - f(x)}{\delta x} = a$$

and so, $$|f(x + \delta x) - f(x)| = |\delta x|(|a| + \varepsilon)$$

where $\varepsilon \to 0$ as $\delta x \to 0$. Since a is finite

$$|f(x) + \delta x) - f(x)| \to 0 \text{ as } |\delta x| \to 0.$$

Hence $f(x)$ is continuous at the point x.

(2) If $f(x)$ is a constant, its derivative is zero, since

$$\lim_{\delta x \to 0} \frac{f(x + \delta x) - f(x)}{\delta x} = \lim \frac{0}{\delta x} = 0$$

(3) If $f(x) = x$, its derivative is unity, since

$$\lim_{\delta x \to 0} \frac{(x + \delta x) - x}{\delta x} = \lim \frac{\delta x}{\delta x} = 1$$

1.6 DIFFERENTIALS

Since in equation (1.5) $\lim_{\delta x \to 0} (\delta y / \delta x)$ has a definite limit $f'(x)$,

$$\delta y / \delta x = f'(x) + \varepsilon$$

where $\varepsilon \to 0$ as $\delta x \to 0$. Alternatively, this may be written

$$\delta y = f'(x) \delta x + \varepsilon \delta x$$

where $\varepsilon \to 0$ as $\delta x \to 0$. In this case, the first term on the right-hand side is called the **differential** of y and is denoted by dy; that is

$$dy = f'(x) \, \delta x, \tag{1.6}$$

and so the differential of y is the product of its derivative and an arbitrary increment δx of the independent variable x.

In particular, when $f(x) = x$, $f'(x) = 1$ and this equation gives

$$dx = \delta x$$

Hence, the differential of the independent variable is defined to be the same as the arbitrary increment of that variable.

Equation (1.6) now becomes

$$dy = f'(x) \, dx$$

or dividing by dx

$$dy/dx = f'(x) . \tag{1.7}$$

Thus it has been shown that the derivative of a function $y = f(x)$, of one variable x, is the ratio of the differentials of the function and the variable.

1.7 GEOMETRICAL INTERPRETATION OF A DIFFERENTIAL

Let P and Q be the points (x,y) and $(x + \delta x, y + \delta y)$ on the curve $y = f(x)$. The derivative $f'(x)$ is the slope of the tangent to the curve at P and so

$$f'(x) = \tan \angle T \, PR = RT/PR = RT/MN$$

By equation (1.7), $$dy/dx = f'(x)$$

and MN $= \delta x$, which for the independent variable is the same as dx, so that $dy =$ RT while $\delta y =$ RQ. This serves to illustrate the important point that δy and dy are not the same. This geometrical consideration suggests that the

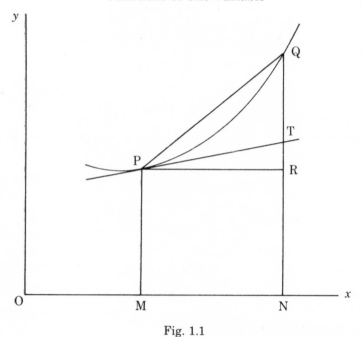

Fig. 1.1

nearer Q is to P, that is the smaller δx (or dx), the smaller the difference between δy and dy. Hence it assists in understanding that as

$$\delta x \to 0, \ \delta y/\delta x \to dy/dx$$

Referring back to equation (1.5), when there is no unique limit $f'(x)$ for a particular value of x in (a,b), the function is said to be not differentiable at that point. However, if a unique limit does exist for some point, the function is said to be differentiable at that point and, if the function possesses a unique derivative at all points in a range, it is said to be differentiable in that range.

If $f(x)$ is, in fact, a differentiable function of x in any given range of values of x, then as has been seen already

$$\delta y/\delta x = f'(x) + \varepsilon$$

where $\varepsilon \to 0$ as $\delta x \to 0$. Suppose that $f'(x) > 0$, then since $\varepsilon \to 0$ as $\delta x \to 0$, x may be chosen to be so small that $f'(x) + \varepsilon > 0$ even when ε is negative. Hence, for all sufficiently small values of δx, δy and δx will have the same sign. Therefore, if δx is positive and sufficiently small,

$$\delta y = f(x + \delta x) - f(x) > 0 \quad \text{or} \quad f(x + \delta x) > f(x).$$

A function which satisfies this latter inequality is said to be an increasing function of x.

Similarly, if $f'(x) < 0$, δy is negative when δx is small and positive, so that $f(x + \delta x) < f(x)$ for small positive δx. A function satisfying this inequality is said to be a decreasing function of x.

Finally, to summarise,

(i) $f'(x) > 0$, $f(x)$ is increasing with x,

(ii) $f'(x) < 0$, $f(x)$ is decreasing with x.

1.8 GENERAL RESULTS

Suppose that $u(x)$ and $v(x)$ are two differentiable functions of x in a given range (a,b) then,

(i) if $y = u \pm v$, $\quad \dfrac{dy}{dx} = \dfrac{du}{dx} \pm \dfrac{dv}{dx}$, $\qquad$ (1.8)

(ii) if $y = uv$, $\quad \dfrac{dy}{dx} = u\dfrac{dv}{dx} + v\dfrac{du}{dx}$, $\qquad$ (1.9)

(iii) if $y = u/v$, $\quad \dfrac{dy}{dx} = \left(v\dfrac{du}{dx} - u\dfrac{dv}{dx} \right) \Big/ v^2 \ (v \neq 0)$. $\qquad$ (1.10)

To illustrate the method of proof it will be sufficient to prove (iii). Let δy, δu and δv be increments of the functions y, u, v corresponding to the increment of δx of x, then

$$\frac{\delta y}{\delta x} = \frac{\dfrac{u + \delta u}{v + \delta v} - \dfrac{u}{v}}{\delta x} = \frac{v\dfrac{\delta u}{\delta x} - u\dfrac{\delta v}{\delta x}}{v(v + \delta v)} .$$

By taking the limit when $\delta x \to 0$ it follows that

$$\frac{dy}{dx} = \left(v\frac{du}{dx} - u\frac{dv}{dx} \right) \Big/ v^2 .$$

1.9 DERIVATIVE OF A FUNCTION OF A FUNCTION

Suppose $y = f(x)$ and $x = g(t)$ are functions such that $f'(x)$ is finite at a certain point and $g'(t)$ is finite at the corresponding point, then y is a function of t having a finite derivative at that point given by

$$\frac{dy}{dt} = \frac{dy}{dx} \cdot \frac{dx}{dt} \qquad (1.11)$$

Since x and t are related by $x = g(t)$, if t is given a small increment δt, the corresponding increment δx in x is given by

$$\delta x = g'(t)\delta t + \varepsilon_1 \delta t$$

where $\varepsilon_1 \to 0$ as $\delta t \to 0$.

The increment δx produces in turn an increment δy in y

$$\delta y = f'(x)\delta x + \varepsilon_2 \delta x .$$

Since $g'(t)$ is finite, $\delta x \to 0$ as $\delta t \to 0$ and hence it follows that $\varepsilon_2 \to 0$ as $\delta t \to 0$.

Then

$$\delta y = f'(x)g'(t)\delta t + f'(x)\varepsilon_1\delta t + \varepsilon_2 \frac{\delta x}{\delta t}\delta t$$

that is,

$$\frac{\delta y}{\delta t} = f'(x)g'(t) + \left(f'(x)\varepsilon_1 + \frac{\delta x}{\delta t}\varepsilon_2\right) \to f'(x)g'(t) \text{ as } \delta t \to 0 .$$

Thus

$$\frac{dy}{dt} = f'(x)g'(t) = \frac{dy}{dx}\frac{dx}{dt} . \tag{1.12}$$

1.10 DERIVATIVE OF AN INVERSE FUNCTION

Suppose $y = f(x)$ is a single-valued, continuous function which increases (or decreases) steadily in a given range of values of x, and let $x = g(y)$ be the inverse function. Then, if $f'(x)$ is finite and non-zero

$$g'(y) = 1/f'(x) .$$

Since $f(x)$ is monotonic, that is $f(x)$ increases (or decreases) steadily in the given range, the identity

$$\frac{\delta x}{\delta y} = 1 \bigg/ \frac{\delta y}{\delta x}$$

nowhere involves division by zero. The required result follows by proceeding to the limit.

Examples

(1) Using equation (1.11) find the derivative dy/dx when $y = \sin^2 x$
Let $\sin x = t$ then $y = t^2$, then $\cos x = dt/dx$ and $dy/dt = 2t$.
Using (1.11)

$$\frac{dy}{dx} = \frac{dy}{dt}\frac{dt}{dx} = 2t. (\cos x)$$

$$= 2 \sin x \cos x .$$

(2) If $y = \sin^{-1} x$ where $-1 < x < 1$ then $x = \sin y$ and is increasing steadily in the range $-\pi/2 < y < \pi/2$. Since $dx/dy = \cos y$, it follows from (1.12) that

$$\frac{dy}{dx} = \frac{1}{\cos y}$$

However, in the range $-\pi/2 < y < \pi/2$, $\cos y$ is positive and given by

$$\cos y = (1 - \sin^2 y)^{\frac{1}{2}} = (1 - x^2)^{\frac{1}{2}}$$

Hence

$$\frac{dy}{dx} = \frac{1}{(1 - x^2)^{\frac{1}{2}}}$$

It might be noted that, if $y = f(x)$ is a differentiable function of x, the derivative $dy/dx = f'(x)$ often turns out to be a differentiable function of x also. The deriv-

ative of dy/dx may be written $\dfrac{d}{dx}\left(\dfrac{dy}{dx}\right)$ but is denoted by d^2y/dx^2 or $f''(x)$ usually and is called the **second derivative** of y with respect to x. By repeated
differentiation the third, fourth, up to the nth derivatives may be obtained and
these are denoted by d^3y/dx^3 or $f'''(x)$, d^4y/dx^4 or $f''''(x)$, d^ny/dx^n or $f^n(x)$ where
the n is not a power but really denotes n primes.

1.11 LEIBNIZ'S THEOREM

Let $y = uv$, where u and v are two given functions of x. If the suffices 1, 2, $\ldots$,
n, $\ldots$ denote the first, second, $\ldots$, nth, $\ldots$ derivatives respectively, using
(1.9) it is seen that

$$y_1 = uv_1 + u_1v$$

$$y_2 = uv_2 + 2u_1v_1 + u_2v$$

$$y_3 = uv_3 + 3u_1v_2 + 3u_2v_1 + u_3v \tag{1.13}$$

which suggest that the law of the coefficients is the same as in the binomial
theorem. Leibniz's theorem states that the nth derivative of the product is
given by

$$y_n = uv_n + nu_1v_{n-1} + \frac{n(n-1)}{2!}\,u_2v_{n-2} + \cdots + nu_{n-1}v_1 + u_nv \ . \tag{1.14}$$

This result may be proved by using the method of induction. This necessitates
assuming the result valid for $n = m$ and proving it for $n = m + 1$. If the result
is true for $n = m$,

$$y_m = uv_m + mu_1v_{m-1} + \frac{m(m-1)}{2!}\,u_2v_{m-2} + \cdots + u_mv$$

$$= uv_m + \binom{m}{1}u_1v_{m-1} + \cdots + \binom{m}{r}u_rv_{m-r} + \cdots + u_mv \tag{1.15}$$

where $$\binom{m}{r} = m!/r!\,(m-r)!$$

Differentiating (1.15) with respect to x gives

$$y_{m+1} = uv_{m+1} + u_1v_m + \binom{m}{1}\{u_1v_m + u_2v_{m-1}\} + \cdots$$

$$+ \binom{m}{r}\{u_rv_{m-r+1} + u_{r+1}v_{m-r}\} + \cdots + u_mv_1 + u_{m+1}v$$

$$= uv_{m+1} + \left\{1 + \binom{m}{1}\right\}u_1v_m + \cdots + \left\{\binom{m}{r-1} + \binom{m}{r}\right\}u_rv_{m-r+1} + \cdots$$

$$+ u_{m+1}v \ .$$

But
$$\binom{m}{r-1} + \binom{m}{r} = \binom{m+1}{r} \quad \text{and so}$$

$$y_{m+1} = uv_{m+1} + \binom{m+1}{1}u_1 v_m + \cdots + \binom{m+1}{r}u_r v_{m+1-r} + \cdots + u_{m+1}v .$$

This result is precisely equation (1.15) with $m + 1$ replacing m. Hence, if the result is true for $n = m$, it is true for $n = m + 1$. Also, by equation (1.13), the result is true for $n = 1$ and so by the method of induction it is true for all integral values of n.

Example

Using Leibniz's theorem find d^3y/dx^3 when $y = x^3 \cos 2x$

Let $u(x) = x^3$, $v(x) = \cos 2x$ so that

$$u'(x) = 3x^2 , \quad u''(x) = 6x , \quad u'''(x) = 6$$

and $v'(x) = -2\sin 2x, v''(x) = -4 \cos 2x, v'''(x) = 8 \sin 2x .$

Then using (1.14) with $n = 3$ gives

$$\frac{d^3y}{dx^3} = 8x^3 \sin 2x - 3.12x^2 \cos 2x$$

$$- 3.12x \sin 2x + 6 \cos 2x$$

$$= 4 \sin 2x \, (2x^3 - 9x) + 6 \cos 2x \, (1 - 6x^2) .$$

1.12 SOME IMPORTANT THEOREMS OF THE DIFFERENTIAL CALCULUS

The theorems which will be considered now are concerned with continuous and differentiable functions and are of great importance, as well as of frequent application, in the further development of the analysis of functions of one variable. The proofs of the theorems, although not difficult in themselves, are based on the properties of continuous functions, and the proofs of these pro-perties are based on the so-called **Heine-Borel theorem**. It is the difficulty of this theorem which proves the main obstacle to a rigorous *elementary* account of this part of the subject.

Since the proofs of the Heine-Borel theorem and those other theorems immediately dependent upon it are outside the scope of this book, the theorems to be considered here will be stated without complete rigorous proofs.

Consider a function $f(x)$. In the interval $[a,b]$, suppose that the values taken by $f(x)$ for x given by x_0 $(=a)$, x_1, x_2, ..., x_n $(=b)$ are $f(x_0)$, $f(x_1)$, $f(x_2)$, ... $f(x_n)$. If there exists a number M such that $f(x) \leqslant M$ for all values of x in $[a,b]$, the function $f(x)$ is said to be **bounded above**. The least value of M, say Λ, for which this condition holds is called the **least upper bound**. Thus, if Λ is the least upper bound of $f(x)$ then

$$f(x) \leqslant \Lambda$$

for all x in $[a,b]$ and for any small positive number, ε,

$$f(x) > \Lambda - \varepsilon$$

for at least one value of x in $[a,b]$.

The **greatest lower bound**, λ, of $f(x)$ in the interval $[a,b]$ is defined similarly by

$$f(x) \geqslant \lambda$$

for all x in $[a,b]$ and

$$f(x) < \lambda + \varepsilon$$

for at least one value of x in $[a,b]$.

The properties of continuous functions which will be required for the further development of the subject but for which no proof will be given are

1) A function which is continuous in an interval $[a,b]$ is bounded therein.
2) A function which is continuous in an interval $[a,b]$ attains its bounds therein.

1.12.1 Rolle's theorem

Let $f(x)$ be a function such that
(i) $f(x)$ is a continuous function in the interval $a \leqslant x \leqslant b$,
(ii) $f'(x)$ exists in the open interval $a < x < b$,
(iii) $f(a) = f(b)$;

then there exists a point c, such that $a < c < b$, at which $f'(c) = 0$.

By the above theorems on continuous functions, $f(x)$ is bounded in $[a,b]$ and it attains its bounds. Hence, either $f(x)$ is constant throughout $[a,b]$, in which case the theorem is obvious, or one of the bounds of $f(x)$ is different from $f(a)$ and is attained at $x = c$.

Suppose it is the upper bound which is attained at $x = c$,

then $$f(c \pm h) \leqslant f(c)$$

where h is positive.

Hence $$\frac{f(c \pm h) - f(c)}{h} \leqslant 0$$

That is $$\frac{f(c + h) - f(c)}{h} \leqslant 0$$

$$\frac{f(c - h) - f(c)}{-h} \geqslant 0 .$$

Now, in the limit as $h \to 0$, the first of these inequalities gives $f'(c) \leqslant 0$, while the second gives $f'(c) \geq 0$. Hence,

$$f'(c) = 0 .$$

This result may be obtained in a similar way if it is the lower bound which is attained at $x = c$.

1.12.2 The mean-value theorem
Let $f(x)$ be a function such that
(i) $f(x)$ is a single-valued and continuous in $a \leq x \leq b$,
(ii) $f'(x)$ exists in the open interval $a < x < b$;
then there exists a point c, such that $a < c < b$, for which

$$f(b) - f(a) = (b - a) f'(c) .$$

The conditions satisfied by $f(x)$ here are the same as those in Rolle's theorem except that $f(b)$ does not equal $f(a)$. Define a new funciton $\Phi(x)$ by

$$\Phi(x) = f(x) - Lx$$

where L is a constant to be chosen so that $\Phi(b) = \Phi(a)$. Therefore, L is given by

$$L = (f(b) - f(a))/(b - a) \tag{a}$$

Also, since $f(x)$ and x are continuous functions, $\Phi(x)$ is a continuous function. Again

$$\Phi'(x) = f'(x) - L \tag{b}$$

and so $\Phi'(x)$ exists for $a < x < b$.

Hence, $\Phi(x)$ satisfies all the conditions of Rolle's theorem,

and so $$\Phi'(c) = 0$$

for some value of c such that $a < c < b$.

Therefore, from equations (a) and (b),

$$f'(c) = L = (f(b) - f(a))/(b - a)$$

1.12.3 Geometrical interpretations
Rolle's theorem is almost obvious geometrically since, if $f(x)$ is a continuous function which possesses a graph, and $f(a) = f(b)$, the diagram shown in Fig. 1.2 indicates the existence of a point or points, between a and b, at which $f'(x)$ vanishes; that is, at which the tangent to the curve $y = f(x)$ is parallel to the x-axis.

The conditions of the theorem involve the graph of $f(x)$ possessing a tangent at every point of the interval $[a,b]$, except possibly at the end-points. Since $f'(x)$ may be infinite, the graph may have points of inflexion with vertical tangents. However, the curve must not possess a sharp bend or kink since, at

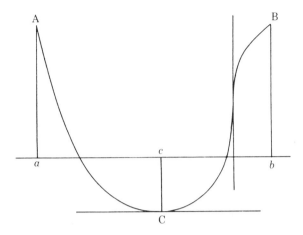

Fig. 1.2

such a point, $f'(x)$ does not exist and condition (ii) would not be fulfilled.

The geometrical interpretation of the mean-value theorem is obvious also and is illustrated in Fig. 1.3. The expression

$$L = (f(b) - f(a))/(b - a)$$

is the slope of the chord AB, and $f'(c)$ is the slope of the tangent at the point C where $x = c$. The theorem simply states that there must be point such as C on the curve between A and B where the tangent is parallel to the chord AB.

1.13 CAUCHY'S FORMULA

Suppose $f(x)$ and $g(x)$ are two functions such that
(i) $f(x)$ and $g(x)$ are continuous in $a \leqslant x \leqslant b$.
(ii) $f'(x)$ and $g'(x)$ exist in the open interval $a < x < b$,
(iii) $g'(x) \neq 0$ anywhere in (a,b),
then there exists a point c, such that $a < c < b$, for which

$$\frac{f(b) - f(a)}{g(b) - g(a)} = \frac{f'(c)}{g'(c)}.$$

Define a new function $\Phi(x)$ by

$$\Phi(x) = f(x) - Ag(x)$$

and choose A so that

$$\Phi(a) = \Phi(b) .$$

Thus

$$A = \frac{f(b) - f(a)}{g(b) - g(a)}.$$

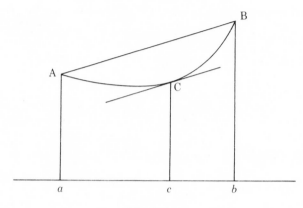

Fig. 1.3

and since $g'(x) \neq 0$ anywhere in (a,b), $g(b) \neq g(a)$. This follows since, if $g(b) = g(a)$, the function $g(x)$ would satisfy in (a,b) all the conditions of Rolle's theorem, and so $g'(x)$ would vanish at some point in (a,b). Hence A is finite and determinate always.

Now $\Phi(x)$ satisfies all the conditions of Rolle's theorem,

and so
$$\Phi'(c) = 0, \quad a < c < b.$$

Hence
$$0 = \Phi'(c) = f'(c) - Ag'(c),$$

and substituting for A gives

$$\frac{f'(c)}{g'(c)} = A = \frac{f(b) - f(a)}{g(b) - g(a)}$$

1.14 INDETERMINATE FORMS

Consider the function $f(x)/g(x)$ for which $f(a) = g(a) = 0$. This function is such that, when $x = a$, its value is indeterminate of the form $0/0$. Often, however, in cases like this $\lim_{x \to a} \{f(x)/g(x)\}$ is definite and limits of this type are evaluated easily by application of Cauchy's formula.

Many important limits may be evaluated by the methods to be considered. Several different cases will be discussed in detail but, in each case, it will be supposed that $f(a) = g(a) = 0$.

(1) Suppose $f(a) = g(a) = 0$ but both $f'(a)$ and $g'(a)$ are assumed to exist and have a definite ratio.

Now
$$\frac{f(x)}{g(x)} = \frac{f(x) - f(a)}{g(x) - g(a)} = \frac{\{f(x) - f(a)\}/(x - a)}{\{g(x) - g(a)\}/(x - a)}$$

so that
$$\lim_{x \to a} \frac{f(x)}{g(x)} = \frac{f'(a)}{g'(a)}.$$

(2) Suppose $f'(x)$ and $g'(x)$ exist near, but not necessarily at, a. Then, if

$$f'(x)/g'(x)$$

tends to a limit λ as $x \to a$, the limit of $f(x)/g(x)$ exists and equals λ also.

By Cauchy's formula, if $a < z_1 < x$,

$$\frac{f(x)}{g(x)} = \frac{f(x) - f(a)}{g(x) - g(a)} = \frac{f'(z_1)}{g'(z_1)}$$

Hence, assuming the limit in question exists,

$$\lim_{x \to a+0} \frac{f(x)}{g(x)} = \lim_{z_1 \to a+0} \frac{f'(z_1)}{g'(z_1)} = \lambda$$

Here it has been assumed that $x > a$ and so only the right-hand limits have been taken–the point a being approached from above.

If $x < a$, that is if $x < z_2 < a$, a similar argument yields

$$\lim_{x \to a-0} \frac{f(x)}{g(x)} = \lim_{z_2 \to a-0} \frac{f'(z_2)}{g'(z_2)} = \lambda$$

where left-hand limits have been taken.

Hence, it has been proved that, if $f'(x)/g'(x)$ possesses a unique finite limit λ when x tends to a, the limit of $f(x)/g(x)$ equals λ also.

This result is known as **l'Hospital's rule**.

(3) Suppose that both $f(x)/g(x)$ and $f'(x)/g'(x)$ assume the indeterminate form $0/0$ when $x = a$. By the same argument as used in (2)

$$\lim_{x \to a} \frac{f(x)}{g(x)} = \lim_{z \to a} \frac{f'(z)}{g'(z)}$$

provided the right-hand side exists.

If $f'(a) = g'(a) = 0$ but $f''(a)/g''(a)$ is determinate, by (1) the right-hand side does exist and equals $f''(a)/g''(a)$. Then, by (2),

$$\lim_{x \to a} \frac{f'(x)}{g'(x)} = \lim_{x \to a} \frac{f''(x)}{g''(x)}$$

whenever the right-hand side exists.

In general, if $f^{(n)}(a)$ and $g^{(n)}(a)$ both vanish for $n < m$, but $f^{(m)}(a)/g^{(m)}(a)$ tends to a limit as $x \to a$, then repeated application of l'Hospital's rule yields

$$\lim_{x \to a} f(x)/g(x) = \lim_{x \to a} f^{(m)}(a)/g^{(m)}(a) \,.$$

Examples

(i) If $f(x) = (e^{mx} - e^{ma})$ and $g(x) = (x-a)$ then, when $x = a$, $f(x)/g(x)$ is indeterminate of the form $0/0$.

But
$$f'(x)/g'(x) = me^{mx}/1 \quad \text{and so}$$

$$\lim_{x \to a} \frac{f(x)}{g(x)} = \lim_{x \to a} \frac{f'(x)}{g'(x)} = me^{ma}$$

(ii) If $f(x) = (e^x - e^{\sin x})$ and $g(x) = (x - \sin x)$, then when $x = 0$, $f(x)/g(x)$ is indeterminate of the form $0/0$.

For this case

$$\lim_{x \to 0} \frac{e^x - e^{\sin x}}{x - \sin x} = \lim_{x \to 0} \frac{e^x - \cos x \, e^{\sin x}}{1 - \cos x}$$

$$= \lim_{x \to 0} \frac{e^x + \sin x \, e^{\sin x} - \cos^2 x \, e^{\sin x}}{\sin x}$$

$$= \lim_{x \to 0} \frac{e^x + \cos x \, e^{\sin x} + 3 \sin x \cos x \, e^{\sin x} - \cos^3 x \, e^{\sin x}}{\cos x} = 1 .$$

The indeterminate form ∞/∞

Suppose $f(x)$ and $g(x)$ are two functions each of which tends to infinity as x tends to a. Also suppose that both $f'(x)$ and $g'(x)$ exist near, but not necessarily at, $x = a$. If $f'(x)/g'(x)$ tends to a finite limit λ as x tends to a, the same rules may be applied as were used when $f(x)$ and $g(x)$ both tended to zero as x tended to a.

Now
$$f(x)/g(x) = [g(x)]^{-1}/[f(x)]^{-1} ,$$

and when $x = a$, the latter ratio is of the indeterminate from $0/0$. Hence, using earlier results,

$$\lim_{x \to a} \frac{f(x)}{g(x)} = \lim_{x \to a} \frac{[g(x)]^{-1}}{[f(x)]^{-1}} = \lim_{x \to a} \frac{g'(x)}{[g(x)]^2} \frac{[f(x)]^2}{f'(x)}$$

$$= \lim_{x \to a} \frac{g'(x)}{f'(x)} \left\{ \lim_{x \to a} \frac{f(x)}{g(x)} \right\}^2$$

and so
$$\lim_{x \to a} \frac{f(x)}{g(x)} = \left\{ \lim_{x \to a} \frac{g'(x)}{f'(x)} \right\}^{-1} .$$

But if
$$\lim_{x \to a} \{f'(x)/g'(x)\} = \lambda ; \quad \text{then} \lim_{x \to a} \{g'(x)/f'(x)\} = \lambda^{-1}$$

and so
$$\lim_{x \to a} \frac{f(x)}{g(x)} = \lambda .$$

Example

If $f(x) = \log(1/x)$ and $g(x) = 1/x$ then, when $x = 0$, $f(x)/g(x)$ is indeterminate of the form ∞/∞.

Now
$$f'(x)/g'(x) = (-1/x)/(-1/x^2) = x$$

and so
$$\lim_{x \to 0} \frac{f(x)}{g(x)} = \lim_{x \to 0} \frac{f'(x)}{g'(x)} = 0 .$$

Occasionally, other indeterminate forms occur but, usually, they may be reduced to the form 0/0. A note of some of the most common cases follows now and, in each instance, the limits are as $x \to a$.

(a) Suppose $f(x) \to 0$, $g(x) \to \infty$ and the function to be considered is $f(x)\,g(x)$. In the limit the product $f(x)\,g(x)$ is of the form of $0.\infty$, but by putting

$$f(x)\,g(x) = f(x)/\{1/g(x)\}$$

the form becomes of the type 0/0.

(b) Suppose $f(x) \to \infty$, $g(x) \to \infty$ and the function to be considered is $f(x) - g(x)$. In this case, since

$$f(x) - g(x) = \left\{ \frac{1}{g(x)} - \frac{1}{f(x)} \right\} \bigg/ \frac{1}{f(x)g(x)}$$

this form reduces to the type 0/0 also.

(c) Suppose $f(x) \to 0$, $g(x) \to 0$ and the function to be considered is $[f(x)]^{g(x)}$. In this case, if $f(x) > 0$, put $y(x) = [f(x)]^{g(x)}$,

then
$$\log y(x) = g(x) \log f(x) = g(x) \bigg/ \left\{ \frac{1}{\log f(x)} \right\}$$

which is of the form 0/0.

1.15 TAYLOR'S THEOREM

If $f(x)$ is a single-valued continuous function of x, the object of Taylor's theorem is to obtain an expansion for $f(a + h)$ in ascending powers of h up to the term of any given order n.

Suppose that $f(x)$ is such a function and that

(i) $f(x)$ and all its derivatives up to and including $f^{(n-1)}(x)$ exist and are continuous in the interval $[a,b]$,

(ii) $f^{(n)}(x)$ exists in the interval (a,b),

then there exists a point c, such that $a < c < b$, for which

$$f(b) = f(a) + (b - a)f'(a) + \frac{(b - a)^2}{2!}\, f''(a) + \cdots$$

$$+ \frac{(b - a)^{n-1}}{(n - 1)!}\, f^{(n-1)}(a) + \frac{(b - a)^p\, (b - c)^{n-p}}{p(n - 1)!}\, f^{(n)}(c) \qquad (1.16)$$

where p is a fixed integer and $1 \leqslant p \leqslant n$.

Now let
$$\Phi(x) = f(x) - f(b) + (b - x)f'(x) + \frac{(b - x)^2}{2!}\, f''(x) + \cdots$$

$$+ \frac{(b - x)^{n-1}}{(n - 1)!}\, f^{(n-1)}(x) + K(b - x)^p$$

Then, it is seen immediately that $\Phi(b) = 0$ and K may be chosen so that $\Phi(a) = 0$, that is

$$f(b) = f(a) + (b - a) f'(a) + \cdots + \frac{(b - a)^{n-1}}{(n - 1)!} f^{(n-1)}(a) + K(b - a)^p$$

$\Phi(x)$ is a function which is continuous in the interval $[a,b]$ and for which $\Phi(a) = \Phi(b) = 0$. Also

$$\Phi'(x) = \frac{(b - x)^{n-1}}{(n - 1)!} f^n(x) - Kp\,(b - x)^{p-1}$$

and so $\Phi'(x)$ exists in the interval (a,b). It follows, therefore, that $\Phi(x)$ satisfies the conditions of Rolle's theorem, and so there exists a point c, such that $a < c < b$, for which $\Phi'(c) = 0$. Therefore,

$$K = \frac{(b - c)^{n-p}}{p(n - 1)!} f^{(n)}(c) \ .$$

Hence, finally,

$$f(b) = f(a) + (b - a) f'(a) + \frac{(b - a)^2}{2!} f''(a) + \cdots$$

$$+ \frac{(b - a)^{n-1}}{(n - 1!} f^{(n-1)}(a) + \frac{(b - a)^p (b - c)^{n-p}}{p\,(n - 1)!} f^{(n)}(c).$$

Note that if b is put equal to $(a + h)$ and c to $(a + \Theta h)$, where Θ is such that $0 < \Theta < 1$, the expansion takes the form

$$f(a + h) = f(a) + hf'(a) + \frac{h^2}{2!} f''(a) + \cdots$$

$$+ \frac{h^{n-1}}{(n - 1)!} f^{(n-1)}(a) = \frac{h^n (1 - \Theta)^{n-p}}{p(n - 1)!} f^{(n)} (a + \Theta h) \ . \tag{1.17}$$

The final term in equation (1.16) is the difference between the function and its polynomial approximation. Although a general form of this 'remainder' is given, two special cases deserve particular mention:

(a) if $p = n$ the Lagrange form of the remainder is obtained; that is

$$\frac{(b - a)^n}{n!} f^{(n)}(c) \ ,$$

or putting $\quad b = a + h$, $\quad c = a + \Theta h$ once more, $\dfrac{h^n}{n!} f^{(n)} (a + \Theta h)$.

(b) if $p = 1$, the Cauchy form of the remainder is obtained; that is

$$\frac{(b - a) (b - c)^{n-1}}{(n - 1)!} f^{(n)}(c) \quad \text{or,}$$

alternatively, $\qquad \dfrac{h^n (1 - \Theta)^{n-1}}{(n - 1)!} f^{(n)} (a + \Theta h)$.

1.16 MACLAURIN'S THEOREM

This theorem is really a special case of Taylor's theorem and may be proved in the same way. However, putting $a = 0$ in equation (1.17) gives Maclaurin's theorem for the expansion of $f(h)$ in ascending powers of h up to the term of order n; that is,

$$f(h) = f(0) + hf'(0) + \frac{h^2}{2!} f''(0) + \cdots$$

$$+ \frac{h^{n-1}}{(n-1)!} f^{(n-1)}(0) + \frac{h^n(1-\Theta)^{n-p}}{p(n-1)!} f^{(n)}(\Theta h) .$$

The forms of the remainder analagous to (a) and (b) above

are $\dfrac{h^n}{n!} f^{(n)}(\Theta h)$ and $\dfrac{h^n(1-\Theta)^{n-1}}{(n-1)!} f^{(n)}(\Theta h)$

respectively.

The infinite series known as Taylor's series (and Maclaurin's series) will be discussed in chapter 4 where the question of their convergence will be considered.

1.17 EXTREME VALUES OF FUNCTIONS OF ONE VARIABLE

In all elementary texts on calculus, the theory of maxima and minima (that is, extreme values) of a function $f(x)$ is considered. For a function $f(x)$ such that $f'(x)$ and $f''(x)$ both exist in the interval $a \leqslant x \leqslant b$, it is shown that the values of x for which $f(x)$ is stationary are the solutions of $f'(x) = 0$ and, provided $f''(x) \neq 0$ at any of these points, the stationary value is a maximum or a minumum according as $f''(x)$ is negative or positive at the point in question. This well-known elementary criterion is a particular case of the more general theorem to be considered here.

A function $f(x)$, defined for $a \leqslant x \leqslant b$, is said to have a *minimum* at the point $x = c$, where $a < c < b$, if $f(x) \geqslant f(c)$ for all values of x near c. A *maximum* is defined with the inequality reversed.

To obtain some conditions for a minimum from this definition, suppose the function $f(x)$ has a Taylor expansion about the point $x = c$. By applying equation (1.17)

$$f(c + h) = f(c) + hf'(c) + \tfrac{1}{2} h^2 f''(c + \Theta h)$$

where the Lagrange form of the remainder has been used and Θ is such that $0 < \Theta < 1$. Then, the definition of a minimum given above is equivalent to

$$\Delta f = f(c + h) - f(c)$$

$$= hf'(c) + \tfrac{1}{2}h^2 f''(c + \Theta h) \geqslant 0$$

for all values of h sufficiently close to zero.

Suppose $f'(c) \neq 0$. In this case, provided h is small enough, the sign of Δf is determined by the sign of $hf'(c)$ and this may be made positive or negative by changing the sign of h. But $\Delta f \geq 0$, and so it is necessary that $hf'(c) = 0$. Since h is arbitrary and non-zero, this implies that $f'(c) = 0$. This is the first necessary condition for an extreme value (that is, either maximum or a minimum). The point $x = c$ at which $f'(c) = 0$ is called a **stationary point** of $f(x)$, and the value $f(c)$ is the corresponding **stationary value** of $f(x)$.

This stationary condition gives no indication of whether $f(x)$ has a maximum, a minimum, or a point of inflexion at $x = c$. To separate these, consider the second derivative, and from above it is seen that, if $f'(c) = 0$, then

$$f''(c) > 0 \Rightarrow \Delta f \geq 0$$
$$\Rightarrow f(c) \quad \text{a minimum,}$$

and
$$f''(c) < 0 \Rightarrow \Delta f \leq 0$$
$$\Rightarrow f(c) \quad \text{a maximum.}$$

Also, if $f''(c)$ changes sign for points near $x = c$, it is a point of inflexion, but more of that later. Firstly, consider the more general theorem covering criteria for extreme values.

Let $f(x)$ be defined in the interval $a \leq x \leq b$ and let c be a point such that $a < c < b$. Also, suppose that
(i) $f^{(n)}(c)$ exists and is not zero,
(ii) $f'(c) = f''(c) = \cdots = f^{(n-1)}(c) = 0$,
then $f(x)$ has no extreme values at $x = c$ if n is odd. If n is even, $f(x)$ has a maximum at $x = c$ if $f^{(n)}(c) < 0$, or a minimum if $f^{(n)}(c) > 0$.

Under the conditions stated, if $f^{(n)}(c)$ is finite, equation (1.17)

yields
$$\Delta f = f(c + h) - f(c) = \frac{h^n}{n!} f^{(n)} (c + \Theta h)$$

where the Lagrange form of the remainder has been used. Since h may be positive or negative, when n is odd Δf does not preserve the same sign in the neighbourhood of the point $x = c$ and so $f(x)$ has no extreme value at that point.

If n is even, the sign of Δf is the same as the sign of $f^{(n)}(c)$, and so
if $f^{(n)}(c) < 0$, there is a maximum at $x = c$,
if $f^{(n)}(c) > 0$, there is a minimum at $x = c$.

The usual elementary criterion for an extreme value is seen to correspond to the above when $n = 2$. Again, by the theorem, if $f''(c) = 0$ the discrimination may be made by considering derivatives of higher orders; for example, if $f'(c) = f''(c) = f'''(c) = 0$ but $f^{iv}(c) \neq 0$, the sign of $f^{iv}(c)$ enables the discrimination to be made. However, if $f'(c) = f''(c) = 0$ but $f'''(c) \neq 0$, the point $x = c$ is not a point at which $f(x)$ has an extreme value. In this case there is a point of inflexion at $x = c$.

1.17.1 Concavity and Convexity

When the gradient of an arc of a curve is increasing with x, the arc bends upwards and so lies above the tangent at any point on the arc. In these circumstances, the arc is said to be **concave upwards** or **convex downwards**. Following from this geometrical idea of the meaning of concave upwards, a curve is said to be concave upwards at a point P if, in the immediate neighbourhood of P, it lies completely above its tangent at P. Therefore, at P, $f'(x)$ must be increasing, and so $f''(x)$ must be positive.

Similarly, a curve is said to be **convex upwards** or **concave downwards**, at a point P if, in the immediate neighbourhood of P, the curve lies below its tangent at P. Hence, in this case, $f'(x)$ is decreasing, and so $f''(x)$ must be negative at P.

At points where $f''(x) = 0$ and changes sign, the curve must be changing from concave upwards to convex upwards or vice versa. Therefore, at such points the curve cannot lie completely above or below the tangent; the curve in fact crosses its tangent at such points, and these points are called **points of inflexion**. It is important to realise that, at such points, $f'(x)$ is not necessarily equal to zero (that is, the tangent is not necessarily parallel to the x axis), but it is necessary that $f''(x)$ be zero and changes sign.

Since $f''(x)$ must change sign at the given point, as x increases through the given value, $f''(x)$ must be either increasing or decreasing and so $f'''(x)$, must be positive or negative. Thus a function $f(x)$ is said to have a point of inflexion at the point $x = c$, where $a < c < b$, if $f''(c) = 0$ and $f'''(c) \neq 0$. This is the usual elementary criterion for a point of inflexion. The more general one is that the function $f(x)$ is said to have a point of inflexion at $x = c$, where $a < c < b$, if $f''(c) = 0$ and the first non-vanishing higher derivative at $x = c$ is odd.

Example

Find the maximum and minimum points and points of inflexion on the curve $y = f(x) = 4x^3 + 9x^2 + 6x + 1$.

For this curve

$$f'(x) = 12x^2 + 18x + 6$$

$$= 6 (2x + 1)(x + 1) \qquad \text{(a)}$$

$$f''(x) = 24x + 18$$

$$= 6 (4x + 3) \qquad \text{(b)}$$

$$f'''(x) = 24 . \qquad \text{(c)}$$

From (a) it is seen that $f'(x) = 0$ when $x = -\frac{1}{2}$ or $x = -1$.

Further, from (b) it follows that, when $x = -\frac{1}{2}$, $f''(x) = 6$ but, when $x = -1$, $f''(x) = -6$. Hence, at $x = -\frac{1}{2}$ the curve has a minimum value, while at $x = -1$, the curve has a maximum value.

Also, from (b), it is seen that $f''(x) = 0$ when $x = -\frac{3}{4}$ and so, since $f'''(x)$ is non-zero, the curve has a point of inflexion at $x = -\frac{3}{4}$.

EXERCISES 1

Differentiate the functions in nos. (1)–(4) with respect to x,

(1) $(x - 3)^5$, $x^2(1 - x)^2$, $\{(4 - x^2)/x\}^{\frac{1}{2}}$.

(2) $x - \tan x$, $\sin(x^{\frac{1}{2}})$, $x/\sin(x^{\frac{1}{2}})$.

(3) $\sin^3 x \cos 3x$, $\sin 3x/\cos^3 x$, $\sin^3 3x/\cos 3x$.

(4) $x^n(a^2 - x^2)^n$, $\{(a - x)/(b - x)\}^n$, $x^2(3 - 4x + 2x^2)^{\frac{1}{2}}$.

(5) Find the nth derivative with respect to x of $e^{-ax} \cos ax$.

(6) Find the 10th derivative with respect to x of $x^2 e^x$.

(7) Show that the conditions of Rolle's theorem are satisfied for the interval $[-\frac{1}{2}, \sqrt{2}]$ for the function

$$f(x) = 2x^3 + x^2 - 4x - 2 .$$

Verify the conclusion of the theorem for this function.

(8) Use the mean value theorem with $f(x) = \log x$, $b = x$ and $a = 1$ to show that, if $x > 1$, $x - 1 > \log x > (x - 1)/x$.

(9) Show that

$$\text{(i)} \quad \lim_{x \to 0} \sin x/x = 1, \quad \text{(ii)} \quad \lim_{x \to 0} (1 - \cos x)/\sin x = 0 .$$

Evaluate the limits in nos. (10) and (11).

(10) $\displaystyle\lim_{x \to 0} \frac{e^x - 1}{x}$, $\displaystyle\lim_{x \to 0} \frac{\sin x - x}{\tan x - x}$.

(11) $\displaystyle\lim_{x \to \infty} \frac{x^2}{e^x}$, $\displaystyle\lim_{x \to \infty} \frac{3x^2 - 2x + 1}{5x^2 + 3x - 2}$.

(12) For the following curves, find their maxima, minima, and points of inflexion. Also determine where they are concave upwards, and where downwards.

(a) $y = x^4 - 10x^2 + 9$;   (b) $y = (1 - x^2)^2$.

Chapter 2
Complex Numbers

2.1 INTRODUCTION.

Complex numbers were introduced first by Cardan in his examination of the solutions of cubic equations. Hence, consider the cubic equation $x^3 - 1 = 0$. This may be written

$$(x - 1)(x^2 + x + 1) = 0.$$

Hence, the roots of the original cubic equation are $x = 1$ and the roots of the quadratic equation

$$x^2 + x + 1 = 0 ,$$

and the roots of this equation are

$$x = \tfrac{1}{2}(-1 \pm \sqrt{-3}) .$$

Now, there is no real number whose square is minus three, and so it is necessary to extend the concept of numbers so that this cubic equation may be said to possess three roots. To achieve this end, the square root of a negative real number is defined to be an imaginary number. Also, it may be noticed that any imaginary number, $\sqrt{-a}$, may be expressed as the product of a real number, $\sqrt{a}$, and the imaginary number $\sqrt{-1}$. Obviously, $\sqrt{-1}$ plays a central role in the theory of imaginary numbers, and mathematicians usually denote it by the letter i. However, since i is also the symbol for current, many people prefer to let j denote $\sqrt{-1}$. This latter symbol will be used here.

The two roots of the quadratic equation

$$x^2 + x + 1 = 0$$

may be written

$$x = \tfrac{1}{2}(-1 \pm \sqrt{3}\mathrm{j}) .$$

Writing the roots in terms of imaginary numbers really only makes sense provided $x^2 + x + 1$ may be factorised into

$$(x - \tfrac{1}{2}(-1 + \sqrt{3}\mathrm{j}))(x - \tfrac{1}{2}(-1 - \sqrt{3}\mathrm{j})).$$

These two brackets may be multiplied out to give $x^2 + x + 1$ provided the imaginary number j is manipulated like a real number in any arithmetic operation and if j^2 is replaced by -1 whenever it occurs.

The roots of the quadratic equation found above are neither real nor imaginary numbers but are the formal sums of a real and an imaginary number. Such a sum is called a **complex number**, and so a complex number z is the sum $z = x + jy$, where x and y are real. The real numbers x and y are referred to as the **real** and **imaginary parts** of the complex number z and are denoted by Re z and Im z sometimes.

The following axioms provide the formal expression of the postulate that complex numbers obey the usual rules of addition, subtraction and multiplication: if $x_1 + jy_1$ and $x_2 + jy_2$ are two complex numbers

$$(x_1 + jy_1) \pm (x_2 + jy_2) = x_1 \pm x_2 + j(y_1 \pm y_2)$$

and $\qquad (x_1 + jy_1)(x_2 + jy_2) \quad = x_1x_2 - y_1y_2 + j(x_1y_2 + x_2y_1).$

These axioms may be used to show that, if $z_1 = x_1 + jy_1$, $z_2 = x_2 + jy_2$, $z_3 = x_3 + jy_3$ are any three complex numbers, then

$$z_1 + z_2 = z_2 + z_1 \; ; z_1z_2 = z_2z_1 \qquad \text{(commutative laws)}$$

$$z_1 + (z_2 + z_3) = (z_1 + z_2) + z_3 \; ; z_1(z_2z_3) = (z_1z_2)z_3 \qquad \text{(associative laws)}$$

$$z_1 (z_2 + z_3) = z_1z_2 + z_1z_3 . \qquad \text{(distributive law)}$$

Also the complex number $-x - jy$ is defined to be minus z and is denoted by $-z$.

The roots of the quadratic equation $x^2 + x + 1 = 0$ considered earlier, are seen to be related simply. Although their real parts are equal, their imaginary parts differ by the factor -1. This prompts the definition that if $z = x + jy$, the complex number $x - jy$ is the complex conjugate of z which is denoted by $\bar{z}$ or sometimes by z^*. Since $z = x + jy$ and $\bar{z} = x - jy$, it follows that $x = \text{Re } z = \frac{1}{2}(z + \bar{z})$ and $y = \text{Im } z = (z - \bar{z})/(2j)$. Hence, if z is real, Im $z = 0$ and $z = \bar{z}$; while if z is imaginary, Re $z = 0$ and $z = -\bar{z}$.

It is fairly straightforward to show that the complex conjugate obeys the following rules

$$\bar{\bar{z}} \quad = z$$

$$\overline{z_1 + z_2} = \bar{z}_1 + \bar{z}_2$$

$$\overline{z_1z_2} \quad = \bar{z}_1\bar{z}_2 .$$

A consequence of this last rule is that $\overline{z^n} = \bar{z}^n$, although a rigorous proof of this would be by induction.

Now consider the quadratic equation

$$az^2 + bz + c = 0$$

where a, b, c are real. Then

$$\overline{az^2 + bz + c} = \bar{a}\,\bar{z}^2 + \bar{b}\,\bar{z} + \bar{c} = 0,$$

that is, $a\bar{z}^2 + b\bar{z} + c = 0$
since a, b, c are real.

Hence, if z_1 is a root of the quadratic equation, so is $\bar{z}_1$. This result is extended easily to polynomial equations of higher order, and means that complex roots occur in pairs of complex conjugates.

2.2 THE ARGAND DIAGRAM

The complex number $z = x + jy$ consists essentially of a pair of real numbers x and y liked by the symbol j which denotes the imaginary number $\sqrt{-1}$. Therefore, z may be viewed as an *ordered pair* of real numbers, the actual ordering being important since, for example, the two complex numbers $2 + 3j$ and $3 + 2j$ are quite distinct. It follows that a complex number z may be represented by an ordered pair of real numbers, and written as (x,y), in which the first component of the pair corresponds to the real part and the second component to the imaginary part of z.

Consider the two complex numbers

$$z_1 = x_1 + jy_1 ; \quad z_2 = x_2 + jy_2 .$$

Applying the rules of manipulation introduced earlier,

$$z_1 + z_2 = (x_1 + jy_1) + (x_2 + jy_2)$$
$$= (x_1 + x_2) + j(y_1 + y_2).$$

If follows that, in the ordered pair notation,

$$(x_1,y_1) + (x_2,y_2) = (x_1 + x_2, y_1 + y_2).$$

Also,
$$z_1z_2 = (x_1 + jy_1)(x_2 + jy_2)$$
$$= x_1x_2 + jy_1x_2 + jx_1y_2 - y_1y_2$$
$$= (x_1x_2 - y_1y_2) + j(x_1y_2 + y_1x_2)$$

Hence,
$$(x_1,y_1) \times (x_2,y_2) = (x_1x_2 - y_1y_2, x_1y_2 + y_1x_2) .$$

Now an ordered pair (x,y) may be interpreted geometrically by taking the two real numbers x and y, in assigned order, to be the Cartesian coordinates of a point P in a plane. (Such coordinates are named after the Frenchman, Descartes.) Given a set of rectangular Cartesian axes, the complex number $z = x + jy$ is represented uniquely by the point P.

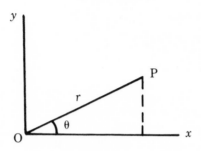

Fig. 2.1

Here P is said to represent the complex number z, and the diagram in which complex numbers are represented is called an **Argand diagram** and the plane in which it is drawn is called the **complex plane**.

As indicated in Fig. 2.1, the position of the point P may be described alternatively in terms of polar coordinates r and θ, where r is the *positive* distance OP and θ is the angle $\angle x$OP, positive angles being measured in the counter-clockwise sense from Ox. Except at the origin, r is defined uniquely whereas θ is defined only up to additive multiples of 2π.

From the diagram, if P is the point (x,y) then

$$x = r\cos\theta, \quad y = r\sin\theta. \tag{2.1}$$

Squaring and adding these relations gives $r^2 = x^2 + y^2$. Hence, since r is positive, $r = +\sqrt{(x^2 + y^2)}$.

This quantity r is called the **modulus**, or absolute value, of z. It is customary to write $r = |z| = \mathrm{mod}\ z$. Notice that $x^2 + y^2 = z\bar{z}$, so that $r^2 = |z|^2 = z\bar{z}$.

The angle θ is defined by equation (2.1) only up to an addive integral multiple of 2π. Any angle θ satisfying (2.1) is called an **argument** of z and is written $\theta = \mathrm{Arg}\ z$.

The particular angle θ satisfying (2.1) and lying in the interval $-\pi < \theta \leqslant \pi$ is called the **principal value** of the argument and is written $\theta = \arg z$.

A common method for determining θ is to eliminate r between the equations (2.1) to obtain $\tan\theta = y/x$.

Notice, however, that not every angle $\theta = \tan^{-1}(y/x)$ satisfies the equations (2.1), and so care must be taken when using this method. The form

$$z = r(\cos\theta + \mathrm{j}\sin\theta)$$

is called the **polar form** of the complex number.

In Fig. 2.2, suppose the point P represents the complex number

$$z = x + \mathrm{j}y = r(\cos\theta + \mathrm{j}\sin\theta)$$

If PN is drawn perpendicular to Ox to meet this axis in N, and is produced to

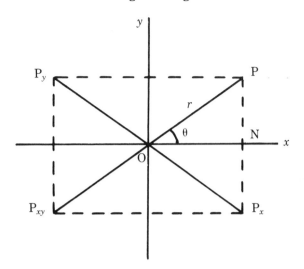

Fig. 2.2

P_x where $PN = NP_x$, the point P_x is seen to represent the complex number

$$x - jy = r(\cos\theta - j\sin\theta),$$

that is, the point P_x, which is the reflection of P in the *real* axis Ox, represents the complex *conjugate* number $\bar{z}$.

Similarly, if P_y is the reflection of P in the *imaginary* axis Oy, then P_y represents $-\bar{z}$. Also, reflection of P in both axes, sometimes referred to as reflection of P in the origin, produces the point P_{xy} which is $-z$.

It is possible now to interpret addition and subtraction on an Argand diagram.

Consider the two complex numbers

$$z_1 = x_1 + jy_1 , \quad z_2 = x_2 + jy_2$$

and suppose them to be represented by the points P and Q respectively as in Fig. 2.3. Now

$$z_1 + z_2 = (x_1 + x_2) + j(y_1 + y_2) ,$$

and this complex number is represented by the point R where OPRQ is a parallelogram.

Since $$z_1 - z_2 = z_1 + (-z_2)$$

it follows that $(z_1 - z_2)$ is represented by the point R' where OPR'Q' is a parallelogram and OQ' is equal in length but opposite in sense to OQ, (that is, Q' is the reflection in O of the point Q).

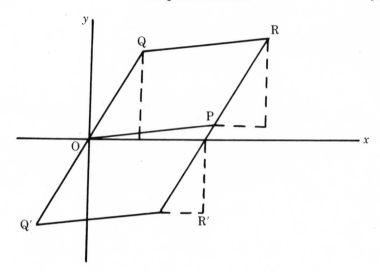

Fig. 2.3

Note that OR' = QP so that $|z_1 - z_2| = $ OR' = QP, and so $|z_1 - z_2|$ is the length of the line joining the points representing z_1 and z_2 in the Argand diagram.

In Fig. 2.4 let the point P represent the complex number

$$z = x + jy = r\,(\cos\theta + j\sin\theta)$$

once again. Suppose the straight line OP is produced to the point M where OM = aOP, a being a real number. This process is called **magnification**, a being the magnification factor. If the point M represents the complex number z_M then

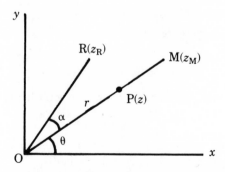

Fig. 2.4

$$\arg z_{\mathrm{M}} = \theta \quad \text{and} \quad |z_{\mathrm{M}}| = ar .$$

Hence,
$$z_{\mathrm{M}} = ar(\cos\theta + \mathrm{j}\sin\theta) = az ,$$

and so magnification corresponds to multiplication by a positive real number.

Now suppose that OR is obtained by rotating OP counter-clockwise through an angle α. If the point R represents the complex number z_{R}, then

$$\arg z_{\mathrm{R}} = \theta + \alpha \quad \text{and} \quad |z_{\mathrm{R}}| = r .$$

Hence,
$$\begin{aligned}
z_{\mathrm{R}} &= r\{\cos(\theta + \alpha) + \mathrm{j}\sin(\theta + \alpha)\} \\
&= r\{\cos\theta\cos\alpha - \sin\theta\sin\alpha + \mathrm{j}(\sin\theta\cos\alpha + \cos\theta\sin\alpha)\} \\
&= r(\cos\alpha + \mathrm{j}\sin\alpha)(\cos\theta + \mathrm{j}\sin\theta) \\
&= (\cos\alpha + \mathrm{j}\sin\alpha)z .
\end{aligned}$$

Therefore, rotation corresponds to multiplication by a factor $(\cos\alpha + \mathrm{j}\sin\alpha)$. In the special case $\alpha = \pi/2$ the factor reduces to j, and so multiplication by j corresponds to rotation through a right-angle in the counter-clockwise sense.

The operations of multiplication and division are more easily discussed on the Argand diagram in terms of polar coordinates. Hence consider

$$z_1 = x_1 + \mathrm{j}y_1 = r_1(\cos\theta_1 + \mathrm{j}\sin\theta_1)$$

and
$$z_2 = x_2 + \mathrm{j}y_2 = r_2(\cos\theta_2 + \mathrm{j}\sin\theta_2)$$

Then
$$\begin{aligned}
z_1 z_2 &= r_1 r_2(\cos\theta_1 + \mathrm{j}\sin\theta_1)(\cos\theta_2 + \mathrm{j}\sin\theta_2) \\
&= r_1 r_2\{\cos(\theta_1 + \theta_2) + \mathrm{j}\sin(\theta_1 + \theta_2)\}
\end{aligned} \tag{2.2}$$

Also,
$$\begin{aligned}
\frac{z_1}{z_2} &= \frac{r_1}{r_2}\frac{(\cos\theta_1 + \mathrm{j}\sin\theta_1)}{(\cos\theta_2 + \mathrm{j}\sin\theta_2)} \\
&= \frac{r_1}{r_2}(\cos\theta_1 + \mathrm{j}\sin\theta_1)(\cos\theta_2 - \mathrm{j}\sin\theta_2) \\
&= \frac{r_1}{r_2}\{\cos(\theta_1 - \theta_2) + \mathrm{j}\sin(\theta_1 - \theta_2)\} .
\end{aligned} \tag{2.3}$$

From (2.2) and (2.3) it follows that

$$|z_1 z_2| = |z_1|\,|z_2| , \quad |z_1/z_2| = |z_1|/|z_2|$$

and
$$\mathrm{Arg}\,(z_1 z_2) = \arg z_1 + \arg z_2$$

$$\mathrm{Arg}\,(z_1/z_2) = \arg z_1 - \arg z_2 .$$

Care must be taken when using principal values of the argument, since, for example, if $\arg z_1 = 5\pi/6$ and $\arg z_2 = 3\pi/6$, then

$$\arg z_1 + \arg z_2 = 8\pi/6$$

and so $\arg(z_1 z_2) = -4\pi/6 \neq \arg z_1 + \arg z_2$.

From (2.2), it is seen that multiplication by a complex number

$$z_2 = r_2(\cos\theta_2 + j\sin\theta_2)$$

corresponds on an Argand diagram to the composition of a magnification, with factor r_2, and a rotation through an angle θ_2. Similarly, from (2.3), division is seen to correspond to the composition of a magnification, with factor $1/r_2$ and a rotation through an angle $-\theta_2$.

It is possible now to consider constructions by which points representing $(z_1 z_2)$ and (z_1/z_2) may be found on an Argand diagram.

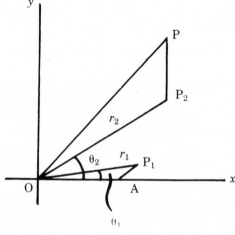

Fig. 2.5

Suppose the complex numbers z_1 and z_2 are represented in Fig. 2.5 by the points P_1 and P_2 respectively. Also, let A be the point $z = 1$. Then, with OP_2 as base corresponding to OA, the triangle OP_2P is constructed to be similar to triangle OAP_1. Now,

$$OP/r_2 = OP/OP_2 = OP_1/OA = r_1/1$$

$$OP = r_1 r_2 .$$

Also $\angle POP_2 = \angle P_1OA = \theta_1$

and so $\angle POA = \theta_1 + \theta_2$.

Hence, the point P on the Argand diagram, Fig. 2.5, represents the number

$$r_1 r_2 \{\cos(\theta_1 + \theta_2) + j\sin(\theta_1 + \theta_2)\} ,$$

that is, the number $z_1 z_2$.

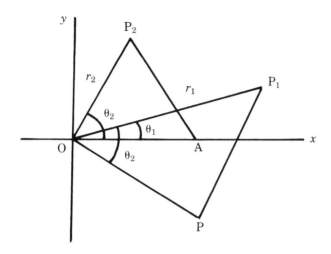

Fig. 2.6

Again suppose that, in Fig. 2.6, P_1, P_2 and A represent the numbers z_1, z_2, $z = 1$ respectively. Then, with OP_1 as base corresponding to OP_2 construct the triangle P_1OP to be similar to triangle P_2OA. Now

$$r_1/r_2 = OP_1/OP_2 = OP/OA = OP/1$$

and so $$OP = r_1/r_2 .$$

Also, $$\angle AOP = \theta_1 - \theta_2 .$$

Hence, the point P in Fig. 2.6 represents the number

$$\frac{r_1}{r_2}\{\cos(\theta_1 - \theta_2) + j\sin(\theta_1 - \theta_2)\} ,$$

that is, the number z_1/z_2.

2.3 THE EXPONENTIAL AND DE MOIVRE'S THEOREM

The complex number $\cos\theta + j\sin\theta$ occurred frequently in the last section. In terms of the power series expansion for $\cos\theta$ and $\sin\theta$,

$$\cos\theta + j\sin\theta = (1 - \frac{1}{2!}\theta^2 + \frac{1}{4!}\theta^4 + \cdots) + j(\theta - \frac{1}{3!}\theta^3 + \frac{1}{5!}\theta^5 + \cdots)$$

$$= 1 + j\theta - \frac{1}{2!}\theta^2 - \frac{1}{3!}j\theta^3 + \frac{1}{4!}\theta^4 + \frac{1}{5!}j\theta^5 + \cdots$$

$$= 1 + j\theta + \frac{1}{2!}(j\theta)^2 + \frac{1}{3!}(j\theta)^3 + \frac{1}{4!}(j\theta)^4 + \frac{1}{5!}(j\theta)^5 + \cdots$$

Comparing the series appearing on the right-hand side with the power series expansion for e^x, where x is real,

$$e^x = 1 + x + \frac{1}{2!}x^2 + \frac{1}{3!}x^3 + \frac{1}{4!}x^4 + \frac{1}{5!}x^5 + \cdots$$

suggests that $\cos\theta + j\sin\theta$ may be written as $e^{j\theta}$. In fact this could be taken as the definition of the exponential of an imaginary number, so that

$$e^{j\theta} = \cos\theta + j\sin\theta .$$

The exponential of a real number has the property that the exponential of a sum of real numbers is equal to the product of the exponentials of the two real numbers, so that $e^{a+b} = e^a e^b$.

With the definition given above the exponential of an imaginary number has the analagous property,

$$e^{j\theta + j\phi} = e^{j\theta}\, e^{j\phi}.$$

The proof is as follows:

$$e^{j\theta + j\phi} = e^{j(\theta + \phi)} = \cos(\theta + \phi) + j\sin(\theta + \phi)$$

$$= \cos\theta\,\cos\phi - \sin\theta\,\sin\phi + j(\sin\theta\cos\phi + \cos\theta\sin\phi)$$

$$= (\cos\theta + j\sin\theta)\,(\cos\phi + j\sin\phi)$$

$$= e^{j\theta}e^{j\phi}.$$

The exponential of the complex number $z = x + jy$ is defined by

$$e^z = e^x\, e^{jy} ,$$

and it may be noticed that

$$e^{z_1 + z_2} = e^{z_1}\, e^{z_2} .$$

The equation $z = r(\cos\theta + j\sin\theta)$ which defines the polar form of the complex number z may be written now as $z = re^{j\theta}$. As has been mentioned already, the modulus r is defined uniquely, whereas the argument θ is defined only up to an additive multiple of 2π. Hence, if $z_1 = z_2$, that is, if $r_1\, e^{j\theta_1} = r_2\, e^{j\theta_2}$, then $r_1 = r_2$ and $\theta_1 = \theta_2 + 2\pi k$ where k is an integer.

Now consider the equation $z^3 = 1$ which was used earlier to motivate the introduciton of complex numbers. Write $z = re^{j\theta}$ and $1 = \cos 0 + j\sin 0 = e^{j0}$, then

$$r^3\, e^{j3\theta} = 1\, e^{j0}.$$

Thus, $r^3 = 1$, so that $r = 1$ and $3\theta = 0 + 2\pi k$. Hence the cube roots of unity are given by

$$z = e^{j(2\pi k/3)} .$$

In fact there are only three *distinct* roots. If they are expressed in terms of the principal values of their arguments, then k must be chosen so that $-\pi < 2\pi k/3 \leqslant \pi$, that is $k = -1, 0, 1$. The three cube roots of unity are therefore

$$e^{-j2\pi/3}, \quad e^0, \quad e^{+j2\pi/3}.$$

Since $\cos 2\pi/3 = -\frac{1}{2}$ and $\sin 2\pi/3 = \dfrac{\sqrt{3}}{2}$ these roots may be written as

$$-\tfrac{1}{2} - j\,\dfrac{\sqrt{3}}{2}, 1, -\tfrac{1}{2} + j\,\dfrac{\sqrt{3}}{2}$$

which agrees with the expressions for the roots given earlier.

The method given above for computing the cube roots of unity may be extended to compute the nth root of any given complex number w.

Let $\qquad\qquad\qquad z^n = w, \quad$ so that $\quad z = \sqrt[n]{w}$

Put $z = re^{j\theta}$ and $w = Re^{j\Theta}$ where $-\pi < \Theta \leqslant \pi$, then

$$r^n\, e^{jn\theta} = Re^{j\Theta}$$

It follows that $\qquad\qquad\qquad r^n = R$

and $\qquad\qquad\qquad\qquad n\theta = \Theta + 2\pi k.$

Since r is real the roots may be written

$$z = R^{1/n}\, e^{j(\Theta + 2\pi k)/n}.$$

There are n distinct roots and, if they are to be expressed in terms of the principal values of their arguments, k must be chosen so that

$$-\pi < \frac{\Theta}{n} + \frac{2\pi k}{n} \leqslant \pi.$$

These roots may be plotted on an Argand diagram. They all lie on a circle of radius $R^{1/n}$ centered at the origin, and form the vertices of a regular n-sided polygon, one vertex being located at $\theta = \Theta/n$.

The above computations depend upon the result that for a positive integer n

$$(e^{j\theta})^n = e^{jn\theta}.$$

This is certainly true, because the product of the exponentials of two imaginary numbers is equal to the exponential of their sum. Repeated use of this fact shows that the product of $e^{j\theta}$ with itself n times is equal to the exponential of the sum of $j\theta$ with itself n times. The rigorous proof is by induction.

In terms of $\cos\theta + j\sin\theta$ the above result may be written

$$(\cos\theta + j\sin\theta)^n = \cos n\theta + j\sin n\theta.$$

This is know as **De Moivre's Theorem**. The previous result that $(e^{j\theta})^n = e^{jn\theta}$ then follows from it.

The theorem is certainly true for $n = 1$. Assume it is true for $n \leqslant p - 1$, then

$$(\cos\theta + j \sin\theta)^p = (\cos\theta + j \sin\theta)^{p-1} (\cos\theta + j \sin\theta)$$

$$= (\cos(p-1)\theta + j \sin (p-1)\theta)(\cos\theta + j \sin\theta)$$

$$= \cos p\theta + j \sin p\theta ,$$

since it has already been shown that

$$(\cos\theta + j \sin\theta) (\cos\phi + j \sin\phi) = \cos(\theta+\phi) + j \sin (\theta+\phi) .$$

De Moivre's Theorem follows by induction. If n is a negative integer and if $n = -m$ then,

$$(\cos\theta + j \sin\theta)^n = \frac{1}{(\cos\theta + j \sin\theta)^m} = \frac{(\cos\theta - j \sin\theta)^m}{(\cos\theta + j \sin\theta)^m(\cos\theta-j \sin\theta)^m}$$

$$= (\cos(-\theta) + j \sin (-\theta))^m$$

$$= \cos(-m\theta) + j \sin(-m\theta)$$

$$= \cos n\theta + j \sin n\theta .$$

Hence De Moivre's Theorem also holds for negative integers n. The situation is rather more difficult when n is a rational number, that is when $n = p/q$ where p and q are integers. Write

$$z = (\cos\theta + j \sin\theta)^{p/q}$$

so that $z^q = (\cos\theta + j \sin\theta)^p = \cos p\theta + j \sin p\theta = e^{jp\theta} .$

If q is positive, the general expression for z will be

$$z = \exp\left\{j\left(\frac{p}{q}\theta + 2\pi \frac{k}{q}\right)\right\} = \exp\left(j\frac{p}{q}\theta\right) \exp\left(j2\pi \frac{k}{q}\right) .$$

where k is an integer. Hence

$$(\cos\theta + j \sin\theta)^{p/q} = (\cos(p/q)\theta + j \sin(p/q)\theta)\, e^{j2\pi k/q}$$

There are q distinct values of $(\cos\theta + j \sin\theta)^{p/q}$, the value given by $k = 0$ alone corresponding to the right-hand side of De Moivre's Theorem. De Moivre's Theorem, therefore, only holds for integral values of n.

2.4 HYPERBOLIC FUNCTIONS

Consider the circle $x^2 + y^2 = 1$. This equation may be written

$$(x + jy) (x - jy) = 1 .$$

Here $(x + jy)$ is a complex number of unit modulus, and so may be written as

$$x + jy = e^{j\theta}$$

where θ is a real number. Then,

$$x - jy = e^{-j\theta}$$

so that the coordinates of any point on the circle may be written as the following functions of θ:

$$x = \tfrac{1}{2}(e^{j\theta} + e^{-j\theta}), \quad y = \frac{1}{2j}(e^{j\theta} - e^{-j\theta}). \tag{2.4}$$

Now consider the rectangular hyperbola $x^2 - y^2 = 1$.
This equation may be written as $(x + y)(x - y) = 1$.
Now $x + y$ is a real number. If it is positive then it may be written as

$$x + y = e^{\theta}$$

where θ is a real number. Then from the equation of the hyperbola, it follows that

$$x - y = e^{-\theta}$$

so that the coordinates of those points on the hyperbola for which $x + y > 0$ may be written as the following functions of θ:

$$x = \frac{1}{2}(e^{\theta} + e^{-\theta}), \quad y = \frac{1}{2}(e^{\theta} - e^{-\theta}). \tag{2.5}$$

The two functions appearing in equations (2.4) may be recognised from definitions given earlier. In fact

$$\frac{1}{2}(e^{j\theta} + e^{-j\theta}) = \cos\theta \quad \text{and} \quad \frac{1}{2j}(e^{j\theta} - e^{-j\theta}) = \sin\theta$$

By analogy, the two functions appearing in (2.5) are defined to be the hyperbolic cosine and hyperbolic sine. These are written $\cosh\theta$ and $\sinh\theta$ and

$$\cosh\theta = \frac{1}{2}(e^{\theta} + e^{-\theta}), \quad \sinh\theta = \frac{1}{2}(e^{\theta} - e^{-\theta}).$$

Summing up, the coordinates of any point on the circle may be written as

$$x = \cos\theta, \quad y = \sin\theta$$

whereas the coordinates of those points on the hyperbola for which $x + y > 0$ may be written as

$$x = \cosh\theta, \quad y = \sinh\theta.$$

Clearly the coordinates of any point on the circle may also be written as

$$x = -\cos\theta , \quad y = -\sin\theta .$$

Those points whose coordinates are written as

$$x = -\cosh\theta , \quad y = -\sinh\theta$$

are in fact, the 'missing points' of the hyperbola corresponding to $x + y < 0$.

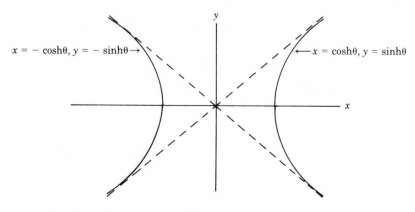

Fig. 2.7

The hyperbola consists of two disjoint curves as illustrated in Fig. 2.7. These are the two branches of the hyperbola. For one $x + y > 0$ and for the other $x + y < 0$. The asymptotes are the straight lines $x \pm y = 0$.

The hyperbolic tangent, cotangent, secant and cosecant are denoted by $\tanh\theta$, $\coth\theta$, $\mathrm{sech}\theta$ and $\mathrm{cosech}\theta$ and are defined by

$$\tanh\theta = \sinh\theta/\cosh\theta = 1/\coth\theta$$

$$\mathrm{sech}\theta = 1/\cosh\theta$$

$$\mathrm{cosech}\theta = 1/\sinh\theta .$$

A succession of properties of $\cosh x$ and $\sinh x$, similar to those of cosine and sine, will be established now.

(a) From earlier results it follows that the series expansion for $\cosh x$ and $\sinh x$ are

$$\cosh x = \frac{1}{2}\,(e^x + e^{-x}) = 1 + \frac{x^2}{2!} + \frac{x^4}{4!} + \cdots$$

and

$$\sinh x = \frac{1}{2}\,(e^x - e^{-x}) = x + \frac{x^3}{3!} + \frac{x^5}{5!} + \cdots$$

Hence, $\cosh x$ is an even function of x which must be greater than unity for all real values of x, and sinh$x$ is an odd function which is positive for positive values of x and negative for negative values of x. Also, it may be noted that

$$\cosh 0 = 1, \quad \sinh 0 = 0 .$$

(b) From the definitions (2.4) it follows that

$$\cosh^2 x - \sinh^2 x = \tfrac{1}{4}\{(e^x + e^{-x})^2 - (e^x - e^{-x})^2\}$$

$$= \tfrac{1}{4}\{e^{2x} + 2 + e^{-2x} - (e^{2x} - 2 + e^{-2x})\} = 1$$

$$\underline{\cosh^2 x - \sinh^2 x = 1} \qquad\qquad (2.6)$$

(c) Again, using the definitions (2.4),

$$\cosh x \cosh y - \sinh x \sinh y = \tfrac{1}{4}\{(e^x + e^{-x})(e^y + e^{-y}) + (e^x - e^{-x})(e^y - e^{-y})\}$$

$$= \tfrac{1}{2}(e^{x+y} + e^{-x-y}) = \cosh(x + y)$$

$$\underline{\cosh(x + y) = \cosh x \cosh y + \sinh x \sinh y .}$$

Similarly, it may be shown that

$$\sinh(x + y) = \sinh x \cosh y + \cosh x \sinh y .$$

In the particular case when $x = y$, these two results give

$$\cosh 2x = \cosh^2 x + \sinh^2 x, \quad \sinh 2x = 2\sinh x \cosh x .$$

Combining the first of these latter two results with (2.6) gives

$$\cosh^2 x = \tfrac{1}{2}(\cosh 2x + 1) .$$

(d) From (2.4)

$$\cosh(-x) = \tfrac{1}{2}(e^{-x} + e^{-(-x)})$$

$$= \tfrac{1}{2}(e^{-x} + e^x) = \cosh x .$$

Also, $$\sinh(-x) = \tfrac{1}{2}(e^{-x} - e^{-(-x)})$$

$$= \tfrac{1}{2}(e^{-x} - e^x) = -\sinh x .$$

2.4.1 The graphs of cosh x and sinh x

Cosh$x$ being an even function of x, has a graph which is symmetrical about the axis of y (Fig. 2.8). Also, as x increases from 0 to ∞, cosh$x$ increases from 1 to ∞.

Sinh$x$, however, is an odd function of x and has a graph which is symmetrical about the origin. As x increases from 0 to ∞, sinh$x$ increases from 0 to ∞. It is evident, from definitions (2.4), that sinh$x$ is always less than cosh$x$ but becomes nearly equal to it as x becomes large since, as $x \to \infty$, $e^{-x} \to 0$.

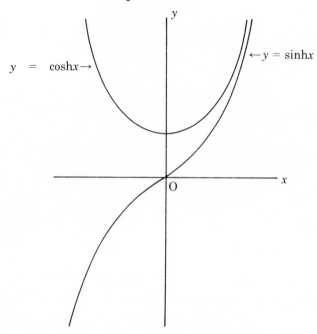

Fig. 2.8

2.5 DIFFERENTIATION OF HYPERBOLIC FUNCTIONS

Consider $\cosh x$.

$$\frac{d}{dx}(\cosh x) = \frac{1}{2}\frac{d}{dx}(e^x + e^{-x})$$

$$= \frac{1}{2}(e^x - e^{-x}) = \sinh x\,.$$

Similarly, for $\sinh x$,

$$\frac{d}{dx}(\sinh x) = \frac{1}{2}\frac{d}{dx}(e^x - e^{-x})$$

$$= \frac{1}{2}(e^x + e^{-x}) = \cosh x$$

2.6 INVERSE HYPERBOLIC FUNCTIONS

In practice, it is sometimes necessary to determine a function whose hyperbolic cosine has a given value x. If the function is y, then $x = \cosh y$. The notation

$y = \cosh^{-1}x$ is used to denote the inverse hyperbolic cosine.

From the properties of the hyperbolic cosine, it follows that

(i) if $x < 1$, the value of $\cosh^{-1}x$ does not exist;

(ii) if $x > 1$, there are two values of $\cosh^{-1}x$, equal in magnitude but opposite in sign.

$\cosh^{-1}x$ may be expressed in terms of logarithms as follows:

If $$y = \cosh^{-1}x$$

then $$x = \cosh y = \tfrac{1}{2}(e^y + e^{-y})$$

and so $$e^{2y} - 2xe^y + 1 = 0 .$$

Regarding this as a quadratic equation in e^y,

$$e^y = x \pm (x^2 - 1)^{\frac{1}{2}}$$

and so, $$y = \log\{(x \pm (x^2 - 1)^{\frac{1}{2}}\} .$$

These are the two values of y, and their sum is seen to be

$$\log(x + (x^2 - 1)^{\frac{1}{2}}) + \log(x - (x^2 - 1)^{\frac{1}{2}})$$

$$= \log(x + (x^2 - 1)^{\frac{1}{2}}) (x - (x^2 - 1)^{\frac{1}{2}})$$

$$= \log(x^2 - (x^2 - 1)) = \log 1 = 0 .$$

The two roots are equal and opposite.

To find the differential coefficient of $\cosh^{-1}x$, the relation $\cosh y = x$ is differentiated with respect to x. Then

$$\sinh y \frac{dy}{dx} = 1 .$$

$$\frac{dy}{dx} = \frac{1}{\sinh y} = \pm \frac{1}{(\cosh^2 y - 1)^{\frac{1}{2}}} = \pm \frac{1}{(x^2 - 1)^{\frac{1}{2}}} .$$

The gradient is positive when y is positive and negative when y is negative.

Similarly, the inverse hyperbolic sine of x; that is, the number whose hyperbolic sine is x is denoted by $y = \sinh^{-1}x$. The function is single-valued and is determined uniquely for all values of x.

$\sinh^{-1}x$ may be expressed in terms of logarithms also as follows. If

$$\sinh^{-1}x = y$$

then $$x = \sinh y = \tfrac{1}{2}(e^y - e^{-y}),$$

and so $$e^{2y} - 2xe^{-y} - 1 = 0 .$$

Solving this quadratic for e^y gives

$$e^y = x \pm (x^2 + 1)^{\frac{1}{2}} .$$

However, the exponential function is positive, and so the positive sign must be taken for the square root.

$$e^y = x + (x^2 + 1)^{\frac{1}{2}}$$

$$y = \log(x + (x^2 + 1)^{\frac{1}{2}}).$$

In order to find the differential coefficient of $\sinh^{-1}x$ consider

$$\sinh y = x,$$

then

$$\cosh y \, \frac{dy}{dx} = 1$$

$$\frac{dy}{dx} = \frac{1}{\cosh y} = \pm \frac{1}{(\sinh^2 y + 1)^{\frac{1}{2}}} = \pm \frac{1}{(x^2 + 1)^{\frac{1}{2}}}.$$

However, $\cosh y$ is positive always, and so the gradient must be positive always.

$$dy/dx = 1/(x^2 + 1)^{\frac{1}{2}}.$$

2.7 THE LOGARITHMIC FUNCTION

The natural logarithm of a complex number, denoted by $\mathrm{Log}z$, is defined by analogy with the Naperian logarithm of a real number by the equation

$$e^{\mathrm{Log}z} = z.$$

Substituting $\mathrm{Log}z = \alpha + j\beta$ and $z = re^{j\theta}$, where $-\pi < \theta \leq \pi$, into this equation gives

$$e^{\alpha} e^{j\beta} = re^{j\theta}.$$

Hence, since α and β are both real,

$$e^{\alpha} = r \quad \text{or} \quad \alpha = \log_e r$$

and

$$\beta = \theta + 2\pi k; \quad k = 0, 1, 2, \dots$$

Thus

$$\mathrm{Log}z = \log_e r + j(\theta + 2\pi k).$$

From this expression it is seen that the value of $\mathrm{Log}z$ is defined only up to additive multiples of $2\pi j$. The principal value of $\mathrm{Log}z$ is denoted by $\log z$ and corresponds to the choice $k = 0$.

Hence

$$\log z = \log_e r + j\theta,$$

that is

$$\log z = \log_e |z| + j \arg z.$$

It follows that

$$\mathrm{Log}z = \log z + 2\pi kj, \quad k \text{ any integer.}$$

Now consider the two complex numbers

$$z_1 = r_1(\cos\theta_1 + j\sin\theta_1),\, z_2 = r_2(\cos\theta_2 + j\sin\theta_2)$$

where θ_1 and θ_2 are the principal values of the respective arguments.

Then, $\text{Log } z_1 = \log_e r_1 + j(\theta_1 + 2n\pi)$

$$\text{Log } z_2 = \log_e r_2 + j(\theta_2 + 2m\pi)$$

where n and m are integers. Adding gives

$$\text{Log} z_1 + \text{Log} z_2 = \log_e r_1 r_2 + j(\theta_1 + \theta_2 + 2p\pi)$$

where $p = n + m$.

It is known that

$$z_1 z_2 = r_1 r_2(\cos(\theta_1 + \theta_2) + j\sin(\theta_1 + \theta_2))$$

so that

$$\text{Log} z_1 z_2 = \log_e r_1 r_2 + j(\theta_1 + \theta_2 + 2q\pi)$$

where q is an integer. Consequently,

$$\text{Log} z_1 + \text{Log} z_2 = \text{Log} z_1 z_2 \tag{2.7}$$

where every value of the left-hand side equals some value of $\text{Log} z_1 z_2$, and conversely.

As far as principal valued logarithms are concerned, the result is

$$\log z_1 + \log z_2 = \text{Log} z_1 z_2$$

where the right-hand side will be principal valued itself if and only if

$$-\pi < \arg z_1 + \arg z_2 \leqslant \pi.$$

In the manner used to obtain (2.4) it may be shown that

$$\text{Log} z_1 - \text{Log} z_2 = \text{Log}(z_1/z_2). \tag{2.8}$$

The exponential and logarithm may be used to provide a suitable method for defining complex powers of complex numbers. Consider two complex numbers z and γ, then z^γ may be defined by

$$z^\gamma = \exp(\gamma \text{Log} z).$$

$\text{Log} z$ is multivalued, and so z will be multivalued also. The principal value of z^γ is defined by $\exp(\gamma \log z)$; where the principal value of $\text{Log} z$ has been chosen so that, since the exponential is single valued, $\exp(\gamma \log z)$ has a unique value.

EXERCISES 2

(1) Express the following in the form $x + jy$, where x and y are both real numbers:

$$(3 + 5j) + (7 - 2j)\,;\quad 3j + (2 - j)\,;$$

$$j\,(1 + j) \qquad ; \quad (3 - j)\,(2 - j)\,.$$

(2) Write down the complex conjugate $\bar{z}$ of the number $z = x + jy$ and show that

$$z\,\bar{z} = x^2 + y^2\,.$$

(3) Express the following quotients in the form $x + jy$, where x and y are real numbers

$$\frac{1}{j}\,;\; \frac{3 + 5j}{1 + 6j}\,;\; \frac{1 + j}{1 - j}\,.$$

(4) Prove that $x_1 + jy_1 = x_2 + jy_2$ if and only if $x_1 = x_2$ and $y_1 = y_2$.

(5) Express $\qquad \dfrac{(3 + j)(1 - j) + (4 + 2j)}{(1 - 2j)} \qquad$ in the form $x + jy$

where x and y are real numbers.

(6) Find the modulus of $(1 + 2j)^2/(3 - 4j)$ by first simplifying the complex number and then verify the result by using $|z_1 z_2| = |z_1|\,|z_2|$ and $|z_1/z_2| = |z_1|/|z_2|$.

(7) Find the loci in an Argand diagram of the points representing the complex number z subject to the relations:

(a) $\qquad\qquad\qquad |z - 2| = |z|$: (b) $|z + 2| = |z - 5j|$;

(c) $\qquad\qquad\qquad |z - a| = k$; (d) $|z - p| = 2\,|z|$.

(8) Find the six roots of the equation $z^6 + 1 = 0$ in the form $a + jb$ where a and b are real, and represent them on an Argand diagram.

(9) (a) solve the equation $(z + 1)^4 = 81z^4$, giving the complex roots in the form $a + jb$ where a and b are real.

(b) The n roots of the equation $z^n = 1$ are represented in the Argand diagram by the n vertices of a regular polygon. Show that the mid-points of the sides of this polygon represent the complex numbers which are the roots of the equation $z^n = -\cos^n (\pi/n)$.

(10) Using De Moivre's Theorem evaluate $(1 + j)^4 + (1 - j)^4$.

(11) Use De Moivre's Theorem to express $\sin 3\theta$ and $\cos 3\theta$ in terms of $\sin\theta$ and $\cos\theta$ respectively. Hence show that, if $\sin 3\theta + \cos 3\theta = 0$, either $\tan\theta = 1$ or $\sin 2\theta = -\frac{1}{2}$.

(12) Show that

$$\sinh x \pm \sinh y = 2 \sinh \frac{x \pm y}{2} \cosh \frac{x \mp y}{2}$$

$$\cosh x + \cosh y = 2 \cosh \frac{x+y}{2} \cosh \frac{x-y}{2}$$

$$\cosh x - \cosh y = 2 \sinh \frac{x+y}{2} \sinh \frac{x-y}{2}.$$

Chapter 3
Integration

3.1 INTRODUCTION.

In Chapter 1, the process of differentiation of a function of one variable was defined and studied. However, the inverse process occurs frequently in many branches of mathematics, engineering, and physical science; that is, given the value of the derivative dy/dx as a function of x, it is required to find the value of y itself. The process of carrying out this evaluation is termed **integration**, and it may be regarded as simply the inverse process to differentiation. Viewed in this way, the problem is seen to be to solve the equation

$$dy/dx = f(x) \qquad (3.1)$$

for y, where $f(x)$ is a given function of x. If a function $\Phi(x)$ may be found whose derivative $\Phi'(x)$ equals $f(x)$ then equation (3.1) is seen to be satisfied by

$$y = \Phi(x) + c \qquad (3.2)$$

where c is an arbitrary constant.

The constant c is arbitrary unless further restrictions are placed on the relation between the variables y and x; for example, if it is given that $y = 0$ when $x = a$, then (3.2) must satisfy $0 = \Phi(a) + c$ also. In this case, the solution of (3.1) which satisfies the added condition is $y = \Phi(x) - \Phi(a)$.

The process of finding a function $\Phi(x)$ whose derivative is $f(x)$ is called **integration with respect to** x. $\Phi(x)$ is termed the **integral** of $f(x)$ and the notation used is

$$\Phi(x) = \int f(x) dx .$$

Here $f(x)$ is called the **integrand**, and the symbolism $\int \ldots dx$ will be explained later.

In general, the determination of $\Phi(x)$ for some given function $f(x)$ is more difficult than the evaluation of derivatives. However, some simple rules may be given, and several integrals may be written down immediately since they are obvious from the corresponding results for differentiation.

For example, if $y = x^{n+1}$ $(n \neq -1)$, $dy/dx = (n + 1) x^n$, and so the derivative of $x^{n+1}/(n + 1)$ is x^n.

Hence, $\int x^n dx = x^{n+1}/(n+1)$.

Similarly, it is seen that

$$\int x^{-1} dx \quad = \log x$$

$$\int e^x dx \quad = e^x$$

$$\int \cos x dx \quad = \sin x$$

$$\int \sin x dx \quad = -\cos x$$

$$\int \sec^2 x dx \quad = \tan x$$

where the arbitrary constant c has been omitted in each case.

Also, it follows quite simply by differentiation that these standard forms for integrals may be extended to slightly more difficult cases:

(i) the addition of a constant to x makes no difference to the form of the integral, since the derivative of $f(x + b)$ is $f'(x + b)$ and so

$$\int f'(x + b) \, dx = f(x + b) .$$

(ii) if x is multiplied by a constant, the integral is of the same form but is divided by the constant, since the derivative of $f(ax + b)$ is $af'(ax + b)$ and so

$$\int f'(ax + b) \, dx = \frac{1}{a} f(ax + b) .$$

3.2 METHODS OF INTEGRATION

3.2.1 Integration of rational algebraic functions

If the degree of the numerator is equal to, or higher than, the degree of the denominator, the numerator must be divided by the denominator until the remainder is of lower degree than the denominator. This gives one or more terms whose integrals may be written down immediately, together with a fraction whose numerator is of lower degree than its denominator. It remains to consider the integration of such fractions.

(a) Suppose the denominator is of the first degree. In this case, after division the remainder will be independent of x, and so the process described above leads to the integral being given as the sum of a number of powers of x, together with a logarithm.

For example,

(i)
$$\int \frac{x^3}{x - 2} \, dx = \int \left\{ x^2 + 2x + 4 + \frac{8}{x - 2} \right\} \, dx$$

$$= \frac{1}{3} x^3 + x^2 + 4x + 8\log(x - 2) .$$

(ii) $\displaystyle\int \frac{x^3}{a-2x}\,dx = \int\left\{-\tfrac{1}{2}x^2 - \tfrac{1}{4}ax - \tfrac{1}{8}a^2 + \frac{a^3}{8(a-2x)}\right\}\,dx$

$$= -\frac{1}{6}x^3 - \tfrac{1}{8}ax^2 - \tfrac{1}{8}a^2x - \frac{1}{16}a^3\log(a-2x).$$

(b) Suppose the denominator is of the second degree, and first consider the case when the denominator breaks up into rational factors. In this particular case, the method of partial fractions may be used, and this is illustrated by the following examples.

(i) Using the method of partial fractions, it is seen that

$$\frac{5x-4}{x^2-8x+12} = \frac{13}{2(x-6)} - \frac{3}{2(x-2)},$$

and so

$$\int \frac{5x-4}{x^2-8x+12}\,dx = \frac{13}{2}\int\frac{dx}{x-6} - \frac{3}{2}\int\frac{dx}{x-2}$$

$$= \frac{13}{2}\log(x-6) - \frac{3}{2}\log(x-2).$$

(ii) Consider $\displaystyle\int \frac{x^2}{2x^2+x-3}\,dx.$

In this particular example it shoud be noticed that the numerator and denominator are of the same degree, and so the first step must be to divide the numerator by the denominator.

$$\frac{x^2}{2x^2+x-3} = \frac{1}{2} - \frac{(x-3)}{2(x-1)(2x+3)}.$$

The final term may be resolved into partial fractions, and it is seen that

$$\frac{(x-3)}{(x-1)(2x+3)} = -\frac{2}{5(x-1)} + \frac{9}{5(2x+3)},$$

and so $\displaystyle\int \frac{x^2}{2x^2+x-3}\,dx = \frac{x}{2} + \frac{1}{5}\log(x-1) - \frac{9}{20}\log(2x+3).$

The general method outlined in this section may be used to evaluate the two integrals

$$\int \frac{dx}{x^2-a^2}\,;\quad \int\frac{dx}{a^2-x^2}.$$

Now $\displaystyle\frac{1}{x^2-a^2} = \frac{1}{2a}\left\{\frac{1}{x-a} - \frac{1}{x+a}\right\}$

and so
$$\int \frac{dx}{x^2 - a^2} = \frac{1}{2a}\{\log(x - a) - \log(x + a)\}$$

$$= \frac{1}{2a}\log\frac{x - a}{x + a}$$

Similarly,
$$\int \frac{dx}{a^2 - x^2} = \frac{1}{2a}\log\frac{a + x}{a - x}.$$

Bearing in mind the properties of logarithms, it will be realised that in the first of these two expressions x^2 is greater than a^2, while in the second x^2 is less than a^2.

Now consider the case when the denominator, although still of the second degree, does not break up into rational factors. As has just been shown

$$\text{if } x^2 > a^2, \quad \int \frac{dx}{x^2 - a^2} = \frac{1}{2a}\log\frac{x - a}{x + a}$$

$$\text{if } x^2 < a^2, \quad \int \frac{dx}{a^2 - x^2} = \frac{1}{2a}\log\frac{a + x}{a - x}.$$

Again, consider $\qquad y = \tan^{-1}(x/a),$

that is $\qquad x = a\tan y.$

$$dx/dy = a\sec^2 y$$

$$= a(1 + \tan^2 y) = \frac{1}{a}(a^2 + x^2)$$

and so $\qquad dy/dx = a/(a^2 + x^2).$

Reversing this result, it is seen that

$$\int \frac{dx}{a^2 + x^2} = \frac{1}{a}\tan^{-1}(x/a).$$

For integrals in which the denominator does not resolve into rational factors but which have a numerator of unity, the solution may be obtained by dividing the denominator by the coefficient of x^2 and completing the square of the terms containing x. This procedure reduces the integral to one of the three standards forms just mentioned. For example,

$$\int \frac{dx}{3x^2 - 4x + 7} = \frac{1}{3}\int \frac{dx}{x^2 - \frac{4x}{3} + \frac{7}{3}}$$

$$= \frac{1}{3}\int \frac{dx}{\left(x - \frac{2}{3}\right)^2 + \frac{17}{9}}$$

$$= \frac{1}{3} \frac{1}{\frac{1}{3}\sqrt{17}} \tan^{-1} \frac{(x - 2/3)}{\frac{1}{3}\sqrt{17}}$$

$$= \frac{1}{\sqrt{17}} \tan^{-1} \frac{(3x - 2)}{\sqrt{17}}$$

where the third of the above standard forms has been used.

Before proceeding further, it should be noted that the integral of a fraction whose numerator is the derivative of its denominator is the logarithm of the denominator; that is, the integral of $f'(x)/f(x)$ with respect to x is $\log f(x)$. This simple result is obvious from the method of differentiating the logarithm of any function of x. Its use is illustrated by the following examples:

(i) $\displaystyle\int \frac{2x + 3}{x^2 + 3x - 4} \, dx = \log(x^2 + 3x - 4)$.

(ii) $\displaystyle\int \frac{x^3}{x^4 + a^4} \, dx = \frac{1}{4} \int \frac{4x^3}{x^4 + a^4} \, dx$.

$$= \frac{1}{4} \log (x^4 + a^4)$$

(iii) $\displaystyle\int \cot x \, dx \quad = \int \frac{\cos x}{\sin x} \, dx = \log \sin x$.

Now, returning to the integration of rational functions, the next case to consider is that in which the denominator is of the second degree and the numerator is of the first degree. In this case, first put the numerator equal to ($k \times$ derivative of the denominator) + l, where k and l are constants which may be determined by inspection. The integral may be divided into two parts, of which the first is a fraction whose numerator is the derivative of its denominator and whose integral, therefore, is the logarithm of the denominator. The second part of the integral is a fraction of a kind considered already.

If the numerator is of the second or higher degree, it may be divided by the denominator until the remainder is of the first degree. Hence, it has been shown how to integrate *any* rational algebraic function whose denominator is of the first or second degree.

The following examples will illustrate the method outlined above:

(i) $\displaystyle\int \frac{4x + 5}{x^2 + 2x + 2} \, dx = \int \frac{2(2x + 2) + 1}{x^2 + 2x + 2} \, dx$

$$= 2 \int \frac{2x + 2}{x^2 + 2x + 2} \, dx + \int \frac{dx}{x^2 + 2x + 2}$$

$$= 2\log(x^2 + 2x + 2) + \int \frac{dx}{(x + 1)^2 + 1}$$

$$= 2\log(x^2 + 2x + 2) + \tan^{-1}(x + 1)$$

(ii) $\displaystyle\int \frac{x^3 + 1}{x^2 + 4}\, dx = \int \left\{ x - \frac{4x - 1}{x^2 + 4} \right\}\, dx$

$$= \frac{x^2}{2} - \int \frac{2(2x) - 1}{x^2 + 4}\, dx$$

$$= \frac{x^2}{2} - 2\int \frac{2x}{x^2 + 4}\, dx + \int \frac{dx}{x^2 + 4}$$

$$= \frac{x^2}{2} - 2\log(x^2 + 4) + \frac{1}{2}\tan^{-1}\frac{x}{2}$$

(c) Suppose the denominator is of a degree higher than the second. If the denominator breaks up into rational factors of the first and second degree, the method of partial fractions may be used. The following examples will illustrate the method:

(i) Consider $\displaystyle \frac{x^2 + 1}{x(x^2 - 4)} = \frac{A}{x} + \frac{B}{x - 2} + \frac{C}{x + 2}$.

It may be shown that

$$A = -\tfrac{1}{4}, \quad B = \tfrac{5}{8}, \quad C = \tfrac{5}{8}.$$

Then

$$\int \frac{x^2 + 1}{6x(x^2 - 4)}\, dx = \int \left\{ -\frac{1}{4x} + \frac{5}{8(x - 2)} + \frac{5}{8(x + 2)} \right\}\, dx$$

$$= -\frac{1}{4}\log x + \frac{5}{8}\log(x - 2) + \frac{5}{8}\log(x + 2).$$

(ii) Consider $\displaystyle \frac{1}{(x - 1)^2 (x^2 + 1)} = \frac{A}{x - 1} + \frac{B}{(x - 1)^2} + \frac{Cx + D}{x^2 + 1}$.

It may be shown that

$$A = -\frac{1}{2}, \quad B = \frac{1}{2}, \quad C = \frac{1}{2}, \quad D = 0.$$

Then

$$\int \frac{dx}{(x - 1)^2 (x^2 + 1)} = -\frac{1}{2}\int \frac{dx}{x - 1} = \frac{1}{2}\int \frac{dx}{(x - 1)^2} + \frac{1}{4}\int \frac{2x\,dx}{x^2 + 1}$$

$$= -\frac{1}{2}\log(x - 1) + \frac{1}{2(x - 1)} + \frac{1}{4}\log(x^2 + 1)$$

3.2.2 Integration of irrational fractions of the form
$(px + q)/\sqrt{(x^2 + bx + c)}$

As will be shown later, many irrational expressions may be rationalised by making a suitable change of variable. However, here a fraction will be considered whose numerator is constant or of the first degree and whose denominator is the square root of a second-degree expression.

Earlier it was shown that

$$\int \frac{dx}{a^2 + x^2} = \frac{1}{a} \tan^{-1}(x/a) .$$

In a similar manner, it may be shown that

$$\int \frac{dx}{(a^2 - x^2)^{1/2}} = \sin^{-1}(x/a)$$

$$\int \frac{dx}{(x^2 + a^2)^{1/2}} = \sinh^{-1}(x/a)$$

$$\int \frac{dx}{(x^2 - a^2)^{1/2}} = \cosh^{-1}(x/a)$$

Also, it may be seen that the differential coefficient of $\log\{x + (x^2 \pm a^2)^{1/2}\}$ is $(x^2 \pm a^2)^{-1/2}$ and so, of the above three new standard forms, the last two may be expressed in the alternative form

$$\int \frac{dx}{(x^2 \pm a^2)^{1/2}} = \log\{x + (x^2 \pm a^2)^{1/2}\} .$$

Now consider fractions of the type mentioned in the heading to this section. There are two subtypes to be investigated:

(a) Let the numerator be unity

In this case, divide the expression under the square root sign by the numerical value of the coefficient of x^2 and complete the square of the terms which contain x. Then the integral reduces to one of the three forms mentioned above. For example

(i)
$$\int \frac{dx}{(x^2 + 4x + 13)^{1/2}} = \int \frac{dx}{[(x + 2)^2 + 9]^{1/2}}$$

$$= \sinh^{-1} \frac{x + 2}{3}$$

$$\text{or } \log[x + 2 + (x^2 + 4x + 13)^{1/2}] .$$

(ii)
$$\int \frac{dx}{(8 - 5x - 3x^2)^{1/2}} = \frac{1}{\sqrt{3}} \int \frac{dx}{\left(\frac{8}{3} - \frac{5}{3}x - x^2\right)^{1/2}}$$

$$= \frac{1}{\sqrt{3}} \int \frac{dx}{\left[\dfrac{121}{36} - (x + \text{⅚})^2 \right]^{\frac{1}{2}}}$$

$$= \frac{1}{\sqrt{3}} \sin^{-1} \frac{x + \text{⅚}}{\text{11/6}} = \frac{1}{\sqrt{3}} \sin^{-1} \frac{6x + 5}{11}.$$

(b) Let the numerator be of the first degree

The derivative of $x^{\frac{1}{2}}$ is $\frac{1}{2} x^{-\frac{1}{2}}$, and it follows that the derivative of $u^{\frac{1}{2}}$ with respect to x is

$$\frac{1}{2} u^{-\frac{1}{2}} \frac{du}{dx} \quad \text{or} \quad \frac{\frac{1}{2} du/dx}{u^{\frac{1}{2}}},$$

a fraction whose denominator is $u^{\frac{1}{2}}$ and whose numerator is half the derivative of u. Conversely, the integral of such a fraction is $u^{\frac{1}{2}}$.

Hence, to integrate

$$\frac{px + q}{(ax^2 + bx + c)^{\frac{1}{2}}}$$

put the numerator equal to $k \times$ (half the derivative of the expression under the square root) $+ l$, where k and l are constants whose values in a particular case are obvious by inspection. The integral splits up into two parts of which the first part is a fraction of the form described here (and whose integral, therefore, equals the denominator), and the second part is of the type considered in section (a). For example

(i)
$$\int \frac{x}{(4 - x^2)^{\frac{1}{2}}} \, dx = - \int \frac{\frac{1}{2}(- 2x)}{(4 - x^2)^{\frac{1}{2}}} \, dx$$

$$= - (4 - x^2)^{\frac{1}{2}}$$

(ii)
$$\int \frac{x + 1}{[x (x - 2)]^{\frac{1}{2}}} \, dx = \int \frac{\frac{1}{2}(2x - 2) + 2}{[x^2 - 2x]^{\frac{1}{2}}} \, dx$$

$$= (x^2 - 2x)^{\frac{1}{2}} + 2 \int \frac{dx}{[(x - 1)^2 - 1]^{\frac{1}{2}}}$$

$$= (x^2 - 2x)^{\frac{1}{2}} + 2 \cosh^{-1} (x - 1) \, .$$

3.2.3 Standard forms
There are several standard forms, which have been mentioned already, which

it is absolutely necessary to remember. They are:

$$\int x^n \, dx = \frac{x^{n+1}}{n+1}, \text{ for all } n \text{ except } n = -1,$$

and in that case

$$\int \frac{1}{x} \, dx = \log x$$

$$\int e^x \, dx = e^x$$

$$\int \sin x \, dx = -\cos x$$

$$\int \cos x \, dx = \sin x$$

$$\int \sec^2 x \, dx = \tan x$$

$$\int \frac{dx}{a^2 + x^2} = \frac{1}{a} \tan^{-1} \frac{x}{a}$$

$$\int \frac{dx}{a^2 - x^2} = \frac{1}{2a} \log \frac{a+x}{a-x}, \; x^2 < a^2$$

$$\int \frac{dx}{x^2 - a^2} = \frac{1}{2a} \log \frac{x-a}{x+a}, \; x^2 > a^2$$

$$\int \frac{dx}{(a^2 - x^2)^{1/2}} = \sin^{-1} \frac{x}{a}$$

$$\int \frac{dx}{(a^2 + x^2)^{1/2}} = \sinh^{-1} \frac{x}{a}$$

$$= \log [x + (x^2 + a^2)^{1/2}]$$

$$\int \frac{dx}{(x^2 - a^2)^{1/2}} = \cosh^{-1} \frac{x}{a}$$

$$= \log [x + (x^2 - a^2)^{1/2}].$$

3.2.4 Integration by substitution or change of variable
This is the most frequently used device for converting expressions into standard forms. The theory is as follows

Let $$y = \int f(x) dx .$$

It is required to change the variable from x to u, where u is a given function of x.

Now since $$y = \int f(x) \, dx$$

$$\frac{dy}{dx} = f(x)$$

$$\frac{dy}{du} = \frac{dy}{dx} \cdot \frac{dx}{du} = f(x) \frac{dx}{du}$$

and so

$$y = \int f(x) \frac{dx}{du} \, du \, ,$$

that is

$$\int f(x) \, dx = \int f(x) \frac{dx}{du} \, du \, .$$

Conversely, if (interchanging x and u in this result) an integral is recognised to be of the form

$$\int f(u) \frac{du}{dx} \, dx \, ,$$

it may be replaced by $\int f(u) \, du$.

This is a form of the theorem which is very convenient for use; that is, the integral of the product of $f(u)$ and du/dx with respect to x is the same as the integral of $f(u)$ with respect to u. In practice, the main difficulty encountered (particularly at first) is deciding what function of x should be adopted as u in any particular case. It is experience alone which enables this question to be answered.

If the result is used in the form last mentioned, it must be noted that the substitution adopted must be such that

    (1) one factor of the given expression supplies the du/dx which has to be introduced,

and (2) the remainder of the expression is expressible easily in terms of u.

The method will be illustrated by the following examples:

(i) $$\int \sin^4 x \cos x \, dx$$

Let $u = \sin x$, then $du/dx = \cos x$.
The integral becomes

$$\int u^4 \frac{du}{dx} \, dx = \int u^4 \, du = \frac{u^5}{5} = \frac{1}{5} \sin^5 x \, .$$

(ii) $$\int \frac{\sin x}{\cos^n x} \, dx \, .$$

Let $u = \cos x$. Then $du/dx = -\sin x$.
The integral becomes

$$-\int \frac{1}{u^n} \frac{du}{dx} \, dx = -\int \frac{du}{u^n} = \frac{1}{(n-1) \, u^{n-1}} = \frac{1}{(n-1)\cos^{n-1} x} \, .$$

(iii) $$\int x^2 (a^3 + x^3)^{1/2} dx .$$

Apart from a constant factor, x^2 is the derivative of $(a^3 + x^3)$. Hence, let $u = a^3 + x^3$, then $du/dx = 3x^2$ and the integral becomes

$$\frac{1}{3} \int \frac{du}{dx} u^{1/2} dx = \frac{1}{3} \int u^{1/2} du$$

$$= \frac{1}{3} \frac{u^{3/2}}{3/2} = \frac{2}{9} (a^3 + x^3)^{3/2}$$

(iv) $$\int x (a - bx^2)^n dx .$$

Let $u = a - bx^2$, then $du/dx = -2bx$.
The integral becomes

$$- \frac{1}{2b} \int \frac{du}{dx} u^n dx = - \frac{1}{2b} \int u^n du$$

$$= - \frac{1}{2b} \frac{u^{n+1}}{(n + 1)}$$

$$= - \frac{(a - bx^2)^{n+1}}{2b(n + 1)} .$$

(v) $$\int \frac{x^5}{a^6 + x^6} dx .$$

Since the numerator is $\frac{1}{6}$ the derivative of the denominator, let $u = a^6 + x^6$, then $du/dx = 6x^5$ and the integral becomes

$$\frac{1}{6} \int \frac{1}{u} \frac{du}{dx} dx = \frac{1}{6} \int \frac{1}{u} du = \frac{1}{6} \log u$$

$$= \frac{1}{6} \log(a^6 + x^6) .$$

(vi) $$\int \frac{x^2}{a^6 + x^6} dx .$$

Since the numerator is only x^2 in this case, let $u = x^3$, then $du/dx = 3x^2$ and the integral becomes

$$\frac{1}{3} \int \frac{1}{a^6 + u^2} \frac{du}{dx} dx = \frac{1}{3} \int \frac{1}{a^6 + u^2} du$$

$$= \frac{1}{3} \frac{1}{a^3} \tan^{-1} \frac{u}{a^3}$$

$$= \frac{1}{3a^3} \tan^{-1} \frac{x^3}{a^3} .$$

Generally, if the function to be integrated is the product of x^{n-1} and some function of x^n or of $a + bx^n$, which is recognised to be of a type whose integral is known, the substitution

$$u = x^n \quad \text{or} \quad u = a + bx^n$$

will effect the integration.

Any algebraic expression involving only the one irrational quantity

$$(ax + b)^{1/2}$$

may be rationalised by using the substitution $u^2 = ax + b$. Its integral may be found then by the methods discussed in section 3.2.1. The following examples will illustrate this approach.

(i) Let
$$y = \int \frac{x^2}{(x + 2)^{1/2}} \, dx \,, \quad \text{then} \quad \frac{dy}{dx} = \frac{x^2}{(x + 2)^{1/2}} \,.$$

Now put
$$u^2 = x + 2 \,, \quad \text{then} \quad 2u = dx/du$$

and
$$\frac{dy}{du} = \frac{dy}{dx} \frac{dx}{du} = \frac{x^2}{(x + 2)^{1/2}} \,. \quad 2u = 2(u^2 - 2)^2 \,.$$

Thus
$$y = 2\int (u^4 - 4u^2 + 4) \, du$$

$$= 2u \left(\frac{1}{5} u^4 - \frac{4}{3} u^2 + 4 \right)$$

$$= 2 (x + 2)^{1/2} \left[\frac{1}{5} (x + 2)^2 - \frac{4}{3} (x + 2) + 4 \right]$$

(ii) Let
$$y = \int \frac{dx}{3 + x^{1/2}} \,,$$

then
$$\frac{dy}{dx} = \frac{1}{3 + x^{1/2}} \,.$$

Now put $u^2 = x$, then $2u = dx/du$ and

$$\frac{dy}{du} = \frac{dy}{dx} \frac{dx}{du} = \frac{1}{3 + u} 2u \,.$$

Thus,
$$y = 2 \int \frac{u}{u + 3} \, du = 2 \int \left(1 - \frac{3}{u + 3} \right) du$$

$$= 2 \left[u - 3 \log(u + 3) \right]$$

$$= 2 \left[x^{1/2} - 3 \log(x^{1/2} + 3) \right] \,.$$

It should be noted that, occasionally, two (or even more) substitutions in succession are needed:

(iii) Let

$$y = \int \frac{dx}{(a^2 - x^2)^{3/2}}$$

then

$$\frac{dy}{dx} = \frac{1}{(a^2 - x^2)^{3/2}}.$$

Put $x = 1/u$, then $dx/du = -1/u^2$ and

$$\frac{dy}{du} = \frac{dy}{dx}\frac{dx}{du} = -\frac{1}{\left(a^2 - \dfrac{1}{u^2}\right)^{3/2}}\frac{1}{u^2} = -\frac{u}{(a^2 u^2 - 1)^{3/2}}$$

$$y = -\int \frac{u\,du}{(a^2 u^2 - 1)^{3/2}}.$$

Now put $a^2 u^2 = z$, then $2a^2 u = dz/du$ and

$$y = -\int \frac{\dfrac{1}{2a^2}\dfrac{dz}{du}}{(z - 1)^{3/2}}\,du = -\frac{1}{2a^2}\int (z - 1)^{-3/2}\,dz$$

$$= -\frac{1}{2a^2}\frac{(z - 1)^{-1/2}}{(-1/2)} = \frac{1}{a^2 (z - 1)^{1/2}}$$

$$= \frac{1}{a^2 (a^2 u^2 - 1)^{1/2}} = \frac{x}{a^2 (a^2 - x^2)^{1/2}}.$$

(iv) Let

$$y = \int \frac{dx}{x\,(x^2 - a^2)^{1/2}}$$

then

$$\frac{dy}{dx} = \frac{1}{x\,(x^2 - a^2)^{1/2}}.$$

Again put $x = 1/u$, then $dx/du = -1/u^2$

and

$$\frac{dy}{du} = \frac{dy}{dx}\frac{dx}{du} = -\frac{1}{\dfrac{1}{u}\left(\dfrac{1}{u^2} - a^2\right)^{1/2}}\frac{1}{u^2} = -\frac{1}{(1 - a^2 u^2)^{1/2}}.$$

Therefore,

$$y = -\int \frac{du}{(1 - a^2 u^2)^{1/2}}$$

$$= -\frac{1}{a}\sin^{-1} au = -\frac{1}{a}\sin^{-1}\frac{a}{x}.$$

It might be noted that any expression of the form

$$\frac{1}{(x - k)\,(ax^2 + bx + c)^{1/2}}$$

may be integrated by making use of the substitution $x - k = 1/u$, as in example (iv) above. Using this substitution reduces the expression to the form

$$\frac{1}{(Ax^2 + Bc + C)^{1/2}}$$

which is of the type considered in section 3.2.2(a).

(v) Consider
$$\int \frac{dx}{x\,(ax^n + b)}.$$

This integral may be written

$$\int \frac{x^{n-1}\,dx}{x^n\,(ax^n + b)}$$

and, therefore, may be evaluated by using the substitution $x^n = u$, $nx^{n-1} = du/dx$. Then, the integral becomes

$$\int \frac{\frac{1}{n}\frac{du}{dx}\,dx}{u\,(au + b)} = \frac{1}{n}\int \frac{1}{b}\left\{\frac{1}{u} - \frac{a}{au + b}\right\}\,du$$

$$= \frac{1}{nb}\{\log u - \log(au + b)\}$$

$$= \frac{1}{nb}\log\frac{x^n}{ax^n + b}.$$

However, this integral may be evaluated also by using the substitution $x^n = 1/u$, and the method for obtaining dx/du in this case should be noted. Since $x^n = 1/u$, it follows that

$$n\log x = -\log u$$

and so
$$\frac{n}{x}\frac{dx}{du} = -\frac{1}{u}, \quad \frac{dx}{du} = -\frac{x}{nu}.$$

Therefore,
$$\frac{dy}{du} = \frac{dy}{dx}\frac{dx}{du} = -\frac{1}{x\left(\dfrac{a}{u} + b\right)}\frac{x}{nu} = -\frac{1}{n\,(a + bu)}.$$

Then
$$y = -\frac{1}{nb}\,\log(a + bu)$$

$$= -\frac{1}{nb}\log(a + bx^{-n})$$

$$= \frac{1}{nb}\log\frac{x^n}{ax^n + b}$$

as before.

3.2.5 Trigonometrical integrals

As has been seen in the list of standard forms

$$\int \sin x\, dx = -\cos x, \quad \int \cos x\, dx = \sin x,$$

Also,

$$\int \tan x\, dx = \int \frac{\sin x}{\cos x}\, dx = -\log \cos x.$$

$$\int \cot x\, dx = \int \frac{\cos x}{\sin x}\, dx = \log \sin x.$$

Now consider

$$\int \sec x\, dx = \int \frac{1}{\cos x}\, dx = \int \frac{\cos x}{\cos^2 x}\, dx = \int \frac{\cos x}{1 - \sin^2 x}\, dx.$$

Now put $\sin x = u$, then $\cos x = du/dx$ and the integral becomes

$$\int \frac{du}{1 - u^2} = \frac{1}{2} \log \frac{1 + u}{1 - u} = \frac{1}{2} \log \frac{1 + \sin x}{1 - \sin x}.$$

By noting that

$$\cos \left(\frac{\pi}{2} + x \right) = -\sin x$$

it is seen that this final expression may be written

$$\frac{1}{2} \log \left\{ \frac{1 - \cos \left(\dfrac{\pi}{2} + x \right)}{1 + \cos \left(\dfrac{\pi}{2} + x \right)} \right\} = \log \left\{ \frac{\sin \left(\dfrac{\pi}{4} + \dfrac{x}{2} \right)}{\cos \left(\dfrac{\pi}{4} + \dfrac{x}{2} \right)} \right\}$$

$$= \log \tan \left(\frac{\pi}{4} + \frac{x}{2} \right).$$

Alternatively

$$\frac{1}{2} \log \frac{1 + \sin x}{1 - \sin x} = \frac{1}{2} \log \frac{(1 + \sin x)^2}{1 - \sin^2 x}$$

$$= \log \frac{1 + \sin x}{\cos x} = \log(\sec x + \tan x)$$

Therefore,

$$\int \sec x\, dx = \log \tan \left(\frac{\pi}{4} + \frac{x}{2} \right) = \log (\sec x + \tan x).$$

Finally, consider

$$\int \csc x \, dx = \int \frac{1}{\sin x} \, dx = \int \frac{\sin x}{\sin^2 x} \, dx = \int \frac{\sin x}{1 - \cos^2 x} \, dx .$$

Now put $\cos x = u$, then $-\sin x = du/dx$ and the integral becomes

$$-\int \frac{du}{1 - u^2} = -\frac{1}{2} \log \frac{1 + u}{1 - u}$$

$$= \frac{1}{2} \log \frac{1 - \cos x}{1 + \cos x} = \log \tan \left(\frac{x}{2} \right) .$$

As an alternative, the latter two integrals may be evaluated as follows:

$$\int \csc x \, dx = \int \frac{dx}{\sin x} = \int \frac{dx}{2 \sin \dfrac{x}{2} \cos \dfrac{x}{2}}$$

$$= \int \frac{dx}{2 \tan \dfrac{x}{2} \cos^2 \dfrac{x}{2}}$$

$$= \int \frac{\frac{1}{2} \sec^2 \dfrac{x}{2} \, dx}{\tan \dfrac{x}{2}} = \log \tan \left(\frac{x}{2} \right) .$$

Then

$$\int \sec x \, dx = \int \csc \left(\frac{\pi}{2} + x \right) dx$$

$$= \log \tan \left(\frac{\pi}{4} + \frac{x}{2} \right) .$$

Now consider the integrals of the squares of the circular functions. As is known already

$$\int \sec^2 x \, dx = \tan x , \quad \int \csc^2 x \, dx = - \cot x .$$

Then, using these

$$\int \tan^2 x \, dx = \int (\sec^2 x - 1) dx \quad = \tan x - x$$

$$\int \cot^2 x \, dx = \int (\csc^2 x - 1) dx \quad = - \cot x - x .$$

The remaining two integrals in this group occur very frequently, and the results, together with the method of obtaining them, should be noted.

$$\int \sin^2 x \, dx = \frac{1}{2} \int (1 - \cos 2x) dx$$

$$= \frac{1}{2} \left(x - \frac{1}{2} \sin 2x \right)$$

and

$$\int \cos^2 x \, dx = \tfrac{1}{2} \int (1 + \cos 2x) dx$$

$$= \tfrac{1}{2} (x + \tfrac{1}{2} \sin 2x) \, .$$

Some more examples of trigonometrical integrals, which illustrate various devices which may be used, will be considered now.

(i) $\int \cos^4 x \sin^3 x \, dx$

Let $\cos x = u$, then $-\sin x = du/dx$.

Now, from the $\sin^3 x$, one factor $\sin x$ is removed to supply the $(-du/dx)$ and the remaining $\sin^2 x$ is written as

$$1 - \cos^2 x = 1 - u^2 \, .$$

Hence, the integral becomes

$$-\int u^4 (1 - u^2) \frac{du}{dx} \, dx = - \int (u^4 - u^6) \, du$$

$$= - \frac{1}{5} u^5 + \frac{1}{7} u^7 = \frac{1}{7} \cos^7 x - \frac{1}{5} \cos^5 x \, .$$

(ii) $\int \dfrac{\cos^3 x}{\sin^2 x} \, dx \, .$

Let $\sin x = u$, then $\cos x = du/dx$ and the integral becomes

$$\int \frac{(1 - u^2)}{u^2} \frac{du}{dx} \, dx = \int \left(\frac{1}{u^2} - 1 \right) du$$

$$= - \frac{1}{u} - u = - \operatorname{cosec} x - \sin x \, .$$

Integrals of the general form $\int \sin^m x \cos^n x \, dx$ may be evaluated as in these two examples provided either m or n is an odd number. If m is odd, put $\cos x = u$; if n is odd, put $\sin x = u$.

When $(m + n)$ is an even negative integer, the method illustrated in the following three examples should be adopted.

(iii) $\int \dfrac{\cos^4 x}{\sin^6 x} \, dx = \int \cot^4 x \operatorname{cosec}^2 x \, dx \, .$

Since the derivative of $\cot x$ is $- \operatorname{cosec}^2 x$, put $\cot x = u$. Then, the integral becomes

$$-\int u^4 \frac{du}{dx} \, dx = -\int u^4 \, du = - \frac{u^5}{5} = - \frac{\cot^5 x}{5} \, .$$

(iv)
$$\int \sec^4 x\, dx = \int \sec^2 x\ \sec^2 x\ dx$$

$$= \int (1 + \tan^2 x)\, \sec^2 x\ dx .$$

Now put $\tan x = u$, then $\sec^2 x = du/dx$ and the integral becomes

$$\int (1 + u^2)\, \frac{du}{dx}\, dx = \int (1 + u^2)\, du$$

$$= u + \frac{1}{3}\, u^3 = \tan x + \frac{1}{3}\, \tan^3 x .$$

(v)
$$\int \frac{1}{\sin^2 x \cos^2 x}\, dx = \int \frac{dx}{\tan^2 x\ \cos^4 x} = \int \frac{\sec^2 x\ \sec^2 x}{\tan^2 x}\, dx .$$

Again, putting $\tan x = u$, this integral becomes

$$\int \frac{(1 + u^2)}{u^2}\, \frac{du}{dx}\, dx = \int \left(\frac{1}{u^2} + 1 \right) du$$

$$= -\frac{1}{u} + u$$

$$= \tan x - \cot x .$$

The product of a sine and a cosine, or of two sines or two cosines, may be integrated immediately by expressing it as a sum or difference. This technique is illustrated by the following two examples.

(vi)
$$\int \sin 2x \cos x\, dx = \frac{1}{2} \int (\sin 3x + \sin x)\, dx$$

$$= -\frac{1}{6} \cos 3x - \frac{1}{2} \cos x .$$

(vii)
$$\int \sin 3x\ \sin 4x\, dx = \frac{1}{2} \int (\cos x - \cos 7x)\, dx$$

$$= \frac{1}{2} \sin x - \frac{1}{14} \sin 7x .$$

Any rational function of $\sin x$ and $\cos x$ may be transformed into a rational algebraic function by using the substitution $\tan \frac{1}{2} x = u$. Then

$$\frac{du}{dx} = \frac{1}{2} \sec^2 \frac{1}{2} x = \frac{1}{2} (1 + u^2)$$

and

$$\sin x = 2 \sin \frac{1}{2} x \cos \frac{1}{2} x = \frac{2 \tan \frac{1}{2} x}{1 + \tan^2 \frac{1}{2} x} = \frac{2u}{1 + u^2} .$$

$$\cos x = \cos^2 \frac{1}{2} x - \sin^2 \frac{1}{2} x = \frac{1 - \tan^2 \frac{1}{2} x}{1 + tan^2 \frac{1}{2} x} = \frac{1 - u^2}{1 + u^2}$$

An example will be considered now to illustrate the use of this particular substitution.

(viii)
$$\int \frac{dx}{5 + 4 \cos x} = y \text{ , say ,}$$

then
$$\frac{dy}{dx} = \frac{1}{5 + 4 \cos x} \text{ ,}$$

$$\frac{dy}{du} = \frac{dy}{dx} \frac{dx}{du} = \frac{1}{5 + 4(1-u^2)/(1 + u^2)} \cdot \frac{2}{(1 + u^2)} = \frac{2}{9 + u^2} \text{ .}$$

Thus,
$$y = \int \frac{2du}{9 + u^2} = \frac{2}{3} \tan^{-1} \frac{u}{3} = \frac{2}{3} \tan^{-1} \left(\frac{1}{3} \tan \frac{x}{2} \right) \text{ .}$$

Trigonometrical substitutions

Many algebraic functions which involve the square root of a quadratic expression may be rationalised by making a trigonometrical substitution. This procedure frequently simplifies the integration considerably. For example, suppose an expression involves the irrational quantity $(a^2 - x^2)^{1/2}$. The substitution $x = a \sin\theta$ would change $(a^2 - x^2)^{1/2}$ *into* $[a^2 (1 - \sin^2\theta)]^{1/2} = a\cos\theta$. Obviously, the substitution $x = a\cos\theta$ would have served equally well. These substitutions are quite legitimate since $a\sin\theta$ and $a\cos\theta$ may take all values from $-a$ to $+a$ inclusive, and these are all the values for which $(a^2 - x^2)^{1/2}$ is real.

The following examples will serve to illustrate the use of these substitutions:

(i)
$$\int (a^2 - x^2)^{1/2} = y \text{ , \quad say.}$$

Let $x = a\sin\theta$, then $dx/d\theta = a\cos\theta$ and

$$\frac{dy}{d\theta} = \frac{dy}{dx} \frac{dx}{d\theta} = a^2\cos^2\theta \text{ .}$$

Thus,
$$y = a^2 \int \cos^2\theta d\theta = a^2 \int \frac{1}{2} (1 + \cos 2\theta) d\theta$$

$$= \frac{1}{2} a^2 \left(\theta + \frac{1}{2} \sin 2\theta \right)$$

$$= \frac{1}{2} a^2 (\theta + \sin\theta\cos\theta)$$

$$= \frac{1}{2} a^2 \sin^{-1} (x/a) + \frac{1}{2} x (a^2 - x^2)^{1/2} \text{ .}$$

(ii)
$$\int \frac{(a^2 - x^2)^{1/2}\, dx}{x^2} = y \text{ , say.}$$

Let $x = a\cos\theta$, then $dx/d\theta = -a\sin\theta$ and

$$\frac{dy}{d\theta} = \frac{dy}{dx}\frac{dx}{d\theta} = -\frac{a\sin\theta}{a^2\cos^2\theta}\, a\sin\theta = -\tan^2\theta \text{ .}$$

Thus,
$$y = -\int \tan^2\theta\, d\theta = -\int (\sec^2\theta - 1)\, d\theta$$

$$= \theta - \tan\theta$$

$$= \cos^{-1}\left(\frac{x}{a}\right) - \frac{(a^2 - x^2)^{1/2}}{x} \text{ .}$$

Again, expressions involving $(a^2 + x^2)^{1/2}$ may be rationalised by using the substitution $x = a\tan\theta$, which turns $(a^2 + x^2)^{1/2}$ into $a(1 + \tan^2\theta)^{1/2} = a\sec\theta$. The hyperbolic substitution $x = a\sinh u$ will do equally well in this case since it changes $(a^2 + x^2)^{1/2}$ into $a\cosh u$.

Expressions involving $(x^2 - a^2)^{1/2}$ may be rationalised easily by using the substitution $x = a\sec\theta$ which makes $(x^2 - a^2)^{1/2}$ into $a\tan\theta$. Or, alternatively, the hyperbolic substitution, $x = a\cosh u$, will serve equally well as it changes $(x^2 - a^2)^{1/2}$ into $a\sinh u$.

The following examples will illustrate the use of these substitutions:

(i)
$$y = \int \frac{dx}{x^2 (4 + x^2)^{1/2}} \text{ .}$$

Let $x = 2\tan\theta$, then $dx/d\theta = 2\sec^2\theta$ and

$$\frac{dy}{d\theta} = \frac{dy}{dx}\frac{dx}{d\theta} = \frac{2\sec^2\theta}{4\tan^2\theta\, 2\sec\theta} = \frac{\cos\theta}{4\sin^2\theta} \text{ .}$$

Thus
$$y = \frac{1}{4}\int \frac{\cos\theta}{\sin^2\theta}\, d\theta \text{ .}$$

This integral is solved by putting

$$u = \sin\theta , \quad \text{then} \quad du/d\theta = \cos\theta \text{ .}$$

This gives

$$y = -1/4\sin\theta = -(x^2 + 4)^{1/2}/4x \text{ .}$$

Note particularly that, in this case, to solve the original integral, *two* substitutions must be used.

(ii)
$$y = \int (x^2 + a^2)^{1/2}\, dx \text{ .}$$

Let $x = a\sinh u$, then $dx/du = a\cosh u$ and

$$\frac{dy}{du} = \frac{dy}{dx}\frac{dx}{du} = a^2\cosh^2 u = \frac{1}{2}a^2(1 + \cosh 2u).$$

Then,
$$y = \frac{1}{2}a^2 \int(1 + \cosh 2u)du$$

$$= \frac{1}{2}a^2\left(u + \frac{1}{2}\sinh 2u\right)$$

$$= \frac{1}{2}a^2 u + \frac{1}{2}a^2 \sinh u \cosh u$$

$$= \frac{1}{2}a^2 \sinh^{-1}\left(\frac{x}{a}\right) + \frac{1}{2}x(a^2 + x^2)^{1/2}.$$

As a minor generalisation, it might be noted that the substitution x, or $x - k$, equals $a\tan\theta$ often proves useful in dealing with certain types of rational expressions. For example, consider

$$y = \int\frac{dx}{(x^2 - 2x + 5)^2}.$$

Now
$$x^2 - 2x + 5 = (x - 1)^2 + 4$$

then, if $x - 1 = 2\tan\theta$, this becomes $4\sec^2\theta$. Hence

$$\frac{dy}{d\theta} = \frac{dy}{dx}\frac{dx}{d\theta} = \frac{1}{(4\sec^2\theta)^2}\cdot 2\sec^2\theta = \frac{\cos^2\theta}{8} = \frac{1 + \cos 2\theta}{16}.$$

Then,
$$y = \frac{1}{16}\int(1 + \cos 2\theta)\,d\theta$$

$$= \frac{1}{16}(\theta + \sin\theta\cos\theta)$$

$$= \frac{1}{16}\left\{\tan^{-1}\frac{x-1}{2} + \frac{x-1}{[(x-1)^2+4]^{1/2}}\cdot\frac{2}{[(x-1)^2+4]^{1/2}}\right\}$$

$$= \frac{1}{16}\left\{\tan^{-1}\frac{x-1}{2} + \frac{2(x-1)}{x^2 - 2x + 5}\right\}.$$

Finally, it might be noticed that the expressions

$$[(x - \alpha)(\beta - x)]^{1/2}, \quad \frac{1}{[(x - \alpha)(\beta - x)]^{1/2}}, \quad \left[\frac{x - \alpha}{\beta - x}\right]^{1/2},$$

where $\beta > \alpha$, are all rationalised by using the substitution

$$x = \alpha\cos^2\theta + \beta\sin^2\theta.$$

This expression admits all values from α to β inclusive and it is for these values—and these values alone—that the preceding expressions are real. Using the above substitution

$$(x - \alpha) \quad \text{becomes} \quad \alpha(\cos^2\theta - 1) + \beta\sin^2\theta = (\beta - \alpha)\sin^2\theta .$$

$$(\beta - x) \quad \text{becomes} \quad (\beta - \alpha)\cos^2\theta$$

and

$$dx/d\theta = -2\alpha\cos\theta\sin\theta + 2\beta \sin\theta\cos\theta = 2(\beta - \alpha)\sin\theta \cos\theta .$$

The following example will illustrate the use of this substitution:

Consider
$$y = \int \sqrt{\frac{x - a}{2a - x}} \, dx .$$

Let
$$x = a\cos^2\theta + 2a\sin^2\theta ,$$

and so
$$x - a = a\sin^2\theta , \quad 2a - x = a\cos^2\theta ,$$

$$dx/d\theta = 2a \sin\theta \cos\theta,$$

and
$$\frac{dy}{d\theta} = \frac{dy}{dx}\frac{dx}{d\theta} = \tan\theta . \quad 2a\sin\theta\cos\theta$$

$$= 2a\sin^2\theta = a(1 - \cos 2\theta) .$$

Then
$$y = a\int(1 - \cos 2\theta) \, d\theta = a (\theta - \sin\theta \cos\theta) .$$

But $x - a = a\sin^2\theta , \quad 2a - x = a\cos^2\theta ,$

and so
$$y = a \sin^{-1} \left(\frac{x - a}{a}\right)^{1/2} - [(x - a) (2a - x)]^{1/2} .$$

3.2.6 Integration by parts
One important method of integration, known as integration by parts, remains to be discussed. This is the converse of the rule for obtaining the derivative of a product of two functions of x:

$$\frac{d}{dx} (uv) = u \frac{dv}{dx} + v \frac{du}{dx} ,$$

where u and v are the two functions of x. Integrating term by term gives, apart from an arbitrary constant to be added,

$$uv = \int u \frac{dv}{dx} \, dx + \int v \frac{du}{dx} \, dx ,$$

whence

$$\int u \frac{dv}{dx} \, dx = uv - \int v \frac{du}{dx} \, dx .$$

In many instances, the integral on the right-hand side is much easier to evaluate then the one on the left-hand side. It might be noted that this method proves particularly useful in cases where the expression to be integrated contains such functions as $\log x$, or an inverse trigonometrical or hyperbolic function. If such a function is taken as the u on the left-hand side, the du/dx on the right-hand side becomes a simple algebraic function.

The following examples will illustrate the use of this method:

(i) $$y = \int x^2 \log x\, dx .$$

Take $u = \log x$, $dv/dx = x^2$,

then $du/dx = 1/x$, $v = \int x^2 dx = \dfrac{1}{3} x^3$.

Therefore

$$y = \frac{1}{3} x^3 \log x - \int \frac{1}{3} x^3 . x^{-1} dx$$

$$= \frac{1}{3} x^3 \log x - \frac{1}{9} x^3 .$$

(ii) $$y = \int x \tan^{-1} x\, dx .$$

Take $u = \tan^{-1} x$, $dv/dx = x$,

then $du/dx = (1 + x^2)^{-1}$, $v = \dfrac{1}{2} x^2$.

Therefore

$$y = \frac{1}{2} x^2 \tan^{-1} x - \frac{1}{2} \int \frac{x^2}{(1 + x^2)}\, dx$$

$$= \frac{1}{2} x^2 \tan^{-1} x - \frac{1}{2} \int \left\{ 1 - \frac{1}{1 + x^2} \right\} dx$$

$$= \frac{1}{2} (x^2 + 1) \tan^{-1} x - \frac{1}{2} x .$$

(iii) $$y = \int \tan^{-1} x\, dx$$

Take $u = \tan^{-1} x$ and $dv/dx = 1$

then $du/dx = (1 + x^2)^{-1}$, $v = x$,

and so

$$y = x \tan^{-1} x - \int \frac{x}{1 + x^2}\, dx$$

$$= x \tan^{-1} x - \frac{1}{2} \int \frac{2x}{1 + x^2}\, dx$$

$$= x \tan^{-1} x - \frac{1}{2} \log (1 + x^2) .$$

(iv) $$y = \int x \sin x\, dx .$$

In this example, it is not obvious immediately which function should be chosen as u. However, if $\sin x$ is taken as u and x as dv/dx, then

$$du/dx = \cos x \,, \ v = \frac{1}{2} x^2 \,,$$

and the integral on the right-hand side becomes

$$\frac{1}{2} \int x^2 \cos x \, dx \,,$$

which is more complicated than the original integral. Hence, take

$$u = x \,, \ dv/dx = \sin x \,,$$

then

$$du/dx = 1 \,, \ v = -\cos x \,,$$

and

$$y = -x\cos x + \int \cos x \, dx = -x\cos x + \sin x$$

(v)

$$y = \int x^2 \, e^{2x} \, dx \,.$$

Since x^2 becomes simpler when differentiated and e^{2x} does not become more complicated when integrated, take

$$u = x^2 \,, \ dv/dx = e^{2x}$$

then

$$du/dx = 2x \,, \ v = \frac{1}{2} e^{2x}$$

$$y = \frac{1}{2} x^2 e^{2x} - \int x e^{2x} \, dx \,.$$

Although the integral on the right-hand side may not be evaluated immediately, it is simpler in form than the original integral. Now integrate by parts again, taking

$$u = x \,, \ dv/dx = e^{2x}$$

then

$$du/dx = 1 \,, \ v = \frac{1}{2} e^{2x}$$

and

$$\int x e^{2x} dx = \frac{1}{2} x e^{2x} - \frac{1}{2} \int e^{2x} dx = \frac{1}{2} x e^{2x} - \frac{1}{4} e^{2x} \,.$$

Therefore,

$$y = \frac{1}{2} x^2 e^{2x} - \frac{1}{2} x e^{2x} + \frac{1}{4} e^{2x} = \frac{1}{4} e^{2x}(2x^2 - 2x + 1) \,.$$

This last example is a simple case of a general method, based on integration by parts, known as **integration by successive reduction**. Some expressions may be integrated only in stages with the integral obtained at the end of each stage being simpler than the integral at the beginning of the stage, until finally an integral results whose value is known.

There are two important types of integrals which may be evaluated by this method.

(A) $$y = \int (x^2 + a^2)^{\frac{1}{2}} dx .$$

Take $$u = (x^2 + a^2)^{\frac{1}{2}} , \, dv/dx = 1$$

then $$\frac{du}{dx} = \frac{x}{(x^2 + a^2)^{\frac{1}{2}}} , \, v = x$$

and $$y = x(x^2 + a^2)^{\frac{1}{2}} - \int \frac{x^2}{(x^2 + a^2)^{\frac{1}{2}}} dx$$

$$= x(x^2 + a^2)^{\frac{1}{2}} - \int \frac{(x^2 + a^2) - a^2}{(x^2 + a^2)^{\frac{1}{2}}} dx$$

$$= x(x^2 + a^2)^{\frac{1}{2}} - \int (x^2 + a^2)^{\frac{1}{2}} dx$$

$$+ \int \frac{a^2}{(x^2 + a^2)^{\frac{1}{2}}} dx .$$

The second term on the right-hand side is the original integral, and so

$$2y = x(x^2 + a^2)^{\frac{1}{2}} + \int \frac{a^2}{(x^2 + a^2)^{\frac{1}{2}}} dx$$

$$= x(x^2 + a^2)^{\frac{1}{2}} + a^2 \sinh^{-1}(x/a) .$$

Therefore, $$y = \frac{1}{2} x(x^2 + a^2)^{\frac{1}{2}} + \frac{1}{2} a^2 \sinh^{-1}(x/a) .$$

Similarly,

$$\int (a^2 - x^2)^{\frac{1}{2}} dx = \frac{1}{2} x(a^2 - x^2)^{\frac{1}{2}} + \frac{1}{2} a^2 \sin^{-1}(x/a)$$

$$\int (x^2 - a)^{\frac{1}{2}} dx = \frac{1}{2} x(x^2 - a^2)^{\frac{1}{2}} - \frac{1}{2} a^2 \cosh^{-1}(x/a) .$$

In the general case, $\int (ax^2 + bx + c)^{\frac{1}{2}} dx$, first divide the expression under the root sign by a, then complete the square of the terms which contain x. This procedure will reduce the given integral to one of the three forms mentioned above.

(B) $$\int e^{ax} \cos bx \, dx \quad \text{and} \quad \int e^{ax} \sin bx \, dx .$$

If each of these integrals is evaluated by parts, the other one is obtained. Hence, two equations are obtained to be solved for the two integrals.

First consider $\int e^{ax} \cos bx \, dx$ and take

$$u = e^{ax}, \quad dv/dx = \cos bx$$

then
$$du/dx = ae^{ax}, \quad v = \frac{1}{b} \sin bx$$

and
$$\int e^{ax}\cos bx\, dx = \frac{1}{b} e^{ax}\sin bx - \frac{a}{b} \int e^{ax}\sin bx\, dx .$$

Similarly,

$$\int e^{ax}\sin bx\, dx = -\frac{1}{b} e^{ax}\cos bx + \frac{a}{b} \int e^{ax}\cos bx\, dx .$$

From these two equations, it is seen immediately that

$$\int e^{ax}\cos bx\, dx = \frac{e^{ax}(b\sin bx + a\cos bx)}{a^2 + b^2}$$

and

$$\int e^{ax}\sin bx\, dx = \frac{e^{ax}(a\sin bx - b\cos bx)}{a^2 + b^2}$$

Integration by successive reduction

This particular technique, which has been mentioned already, will be illustrated by the following examples:

(i)
$$y = \int x^n e^{ax} dx .$$

Take
$$u = x^n, \ dv/dx = e^{ax},$$

then
$$du/dx = nx^{n-1}, \ v = \frac{1}{a} e^{ax}$$

and so
$$y = \frac{1}{a} x^n e^{ax} - \frac{n}{a} \int x^{n-1} e^{ax} dx .$$

The integral remaining on the right-hand side is of the same form as the original integral, but the power to which x is raised is reduced by unity. By repeating the process, the integral is made to depend on $\int x^{n-2} e^{ax}\, dx$, and so on until finally $\int e^{ax}\, dx$, which may be evaluated to give $\frac{1}{a} e^{ax}$, is reached. The actual process of integration by parts has been performed once only for the general case; all the successive steps follow by substituting numerical values for n. The above equation for y is said to give the **reduction formula** for the original integral.

(ii)
$$y = \int x^n \cos ax\, dx .$$

Take
$$u = x^n, \ dv/dx = \cos ax$$

then
$$\mathrm{d}u/\mathrm{d}x = nx^{n-1}\, ,\; v = \frac{1}{a}\sin ax\, ,$$

and so
$$y = \frac{1}{a}x^n \sin ax - \frac{n}{a}\int x^{n-1}\sin ax\, \mathrm{d}x\, .$$

Similarly,

$$\int x^{n-1}\sin ax\, \mathrm{d}x = -\frac{1}{a}x^{n-1}\cos ax + \frac{n-1}{a}\int x^{n-2}\cos ax\, \mathrm{d}x\, .$$

Each step reduces the index of x by unity, and the trigonometrical factors are sin ax and cos ax alternately. The process is continued until finally the integral reduces to either

$$\int \cos ax\, \mathrm{d}x \qquad \text{if } n \text{ is even}$$

or

$$\int \sin ax\, \mathrm{d}x \qquad \text{if } n \text{ is odd}\, .$$

Exactly the same technique may be used to evaluate

$$\int x^n \sin ax\, \mathrm{d}x\, ,\; \int x^n \sinh ax\, \mathrm{d}x\, ,\; \int x^n \cosh ax\, \mathrm{d}x\, .$$

3.3 DEFINITE INTEGRALS: AREA BENEATH PLANE CURVES

Thought of as the inverse of differentiation, integration has little apparent application to problems in mathematics, physical science, or engineering. In order to relate it to such problems, the definite integral must be introduced. One way of carrying out this introduciton is via the evaluation of the area beneath a plane curve.

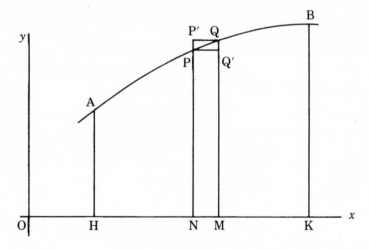

Fig. 3.1

Suppose $f(x)$ is a continuous function of x which is positive for values of x in the range $a \leqslant x \leqslant b$. The graph of $y = f(x)$ is then a curve such as AB of Fig. 3.1, in which HA is the ordinate at $x = a$, KB the ordinate at $x = b$. Let P be a point on the curve with coordinates (x,y) and let the area AHNP between the curve, the x-axis and the ordinates AH and PN be denoted by z. The value of z varies as the position of N varies, so that z is a function of x.

Now let x increase to $x + \delta x$ and let Q be the corresponding point on the curve and MQ its ordinate. Then the area PNMQ is δz, the increase in z due to the increase δx in x, and MQ is $y + \delta y$.

In Fig. 3.1, if the rectangles PNMQ$'$ and P$'$NMQ are completed and if the slope from P to Q is positive,

$$\text{rect. } P'NMQ > \quad \delta z \quad > \text{rect. } PNMQ' \tag{3.3}$$

$$(y + \delta y)\,\delta x > \quad \delta z \quad > y\delta x \,,$$

that is, $\qquad\qquad\qquad y + \delta y > \delta z/\delta x > y \,.$

Then, in the limit as $\delta x \rightarrow 0$, $\delta y \rightarrow 0$ and

$$\lim_{\delta x \to 0} \frac{\delta z}{\delta x} = \frac{dz}{dx} = y = f(x) \,.$$

This equation is of the same form as (3.1), and so

$$z = \phi(x) + c$$

where $\phi(x)$ is an integral of $f(x)$ and c is an arbitrary constant. However, in the present situation there is the added condition that z is the area HAPN, and this is zero when $x = a$. Hence, c must satisfy $0 = \phi(a) + c$ and so $z = \phi(x) - \phi(a)$.

The total area HABK will be the value of z when N is at K; that is, when $x = b$, and its value is $\phi(b) - \phi(a)$.

This result may be expressed in terms of the function $f(x)$ by using the notation

$$\int_a^b f(x)\,dx = \phi(b) - \phi(a) \,. \tag{3.4}$$

The expression $\int_a^b f(x)\,dx$ is called a **definite integral;** a and b are the lower and upper limits; $f(x)$ is the integrand, and the interval $[a,b]$ the range of integration. It might be noted that a definite integral depends on a,b and the form of the intergrand, but it is not a function of x. The function $\phi(x) = \int f(x)dx$, an integral of $f(x)$, is called an **indefinite integral** of $f(x)$ to distinguish it from a definite integral. It proves convenient to write

$$\int_a^b f(x)\,dx = [\phi(x)]_a^b = \phi(b) - \phi(a)$$

when evaluating definite integrals.

In this discussion, if the slope from P to Q had been negative, the inequality signs in (3.3) would have been reversed. Also, the slope has been assumed to have the same sign from P to Q, but the range may be taken sufficiently small for this to be so. Finally, the area beneath the curve $y = f(x)$ has been expressed as an integral only when $f(x)$ is positive. If $f(x)$ is negative in the given range, it is necessary to consider the curve $y = -f(x)$ so that the required area is

$$\int_a^b \{-f(x)\}\, dx = [-\phi(x)]_a^b = -\phi(b) + \phi(a) = -\int_a^b f(x)dx .$$

When $f(x)$ is negative, the definite integral $\int_a^b f(x)\, dx$ gives the correct numerical value for the required area, but with a negative sign. This shows that care must be taken when evaluating the area between a curve and the x-axis if $f(x)$ has positive and negative values in the given range of variation of x.

From the definition (3.4) of a definite integral, the following properties are immediately obvious:

(a)
$$\int_a^b f(x)\, dx = \phi(b) - \phi(a) = -\int_b^a f(x)\, dx .$$

(b)
$$\int_a^c f(x)\, dx + \int_c^b f(x)\, dx = \int_a^b f(x)\, dx .$$

(c)
$$\int_a^b \{f(x) + g(x)\}\, dx = \int_a^b f(x)\, dx + \int_a^b g(x)\, dx .$$

3.4 DEFINITE INTEGRALS: LIMIT OF A SUM

Consider once again the area ABKH beneath a plane curve $y = f(x)$ as shown in Fig. 3.2. Suppose the segment AB is divided into n parts by points whose abscissae are

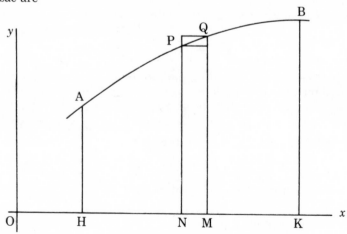

Fig. 3.2

$$a = x_0, x_1, x_2, \ldots x_{r-1}, x_r, \ldots, x_n = b.$$

Suppose N is the point x_{r-1}, M the point x_r, and NP, MQ the ordinates at N and M respectively. Also let $x_r - x_{r-1} = \delta x_r$. In the range $x_{r-1} < x < x_r$, suppose the greatest and least values of $f(x)$ are G_r and L_r respectively. Then, it is seen from the figure that the area NPQM lies between the values

$$G_r(x_r - x_{r-1}) = G_r \delta x_r \quad \text{and} \quad L_r(x_r - x_{r-1}) = L_r \delta x_r.$$

If, as before, this area is denoted by δz_r,

$$L_r \delta x_r \leqslant \delta z_r \leqslant G_r \delta x_r, \tag{3.5}$$

and, since δx_r is positive, this gives

$$L_r \leqslant \frac{\delta z_r}{\delta x_r} \leqslant G_r. \tag{3.6}$$

As $\delta x_r \to 0$, L_r and G_r both tend to the value of $f(x_r)$ provided $f(x)$ is a continuous function. Hence, if x is used to denote any point in the range and δx, δz the corresponding increments, (3.6) gives

$$\frac{dz}{dx} = \lim_{\delta x \to 0} \frac{\delta z}{\delta x} = f(x).$$

Again, summing equations of the form of (3.5) for all values of r, using

$$S = \sum_r G_r \delta x_r = \text{sum of outer rectangles},$$

$$\sigma = \sum_r L_r \delta x_r = \text{sum of inner rectangles},$$

and

$$\sum_r \delta z_r = \sum \text{areas NPQM} = \text{area ABKH},$$

leads to

$$\sigma \leqslant \text{area ABKH} \leqslant S;$$

where the equality sign holds only when the curve $y = f(x)$ is a straight line parallel to the x-axis.

Thus, if the sums σ and S have a common limit as the number of divisions increases in such a manner that the largest division δx_r tends to zero, this limit is the area ABKH. Also, if some point on the curve intermediate between P and Q, with abscissa ξ_r and ordinate $f(\xi_r)$ is taken,

$$L_r \delta x_r \leqslant f(\xi_r) \delta x_r \leqslant G_r \delta x_r,$$

and summing over r,

$$\sigma \leqslant \sum_r f(\xi_r) \delta x_r \leqslant S.$$

Hence, if σ and S have a common limit as $\delta x_r \to 0$, it will be

$$\lim_{\delta x_r \to 0} \sum_r f(\xi_r)\, \delta x_r \,;$$

and so,   area ABKH $= \displaystyle\lim_{\delta x_r \to 0} \sum_r f(\xi_r)\delta x_r$.

This helps explain the notation for an integral. In the limit when $\delta x_r \to 0$, $\xi_r \to x_r$, the integral sign $\int$ replaces the summation sign Σ_r.

The conditions under which σ and S have a common limit depend on the function $f(x)$ but, if $f(x)$ is a continuous function, these conditions may be shown to hold. If σ and S do have a common limit, $f(x)$ is said to be Riemann-integrable and the integral is a **Riemann integral**.

3.5 IMPROPER INTEGRALS
In the definition of the definite integral $\int_a^b f(x)\,dx$, it was assumed that the limits of integration, a and b, were finite and that the function $f(x)$ was continuous, and therefore finite, throughout the range $a \leq x \leq b$. Cases occur frequently in which these conditions are not satisfied, and it remains to consider how the definition of an integral may be extended.

It has been shown that

$$\int_a^b f(x)\, dx = \phi(b) - \phi(a) \,, \text{ where } \phi(x) \text{ is an integral of } f(x)\,.$$

If, as $b \to \infty$, $\phi(b)$ tends to a finite limit l, then $l - \phi(a)$ is defined to be the value of $\int_a^\infty f(x)\,dx$.

Similarly, if as $a \to -\infty$, $\phi(a)$ tends to a finite limit l', then $\phi(b) - l'$ is defined to be the value of $\int_{-\infty}^b f(x)\,dx$.

Examples
(i) $\int_a^b x^{-2}\,dx$, where both a and b are positive so that the value 0, for which x^{-2} is discontinuous, is not in the range of integration. Now

$$\int_a^b x^{-2}\, dx = [-x^{-1}]_a^b = \frac{1}{a} - \frac{1}{b}\,.$$

As $b \to \infty$, $1/b \to 0$ and so

$$\int_a^\infty x^{-2}\, dx = 1/a\,.$$

(ii)
$$\int_0^b \frac{dx}{a^2 + x^2} = \left[\frac{1}{a}\tan^{-1}\frac{x}{a}\right]_0^b = \frac{1}{a}\tan^{-1}\frac{b}{a}\,.$$

As $b \to \infty$, $\tan^{-1}\dfrac{b}{a} \to \dfrac{\pi}{2}$ and so $\displaystyle\int_0^\infty \frac{dx}{a^2 + x^2} = \frac{\pi}{2a}$.

Suppose next that $f(x)$ becomes infinite at one of the extremities of the range of integration; let $f(x) = \infty$ when $x = b$ say. If the integral $\int_a^{b-\varepsilon} f(x)\, dx$ is considered, $f(x)$ will be finite throughout this range of integration. If $\int_a^{b-\varepsilon} f(x)\, dx$ tends to a finite limit, l say, as $\varepsilon \to 0$, the value l is defined to be the value of $\int_a^b f(x)\, dx$.

Similarly, if $f(x) = \infty$ when $x = a$ and if $\int_{a+\varepsilon}^b f(x)\, dx$ tends to a finite limit, l' say, as $\varepsilon \to 0$, then l' is defined to be the value of $\int_a^b f(x)\, dx$.

Finally, if $f(x)$ becomes infinite for a single value of x, $x = c$ say, within the range of integration, then

$$\int_a^b f(x)\, dx = \int_a^c f(x)\, dx + \int_c^b f(x)\, dx$$

and each integral on the right-hand side may be treated in the manner described. This latter result may be extended easily to the case where $f(x)$ becomes infinite at any finite number of points within the range of integration.

Examples

(i) $\int_0^a x^{-\frac{1}{2}}\, dx$; $x^{-\frac{1}{2}}$ is infinite when $x = 0$.

Now $\int_0^a x^{-\frac{1}{2}}\, dx = [2x^{\frac{1}{2}}]_\varepsilon^a = 2(a^{\frac{1}{2}} - \varepsilon^{\frac{1}{2}})$. As $\varepsilon \to 0$, $\varepsilon^{\frac{1}{2}} \to 0$, and so

$$\int_0^a x^{-\frac{1}{2}}\, dx = 2a^{\frac{1}{2}} .$$

(ii)

$$\int_0^4 (x - 3)^{-\frac{1}{3}}\, dx .$$

In this case, the integrand becomes infinite when $x = 3$, so write

$$\int_0^4 (x - 3)^{-\frac{1}{3}}\, dx = \int_0^3 (x - 3)^{-\frac{1}{3}}\, dx + \int_3^4 (x - 3)^{-\frac{1}{3}}\, dx .$$

Now

$$\int_0^{3-\varepsilon} (x - 3)^{\frac{1}{3}}\, dx = \left[\frac{3}{2} (x - 3)^{\frac{2}{3}} \right]_0^{3-\varepsilon} = \frac{3}{2} [(-\varepsilon)^{\frac{2}{3}} - (-3)^{\frac{2}{3}}]$$

and this tends to the limit $-\dfrac{3}{2}(-3)^{\frac{2}{3}}$ as $\varepsilon \to 0$.

Also

$$\int_{3+\varepsilon}^4 (x - 3)^{-\frac{1}{3}}\, dx = \left[\frac{3}{2} (x - 3)^{\frac{2}{3}} \right]_{3+\varepsilon}^4 = \frac{3}{2} (1 + \varepsilon^{\frac{2}{3}})$$

and this tends to the limit $3/2$ as $\varepsilon \to 0$.

Hence,

$$\int_0^4 (x - 3)^{-\frac{1}{3}}\, dx = \frac{3}{2} (1 - (-3)^{\frac{2}{3}}) = \frac{3}{2} (1 - 9^{\frac{1}{3}}) .$$

3.6 FURTHER PROPERTIES OF DEFINITE INTEGRALS

(i) $\int_{-a}^a f(x)\, dx = 0$ or $2\int_0^a f(x)\, dx$ according as $f(x)$ is an odd or even function of x.

Now
$$\int_{-a}^{a} f(x)\, dx = \int_{-a}^{0} f(x)\, dx + \int_{0}^{a} f(x)\, dx .$$

If $f(x)$ is an odd function of x, $f(-x) = -f(x)$ and replacing x by $-u$ in the first integral on the right-hand side gives

$$\int_{-a}^{0} f(x)\, dx = -\int_{a}^{0} f(-u)du = -\int_{0}^{a} f(u)du$$

and so

$$\int_{-a}^{a} f(x)\, dx = 0 \text{ if } f(x) \text{ is an odd function of } x .$$

If $f(x)$ is an even function of x, $f(-x) = f(x)$, and carrying out the same procedure as above gives

$$\int_{-a}^{0} f(x)\, dx = -\int_{a}^{0} f(-u)du = \int_{0}^{a} f(u)du$$

and so

$$\int_{-a}^{a} f(x)\, dx = 2\int_{0}^{a} f(x)\, dx \text{ if } f(x) \text{ is an even function of } x .$$

(ii)
$$\int_{0}^{a} f(x)\, dx = \int_{0}^{a} f(a - x)\, dx .$$

Putting $a - x = u$ in the second integral gives

$$\int_{0}^{a} f(a - x)\, dx = -\int_{a}^{0} f(u)\, du = \int_{0}^{a} f(u)\, du .$$

Hence the result.

An important application of this result is

$$\int_{0}^{\pi/2} f\,(\sin x)dx = \int_{0}^{\pi/2} f\left\{\sin\left(\frac{\pi}{2} - x\right)\right\}dx = \int_{0}^{\pi/2} f(\cos x)dx .$$

Thus,
$$\int_{0}^{\pi/2} \sin^2 x\, dx = \int_{0}^{\pi/2} \cos^2 x\, dx$$

and each of these integrals is equal to their average

$$\frac{1}{2}\int_{0}^{\pi/2} (\sin^2 x + \cos^2 x)\, dx = \frac{1}{2}\int_{0}^{\pi/2} dx = \frac{\pi}{4} .$$

(iii) By a simple change of variable in (i), it may be shown that $\int_{0}^{2a} f(x)\, dx = 0$ or $2\int_{0}^{a} f(x)\, dx$ according as $f(2a - x) = -f(x)$ or $+ f(x)$.

This is particularly useful when dealing with trigonometrical integrals since $\sin(\pi - x) = \sin x$, $\cos(\pi - x) = -\cos x$, and $\tan(\pi - x) = -\tan x$.

Hence
$$\int_0^\pi f(\sin x) \, dx = 2 \int_0^{\pi/2} f(\sin x) \, dx \,,$$

$$\int_0^\pi f(\cos x) \, dx = 0 \quad \text{and} \quad \int_0^\pi f(\tan x) \, dx = 0 \,.$$

3.7 AN IMPORTANT DEFINITE INTEGRAL: $\int_0^\pi \sin^m\theta \cos^n\theta \, d\theta$

Consider the integral

$$I_{m,n} = \int \sin^m\theta \cos^n\theta \, d\theta$$

where m and n are positive integers. Now write

$$I_{m,n} = \int (\sin^m\theta \cos\theta) \cos^{n-1}\theta \, d\theta$$

and integrate by parts to give, for $n > 1$,

$$I_{m,n} = \frac{\sin^{m+1}\theta \cos^{n-1}\theta}{m+1} + \frac{n-1}{m+1} \int \sin^{m+2}\theta \cos^{n-2}\theta \, d\theta \,.$$

Putting $\sin^2\theta = 1 - \cos^2\theta$ in the final integral and collecting terms leads to

$$(m+n) I_{m,n} = \sin^{m+1}\theta \cos^{n-1}\theta + (n-1)\int \sin^m\theta \cos^{n-2}\theta \, d\theta \,.$$

The last integral is now of the same form as the original one but with n replaced by $n - 2$, and so

$$(m+n) I_{m,n} = \sin^{m+1}\theta \cos^{n-1}\theta + (n-1) I_{m,n-2} \,. \tag{3.7}$$

It might be noted that, if the original integral had been written in the form

$$I_{m,n} = \int (\cos^n\theta \sin\theta) \sin^{m-1}\theta \, d\theta$$

before integrating by parts then, for $m > 1$, the result would have been

$$(m+n) I_{m,n} = -\sin^{m-1}\theta \cos^{n+1}\theta + (m-1) I_{m-2,n} \,. \tag{3.8}$$

The process may be repeated, reducing the index of either $\cos\theta$ or $\sin\theta$ by 2 at each step. If both m and n are even, the integral is reduced finally to $\int d\theta$; that is, θ.

If m is odd and n even, the integral ultimately reduces to $\int \sin\theta \, d\theta$; that is, $-\cos\theta$.

If m is even and n odd, the integral ultimately reduces to $\int \cos\theta \, d\theta$; that is, $\sin\theta$.

Finally, if both m and n are odd, the integral ultimately reduces to $\int \sin\theta \cos\theta \, d\theta$; that is, $\frac{1}{2} \sin^2\theta$.

Also note that the special cases when either m or n is zero are included in the general case discussed above.

This discussion shows that it is possible to give general formulae for the indefinite integral $I_{m,n}$. However, in practice, it is definite integrals which tend to occur; and so consider

$$I_{m,n} = \int_0^{\pi/2} \sin^m\theta \cos^n\theta \; d\theta \; .$$

With these limits, (3.7) and (3.8) become, for $n > 1$,

$$(m + n)I_{m,n} = (n - 1)\,I_{m,n-2}$$

and for $m > 1$,

$$(m + n)I_{m,n} = (m - 1)\,I_{m-2,n} \quad \text{respectively.}$$

The integrals on the right-hand sides may be reduced a stage further by using these results with $n - 2$ for n and $m - 2$ for m respectively, so that

$$I_{m,n} = \frac{(n - 1)}{(m + n)}\,\frac{(n - 3)}{(m + n - 2)}\,I_{m,n-4} \quad \text{or} \quad \frac{(m - 1)}{(m + n)}\,\frac{(m - 3)}{(m + n - 2)}\,I_{m-4,n}.$$

By repeated use of these results, the numerical factors in the numerator will be $(n - 1), (n - 3), (n - 5) \ldots$ down to either 2 or 1 (according as n is odd or even) as the index of $\cos\theta$ is reduced, and $(m - 1), (m - 3), (m - 5) \ldots$ down to either 2 or 1 (according as m is odd or even) as the index of $\sin\theta$ is reduced; the last factor in the denominator will exceed by 2 the sum of the remaining indices of $\sin\theta$ and $\cos\theta$ at any stage.

If one index is odd and the other even, the integral reduces to either $\int_0^{\pi/2}\sin\theta \; d\theta$ or $\int_0^{\pi/2}\cos\theta \; d\theta$. Both of these integrals have the value 1, and the last factor in the denominator will be 3.

If both indices are odd, the integral reduces to $\int_0^{\pi/2}\sin\theta \cos\theta \; d\theta$ which equals ½. The last factor in the denominator of the coefficient of this integral will be 4 and so, in the final result, the last factor in the denominator will be 2.

If both indices are even, the integral reduces to $\int_0^{\pi/2} d\theta$ which is $\pi/2$ and the last factor in the preceding denominator is 2.

Hence, finally,

$$\int_0^{\pi/2} \sin^m\theta \cos^n\theta \; d\theta = \frac{(m - 1)(m - 3) \ldots (n - 1)(n - 3) \ldots}{(m + n)(m + n - 2) \ldots}$$

followed by the factor $\pi/2$ only when m and n are both even (0 counts as an even number). All three sets of factor descend 2 at a time to either 1 or 2 according as the first factor of the set is odd or even.

The various properties of definite integrals discussed earlier may be used to help in the evaluation of the integral when the limits are multiples of $\pi/2$.

Examples

(i)
$$\int_0^{\pi/2} \sin^5\theta \cos^2\theta \; d\theta = \frac{4.2.2}{8.6.4.2} = \frac{1}{24} \, .$$

(ii)
$$\int_0^{\pi/2} \sin^4\theta \cos^6\theta \; d\theta = \frac{3.1.5.3.1}{10.8.6.4.2} \cdot \frac{\pi}{2} = \frac{3\pi}{512} \, .$$

(iii) $$\int_{-\pi/2}^{\pi/2} \sin^2\theta \cos^2\theta \, d\theta = 2 \int_0^{\pi/2} \sin^2\theta \cos^2\theta \, d\theta$$

$$= \frac{2.1.2}{5.3.1} = \frac{4}{15}.$$

EXERCISES 3

Integrate the following:

(1) $$\frac{x^2}{2x - 3} \ , \quad \frac{2x + 3}{x - 4} \ , \quad \frac{3}{a - 2x}.$$

(2) $$\frac{x}{x^2 - 1} \ , \quad \frac{5 + x^2}{9 - x^2} \ , \quad \frac{x^4}{x^2 - 5}.$$

(3) $$\frac{1}{x^2 + 2x + 10} \ , \quad \frac{1}{x^2 - 2x - 1} \ , \quad \frac{x^2 + 2x}{x^2 + 2x + 2} \ , \quad \frac{x^4}{x^2 + 7}.$$

(4) $$\frac{x^3}{a^4 - x^4} \ , \quad \frac{\sin x \cos x}{1 + 3\sin^2 x} \ , \quad \tanh x \ , \quad \frac{1}{x \log x}.$$

(5) $$\frac{x + 1}{x^2 + 9} \ , \quad \frac{6x + 3}{x^2 + 4x + 13} \ , \quad \frac{x^2 - x + 1}{x^2 + x + 1}.$$

(6) $$\frac{1}{x^2(x - 1)} \ , \quad \frac{x^2}{(x^2 - 1)(2x + 1)} \ , \quad \frac{x}{x^4 + x^2 - 2} \ , \quad \frac{x^2}{1 - x^4}.$$

(7) $$\frac{1}{(x^2 + 2x + 10)^{\frac{1}{2}}} \ , \quad \frac{1}{[x(1 + x)]^{\frac{1}{2}}} \ , \quad \frac{1}{[x(3 - 2x)]^{\frac{1}{2}}}.$$

(8) $$\frac{x}{(x^2 + 5)^{\frac{1}{2}}} \ , \quad \frac{x}{(4 - 3x - x^2)^{\frac{1}{2}}} \ , \quad \left(\frac{2 + x}{x}\right)^{\frac{1}{2}}.$$

(9) $$\frac{\cos x}{\sin^4 x} \ , \quad \frac{x^2}{a^3 - x^3} \ , \quad \frac{(1 + \log x)^2}{x} \ , \quad \frac{\sin x}{(a - b\cos x)^2}.$$

(10) $$\frac{x}{(1 - x)^{\frac{1}{2}}} \ , \quad x^2(ax + b)^{\frac{1}{2}} \ , \quad \frac{1}{x(x^2 - 1)^{\frac{1}{2}}} \ , \quad \frac{1}{x(2x^2 + 3)}.$$

(11) $$\tan 2x \ , \quad \cos^3 x \ , \quad \tan^4 x \ , \quad \sin^2 x \cos^2 x,$$

$$\frac{1}{\cos x \sin^2 x} \ , \quad \frac{\sin^2 x}{\sin 2x} \ , \quad \frac{1}{2 + \sin x}.$$

(12) $$(9 - x^2)^{\frac{1}{2}} \ , \quad \frac{x^2}{(x^2 + 9)^{\frac{1}{2}}} \ , \quad \sqrt{\frac{x - 1}{2 - x}} \ , \quad \frac{1}{(x^2 + 4x + 5)^2}.$$

(13) $$x^4 \log x \ , \quad x^3 \tan^{-1} x \ , \quad x \cosh\left(\frac{x}{a}\right) \ , \quad x^2 e^{-x}.$$

(14) $$(32 + 2x^2)^{\frac{1}{2}} \ , \quad e^{3x} \cos 2x \ , \quad \cosh x \sin x \ , \quad e^{-Rt/L}\cos(pt + \varepsilon).$$

(15) $x^3 \, e^{ax}$, $x^3 \sin 2x$, $x^2 (\log x)^2$, $x^2 \cosh x$.

Find the values of

(16) $\int_1^4 x^4 \, dx$, $\int_4^9 x^{-\frac{1}{2}} dx$ $\int_0^a (x + a)^n \, dx$.

(17) $\int_0^{\pi/2} \sin x \, dx$, $\int_{-\pi/2}^{\pi/2} \cos^2 x \, dx$, $\int_0^{\pi/2} \dfrac{\sin x}{1 + \cos^2 x} \, dx$.

(18) $\int_0^\pi e^{2x} \sin x \, dx$, $\int_0^1 x^2 \, e^x \, dx$.

(19) $\int_0^a \dfrac{x^2 - a^2}{x^2 + a^2} \, dx$, $\int_0^1 \dfrac{x^3}{x + 2} \, dx$.

(20) $\int_0^1 \dfrac{dx}{1 + 2x \cos\alpha + x^2}$, $\int_0^1 \dfrac{dx}{x^2 + 2x + 5}$.

(21) $\int_0^1 x \, (1 - x)^{\frac{3}{2}} \, dx$, $\int_0^2 x^2 \, (2 - x)^{\frac{1}{2}} \, dx$.

(22) $\int_{-\alpha}^{\alpha} \dfrac{\sin^3 x}{1 + \cos^2 x} \, dx$, $\int_0^{\pi/2} \dfrac{\cos x - \sin x}{\cos x + \sin x} \, dx$.

Find, when they exist, the values of:

(23) $\int_1^\infty x^{-3} \, dx$, $\int_1^\infty x^{-\frac{1}{2}} \, dx$, $\int_0^1 (1 - x^2)^{-\frac{1}{2}} \, dx$.

(24) $\int_0^\infty e^{-x} \sin x \, dx$, $\int_0^a \dfrac{x \, dx}{(a^2 - x^2)^{\frac{1}{2}}}$, $\int_0^1 \log x \, dx$.

(25) $\int_1^\infty \dfrac{dx}{x(1 + x)}$ $\int_{-\infty}^\infty \dfrac{dx}{x^2(1 + x^2)}$, $\int_\alpha^\beta \dfrac{dx}{[(x - \alpha)(\beta - x)]^{\frac{1}{2}}}$.

Find the values of the following:

(26) $\int_0^{\pi/2} \sin^4\theta \cos^4\theta \, d\theta$, $\int_0^{\pi/2} \cos^{10}\theta \, d\theta$, $\int_0^{2\pi} \sin^2\theta \cos^6\theta \, d\theta$.

(27) $\int_0^a x^3 \, (a^2 - x^2)^{\frac{1}{2}} \, dx$, $\int_0^\infty \dfrac{x^3}{(a^2 + x^2)^4} \, dx$, $\int_0^a x^3 (a - x)^3 \, dx$.

(28) $\int_2^5 (7x - 10 - x^2)^{1/2} \, dx$, $\int_a^{3a} \left(\dfrac{x - a}{3a - x} \right)^{1/2} dx$, $\int_1^3 x(4x - 3 - x^2)^{1/2} \, dx$.

Chapter 4
Infinite Series

4.1 SEQUENCES

Any ordered set of numbers $a_1, a_2, \ldots, a_n, \ldots$ is called a **sequence** and is denoted by $\{a_n\}$.

The upper bound U of such a sequence is the least number which is greater than or equal to every member of the sequence. Hence, $a_n \leq U$ for all values of n and, if ε is a small positive number, $U - \varepsilon$ cannot be greater than or equal to every a. Therefore, $a_n > U - \varepsilon$ for at least one value of n.

The lower bound L is defined in a similar manner; that is, $a_n \geq L$ for all values of n and, if ε is a small positive number, $a_n < L + \varepsilon$ for at least one value of n.

Now let $\{a_n\}$ be any bounded sequence, with U and L its upper and lower bounds. A real number A which is such that $A \leq a_n$ for all sufficiently large values of n, is termed an **inferior number**, for $\{a_n\}$. Also, a number B which is such that $B \geq a_n$ for all sufficiently large values of n, is called a **superior number** for $\{a_n\}$.

Consider the set of all superior numbers. It is bounded below since none of its members is less than L. Hence, it has a lower bound which may be denoted by Λ. Similarly, the set of inferior numbers has an upper bound which may be denoted by λ.

The number Λ is called the **upper limit** of the sequence $\{a_n\}$ as n tends to infinity, and the number λ is called the **lower limit** of $\{a_n\}$ as n tends to infinity. From the definition of λ and Λ, it is clear that $L \leq \lambda \leq \Lambda \leq U$.

If $\Lambda = \lambda$, their common value a is defined to be the **unique limit** (or simply the limit) of the sequence $\{a_n\}$ as n tends to infinity. When the sequence $\{a_n\}$ has such a limit, it is said to **converge** to that limit. Symbolically this may be expressed as

$$\lim_{n \to \infty} a_n = a \ .$$

Since $\Lambda - \lambda \geq 0$, a direct consequence of this definition is that the necessary and sufficient condition for the existence of a unique finite limit is that $\Lambda - \lambda < \varepsilon$ for every arbitrary positive ε.

Using this result, the more usual definition of a unique limit may be proved; that is,

The necessary and sufficient condition that the sequence $\{a_n\}$ converges to a limit a is that, given ε, there exists a number N depending on ε such that $|a_n - a| < \varepsilon$ whenever $n \geq N$.

This condition is necessary since, if $a_n \to a$, then every number greater than a is superior for $\{a_n\}$, and every number less than a is inferior for $\{a_n\}$. Hence,

$$a - \varepsilon < a_n \quad \text{for} \quad n \geq N_1$$

$$a + \varepsilon > a_n \quad \text{for} \quad n \geq N_2 .$$

Then, if N is the greater of the two numbers N_1 and N_2,

$$a - \varepsilon < a_n < a + \varepsilon \quad \text{for} \quad n \geq N$$

that is, $$|a_n - a| < \varepsilon \qquad \text{for} \quad n \geq N .$$

Again, the condition is sufficient since, if $|a_n - a| < \varepsilon$ for $n \geq N$, then $a - \varepsilon$ is an inferior number for $\{a_n\}$. However, since ε is arbitrary, every number less than a is an inferior number for $\{a_n\}$. Similarly, every number greater than a is a superior number for $\{a_n\}$. Hence a unique limit exists.

It is now possible to prove **Cauchy's General Principle of Convergence** which states that:

The necessary and sufficient condition for the convergence of any sequence $\{a_n\}$ is that corresponding to every arbitrary ε there exists an integer N such that

$$|a_N - a_{N+P}| < \varepsilon$$

for all positive integral values of P.

The condition is necessary since, by the result proved above, if a_n tends to a limit a whenever $n \geq N$,

$$|a_n - a| < \frac{1}{2}\varepsilon .$$

In particular, $$|a_N - a| < \frac{1}{2}\varepsilon , |a_{N+P} - a| < \frac{1}{2}\varepsilon .$$

Hence,
$$|a_N - a_{N+P}| = |a_N - a + a - a_{N+P}|$$
$$\leq |a_N - a| + |a - a_{N+P}|$$
$$< \varepsilon .$$

Also, the condition is sufficient since, if $|a_N - a_{N+P}| < \varepsilon$ for all positive integral values of P, then

$$a_N - \varepsilon < a_{N+P} < a_N + \varepsilon ;$$

that is, $a_N - \varepsilon$ and $a_N + \varepsilon$ are an inferior number and superior number respectively for the sequence $\{a_{N+P}\}$. Hence,

$$\Lambda - \lambda \leq (a_N + \varepsilon) - (a_N - \varepsilon) = 2\varepsilon .$$

But $\Lambda - \lambda \geq 0$ and ε is arbitrary, and so it follows that $\Lambda - \lambda = 0$. This is the condition that a unique limit exists and so the sufficiency of the condition is established.

In the discussion so far it has been assumed that the sequences under discussion have been bounded; that is, their upper and lower limits have been finite. It is useful to extend the concept of upper and lower limits to unbounded sequences. This is achieved by noting that in certain cases $\Lambda = +\infty$ and $\lambda = -\infty$. In both cases $\{a_n\}$ is a divergent sequence and the sequence may be said to diverge to ∞, or diverge to $-\infty$.

4.1.1 Monotonic sequences

Suppose that $\{a_n\}$ is any given sequence, then if

$$a_1 \leq a_2 \leq \ldots \leq a_n \leq \ldots \tag{i}$$

or
$$a_1 \geq a_2 \geq \ldots \geq a_n \geq \ldots \tag{ii}$$

$\{a_n\}$ is said to be **monotonic**. If the sequence is of type (i), it is said to be **monotonic increasing** or strictly monotonic increasing if the equality signs are not allowed. Similarly, sequences of type (ii) are said to be **monotonic decreasing** or strictly monotonic decreasing if the equality signs are not allowed.

It now remains to prove a useful theorem concerning monotonic sequences, namely that:

A monotonic increasing sequence tends to its upper bound.

If the upper bound of the sequence $\{a_n\}$ is U, then U is either finite or infinite. If U is finite, then

$$a_n \leq U \qquad \text{for all values of } n \tag{i}$$

$$a_n > U - \varepsilon \qquad \text{for at least one value of } n,$$

so suppose $\quad a_N > U - \varepsilon .$

However, the sequence is monotonic increasing, and so $a_n \geqslant a_N$ if $n \geqslant N$. Therefore

$$a_n > U - \varepsilon .\tag{ii}$$

Hence, comparing (i) and (ii)

$$U - \varepsilon < a_n < U + \varepsilon \qquad \text{for } n \geqslant N$$

which implies that, as $n \to \infty$, $a_n \to U$.

If U is infinite, then given any number G, $a_n > G$ for at least one value of n, say $n = N$. Since $\{a_n\}$ is monotonic increasing, for $n \geqslant N$, $a_n > G$ and so $a_n \to \infty$.

Obviously, it may be proved in a similar manner that a monotonic decreasing sequence tends to its lower bound.

4.2 INFINITE SERIES

The discussion of the infinite series

$$u_1 + u_2 + \cdots + u_n + \cdots = \sum_{r=1}^{\infty} u_r$$

may be reduced to the study of the sequence $\{S_n\}$ where

$$S_n = u_1 + u_2 + \cdots + u_n .$$

Here S_n is the sum of the first n terms of the given infinite series and is called the **nth partial sum**. If $\{S_n\}$ converges to a limit S, then the series is said to be convergent to the value S. If a series is not convergent, it is divergent, and there are several types of divergent series:

(i) if $S_n \to \pm\infty$, the series is said to be **properly divergent**,

(ii) if $\{S_n\}$ does not possess a unique limit, the series is said to **oscillate**. If the sequence has finite upper and lower limits, Λ and λ, the series is **finitely oscillating**, and if $\Lambda = \infty$, $\lambda = -\infty$, it is **infinitely oscillating**.

It is relatively easy to see that some infinite series are convergent simply by applying this definition. For example,

(1) Consider the series whose nth term is

$$u_n = \frac{1}{n(n + 1)} = \frac{1}{n} - \frac{1}{n + 1} .$$

In this case

$$S_n = 1 - \frac{1}{2} + \frac{1}{2} - \frac{1}{3} \cdots + \frac{1}{n} - \frac{1}{n + 1} = 1 - \frac{1}{n + 1} ,$$

that is,

$$|S_n - 1| = \frac{1}{n + 1} .$$

Here the right-hand side tends to zero as $n \to \infty$, and so $S_n \to 1$ as $n \to \infty$.

Therefore, the series is convergent and its sum to infinity is 1.

(2) Consider the geometric series

In this case
$$\sum_{i=0}^{\infty} r^i = 1 + r + r^2 + \cdots + r^n + \cdots$$

$$S_n = \frac{1 - r^n}{1 - r}.$$

Then, provided $|r| < 1$, $\lim_{n \to \infty} S_n = (1 - r)^{-1}$ and the series is convergent.

Theorem

If a series converges, its nth term tends to zero as n tends to infinity.

This result may be deduced immediately from the general principle of convergence of a sequence $\{S_n\}$, since if the series $\sum_{r=1}^{\infty} u_r$ converges then, for a large enough value of n and for all positive integral values of p,

$$|S_{n+p} - S_n| < \varepsilon.$$

This relation must hold, in particular, when $p = 1$ and

$$|S_{n+1} - S_n| = |u_{n+1}|$$

and so $|u_{n+1}| < \varepsilon$ or, in other words $u_{n+1} \to 0$ as $n \to \infty$.

A useful corollary to this theorem is that, if u_n does not tend to zero, the series $\sum_{r=1}^{\infty} u_r$ cannot converge. This provides a useful test for showing that a given series does not converge. However, it is vital to note that the condition that u_n must tend to zero is only a necessary condition for $\sum_{r=1}^{\infty} u_r$ to converge, it is not sufficient. For example, if $u_n = 1/n$, then $u_n \to 0$ as $n \to \infty$ but, as will be seen later, $\sum_{r=1}^{\infty} \frac{1}{r}$ diverges.

4.3 SERIES OF POSITIVE TERMS

If all the terms in the series $\sum_{r=1}^{\infty} u_r$ are positive, the sequence $\{S_n\}$ is monotonic increasing. Hence, $\{S_n\}$ must diverge to infinity or tend to a finite limit. If $\{S_n\}$ is bounded, the series of positive terms $\sum_{r=1}^{\infty} u_r$ will be convergent. This follows since, owing to $\{S_n\}$ being monotonic increasing, it tends to its upper bound (as was proved earlier) and so, if S_n is less then some constant K, S_n will tend to a limit S which cannot exceed K. If K is only a rough upper bound, the exact upper bound S will be less than K. If K is the upper bound, S and K coincide. Thus $S_n \to S \leqslant K$.

Now consider the following examples of series of positive terms:

(1)
$$1 + \frac{1}{2} + \frac{1}{3} + \cdots + \frac{1}{n} + \cdots .$$

Now
$$S_{2^n} = 1 + \frac{1}{2} + \left(\frac{1}{3} + \frac{1}{4}\right) + \left(\frac{1}{5} + \frac{1}{6} + \frac{1}{7} + \frac{1}{8}\right) + \cdots$$

$$+ \left(\frac{1}{2^{n-1} + 1} + \cdots + \frac{1}{2^n}\right)$$

$$> 1 + \frac{1}{2} + \left(\frac{1}{4} + \frac{1}{4}\right) + \left(\frac{1}{8} + \frac{1}{8} + \frac{1}{8} + \frac{1}{8}\right) + \cdots + \frac{2^{n-1}}{2^n}$$

that is
$$S_{2^n} > 1 + \frac{1}{2} + \frac{1}{2} + \frac{1}{2} + \cdots + \frac{1}{2} = 1 + \frac{n}{2}.$$

Therefore, given any K, however large, $S_{2^n} > K$ if $n > 2(K - 1)$ and so, the sequence $\{S_n\}$ is not bounded and $S_n \to \infty$ as $n \to \infty$. This means that the given series diverges to infinity.

(2) $1 + 2^{-p} + 3^{-p} + \cdots + n^{-p} + \cdots$, where $p > 1$.

For this series
$$\sum_{r=2}^{n} r^{-p} < \int_1^n x^{-p} \, dx < (p - 1)^{-1}$$

and so
$$S_n = 1 + \sum_{r=2}^{n} r^{-p} < (p - 1)^{-1} + 1.$$

Therefore, $\{S_n\}$ is bounded above, and so the given series is convergent.

4.4 TESTS FOR CONVERGENCE
4.4.1 Comparison tests
(a) Suppose $\Sigma_{r=1}^{\infty} v_r$ is a series which is known to be convergent and let $\Sigma_{r=1}^{\infty} u_r$ be the series to be tested. If $u_n \leq k v_n$ for all n, where k is a positive constant, then $\Sigma_{r=1}^{\infty} u_r$ is convergent.

Let the nth partial sum of the series to be tested be S_n, then

$$S_n = \sum_{r=1}^{n} u_r \leq k \sum_{r=1}^{n} v_r.$$

However, since $\Sigma_{r=1}^{\infty} v_r$ is a convergent series, $\Sigma_{r=1}^{n} v_r$ will tend to a finite limit, V say, as n tends to infinity; and so, $S_n \leq kV$. This means that the sequence $\{S_n\}$ is bounded above and hence tends to a finite limit as n tends to infinity. Therefore, $\Sigma_{r=1}^{\infty} u_r$ is convergent.

(b) Suppose $\Sigma_{r=1}^{\infty} w_r$ is a series which is known to be divergent. If $u_n \geq k w_n$, then $\Sigma_{r=1}^{\infty} u_r$ is divergent.

Let W_n be the nth partial sum of the given divergent series then, given any H however large, there exists m such that

$$W_n > H k^{-1} \qquad \text{if } n > m,$$

that is
$$S_n > H \qquad \text{if } n > m.$$

Thus, as n tends to infinity, S_n tends to infinity also and the series $\Sigma_{r=1}^{\infty} u_r$ is seen to be divergent.

The application of these comparison tests is quite straightforward as is illustrated by the following examples:

(i) Consider
$$1 + \frac{1}{2!} + \frac{1}{3!} + \cdots + \frac{1}{n!} + \cdots$$

The nth term $= u_n = \dfrac{1}{n!} \leqslant \dfrac{1}{2^{n-1}}$ provided $n \geqslant 2$.

The series $\Sigma_{n=2}^{\infty} \dfrac{1}{2^{n-1}}$ is convergent and so, by the comparison test, $\Sigma_{n=1}^{\infty} u_n$ is convergent.

(ii) Consider $\Sigma_{n=1}^{\infty} n^{-p}$ where $p < 1$.
In this case, $n^{-p} > n^{-1}$ and so, since $\Sigma_{n=1}^{\infty} n^{-1}$ is divergent, $\Sigma_{n=1}^{\infty} n^{-p}$ is divergent also.

(iii) Consider
$$\sum_{n=1}^{\infty} \frac{1}{(n^2 + n)}.$$

In this case, $(n^2 + n)^{-1} < n^{-2}$ and so, since $\Sigma_{n=1}^{\infty} n^{-2}$ is convergent, the given series is convergent also.

(iv) Consider
$$\sum_{n=1}^{\infty} \frac{1}{n + \sqrt{n}}.$$

In this case, $(n + \sqrt{n})^{-1} > \dfrac{1}{2n}$ and so, since $\Sigma_{n=1}^{\infty} n^{-1}$ is divergent, the given series is divergent also.

4.4.2 d'Alembert's ratio test

If $\lim\limits_{n\to\infty} u_{n+1}/u_n = \mu$, then the series $\Sigma_{r=1}^{\infty} u_r$ converges if $\mu < 1$ and diverges if $\mu > 1$.

(a) Suppose μ is less than unity and choose k such that $\mu < k < 1$, then, since the values of u_{n+1}/u_n differ from μ by smaller and smaller amounts as n increases, for n greater than or equal to some value m, say,

$$u_{n+1}/u_n < k.$$

Also, since series of positive terms are being considered, this means that

$$u_{m+1} < k u_m, \; u_{m+2} < k^2 u_m, \ldots.$$

Therefore, from the term u_m onwards, the terms of the given series do not exceed those of the convergent geometric series

$$u_m(1 + k + k^2 + \cdots)$$

and so $\Sigma_{r=1}^{\infty} u_r$ does converge.

(b) Suppose μ is greater than unity then, in this case, for $n \geqslant m$, $u_{n+1} > u_n$. Hence, the nth term does not tend to zero, and so the given series cannot converge. Since it is a series of positive terms under discussion, it must diverge.

4.4.3 Cauchy's test

If $\lim\limits_{n \to \infty} \sqrt[n]{u_n} = \mu$, then the series $\Sigma_{r=1}^{\infty} u_r$ converges if $\mu < 1$ and diverges if $\mu > 1$.

(a) Suppose μ is less than unity and choose k such that $\mu < k < 1$, then if $n \geqslant m$,

$$\sqrt[n]{u_n} < k$$

that is

$$u_n < k^n .$$

Therefore, the given series converges by comparison with the convergent geometric series $\Sigma_{r=1}^{\infty} k^r$, $k < 1$.

(b) Suppose μ is greater than unity, then $\sqrt[n]{u_n}$ and, therefore, u_n itself are greater than unity. Hence, the nth term of the given series does not tend to zero and, accordingly, the series under discussion diverges.

4.5 ABSOLUTE CONVERGENCE OF SERIES

The series which have been discussed so far have all been series of positive terms, and the convergence tests considered have been applicable only to such series. Although it is not intended to discuss series of arbitrary terms in detail, it is worth noting that, when series whose terms are not all of the same sign are considered, a distinction has to be made between series which remain convergent when all the terms are replaced by their absolute values, and those which do not. If a convergent series $\Sigma_{r=1}^{\infty} u_r$ is such that $\Sigma_{r=1}^{\infty} |u_r|$ is also convergent, the original series is said to be **absolutely convergent**.

Again, a series $\Sigma_{r=1}^{\infty} u_r$ is convergent if $\Sigma_{r=1}^{\infty} |u_r|$ is convergent since, if $S_n = \Sigma_{r=1}^{\infty} u_r$ and $T_n = \Sigma_{r=1}^{\infty} |u_r|$ then for a large enough value of n and for all positive integral values of p

$$|S_{n+p} - S_n| \leqslant |T_{n+p} - T_n| < \varepsilon .$$

Therefore, $\Sigma_{r=1}^{\infty} u_r$ does converge.

The sum of an infinite series is defined as a limit, and so is different from the sum of a finite series which is obtained by adding together a finite number of terms. Hence, operations, which are justifiable when applied to finite series, may *not* be applied to infinite series without further investigation. The important property of absolutely convergent series is that, in some ways, they may be treated as if they were finite series: an absolutely convergent series may be rearranged without altering the fact that it is an absolutely convergent series and without altering its sum to infinity. Also, it may be proved (although the proof will not be included here) that if $\Sigma_{r=1}^{\infty} u_r$ and $\Sigma_{r=1}^{\infty} v_r$ are two absolutely convergent series,

$$(u_1 + u_2 + u_3 + \cdots)(v_1 + v_2 + v_3 + \cdots) = u_1 v_1 + (u_2 v_1 + u_1 v_2) + \cdots .$$

In order to test for absolute convergence, the same tests are used as when series of positive terms are being examined but, in this case, the modulus of individual terms is used in the application of the particular test. Hence, it is easier to show the convergence of a series of arbitrary terms if that series is absolutely convergent, than it is if the series is not absolutely convergent. As far as series which contain non-positive terms are concerned, the only case to be considered here is the important case of **alternating series**, that is, series whose terms are alternately positive and negative.

4.6 ALTERNATING SERIES TEST

Consider the series

$$u_1 - u_2 + u_3 - u_4 + \cdots$$

in which each u_r is positive. Suppose $u_n \to 0$ as $n \to \infty$ and $u_m \geq u_{m+1}$ for all values of m. Then, the given alternating series is convergent.

Now
$$S_{2n} = (u_1 - u_2) + (u_3 - u_4) + \cdots + (u_{2n-1} - u_{2n})$$

$$= u_1 - (u_2 - u_3) - \cdots - (u_{2n-2} - u_{2n-1}) - u_{2n} .$$

Since $u_m \geq u_{m+1}$ for all values of m, the content of each bracket in these two equations is positive. Thus, the first equation shows that S_{2n} is positive while the second shows that $S_{2n} < u_1$ and so, S_{2n} tends to a limit which is not greater than u_1.

Also, $S_{2n+1} = S_{2n} + u_{2n+1}$; but, by the first condition of the test, $u_{2n+1} \to 0$ as $n \to \infty$ and so, S_{2n+1} and S_{2n} tend to the same limit. Therefore, the given alternating series is convergent.

Using this test, it is seen immediately that

$$1 - \frac{1}{2} + \frac{1}{3} - \frac{1}{4} + \cdots$$

is convergent but it is not absolutely convergent since, as has been shown already,

$$1 + \frac{1}{2} + \frac{1}{3} + \frac{1}{4} + \cdots \quad \text{is divergent.}$$

On the other hand, the series

$$1 - 2^{-p} + 3^{-p} - 4^{-p} + \cdots \quad , \quad \text{where } p > 1,$$

is seen to be absolutely convergent since

$$1 + 2^{-p} + 3^{-p} + 4^{-p} + \cdots \quad , \quad \text{where } p > 1 \,,$$

has been shown to be convergent.

4.7 THE TAYLOR AND MACLAURIN SERIES

The theorems discussed in Chapter 1 provided a means of obtaining expansions for $f(a + h)$ or $f(h)$ in a series of ascending powers of h up to the term of any order n. Also, various forms of the remainder in these expansions were found. Following earlier discussions in this chapter, it is possible now to consider the expansion of $f(a + h)$, or $f(h)$, in an infinite series of ascending powers of h.

Suppose $f(x)$ is a function with continuous derivatives of any order n (however large n is taken), then a necessary and sufficient condition for the convergence of the Taylor or Maclaurin series is that the remainder $R_n(h)$ tend to zero as n tends to infinity.

Let $S_n(h)$ be the sum to n terms of the Maclaurin series. A necessary and sufficient condition that $S_n(h) \rightarrow f(h)$ as $n \rightarrow \infty$ is that, given any ε, there exists N depending on ε such that, for $n \geqslant N$,

$$|S_n(h) - f(h)| < \varepsilon \,.$$

However, $$f(h) = S_n(h) + R_n(h)$$

and so the convergence condition becomes

$$|R_n(h)| < \varepsilon \quad \text{for} \quad n \geqslant N$$

or, in other words, $R_n(h) \rightarrow 0$ as $n \rightarrow \infty$.

It should be noted that $R_n(h)$ is a function of n, h, and an unknown variable θ which is such that $0 < \theta < 1$. Also, it depends on a for Taylor's series. In some cases the above convergence condition is found to hold for all values of h, but $R_n(h)$ usually tends to zero only when h is restricted to be between certain limits.

Examples

(1) Consider $f(x) = e^x$ so that $f^{(n)}(x) = e^x$ and $f^{(n)}(0) = 1$ for all values of n. Therefore, using Maclaurin's theorem with the Lagrange form of the remainder, leads to

$$e^x = 1 + x + \frac{x^2}{2!} + \cdots + \frac{x^{n-1}}{(n-1)!} + \frac{x^n}{n!} e^{\theta x}$$

where $0 < \theta < 1$.

In order to obtain an infinite series for e^x, it is necessary to show that $R_n(x) \rightarrow 0$ as $n \rightarrow \infty$.

Hence, note that

$$n! = 1.2.3. \dots . (n-1)n \quad \text{or} \quad n! = n(n-1)\dots 3.2.1 ,$$

and so $(n!)^2$ is a product of n factors each of the form $p(n-p+1)$ where $1 \leqslant p \leqslant n$. When $p > 1$

$$p(n-p+1) = p(n-p) + p > (n-p) + p = n .$$

Hence, $(n!)^2 > n^n \quad \text{or} \quad n! > (\sqrt{n})^n .$

Therefore, $\dfrac{|x|^n}{n!} < \left(\dfrac{|x|}{\sqrt{n}}\right)^n \to 0 \quad \text{as} \quad n \to \infty ,$

and so, since $e^{\theta x} < e^x$ which is independent of n, $R_n(x) \to 0$ as $n \to \infty$ for all values of x.

(2) Consider $f(x) = \log(1+x)$ so that $f'(x) = (1+x)^{-1}$ and $f^{(n)}(x) = (-1)^{n-1}(n-1)!\,(1+x)^{-n}$. Then using Maclaurin's theorem,

$$\log(1+x) = x - \frac{x^2}{2} + \frac{x^3}{3} - \dots + R_n(x)$$

where, if the Lagrange form of the remainder is used,

$$R_n(x) = (-1)^{n-1}\frac{x^n}{n}(1+\theta x)^{-n} ,$$

and if the Cauchy form is used

$$R_n(x) = (-1)^{n-1}x^n(1-\theta)^{n-1}(1+\theta x)^{-n}$$

It must be assumed throughout that $x > -1$ since otherwise the derivatives of $f(x)$ do not exist in the interval $[x,0]$. Now there are two cases to consider:

(i) $0 \leqslant x \leqslant 1$.

In this case, the Lagrange form of the remainder shows that

$$|R_n(x)| < n^{-1} \quad \text{and so} \quad R_n(x) \to 0 \quad \text{as} \quad n \to \infty.$$

(ii) $-1 < x < 0$.

In this case, the Cauchy form of the remainder must be used and, if the substitution $x = -y\,(0 < y < 1)$ is made, this yields

$$R_n(y) = -y^n(1-\theta)^{n-1}(1-\theta y)^{-n} .$$

In this expression, $(1-\theta)(1-\theta y)^{-1} < 1$ and $(1-\theta y)$ is independent of n. Hence, $R_n(y) \to 0$ as $n \to \infty$; and, therefore, $R_n(x) \to 0$ as $n \to \infty$.

Thus, it may be deduced that

$$\log(1+x) = x - \frac{x^2}{2} + \frac{x^3}{3} - \dots$$

provided $-1 < x \leqslant 1$.

The use of both the Taylor and Maclaurin theorems for finding expansions of functions in ascending powers of the variable is limited by the complicated forms of the remainder $R_n(x)$. It is in relatively few cases that $R_n(x)$ adopts a manageable form. If an infinite series is found for some function $f(x)$ by evaluating successive derivatives of $f(x)$ and using either Taylor's or Maclaurin's theorem, but if no expression can be found for $R_n(x)$, then it has not been proved that the series so found is the Taylor or Maclaurin expansion for $f(x)$. However, normally when a convergent infinite series is found for a function $f(x)$ by this method, it may be expected to represent that function within its range of absolute convergence.

4.8 POWER SERIES

The Taylor and Maclaurin series are examples of an important type of series called **power series**. Power series are of the form

$$a_0 + a_1 x + a_2 x^2 + \cdots = \sum_{r=0}^{\infty} a_r x^r$$

where the coefficients a_r are constants. As written here, the series is a real power series since x is assumed to be real but, in general, the constants a_r and the variable x could be complex. Here attention will be restricted to real power series. The values of x for which the above series converges may be found by using d'Alembert's ratio test. The series is seen to be absolutely convergent when $\mu < 1$ where

$$\lim_{n \to \infty} \left| \frac{u_{n+1}}{u_n} \right| = \lim_{n \to \infty} \left| \frac{a_{n+1} x^{n+1}}{a_n x^n} \right| = \mu \,.$$

Now write

$$\lim_{n \to \infty} \left| \frac{a_n}{a_{n+1}} \right| = R$$

so that

$$\lim_{n \to \infty} \left| \frac{a_{n+1} x}{a_n} \right| = \frac{|x|}{R} \,,$$

and the original series is seen to be absolutely convergent if $|x| < R$. Hence, a power series is always absolutely convergent for values of x in the open interval $(-R, R)$. Whether or not a power series is convergent when $|x| = R$ will depend on the particular series. The value R is termed the **radius of convergence**.

One of the more useful properties of power series is that the series obtained by differentiating (or integrating) a power series term by term is a power series with the same radius of convergence as the original series.

Consider the power series

$$S = a_0 + a_1 x + a_2 x^2 + \cdots$$

which converges if

$$|x| < \lim_{n\to\infty} \left|\frac{a_n}{a_{n+1}}\right| = R \ .$$

For the derived series,

$$\frac{dS}{dx} = a_1 + 2a_2x + 3a_3x^2 + \cdots ,$$

which converges if

$$|x| < \lim_{n\to\infty} \left|\frac{na_n}{(n+1)a_{n+1}}\right| = \lim_{n\to\infty} \left|\frac{n}{n+1}\right| \lim_{n\to\infty} \left|\frac{a_n}{a_{n+1}}\right| = R \ .$$

Also, for the integrated series,

$$\int S dx = a_0x + \frac{1}{2}a_1x + \frac{1}{3}a_2x^3 + \cdots ,$$

which converges if

$$|x| < \lim_{n\to\infty} \left|\frac{(n+2)a_n}{(n+1)a_{n+1}}\right| = \lim_{n\to\infty} \left|\frac{n+2}{n+1}\right| \lim_{n\to\infty} \left|\frac{a_n}{a_{n+1}}\right| = R \ .$$

Hence, the required result.

It may be noted also that it is possible to prove that differentiating or integrating a power series term by term within its radius of convergence is the same as differentiating or integrating the function it represents. However, although these results hold for power series, they are not valid in general for infinite series of arbitrary functions. The conditions under which an arbitrary infinite series may be differentiated, or integrated, term by term depend on the idea of uniform convergence.

To introduce the idea of uniform convergence, consider the series

$$u_1(x) + u_2(x) + \cdots + u_n(x) + \cdots$$

and write
$$S_n(x) = \sum_{r=1}^{n} u_r(x) \ .$$

If $S_n(x)$ tends to the limit $S(x)$ as n tends to infinity then $\{S_n(x)\}$ is said to converge to $S(x)$, and $S(x)$ is termed the **sum-function** of the given series. As has been seen already, for a sequence $\{S_n\}$ which does not depend on x, the number N, involved in the definition of a limit, depends on ε. For the sequence $\{S_n(x)\}$, the number N will be a function of ε and x in general. It is here that the notion of uniformity becomes important. $S_n(x)$ is said to **converge uniformly** to $S(x)$ in $[a,b]$ if, given any $\varepsilon > 0$, there exists $m(\varepsilon)$ *which does not depend on x*, such that

$$|S_n(x) - S(x)| < \varepsilon$$

for $n \geq m(\varepsilon)$ and for all values of x in $a \leq x \leq b$.

Example

Consider $S_n(x) = x^2/n$ in the range $0 \leqslant x \leqslant 1$.

Clearly $|S_n(x)| \leqslant n^{-1}$. Hence, given any $\varepsilon > 0$, $|S_n(x)| < \varepsilon$ if $n > \varepsilon^{-1}$; that is $S_n(x)$ tends to zero uniformly in $[0,1]$.

4.9 THE UNIFORM CONVERGENCE OF SERIES

The case of the uniform convergence of a series follows immediately from the definition of uniform convergence of a sequence $\{S_n(x)\}$ by writing $S_n(x) = \sum_{r=1}^{n} u_r(x)$.

Now the **General Principle of Uniform Convergence** states that the necessary and sufficient condition that a sequence $\{S_n(x)\}$ converges uniformly to $S(x)$ in a range $a \leqslant x \leqslant b$ is that, given any $\varepsilon > 0$, there exists a number $m(\varepsilon)$, independent of x, such that

$$|S_n(x) - S_{n+t}(x)| < \varepsilon$$

for all $n + t > n \geqslant m(\varepsilon)$ and for all values of x in $[a,b]$.

The necessity is obvious. To prove the sufficiency, suppose that the condition is satisfied, then, for each x in $[a,b]$, $\lim_{n \to \infty} S_n(x)$ exists and equals $S(x)$. Also the inequality holds for all values of $(n + t)$. Therefore, let $t \to \infty$ then

$$|S_n(x) - S_{n+t}(x)| \to |S_n(x) - S(x)|$$

and so $|S_n(x) - S(x)| < \varepsilon$ for $n \geqslant m(\varepsilon)$ and for all values of x in $[a,b]$. Hence, $S_n(x)$ tends uniformly to $S(x)$.

An immediate corollary to this result is that the necessary and sufficient condition that the series $\sum_{n=1}^{\infty} u_n(x)$ converges uniformly in a range $a \leqslant x \leqslant b$ is that, given any $\varepsilon > 0$, there exists a number $m(\varepsilon)$, independent of x, such that

$$|u_{m+1}(x) + u_{m+2}(x) + \cdots + u_{m+p}(x)| < \varepsilon$$

for all positive integral values of p.

One of the most useful tests for determining whether or not a series is uniformly convergent is the **Weierstrass M-test**. This states that a series $\sum_{n=1}^{\infty} u_n(x)$ is uniformly convergent for all values of x in a given range $[a,b]$ if $|u_n(x)| < M_n$ for all values of n greater than a fixed number m, where M_n is a function of n only, and if $\sum_{n=1}^{\infty} M_n$ is convergent.

The proof is simple since

$$|u_{m+1}(x) + u_{m+2}(x) + \cdots + u_{m+p}(x)| < \sum_{r=m}^{m+p} M_r < \varepsilon$$

for all positive integral values of p, the number m depending on ε but not x. It follows that the given series is uniformly convergent in the given range.

Examples

(i) Consider the series $1 + x + \dfrac{x^2}{2!} + \dfrac{x^3}{3!} + \cdots$ in the range $[-R,R]$. For this series
$$u_{n+1}(x) = x^n/n!$$

and so
$$|u_{n+1}(x)| \leqslant R^n/n! = v_{n+1} \quad \text{say.}$$

Also,
$$v_{n+1}/v_n = R/n \to 0 \quad \text{as} \quad n \to \infty .$$

Therefore, by d'Alembert's ratio test, $\Sigma_{n=1}^{\infty} v_n$ is convergent.

Hence, by Weierstrass' M-test, the original series is uniformly convergent in the range $[-R,R]$.

(Note that this series is not uniformly convergent for all x.)

(ii) Consider the series $\qquad \displaystyle\sum_{n=1}^{\infty} \frac{x}{n(1 + nx^2)}$ for all x.

The nth term of this series $x/n(1 + nx^2)$ is found to possess a maximum value when $x = n^{-\frac{1}{2}}$ and a minimum value when $x = -n^{-\frac{1}{2}}$; and so,

$$|u_n(x)| \leqslant \frac{1}{2} n^{-\frac{3}{2}}$$

for all x.

However, $\Sigma_{n=1}^{\infty} \dfrac{1}{2} n^{-\frac{3}{2}}$ is convergent and so, by the Weierstrass M-test, the given series is uniformly convergent.

It now remains to prove two important and useful results for uniformly convergent sequences and to note the extension to the case of uniformly convergent series.

Theorem

If the sequence $\{S_n(x)\}$ converges uniformly to $S(x)$ in the range $[a,b]$ then provided the integrals exist,

$$\lim_{n \to \infty} \int_a^b S_n(x)\, dx = \int_a^b S(x)\, dx .$$

Proof

From the conditions of the theorem, it is seen that, given any $\varepsilon > 0$, there exists a number m depending on ε such that

$$|S_n(x) - S(x)| < \varepsilon/(b - a) \quad \text{if} \quad n > m(\varepsilon) .$$

Then
$$\left| \int_a^b S_n(x)\, dx - \int_a^b S(x)\, dx \right| = \left| \int_a^b \{S_n(x) - S(x)\}\, dx \right|$$

$$\leqslant \int_a^b \left| S_n(x) - S(x) \right| dx$$

$$\leq \int_a^b \frac{\varepsilon}{(b-a)}\, dx \quad \text{if} \quad n > m(\varepsilon)$$

$$= \quad \varepsilon \qquad \quad \text{if} \quad n > m(\varepsilon)\,.$$

Hence the required result.

The corresponding result for series is that a uniformly convergent series $\Sigma_{n=1}^{\infty} u_n(x)$, of continuous functions of x, may be integrated term by term.

From the result for sequences, if $S_n(x) = \Sigma_{r=1}^{n} u_r(x)$, it follows that

$$\int_a^b S(x)dx = \lim_{n \to \infty} \int_a^b S_n(x)dx$$

$$= \int_a^b u_1(x)dx + \int_a^b u_2(x)dx + \cdots + \int_a^b u_n(x)dx + \cdots$$

Theorem

If the sequence $\{S_n(x)\}$ converges to $S(x)$ in the range $[a,b]$ and if $S_n'(x)$, (where $S_n'(x)$ is the derivative of $S_n(x)$ with respect to x), is uniformly convergent in $[a,b]$, then

$$\lim_{n \to \infty} S_n'(x) = S'(x)\,.$$

Proof

Suppose $S_n'(x)$ converges uniformly to $\sigma(x)$ for x in the range $[a,b]$ then, since the convergence is uniform in $[a,x]$ where $a \leq x \leq b$,

$$\lim_{n \to \infty} \int_a^x S_n'(t)\, dt = \int_a^x \sigma(t)dt\,,$$

that is

$$\lim_{n \to \infty} \{S_n(x) - S_n(a)\} = \int_a^x \sigma(t)dt\,.$$

Now the left-hand side equals $\{S(x) - S(a)\}$ and so

$$S(x) - S(a) = \int_a^x \sigma(t)dt\,.$$

Also, on the right-hand side provided $\sigma(t)$ is continuous

$$\frac{d}{dx}\int_a^x \sigma(t)dt = \sigma(x)\,.$$

Therefore, $S'(x)$ exists and is equal to $\sigma(x)$ so that

$$S'(x) = \lim_{n \to \infty} S_n'(x)\,.$$

In this case, the corresponding result for series is that, if the series $\Sigma_{n=1}^{\infty} u_n(x)$ is convergent to $S(x)$ and if the series of derivatives $\Sigma_{n=1}^{\infty} u_n'(x)$ is uniformly convergent to $\sigma(x)$ in $[a,b]$, then $S'(x) = \sigma(x)$; that is, the series may be differentiated term by term.

As was mentioned earlier, these two results apply to all power series within their radii of convergence, since a power series $\sum_{r=0}^{\infty} a_r x^r$ with a non-zero radius of convergence R is uniformly convergent in the interval $-r \leq x \leq r$ where $r < R$. This may be seen as follows:

For $-r \leq x \leq r$.

$$\left| a_{n+1} x^{n+1} + a_{n+2} x^{n+2} + \cdots + a_{n+p} x^{n+p} \right|$$
$$\leq \left| a_{n+1} \right| r^{n+1} + \left| a_{n+2} \right| r^{n+2} + \cdots + \left| a_{n+p} \right| r^{n+p} .$$

Also, since the original series converges absolutely for $x = r$, it follows that, given $\varepsilon > 0$, there exists a number N depending on ε, such that

$$\left| a_{n+1} \right| r^{n+1} + \left| a_{n+2} \right| r^{n+2} + \cdots + \left| a_{n+p} \right| r^{n+p} < \varepsilon$$

for $n > N(\varepsilon)$ and for all positive integral values of p.

Hence,

$$\left| a_{n+1} x^{n+1} + a_{n+2} x^{n+2} + \cdots + a_{n+p} x^p \right| < \varepsilon$$

for $n > N(\varepsilon)$, for all values of x in $-r \leq x \leq r$ and for all positive integral values of p.

Since $N(\varepsilon)$ is independent of x, this shows that the original series is uniformly convergent in the interval $-r \leq x \leq r$.

EXERCISES 4

(1) Consider the series $\sum_{r=1}^{\infty} u_r$, where $u_r = [r(r + 1)(r + 2)]^{-1}$. Find an expression for the sum of the first n terms and, by finding the sum to infinity, show that the series is convergent.

(2) By comparing with $\sum_{n=1}^{\infty} n^{-p}$, test the following series for convergence or divergence:

$$\sum_{n=1}^{\infty} (1 + n^2)^{-1} \; ; \; \sum_{n=1}^{\infty} (1 + n)/(1 + n^2) \; ; \; \sum_{n=1}^{\infty} n!/(2n)! .$$

(3) Use either d'Alembert's test or Cauchy's test to show that
(a) $\sum_{n=1}^{\infty} q^{n^2} x^n$, where $0 < q < 1$, converges for any positive value of x;

(b) the series $\quad 1 + \dfrac{a + 1}{b + 1} + \dfrac{(a + 1)(2a + 1)}{(b + 1)(2b + 1)} + \dfrac{(a + 1)(2a + 1)(3a + 1)}{(b + 1)(2b + 1)(3b + 1)} + \cdots$

converges if $b > a > 0$ but diverges if $a \geq b > 0$.

(4) Show that the series $(1 - \frac{1}{2} + \frac{1}{3} - \frac{1}{4} + \cdots)$ is convergent but the series $(1 + \frac{1}{2} - \frac{1}{3} + \frac{1}{4} + \frac{1}{5} - \frac{1}{6} + \cdots)$ is divergent.

(5) Show that the following series are absolutely convergent in the range given:

(a)
$$1 + x + \frac{x^2}{2!} + \cdots + \frac{x^n}{n!} + \cdots$$

for x in the range $(-\infty, \infty)$,

(b)
$$1 + x + \frac{x^2}{2} + \cdots + \frac{x^n}{n} + \cdots$$

for x in the range $(-1, 1)$,

(c)
$$1 + 2x + 3x^2 + \cdots + (n + 1)x^n + \cdots$$

for x in the range $(-1, 1)$.

(6) Find the values of x for which the series

$$\frac{3x}{1 + x^2} + \left(\frac{3x}{1 + x^2}\right)^2 + \left(\frac{3x}{1 + x^2}\right)^3 + \cdots$$

is (a) absolutely convergent and (b) divergent.

(7) Use Maclaurin's theorem to prove the following results:

(a)
$$\sin x = x - \frac{x^3}{3!} + \frac{x^5}{5!} - \frac{x^7}{7!} + \cdots$$

for all finite values of x.

b)
$$\cos x = 1 - \frac{x^2}{2!} + \frac{x^4}{4!} - \frac{x^6}{6!} + \cdots$$

for all finite values of x.

(c)
$$2^x = 1 + x \log 2 + \frac{(x \log 2)^2}{2!} + \frac{(x \log 2)^3}{3!} + \cdots$$

for all finite values of x,

(d)
$$\sec x \tan x = x + \frac{5}{6}x^3 + \frac{61}{120}x^5 + \cdots$$

for x in the range $(-\pi/2, \pi/2)$,

(e)
$$\tan x = 1 + \frac{1}{3}x^3 + \frac{2}{15}x^5 + \frac{17}{315}x^7 + \cdots$$

for x in the range $(-\pi/2, \pi/2)$.

(8) If $f(x) = \sin(m \sin^{-1}x)$, show that $(1 - x)f''(x) - xf'(x) = -m^2f(x)$. Hence by Leibniz' theorem, show that

$$(1 - x^2)f^{(n+2)}(x) - (1 + 2n)xf^{(n+1)}(x) + (m^2 - n^2)f^{(n)}(x) = 0.$$

Use this result to show that

$$\sin(m \sin^{-1} x) = mx - \frac{m(m^2 - 1^2)x^3}{3!} + \frac{m(m^2 - 1^2)(m^2 - 3^2)x^5}{5!} \cdots.$$

(9) Prove that $\sum_{n=1}^{\infty} x^n$ is uniformly convergent in $[-k,k]$ if $k < 1$.

(10) Show that the series $\sum_{n=1}^{\infty} \dfrac{x}{n^p + n^q x^2}$ converges uniformly in $(-\infty,\infty)$ if (i) $p > 1$ or (ii) $p + q > 2$.

(11) Show that the series $\sum_{n=1}^{\infty}(n^3 + n^4x^2)^{-1}$ is uniformly convergent for all x. If the sum of this series is $f(x)$, prove that

$$f'(x) = \sum_{n=1}^{\infty} \frac{d}{dx}[(n^3 + n^4x^2)^{-1}].$$

Chapter 5
Matrices and Determinants

5.1 BASIC CONCEPTS

The concept of a matrix arises in connection with linear relations such as linear transformations or systems of linear equations. For example, the coordinates of two different fixed coordinate systems in the plane might be related via the linear equations

$$x = a_{11}x' + a_{12}y'$$

$$y = a_{21}x' + a_{22}y'$$

where x,y and x',y' are variable quantities but the four coefficients a_{11}, a_{12}, a_{21}, a_{22} are all constants. Arranging the coefficients in the manner in which they occur in the above equations and enclosing them in large brackets yields

$$\begin{pmatrix} a_{11} & a_{12} \\ a_{21} & a_{22} \end{pmatrix}.$$

This array is an example of a **matrix**.

In general, any rectangular array of numbers (numbers which may be real or complex), of the form

$$\begin{pmatrix} a_{11} & a_{12} & \cdots & a_{1n} \\ a_{21} & a_{22} & \cdots & a_{2n} \\ \cdot & \cdot & & \cdot \\ \cdot & \cdot & & \cdot \\ \cdot & \cdot & & \cdot \\ a_{m1} & a_{m2} & \cdots & a_{mn} \end{pmatrix}$$

is called a matrix. The numbers a_{ik} are called the **elements** of the matrix. The horizontal lines are called **rows** and the vertical lines are called **columns** of the matrix. A matrix with m rows and n columns is termed an $(m \times n)$ matrix,—this is read as an 'm by n' matrix. In the special case when m and n are equal, the matrix is said to be **square**.

In common with many texts, matrices will be denoted by bold-face capital letters **A**, **B**, etc., or by (a_{ik}), (b_{ik}), etc., that is by writing the general element of the matrix and enclosing it in brackets. In this notation for elements which involves two subscripts, the first subscript always denotes the row and the second the column containing the particular element.

A matrix $(a_1, a_2, \ldots, a_n)$, which has only one row, is termed a **row matrix** or **row vector** while a matrix

$$\begin{pmatrix} b_1 \\ b_2 \\ \cdot \\ \cdot \\ \cdot \\ b_n \end{pmatrix} ,$$

which has only one column, is termed a **column matrix** or **column vector**. Again in common with other texts, row and column matrices will be denoted by small bold-faced letters.

Before proceeding to discuss the uses of matrices, particularly in connection with the solution of systems of linear equations, it is necessary to set up an algebra defining the various operations with matrices; that is, the operations of addition, multiplication, and so on.

5.2 ALGEBRA OF MATRICES

Two $(m \times n)$ matrices $\mathbf{A} = (a_{ik})$ and $\mathbf{B} = (b_{ik})$ are said to be **equal** if and only if all their corresponding elements are equal, that is

$$a_{ik} = b_{ik} \quad \text{for all } i = 1, \ldots, m \quad \text{and} \quad k = 1, \ldots, n .$$

If this is the case, $\mathbf{A} = \mathbf{B}$.

It is important to note that this definition of equality refers to matrices having the same number of rows and the same number of columns only.

The operations of addition and subtraction will be defined now, and it should be noted that these definitions also apply only to matrices possessing the same number of rows and the same number of columns. The **sum** of two $(m \times n)$ matrices $\mathbf{A} = (a_{ik})$ and $\mathbf{B} = (b_{ik})$ is defined to be the $(m \times n)$ matrix $\mathbf{C} = (c_{ik})$ whose elements are given by

$$c_{ik} = a_{ik} + b_{ik} \quad \text{for } i = 1, \ldots, m \quad \text{and} \quad k = 1, \ldots, n .$$

The sum is written $\mathbf{C} = \mathbf{A} + \mathbf{B}$

Similarly, the **difference** of **A** and **B** is defined to be the $(m \times n)$ matrix $\mathbf{D} = (d_{ik})$ whose elements are given by

$$d_{ik} = a_{ik} - b_{ik} \quad \text{for } i = 1, \ldots, m \quad \text{and} \quad k = 1, \ldots, n .$$

The difference is written $\mathbf{D} = \mathbf{A} - \mathbf{B}$.

Example

Suppose
$$\mathbf{A} = \begin{pmatrix} 2 & -4 & 1 \\ 0 & 3 & 5 \end{pmatrix} \text{ and } \mathbf{B} = \begin{pmatrix} -1 & 3 & 1 \\ 2 & 0 & 5 \end{pmatrix}$$

then
$$\mathbf{C} = \mathbf{A} + \mathbf{B} = \begin{pmatrix} 1 & -1 & 2 \\ 2 & 3 & 10 \end{pmatrix} \text{ and } \mathbf{D} = \mathbf{A} - \mathbf{B} \begin{pmatrix} 3 & -7 & 0 \\ -2 & 3 & 0 \end{pmatrix}.$$

From the above definitions, it is seen that, provided matrices have elements which are real or complex numbers, the laws of addition and subtraction of elementary algebra apply to matrices also. This follows since addition and subtraction of matrices are defined in terms of the addition and subtraction of the individual elements of the matrices. Hence, addition and subtraction of matrices are commutative and associative:

$$\mathbf{A} + \mathbf{B} = \mathbf{B} + \mathbf{A}, (\mathbf{A} + \mathbf{B}) + \mathbf{C} = \mathbf{A} + (\mathbf{B} + \mathbf{C}),$$

where $\mathbf{A}, \mathbf{B}, \mathbf{C}$ are all $(m \times n)$ matrices.

Again, the product of a matrix $\mathbf{A} = (a_{ik})$ with a number h is defined to be the matrix (ha_{ik}) and is denoted by $h\mathbf{A}$ or $\mathbf{A}h$.

In accordance with the above definition of subtraction, if $h = -1, (-1)\mathbf{A}$ is written as $-\mathbf{A}$ and $\mathbf{A} + (-\mathbf{B})$ is written $\mathbf{A} - \mathbf{B}$.

Example

If
$$\mathbf{A} = \begin{pmatrix} 7 & 5 \\ 2 & 6 \end{pmatrix} \text{ then } h\mathbf{A} = \begin{pmatrix} 7h & 5h \\ 2h & 6h \end{pmatrix}.$$

Also, from the above definitions, the following laws of elementary algebra are seen to hold for matrices also

$$h(\mathbf{A} + \mathbf{B}) = h\mathbf{A} + h\mathbf{B}, (h + k)\mathbf{A} = h\mathbf{A} + k\mathbf{A},$$

where $\mathbf{A}, \mathbf{B}$ are $(m \times n)$ matrices and h, k are constants.

Another operation which is used quite frequently is that of transposition of a matrix. The **transpose** of an $(m \times n)$ matrix $\mathbf{A} = (a_{ik})$ is the $(n \times m)$ matrix (a_{ki}) and it is denoted by $\mathbf{A}^{\mathrm{T}}$

Therefore, if
$$\mathbf{A} = (a_{ik}) = \begin{pmatrix} a_{11} & a_{12} & \cdots & a_{1n} \\ a_{21} & a_{22} & \cdots & a_{2n} \\ \cdot & \cdot & & \cdot \\ \cdot & \cdot & & \cdot \\ \cdot & \cdot & & \cdot \\ a_{m1} & a_{m2} & \cdots & a_{mn} \end{pmatrix}$$

then
$$\mathbf{A}^{\mathrm{T}} = (a_{ki}) = \begin{pmatrix} a_{11} & a_{21} & \cdots & a_{m1} \\ a_{12} & a_{22} & \cdots & a_{m2} \\ \cdot & \cdot & & \cdot \\ \cdot & \cdot & & \cdot \\ \cdot & \cdot & & \cdot \\ a_{1n} & a_{2n} & \cdots & a_{mn} \end{pmatrix}.$$

Hence, the rows of $\mathbf{A}$ become the columns of $\mathbf{A}^T$ and vice versa. It might be noted that it follows from the definition of the transpose of a matrix that the transpose of a row matrix is a column matrix and the transpose of a column matrix is a row matrix. .

Examples

(i)   if $\mathbf{A} = \begin{pmatrix} 1 & 3 \\ 7 & 4 \end{pmatrix}$, $\mathbf{A}^T = \begin{pmatrix} 1 & 7 \\ 3 & 4 \end{pmatrix}$

(ii) if $\mathbf{a} = (1\ 5\ 6)$, $\mathbf{a}^T = \begin{pmatrix} 1 \\ 5 \\ 6 \end{pmatrix}$

(iii) if $\mathbf{b} = \begin{pmatrix} 2 \\ 3 \\ 5 \end{pmatrix}$, $\mathbf{b}^T = (2\ 3\ 5)$.

If $\mathbf{A}$ and $\mathbf{B}$ are two $(m \times n)$ matrices and a is a constant then it follows from the definition of the transpose of a matrix that

$$(\mathbf{A} + \mathbf{B})^T = \mathbf{A}^T + \mathbf{B}^T$$

$$(a\mathbf{A})^T = a\mathbf{A}^T$$

$$(\mathbf{A}^T)^T = \mathbf{A}.$$

It has been mentioned already that the elements of a matrix may be real or complex. A matrix, whose elements are all real, is termed a **real** matrix.

Again as has been mentioned already, a matrix which has the same number of rows as columns is called a square matrix and the number of its rows is its **order**. For such a matrix of order n, the diagonal containing the elements $a_{11}, a_{22}, \ldots, a_{nn}$ is called the **leading** or **principal diagonal** and the sum of these elements is the **trace** (or spur) of the matrix. This sum is denoted by Tr (or Sp) usually.

Example

If $\mathbf{A} = \begin{pmatrix} 1 & 4 & 7 \\ 2 & 3 & 8 \\ 9 & 6 & 5 \end{pmatrix}$ then Tr $\mathbf{A} = 1 + 3 + 5 = 9$.

Square matrices turn out to be of particular importance, as will be seen in what follows. A real square matrix $\mathbf{A} = (a_{ik})$ is said to be **symmetric** if it is equal to its transpose, that is, if

$$\mathbf{A}^T = \mathbf{A} \quad \text{or} \quad a_{ki} = a_{ik}, (i,k = 1, \ldots, n).$$

On the other hand, such a matrix is said to be **anti-symmetric** or **skew-symmetric** if

$$\mathbf{A}^T = -\mathbf{A} \, ,$$

that is, if $a_{ki} = -a_{ik}$ $(i,k = 1, \ldots, n)$.

For this definition of an anti-symmetric matrix it is seen that, for $i = k$, a_{ii} $= -a_{ii}$ which implies that the elements along the principal diagonal of an anti-symmetric matrix are all zero. Further, any square matrix $\mathbf{A} = (a_{ik})$ may be written as the sum of a symmetric matrix $\mathbf{R}$ and an anti-symmetric matrix $\mathbf{S}$ since

$$a_{ik} = \tfrac{1}{2}(a_{ik} + a_{ki}) + \tfrac{1}{2}(a_{ik} - a_{ki})$$

or $$\mathbf{A} = \tfrac{1}{2}(\mathbf{A} + \mathbf{A}^T) + \tfrac{1}{2}(\mathbf{A} - \mathbf{A}^T)$$

$$= \mathbf{R} + \mathbf{S} \, .$$

Example

The matrix $\mathbf{A} = \begin{pmatrix} 1 & 2 & 6 \\ 3 & 4 & 7 \\ 5 & 8 & 9 \end{pmatrix}$ may be written in the form $\mathbf{A} = \mathbf{R} + \mathbf{S}$ where

$$\mathbf{R} = \tfrac{1}{2}(\mathbf{A} + \mathbf{A}^T) = \begin{pmatrix} 1 & 2.5 & 5.5 \\ 2.5 & 4 & 7.5 \\ 5.5 & 7.5 & 9 \end{pmatrix}, \; \mathbf{S} = \tfrac{1}{2}(\mathbf{A} - \mathbf{A}^T) = \begin{pmatrix} 0 & -0.5 & 0.5 \\ 0.5 & 0 & -0.5 \\ -0.5 & 0.5 & 0 \end{pmatrix}$$

and $\mathbf{R}$, $\mathbf{S}$ are seen to be symmetric and anti-symmetric respectively.

A square matrix $\mathbf{A} = (a_{ik})$ all of whose elements above, or below, the principal diagonal are zero is called a **triangular matrix**.

$$\mathbf{T}_1 = \begin{pmatrix} 1 & 0 & 0 \\ 6 & 5 & 0 \\ 3 & 2 & 7 \end{pmatrix}, \mathbf{T}_2 = \begin{pmatrix} 1 & 4 & -2 \\ 0 & 3 & 7 \\ 0 & 0 & 5 \end{pmatrix}$$

are typical examples of triangular matrices.

If a square matrix $\mathbf{A} = (a_{ik})$ is such that $a_{ik} = 0$ for all $i \neq k$ (that is, all the elements both above and below the principal diagonal are zero), then that matrix is termed a **diagonal matrix**. A typical example of such a matrix is

$$\begin{pmatrix} 2 & 0 & 0 \\ 0 & 1 & 0 \\ 0 & 0 & 3 \end{pmatrix} .$$

A diagonal matrix whose non-zero elements all equal unity is called **unit matrix** and is denoted by $\mathbf{I}$. The (3×3) unit matrix is

$$\begin{pmatrix} 1 & 0 & 0 \\ 0 & 1 & 0 \\ 0 & 0 & 1 \end{pmatrix} .$$

Finally, a matrix whose elements are all zero is called a **zero** or **null matrix** and is denoted by **0**. Clearly, if **A** is any $(m \times n)$ matrix and **0** is the $(m \times n)$ zero matrix

$$\mathbf{A} + \mathbf{0} = \mathbf{0} + \mathbf{A} = \mathbf{A}.$$

Hence, so far, what is meant by addition and subtraction of matrices as well as by the product of a number and a matrix has been explained and various special matrices have been introduced. The most important operation remaining to be introduced is that of multiplication of one matrix by another. In order to give some justification for the definition of matrix multiplication which will be given shortly, consider once again coordinate systems in the plane. In this case, consider three such systems and let them be denoted by the variables x_1 and x_2, y_1 and y_2, z_1 and z_2. Also, suppose the first two systems are related by

$$x_1 = a_{11}y_1 + a_{12}y_2 = \sum_{k=1}^{2} a_{1k}y_k$$

$$x_2 = a_{21}y_1 + a_{22}y_2 = \sum_{k=1}^{2} a_{2k}y_k$$

where the matrix of the coefficients is $\mathbf{A} = \begin{pmatrix} a_{11} & a_{12} \\ a_{21} & a_{22} \end{pmatrix}$,

and suppose the second and third systems are related by

$$y_1 = b_{11}z_1 + b_{12}z_2 = \sum_{k=1}^{2} b_{1k}z_k$$

$$y_2 = b_{21}z_1 + b_{22}z_2 = \sum_{k=1}^{2} b_{2k}z_k$$

where the matrix of the coefficients is $\mathbf{B} = \begin{pmatrix} b_{11} & b_{12} \\ b_{21} & b_{22} \end{pmatrix}$.

It follows from the above two sets of equations that the first and third systems are related by

$$x_1 = (a_{11}b_{11} + a_{12}b_{21})z_1 + (a_{11}b_{12} + a_{12}b_{22})z_2$$

$$x_2 = (a_{21}b_{11} + a_{22}b_{21})z_1 + (a_{21}b_{12} + a_{22}b_{22})z_2$$

that is, by equations of the form

$$x_1 = c_{11}z_1 + c_{12}z_2$$

$$x_2 = c_{21}z_1 + c_{22}z_2$$

where
$$c_{ik} = a_{i1}b_{1k} + a_{i2}b_{2k} = \sum_{j=1}^{2} a_{ij}b_{jk} \qquad (5.1)$$

Now the product **AB** (with **A** and **B** in this order) of the coefficient matrices **A** and **B** is defined to be the coefficient matrix

$$\mathbf{C} = \begin{pmatrix} c_{11} & c_{12} \\ c_{21} & c_{22} \end{pmatrix}$$

that is, $\mathbf{C} = \mathbf{AB}$ where the elements of **C** are given by (5.1).

This definition covers the product of two (2×2) matrices. However, the approach is generalised easily by considering two quite general linear transformations which could be written

$$x_i = \sum_{k=1}^{n} a_{ik} y_k , \qquad i = 1, 2, \dots, m, \tag{5.2}$$

$$y_i = \sum_{k=1}^{p} b_{ik} z_k , \qquad i = 1, 2, \dots, n . \tag{5.3}$$

By eliminating the y's between these two equations, it is seen that

$$x_i = \sum_{k=1}^{p} c_{ik} z_k , \qquad i = 1, 2, \dots, m, \tag{5.4}$$

where the coefficients c_{ik} are given by

$$c_{ik} = a_{i1}b_{1k} + a_{i2}b_{2k} + \cdots + a_{in}b_{nk} = \sum_{j=1}^{n} a_{ij}b_{jk} .$$

The requirement that the product **AB** of the coefficient matrices $\mathbf{A} = (a_{ik})$ and $\mathbf{B} = (b_{ik})$ of these transformations leads to the coefficient matrix $\mathbf{C} = (c_{ik})$ as above, yields the following definition:

Let $\mathbf{A} + (a_{ik})$ be an $(m \times n)$ matrix and $\mathbf{B} = (b_{ik})$ an $(r \times p)$ matrix, then the product **AB** (with **A** and **B** in this order) is defined only when $r = n$ and is the $(m \times p)$ matrix $\mathbf{C} = (c_{ik})$ whose elements are $c_{ik} = \sum_{j=1}^{n} a_{ij}b_{jk}$.

It might be noted that $\mathbf{A}^2$ is written instead of **AA**, and so on.

Examples

(i) Suppose $\mathbf{A} = \begin{pmatrix} 4 & 6 & -1 \\ 3 & 0 & 2 \\ 1 & -2 & 5 \end{pmatrix}$ and $\mathbf{B} = \begin{pmatrix} 2 & 4 \\ 0 & 1 \\ -1 & 2 \end{pmatrix}$.

Since **A** is a (3×3) matrix and **B** is a (3×2) matrix, the product **BA** is not defined but

$$\mathbf{AB} = \begin{pmatrix} 4 & 6 & -1 \\ 3 & 0 & 2 \\ 1 & -2 & 5 \end{pmatrix} \begin{pmatrix} 2 & 4 \\ 0 & 1 \\ -1 & 2 \end{pmatrix} = \begin{pmatrix} 9 & 20 \\ 4 & 16 \\ -3 & 12 \end{pmatrix} .$$

(ii) Suppose $\mathbf{a} = (5\ 2\ -3)$ and $\mathbf{b} = \begin{pmatrix} 2 \\ -1 \\ 4 \end{pmatrix}$ then

$$\mathbf{a\,b} = (5\ 2\ -3)\begin{pmatrix} 2 \\ -1 \\ 4 \end{pmatrix} = -4$$

$$\mathbf{b\,a} = \begin{pmatrix} 2 \\ -1 \\ 4 \end{pmatrix}(5\ 2\ -3) = \begin{pmatrix} 10 & 4 & -6 \\ -5 & -2 & 3 \\ 20 & 8 & -12 \end{pmatrix}.$$

(iii) Suppose $\mathbf{A} = \begin{pmatrix} a_{11} & a_{12} \\ a_{21} & a_{22} \end{pmatrix}$ and $\mathbf{x} = \begin{pmatrix} x_1 \\ x_2 \end{pmatrix}$ then

$$\mathbf{A\,x} = \begin{pmatrix} a_{11} & a_{12} \\ a_{21} & a_{22} \end{pmatrix}\begin{pmatrix} x_1 \\ x_2 \end{pmatrix} = \begin{pmatrix} a_{11}x_1 + a_{12}x_2 \\ a_{21}x_1 + a_{22}x_2 \end{pmatrix}.$$

Hence, if $\mathbf{y} = \begin{pmatrix} y_1 \\ y_2 \end{pmatrix}$ the system of linear equations

$$a_{11}x_1 + a_{12}x_2 = y_1$$

$$a_{21}x_1 + a_{22}x_2 = y_2$$

is expressible concisely as the matrix equation

$$\mathbf{A\,x} = \mathbf{y}.$$

Referring back to equation (5.2), it is seen that if $\mathbf{x}$ and $\mathbf{y}$ are the column matrices with elements $x_1, x_2, \ldots, x_m$ and $y_1, y_2, \ldots, y_n$ respectively, then (5.2) may be written $\mathbf{x} = \mathbf{A\,y}$ where $\mathbf{A} = (a_{ik})$

Similarly, if $\mathbf{z}$ is the column matrix with elements $z_1, z_2, \ldots, z_p$, (5.3) may be written $\mathbf{y} = \mathbf{B\,z}$ where $\mathbf{B} = (b_{ik})$. Finally, eliminating $\mathbf{y}$ between these two equations yields

$$\mathbf{x} = \mathbf{A(Bz)} = \mathbf{ABz} = \mathbf{Cz}$$

which agrees with (5.4) as was to be expected.

In this discussion it has been assumed that matrix multiplication is associative. However, it is straightforward to show that matrix multiplication is both associative and distributive; that is

$$\mathbf{(AB)C} = \mathbf{A(BC)} = \mathbf{ABC}$$

$$\mathbf{(A + B)C} = \mathbf{AC} + \mathbf{BC}$$

$$\mathbf{A(B + C)} = \mathbf{AB} + \mathbf{AC}$$

provided the matrices $\mathbf{A}$, $\mathbf{B}$, $\mathbf{C}$ are such that the expressions on the left-hand sides are defined. Hence, matrix multiplication has some properties in common with the usual multiplication of numbers but *not all*. Consider the two matrices

$$\mathbf{A} = \begin{pmatrix} 2 & 1 & 3 \\ 3 & 1 & 2 \end{pmatrix}, \quad \mathbf{B} = \begin{pmatrix} 1 & 2 \\ 3 & 1 \\ 2 & 3 \end{pmatrix}.$$

$\mathbf{A}$ is a (2×3) matrix and $\mathbf{B}$ a (3×2) matrix, and so both the products $\mathbf{AB}$ and $\mathbf{BA}$ are defined. However, the product $\mathbf{AB}$ is the (2×2) matrix

$$\begin{pmatrix} 11 & 14 \\ 10 & 13 \end{pmatrix}$$

and $\mathbf{BA}$ is the (3×3) matrix

$$\begin{pmatrix} 8 & 3 & 7 \\ 9 & 4 & 11 \\ 13 & 5 & 12 \end{pmatrix}$$

and so, $\mathbf{AB} \neq \mathbf{BA}$; that is, matrix multiplication is not commutative. This property of matrix multiplication appears also when the matrices $\mathbf{A}$ and $\mathbf{B}$ are such that their products $\mathbf{AB}$ and $\mathbf{BA}$ are of the same type. For example, if

$$\mathbf{A} = \begin{pmatrix} 2 & 1 \\ 3 & 5 \end{pmatrix} \quad \text{and} \quad \mathbf{B} = \begin{pmatrix} -3 & 1 \\ 6 & 2 \end{pmatrix}$$

then
$$\mathbf{AB} = \begin{pmatrix} 0 & 4 \\ 21 & 13 \end{pmatrix} \quad \text{and} \quad \mathbf{BA} = \begin{pmatrix} -3 & 2 \\ 18 & 16 \end{pmatrix}.$$

Hence, once again, $\mathbf{AB} \neq \mathbf{BA}$.

It may be concluded that if $\mathbf{A}$ and $\mathbf{B}$ are two matrices for which both the products $\mathbf{AB}$ and $\mathbf{BA}$ are defined then, in general, $\mathbf{AB} \neq \mathbf{BA}$.

However, if $\mathbf{A}$ is a square matrix of order m and $\mathbf{I}$ is the unit matrix of the same order then

$$\mathbf{IA} = \mathbf{AI} = \mathbf{A}.$$

Also
$$\mathbf{I} = \mathbf{I}^2 = \cdots = \mathbf{I}^n = \cdots$$

where n is a positive integer, and it might be noted that, provided the product is defined, multiplying any matrix by the unit matrix leaves the matrix unaltered.

Example

$$\begin{pmatrix} 1 & 0 & 0 \\ 0 & 1 & 0 \\ 0 & 0 & 1 \end{pmatrix} \begin{pmatrix} 1 & 3 \\ 2 & 2 \\ 3 & 1 \end{pmatrix} = \begin{pmatrix} 1 & 3 \\ 2 & 2 \\ 3 & 1 \end{pmatrix}.$$

Again, a diagonal matrix whose diagonal elements are all equal is called a **scalar matrix** and actually equals the unit matrix of the same order multiplied by a scalar.

Hence, if

$$\mathbf{S} = \begin{pmatrix} k & 0 & 0 \\ 0 & k & 0 \\ 0 & 0 & k \end{pmatrix}$$

and $\mathbf{I}$ is the third-order unit matrix, $\mathbf{S} = k\mathbf{I}$ and if $\mathbf{A}$ is any square matrix of order three also, then it follows that

$$\mathbf{AS} = \mathbf{SA} = k\mathbf{A} \,.$$

In general, a scalar matrix of order n commutes with any square matrix of order n.

It is clear from this discussion that the order of the factors in a matrix product is extremely important, and the relation $\mathbf{AB} = \mathbf{BA}$ holds only in certain special cases. Hence, it is usual to say that, in the product $\mathbf{AB}$, the matrix $\mathbf{A}$ is postmultiplied by the matrix $\mathbf{B}$, or $\mathbf{B}$ is premultiplied by $\mathbf{A}$.

Another unusual property of matrix multiplication is illustrated by noting that

$$\begin{pmatrix} h & h \\ k & k \end{pmatrix}\begin{pmatrix} -1 & 1 \\ 1 & -1 \end{pmatrix} = \begin{pmatrix} 0 & 0 \\ 0 & 0 \end{pmatrix},$$

that is, the product of two matrices, neither of which is the zero matrix, turns out to be the zero matrix. Hence, as far as matrix multiplication is concerned, if $\mathbf{AB} = \mathbf{0}$, it cannot be deduced that either $\mathbf{A} = \mathbf{0}$ or $\mathbf{B} = \mathbf{0}$.

To conclude this section on matrix multiplication, it remains to show that, for the matrices $\mathbf{A}$, $\mathbf{B}$, $\mathbf{C}$, if $\mathbf{C} = \mathbf{AB}$ then

$$\mathbf{C}^{\mathrm{T}} = (\mathbf{AB})^{\mathrm{T}} = \mathbf{B}^{\mathrm{T}}\,\mathbf{A}^{\mathrm{T}} \,.$$

Suppose $\mathbf{A} = (a_{ik})$ is an $(m \times n)$ matrix and $\mathbf{B} = (b_{ik})$ and $(n \times p)$ matrix, then $\mathbf{C} = (c_{ik})$ is an $(m \times p)$ matrix and

$$c_{ik} = \sum_{j=1}^{n} a_{ij}b_{jk} \,.$$

Now, if $\mathbf{C}^{\mathrm{T}} = (c_{ik}^{\mathrm{T}})$, then

$$c_{ik}^{\mathrm{T}} = c_{ki} = \sum_{j=1}^{n} a_{kj}b_{ji} = \sum_{j=1}^{n} b_{ij}^{\mathrm{T}}a_{jk}^{\mathrm{T}}$$

and so $$\mathbf{C}^{\mathrm{T}} = \mathbf{B}^{\mathrm{T}}\mathbf{A}^{\mathrm{T}} \,.$$
Similarly, it may be shown that

$$(\mathbf{ABC})^{\mathrm{T}} = \mathbf{C}^{\mathrm{T}}\mathbf{B}^{\mathrm{T}}\mathbf{A}^{\mathrm{T}}$$

and so on for a finite number of matrices.

Before concluding this section, a few more special matrices will be introduced. In what has gone before, all the examples considered have been of matrices with real elements. However, as has been stated already, the elements of a matrix may be either real or complex. If any matrix $\mathbf{A} = (a_{ik})$ has complex elements than the matrix $\bar{\mathbf{A}} = (\bar{a}_{ik})$ denotes that matrix obtained from $\mathbf{A}$ by replacing each element a_{ik} by its complex conjugate $\bar{a}_{ik}$.

Example

If
$$\mathbf{A} = \begin{pmatrix} 1+j & 4 & -3j \\ 2 & 2+j & 1-j \end{pmatrix}$$

then
$$\bar{\mathbf{A}} = \begin{pmatrix} 1-j & 4 & 3j \\ 2 & 2-j & 1+j \end{pmatrix}.$$

Clearly
$$\overline{(\bar{\mathbf{A}})} = \mathbf{A}.$$

The idea of an **Hermitian matrix** follows almost immediately since an Hermitian matrix is a square matrix $\mathbf{A} = (a_{ik})$ which is unchanged by taking the transpose of its complex conjugate; that is, $\mathbf{A}$ is Hermitian if

$$(\bar{\mathbf{A}})^{\mathrm{T}} = \mathbf{A} \quad (\text{or } \bar{a}_{ki} = a_{ik}).$$

It follows that the elements along the principal diagonal of an Hermitian matrix are always real. Also, if the elements of an Hermitian matrix are real, then the above equation becomes $\mathbf{A}^{\mathrm{T}} = \mathbf{A}$. This means that a real Hermitian matrix is symmetric, and so Hermitian matrices may be regarded as a natural generalisation of real symmetric matrices.

Example

Consider
$$\mathbf{A} = \begin{pmatrix} 3 & 5+2j \\ 5-2j & 7 \end{pmatrix}$$

then
$$\bar{\mathbf{A}} = \begin{pmatrix} 3 & 5-2j \\ 5+2j & 7 \end{pmatrix}$$

and
$$(\bar{\mathbf{A}})^{\mathrm{T}} = \begin{pmatrix} 3 & 5+2j \\ 5-2j & 7 \end{pmatrix} = \mathbf{A},$$

and so $\mathbf{A}$ is an Hermitian matrix.

If the matrix $\mathbf{A}$ is such that $(\bar{\mathbf{A}})^{\mathrm{T}} = -\mathbf{A}$ then $\mathbf{A}$ is said to be **skew-Hermitian**.

In the discussion of the algebra of matrices given so far, addition, subtraction, and multiplication of matrices have been defined. However, no mention has been made of division. This is because division in matrix algebra is not defined. Nevertheless, there are conditions under which the inverse $\mathbf{A}^{-1}$ of a square matrix $\mathbf{A}$ exists. More will be said of this after determinants have been introduced and discussed. For the present, it might be noted that if the inverse $\mathbf{A}^{-1}$ of a square matrix $\mathbf{A}$ exists then

$$\mathbf{A}\mathbf{A}^{-1} = \mathbf{A}^{-1}\mathbf{A} = \mathbf{I}$$

where $\mathbf{I}$ is the unit matrix of the same order as $\mathbf{A}$.

Once the idea of the inverse matrix has been introduced, two other useful special types of matrix may be defined. If $\mathbf{A} = (a_{ik})$ is a square matrix for which

$$(\bar{\mathbf{A}})^{\mathrm{T}} = \mathbf{A}^{-1}$$

then $\mathbf{A}$ is said to be a **unitary matrix**. A real unitary matrix $\mathbf{A}$ is said to be an **orthogonal matrix**, and for such a matrix, the above equation takes the form

$$\mathbf{A}^{\mathrm{T}} = \mathbf{A}^{-1}$$

or, in other words, an orthogonal matrix is a real matrix whose inverse equals its transpose. It follows that, if $\mathbf{A}$ and $\mathbf{B}$ are two orthogonal matrices of the same order, their product $\mathbf{AB}$ is also an orthogonal matrix since

$$(\mathbf{AB})(\mathbf{AB})^{\mathrm{T}} = \mathbf{ABB}^{\mathrm{T}}\mathbf{A}^{\mathrm{T}} = \mathbf{I}$$

and
$$(\mathbf{AB})^{\mathrm{T}}(\mathbf{AB}) = \mathbf{B}^{\mathrm{T}}\mathbf{A}^{\mathrm{T}}\mathbf{AB} = \mathbf{I}\,.$$

It may be shown in a similar manner that the product of two unitary matrices of the same order is also a unitary matrix.

Also, it might be noted that, if $\mathbf{A}_i$ and $\mathbf{A}_k$ are two columns of an orthogonal matrix $\mathbf{A}$ then

$$\mathbf{A}_i^{\mathrm{T}}\mathbf{A}_k = 0 \quad \text{for } i \neq k\,.$$

A similar property holds for the rows of $\mathbf{A}$. If, on the other hand, the two columns (or two rows) satisfy the condition $\mathbf{A}_i^{\mathrm{T}}\mathbf{A}_k = \delta_{ik}$ where δ_{ik} is the Kronecker delta, equalling 1 if $i = k$ and 0 if $i \neq k$, then the columns (or rows) are said to be **orthonormal**. If, however, the elements of the two column (or row) matrices are complex numbers, the condition for orthonormality becomes

$$\bar{\mathbf{A}}_i^{\mathrm{T}}\mathbf{A}_k = \delta_{ik}\,.$$

Examples

(i) If $\quad\quad \mathbf{A} = \dfrac{1}{\sqrt{2}}\begin{pmatrix} 1 & -j \\ -j & 1 \end{pmatrix}\quad$ then $\bar{\mathbf{A}}^{\mathrm{T}} = \dfrac{1}{\sqrt{2}}\begin{pmatrix} 1 & j \\ j & 1 \end{pmatrix}$

and it is seen immediately that

$$\bar{\mathbf{A}}^{\mathrm{T}}\mathbf{A} = \mathbf{A}\bar{\mathbf{A}}^{\mathrm{T}} = \mathbf{I}$$

where $\mathbf{I}$ is the unit matrix of the second order. Thus $\mathbf{A}$ is a unitary matrix.

(ii) If $\quad\quad \mathbf{A} = \dfrac{1}{\sqrt{2}}\begin{pmatrix} 1 & 1 \\ -1 & 1 \end{pmatrix}\quad$ then $\mathbf{A}^{\mathrm{T}} = \dfrac{1}{\sqrt{2}}\begin{pmatrix} 1 & -1 \\ 1 & 1 \end{pmatrix}$

and it is seen immediately that

$$\mathbf{A}^{\mathrm{T}}\mathbf{A} = \mathbf{A}\mathbf{A}^{\mathrm{T}} = \mathbf{I}$$

where $\mathbf{I}$ is the unit matrix of the second order. Thus $\mathbf{A}$ is an orthogonal matrix.

5.3 DETERMINANTS

The formulae for the solution of a set of linear equations lead naturally to determinants. For example, consider the two linear equations

$$a_{11}x_1 + a_{12}x_2 = k_1 ,$$

$$a_{21}x_1 + a_{22}x_2 = k_2 ,$$

where x_1, x_2 are to be found in terms of the given constants a_{11}, a_{12}, a_{21}, a_{22}, k_1, k_2. Solving for x_1, x_2 in the usual way yields

$$x_1 = (k_1 a_{22} - k_2 a_{12})/(a_{11}a_{22} - a_{12}a_{21})$$

$$x_2 = (k_2 a_{11} - k_1 a_{21})/(a_{11}a_{22} - a_{12}a_{21})$$

provided $a_{11}a_{22} - a_{12}a_{21} \neq 0$. This expression in the denominator may be written

$$a_{11}a_{22} - a_{12}a_{21} = \begin{vmatrix} a_{11} & a_{12} \\ a_{21} & a_{22} \end{vmatrix} = D , \text{ say,}$$

and is termed a **determinant of the second order**. Similarly, the numerators of the above two expressions may be written as

$$N_1 = \begin{vmatrix} k_1 & a_{12} \\ k_2 & a_{22} \end{vmatrix} \quad \text{and} \quad N_2 = \begin{vmatrix} a_{11} & k_1 \\ a_{21} & k_2 \end{vmatrix}$$

respectively. Hence, the solution of the two linear equations may be written in terms of second-order determinants as

$$x_1 = N_1/D , \quad x_2 = N_2/D .$$

The solution for a set of three linear equations, $\sum_{j=1}^{3} a_{ij} x_j = k_i$, $(i = 1, 2, 3)$, may be found in a similar way. In this case, the denominator of each solution is

$$\begin{vmatrix} a_{11} & a_{12} & a_{13} \\ a_{21} & a_{22} & a_{23} \\ a_{31} & a_{32} & a_{33} \end{vmatrix} = \begin{aligned} & a_{11}a_{22}a_{33} + a_{12}a_{23}a_{31} \\ + \; & a_{13}a_{21}a_{32} - a_{11}a_{23}a_{32} \\ - \; & a_{12}a_{21}a_{33} - a_{13}a_{22}a_{31} \end{aligned}$$

where a **third-order determinant** has been introduced. On the right-hand side of this latter equation are six products. Each is a product of three factors, one from each row of the determinant. Each column is represented in every product also. It follows that each of these six terms is of the form $a_{1\alpha} a_{2\beta} a_{3\gamma}$ where $\alpha\,\beta\,\gamma$ is some permutation of the column indices 1 2 3. Further examination of the six terms shows that for those prefixed by a positive sign, $\alpha\,\beta\,\gamma$ is an even permutation of 1 2 3, while, for those with a negative sign, $\alpha\,\beta\,\gamma$ is an odd permutation of 1 2 3. Hence, the value of the above third-order determinant could be written $\sum \pm a_{1\alpha}a_{2\beta}a_{3\gamma}$ where the summation is over the 6 $(= 3!)$ possible permutations of 1 2 3, and a positive sign is associated with products for which α β γ is an even permutation of 1 2 3, while a negative sign is associated with those for which α β γ is an odd permutation of 1 2 3.

This third-order determinant has been introduced following an examination of the solution for a set of three linear equations $\sum_{j=1}^{3} a_{ij}x_j = k_i$, $(i = 1, 2, 3)$. In terms of matrices, these equations could be written $\mathbf{Ax} = \mathbf{k}$ where $\mathbf{x}$ and $\mathbf{k}$ are the column matrices with elements x_1, x_2, x_3 and k_1, k_2, k_3 respectively, and $\mathbf{A}$ is the square matrix of order three

$$\begin{pmatrix} a_{11} & a_{12} & a_{13} \\ a_{21} & a_{22} & a_{23} \\ a_{31} & a_{32} & a_{33} \end{pmatrix}.$$

Hence the third-order determinant above may be thought of as the determinant of the third-order square matrix $\mathbf{A} = (a_{ik})$ and may be denoted by $|\mathbf{A}|$ or $|a_{ik}|$.

The above definition of a third-order determinant as the sum over all permutations of 1 2 3 of the product $a_{1\alpha} a_{2\beta} a_{3\gamma}$ may be extended easily to higher orders. Hence, the determinant of the nth-order square matrix $\mathbf{A} = (a_{ik})$ is given by

$$|\mathbf{A}| = \Sigma \pm a_{1\alpha} a_{2\beta} \cdots a_{n\omega} \tag{5.5}$$

where the summation is over the n! possible permutations of 1 2 ... n. Once again, a positive sign is associated with products for which αβ ... ω is an even permutation of 1 2 ... n, while a negative sign is associated with those for which αβ ... ω is an odd permutation of 1 2 ... n. It might be noticed that, in the product $a_{1\alpha} a_{2\beta} \cdots a_{n\omega}$, only one element appears from each column and only one from each row of the matrix $\mathbf{A}$. The value of the determinant is found by taking all n! such products, attaching a positive sign if the row suffices α, β, ..., ω are an even permutation of the column suffices 1, 2, ... n, and a negative sign otherwise, and finally summing the n! products with these signs attached. Clearly, this definition of an nth-order determinant is symmetrical between the rows and columns of the matrix $\mathbf{A}$. Thus, any result for the determinant $|\mathbf{A}|$ of a square matrix $\mathbf{A}$ which involves the rows of $\mathbf{A}$ is true also for the columns of $\mathbf{A}$, and vice versa.

Finally, before proceeding to consider some general results for determinants, it should be pointed out that, as has been mentioned already, square matrices are often of particular importance in applications of matrix algebra, and the determinant is an extremely important quantity associated with a square matrix. Also, equation (5.5) is seen to lead to the correct values for (2×2) and (3×3) determinants appearing at the beginning of this section.

Equation (5.5) may be used to deduce, fairly easily, one of the basic properties of determinants. Consider two $(n \times n)$ matrices $\mathbf{A}$ and $\mathbf{B}$ where $\mathbf{B}$ is formed from $\mathbf{A}$ by interchanging the position of two complete columns. Hence, each term of type $a_{1\alpha}a_{2\beta} \cdots a_{n\omega}$ which occurs in $\mathbf{A}$ will occur in $\mathbf{B}$ also, but the interchange of two columns of **A** is equivalent to the interchange of two column suffices in the permutation $1, 2 \ldots n$ so that even and odd permutations in **A** become odd and even permutations respectively in **B**. Thus, all the signs in (5.5) are altered and $|\mathbf{B}| = -|\mathbf{A}|$. It follows that the interchange of two rows of the matrix **A** also results in a change in the sign of the determinant.

Now consider the determinant $|\mathbf{A}|$ of the nth-order square matrix $\mathbf{A} = (a_{ik})$. If the ith row and kth column of this determinant are deleted, an $(n-1)$th-order determinant remains which is called the **minor** of the element a_{ik} (the element belonging to the deleted row and column) and is denoted by M_{ik}. The minor M_{ik} multiplied by $(-1)^{i+k}$ is termed the **cofactor** of a_{ik} and may be denoted by C_{ik}. For example, consider the third-order determinant

$$\begin{vmatrix} a_{11} & a_{12} & a_{13} \\ a_{21} & a_{22} & a_{23} \\ a_{31} & a_{32} & a_{33} \end{vmatrix} .$$

For this determinant, it follows that

$$C_{11} = (-1)^2 M_{11} = \begin{vmatrix} a_{22} & a_{23} \\ a_{32} & a_{33} \end{vmatrix}$$

and

$$C_{12} = (-1)^3 M_{12} = - \begin{vmatrix} a_{21} & a_{23} \\ a_{31} & a_{33} \end{vmatrix} \quad \text{etc.}$$

An expression may be found expressing $|\mathbf{A}|$ in terms of the minors of the elments of $|\mathbf{A}|$. To see this, consider first all the terms in the sum in (5.5) which contain a_{11}. In each of these terms $\alpha = 1$ and so $\beta \ldots \omega$ is a permutation of $2 \ldots n$. Hence, if $\alpha\beta \ldots \omega$ is an even (or odd) permutation of $1\, 2 \ldots n$, then $\beta \ldots \omega$ is an even (or odd) permutation of $2 \ldots n$, and those terms which contain a_{11} sum to give

$$a_{11} \Sigma \pm a_{2\beta} \cdots a_{n\omega} = a_{11} M_{11}$$

where the summation is over the possible permutations of $2 \ldots n$ and M_{11} is the minor of a_{11}. Now consider all the terms in the sum in (5.5) which contain the element a_{ik}; the element belonging to the ith row and the kth column. If the entire ith row is interchanged with the row above it $(i-1)$ times, it will have become the first row, and the determinant will have altered by a factor $(-1)^{i-1}$. Similarly, if the entire kth column is interchanged with the column on its left $(k-1)$ times, it will have become the first column, and the determinant will have changed by a factor $(-1)^{k-1}$. The final result of carrying out both these manipulations is to change the value of the determinant by a factor $(-1)^{i+k}$ and to place the element a_{ik} in the position occupied previously by a_{11}. Hence, in the rearranged determinant, those terms which contain a_{ik} sum to give $a_{ik} M_{ik}$ and so, the terms in $|\mathbf{A}|$ which contain a_{ik} sum to give $(-1)^{i+k} a_{ik} M_{ik}$ or $a_{ik} C_{ik}$ where C_{ik} is the cofactor of a_{ik}.

It might be noted that each term in the sum in (5.5) contains only one element from the ith row and, as has been shown, those which contain a_{ik} sum to $(-1)^{i+k}a_{ik}M_{ik}$. Thus, (5.5) may be written in the form

$$|\mathbf{A}| = \sum_{k=1}^{n}(-1)^{i+k}a_{ik}M_{ik} = \sum_{k=1}^{n}a_{ik}C_{ik} \,. \tag{5.6}$$

This formula gives the expansion of $\mathbf{A}$ by the ith row. The analogous expansion by the kth column is

$$|\mathbf{A}| = \sum_{i=1}^{n}(-1)^{i+k}a_{ik}M_{ik} = \sum_{i=1}^{n}a_{ik}C_{ik} \,. \tag{5.7}$$

It is now possible to derive further useful properties of determinants quite easily. For example, if all the elements of the ith row of the matrix $\mathbf{A}$ are multiplied by the same factor K, then the determinant of the matrix is seen to have the value $K\,|\mathbf{A}|$. This follows since, if the new determinant is $|\mathbf{B}|$, then

$$|\mathbf{B}| = \sum_{k=1}^{n}(-1)^{i+k}Ka_{ik}M_{ik} = K|\mathbf{A}| \,.$$

A similar result follows if all the elements of one column of a matrix are multiplied by a common factor.

In connection with this simple result it is important to note that, if all the elements of an nth-order square matrix $\mathbf{A}$ are multiplied by the same factor K so that $\mathbf{B} = K\mathbf{A}$, then each element in each of the n rows of $\mathbf{A}$ has been multiplied by K. Hence, in this case

$$|\mathbf{B}| = K^{n}|\mathbf{A}|$$

so that $\mathbf{B} = K\mathbf{A}$ does not imply $|\mathbf{B}| = K\,|\mathbf{A}|$.

It might be noted also that the symmetry between rows and columns in the definition of a determinant implies that, if $\mathbf{A}^{T}$ is the transpose of $\mathbf{A}$, then $|\mathbf{A}| = |\mathbf{A}^{T}|$. However, if $\mathbf{A}$ is an anti-symmetric matrix, the above result shows that

$$|\mathbf{A}^{T}| = (-1)^{n}\,|\mathbf{A}|$$

where n is the order of the matrix, and so, if n is odd,

$$|\mathbf{A}^{T}| = -\,|\mathbf{A}| \,.$$

The combination of these two results for the determinant of the transpose of a matrix shows that the determinant of an anti-symmetric matrix of odd order is zero.

As has been seen, the evaluation of second- and third-order determinants is straightforward. However, for higher-order determinants, this straightforward method is extremely tedious and time-consuming. Several simple facts concerning determinants will be discussed now before being used to simplify some higher-order determinants as a prelude to their evaluation.

(1) If two rows (or two columns) of a matrix $\mathbf{A}$ are identical then $|\mathbf{A}| = 0$. This follows immediately since, if the two rows (or columns) are interchanged, the new determinant has the value $-|\mathbf{A}|$ but, since the rows (or columns) are identical, the value of the determinant is unaltered and so, $|\mathbf{A}| = -|\mathbf{A}|$ or $|\mathbf{A}| = 0$. As a corollary to this, it is seen that, if two rows (or columns) have corresponding elements in a fixed ratio then, once again, $|\mathbf{A}| = 0$. This follows since, by an earlier result, the common factor may be taken outside the determinant leaving a determinant with two equal rows (or columns).

(2) If $\mathbf{A} = (a_{ik})$ and $\mathbf{B} = (b_{ik})$ are two $(n \times n)$ matrices which differ in the ith row only, then $|\mathbf{A}| + |\mathbf{B}| = |\mathbf{C}|$, where $\mathbf{C}$ has elements $a_{ik} + b_{ik}$ in the ith row but is identical with $\mathbf{A}$ otherwise. This result follows immediately if both $|\mathbf{A}|$ and $|\mathbf{B}|$ are expanded by the ith row. Obviously this result applies to matrices with one column different also.

Another useful result which follows directly is that the value of a determinant is unaltered if a constant multiple of one row (or column) is added to another row (or column). This is seen by applying the above result. In this case the determinant resulting from the proposed manipulation would be the sum of two determinants, one the original determinant and the other a determinant with two rows (or columns) proportional to one another. As shown earlier this latter determinant would be zero.

Some examples of evaluation of determinants will be considered now which illustrate just how useful this last result can be.

Example

(i) Evaluate
$$\begin{vmatrix} 7 & 11 & 4 \\ 13 & 15 & 10 \\ 3 & 9 & 6 \end{vmatrix} = D \text{ , say.}$$

First note that all the elements in the third row have 3 as a common factor and all the elements of the third column have 2 as a common factor. Then

$$D = 6 \begin{vmatrix} 7 & 1 & 2 \\ 13 & 15 & 5 \\ 1 & 3 & 1 \end{vmatrix} .$$

Subtract twice the first row from the second row to give

$$D = 6 \begin{vmatrix} 7 & 11 & 2 \\ -1 & -7 & 1 \\ 1 & 3 & 1 \end{vmatrix} .$$

Add the second row to the third row to give

$$D = 6 \begin{vmatrix} 7 & 11 & 2 \\ -1 & -7 & 1 \\ 0 & -4 & 2 \end{vmatrix} .$$

Add twice the third column to the second column to give

$$D = 6 \begin{vmatrix} 7 & 15 & 2 \\ -1 & -5 & 1 \\ 0 & 0 & 2 \end{vmatrix}.$$

Finally,
$$D = 6.2 \begin{vmatrix} 7 & 15 \\ -1 & -5 \end{vmatrix}$$

$$= 12\,(-20) = -240\,.$$

(ii) Evaluate
$$\begin{vmatrix} 1 & 1 & 1 \\ \alpha & \beta & \gamma \\ \beta\gamma & \gamma\alpha & \alpha\beta \end{vmatrix} = D$$

Subtract column one from column three and from column two to give

$$D = \begin{vmatrix} 1 & 0 & 0 \\ \alpha & \beta-\alpha & \gamma-\alpha \\ \beta\gamma & \gamma(\alpha-\beta) & \beta(\alpha-\gamma) \end{vmatrix}.$$

The elements of column two now have a common factor $(\alpha - \beta)$ while those of column three have $(\gamma - \alpha)$ as common factor and so

$$D = (\alpha-\beta)(\gamma-\alpha) \begin{vmatrix} 1 & 0 & 0 \\ \alpha & -1 & 1 \\ \beta\gamma & \gamma & -\beta \end{vmatrix}$$

$$= (\alpha-\beta)(\beta-\gamma)(\gamma-\alpha)\,.$$

Multiplication of determinants will be considered briefly now. Obviously the product of any two determinants may be found by evaluating the two determinants and multiplying the results. However, if the determinants are both of order n, it sometimes proves convenient to be able to write their product as an nth order determinant also. This may be done by realising that, if $\mathbf{A} = (a_{ik})$ and $\mathbf{B} = (b_{ik})$ are two square matrices of order n, the determinant of the matrix product $\mathbf{AB}$ is given by

$$|\mathbf{AB}| = |\mathbf{A}|\,|\mathbf{B}|\,.$$

Although this result will be established for two square matrices of order two, a similar proof applies for matrices of any order.

Consider the following determinant Δ of order four:

$$\Delta = \begin{vmatrix} a_{11} & a_{12} & 0 & 0 \\ a_{21} & a_{22} & 0 & 0 \\ -1 & 0 & b_{11} & b_{12} \\ 0 & -1 & b_{21} & b_{22} \end{vmatrix}.$$

This may be evaluated as follows:

$$\Delta = a_{11}\begin{vmatrix} a_{22} & 0 & 0 \\ 0 & b_{11} & b_{12} \\ -1 & b_{21} & b_{22} \end{vmatrix} - a_{12}\begin{vmatrix} a_{21} & 0 & 0 \\ -1 & b_{11} & b_{12} \\ 0 & b_{21} & b_{22} \end{vmatrix}$$

$$= a_{11}a_{22}\begin{vmatrix} b_{11} & b_{12} \\ b_{21} & b_{22} \end{vmatrix} - a_{12}a_{21}\begin{vmatrix} b_{11} & b_{12} \\ b_{21} & b_{22} \end{vmatrix}$$

$$= |\mathbf{A}|\,|\mathbf{B}|\,.$$

Now transform the determinant Δ as follows: to the first row add a_{11} multiplied by the third row and a_{12} multiplied by the fourth row; to the second row add a_{21} multiplied by the third row and a_{22} multiplied by the fourth row; then

$$\Delta = \begin{vmatrix} 0 & 0 & a_{11}b_{11}+a_{12}b_{21} & a_{11}b_{12}+a_{12}b_{22} \\ 0 & 0 & a_{21}b_{11}+a_{22}b_{21} & a_{21}b_{12}+a_{22}b_{22} \\ -1 & 0 & b_{11} & b_{12} \\ 0 & -1 & b_{21} & b_{22} \end{vmatrix}$$

$$= \begin{vmatrix} a_{11}b_{11}+a_{12}b_{21} & a_{11}b_{12}+a_{12}b_{22} \\ a_{21}b_{11}+a_{22}b_{21} & a_{21}b_{12}+a_{22}b_{22} \end{vmatrix}$$

$$= |\mathbf{AB}|\,.$$

Hence, the result is proved for two square matrices of order two. The result for two square matrices of order n may be proved in a similar manner, but in that case the determinant Δ is of order $2n$ although with the same structure as the Δ used above, that is

$$\begin{vmatrix} a_{11} & \cdot & \cdots & a_{1n} & 0 & \cdots & 0 \\ \cdot & & & \cdot & \cdot & & \cdot \\ \cdot & & & \cdot & \cdot & & \cdot \\ \cdot & & & \cdot & \cdot & & \cdot \\ a_{n1} & \cdot & \cdots & a_{nn} & 0 & \cdots & 0 \\ -1 & 0 & \cdots & 0 & b_{11} & \cdots & b_{1n} \\ 0 & -1 & \cdots & 0 & \cdot & & \cdot \\ \cdot & \cdot & & \cdot & \cdot & & \cdot \\ \cdot & \cdot & & \cdot & \cdot & & \cdot \\ \cdot & \cdot & & \cdot & \cdot & & \cdot \\ 0 & \cdot & \cdots & -1 & b_{n1} & \cdots & b_{nn} \end{vmatrix}.$$

This result may be extended to a product of any number of matrices provided all the matrices have the same order n.

Thus $$|\mathbf{A}\,\mathbf{B}\cdots\mathbf{Y}\,\mathbf{Z}| = |\mathbf{A}|\,|\mathbf{B}|\cdots|\mathbf{Y}|\,|\mathbf{Z}|\,.$$

5.4 CRAMER'S RULE
This is a rule which allows the solution of a system of n linear equations in n unknowns to be evaluated in terms of determinants.

It has been shown already in equations (5.6) and (5.7) that the expansion of the nth order determinant $|\mathbf{A}|$ by the ith row is

$$|\mathbf{A}| = \sum_{k=1}^{n} a_{ik}C_{ik}$$

and the expansion by the kth column is

$$|\mathbf{A}| = \sum_{i=1}^{n} a_{ik}C_{ik}$$

respectively. Here C_{ik} is the cofactor of the element a_{ik}.

A further important result that may be deduced readily is

$$\sum_{k=1}^{n} a_{ik}C_{jk} = 0 , \quad i \neq j . \tag{5.8a}$$

Each term of this summation is the product of an element in the ith row with the cofactor of the corresponding element in the jth row. This is simply the expansion of a determinant with identical ith and jth rows. Such a determinant has value zero, and so the result is proved. Similarly, it may be shown that

$$\sum_{i=1}^{n} a_{ik}C_{ij} = 0 , \quad k \neq j . \tag{5.8b}$$

This result will be used now to help establish Cramer's rule. Consider the n linear equations in the n unknowns $x_1, x_2, \ldots, x_n$:

$$\sum_{k=1}^{n} a_{ik}x_k = b_i , \quad i = 1, 2, \ldots, n .$$

where the a_{ik} and b_i are given numbers. If all the b_i are zero, the system of equations is said to be **homogeneous** but, if just one of the b_i is non-zero, it is said to be **non-homogeneous**. Also, the determinant

$$\Delta = \begin{vmatrix} a_{11} & \cdots & a_{1n} \\ \cdot & & \cdot \\ \cdot & & \cdot \\ \cdot & & \cdot \\ a_{n1} & \cdots & a_{nn} \end{vmatrix}$$

is sometimes referred to as the **determinant** of the system.

In the given system of equations, if the equation with $i = 1$ is multiplied by C_{1j}, that with $i = 2$ by C_{2j} and so on, so that the equation with $i = n$ is multiplied by C_{nj}, and the resulting equations are added together, then

$$\sum_{i=1}^{n} \sum_{k=1}^{n} a_{ik} C_{ij} x_k = \sum_{i=1}^{n} b_i C_{ij} .$$

The sum on the left-hand side may be written

$$x_1(a_{11}C_{1j} + \cdots + a_{n1}C_{nj}) + \cdots + x_n(a_{1n}C_{1j} + \cdots + a_{nn}C_{nj}) .$$

From the results established above it follows that the bracket multiplying x_j in this expression is equal to Δ but the brackets multiplying x_i ($i \neq j$) are zero. Hence, provided $\Delta \neq 0$, the above equation becomes

$$x_j \Delta = \sum_{i=1}^{n} b_i C_{ij}$$

or

$$x_j = \frac{1}{\Delta} \sum_{i=1}^{n} b_i C_{ij} , \quad j = 1, 2, \ldots, n .$$

Alternatively, this solution of the given system of n linear equations in n unknowns may be written

$$x_j = \Delta_j/\Delta , \quad j = 1, 2, \ldots, n .$$

where Δ_j is the determinant obtained from Δ by replacing the elements in the jth column of Δ by the elements $b_1, \ldots, b_n$ and where it has been assumed that $\Delta \neq 0$.

This is a statement of Cramer's rule for solving a system of n linear equations in n unknowns.

Example

Use Cramer's rule to solve the equations

$$3x_1 + 2x_2 - x_3 = -1$$
$$x_1 - 2x_2 + 2x_3 = 7$$
$$2x_1 + x_2 + x_3 = 3 .$$

For this example,

$$\Delta = \begin{vmatrix} 3 & 2 & -1 \\ 1 & -2 & 2 \\ 2 & 1 & 1 \end{vmatrix} = -11$$

Also,

$$\Delta_1 = \begin{vmatrix} -1 & 2 & -1 \\ 7 & -2 & 2 \\ 3 & 1 & 1 \end{vmatrix} = -11$$

$$\Delta_2 = \begin{vmatrix} 3 & -1 & -1 \\ 1 & 7 & 2 \\ 2 & 3 & 1 \end{vmatrix} = 11$$

$$\Delta_3 = \begin{vmatrix} 3 & 2 & -1 \\ 1 & -2 & 7 \\ 2 & 1 & 3 \end{vmatrix} = -22 .$$

Thus, the required solution is

$$x_1 = \Delta_1/\Delta = 1 , \quad x_2 = \Delta_2/\Delta = -1 , \quad x_3 = \Delta_3/\Delta = 2 .$$

There are other methods which may be used for solving a system of linear equations such as that considered above. One method involves evaluating the inverse of a matrix. Although the idea of the inverse of a matrix has been mentioned, it has not been discussed fully and no method for finding such an inverse has been introduced. This will be done now.

5.5 THE INVERSE OF A MATRIX

Suppose $\mathbf{A} = (a_{ik})$ is a square matrix of order n, then the transpose of the matrix of the cofactors of the elements of $\mathbf{A}$ is called the **adjoint** of $\mathbf{A}$ and is denoted by adj $\mathbf{A}$. In other words, if

$$\mathbf{A} = \begin{pmatrix} a_{11} & a_{12} & \cdots & a_{1n} \\ a_{21} & a_{22} & \cdots & a_{2n} \\ \cdot & \cdot & & \cdot \\ \cdot & \cdot & & \cdot \\ \cdot & \cdot & & \cdot \\ a_{n1} & a_{n2} & \cdots & a_{nn} \end{pmatrix}$$

and C_{ik} denotes the cofactor of the element a_{ik}, then

$$\text{adj } \mathbf{A} = \begin{pmatrix} C_{11} & C_{21} & \cdots & C_{n1} \\ C_{12} & C_{22} & \cdots & C_{n2} \\ \cdot & \cdot & & \cdot \\ \cdot & \cdot & & \cdot \\ C_{1n} & C_{2n} & \cdots C_{nn} \end{pmatrix} .$$

Now consider the product of $\mathbf{A}$ and adj $\mathbf{A}$. This is

$$\begin{pmatrix} a_{11} & a_{12} & \cdots & a_{1n} \\ a_{21} & a_{22} & \cdots & a_{2n} \\ \cdot & \cdot & & \cdot \\ \cdot & \cdot & & \cdot \\ \cdot & \cdot & & \cdot \\ a_{n1} & a_{n2} & \cdots & a_{nn} \end{pmatrix} \begin{pmatrix} C_{11} & C_{21} & \cdots & C_{n1} \\ C_{12} & C_{22} & \cdots & C_{n2} \\ \cdot & \cdot & & \cdot \\ \cdot & \cdot & & \cdot \\ \cdot & \cdot & & \cdot \\ C_{1n} & C_{2n} & \cdots & C_{nn} \end{pmatrix} .$$

Using results (5.6), (5.7) and (5.8), it follows immediately that

$$\mathbf{A}\,(\mathrm{adj}\ \mathbf{A}) = \begin{pmatrix} |\mathbf{A}| & 0 & \cdots & 0 \\ 0 & |\mathbf{A}| & \cdots & 0 \\ \cdot & \cdot & & \cdot \\ \cdot & \cdot & & \cdot \\ \cdot & \cdot & & \cdot \\ 0 & 0 & \cdots & |\mathbf{A}| \end{pmatrix} = |\mathbf{A}|\mathbf{I}$$

where $|\mathbf{A}|$ is the determinant of the square matrix $\mathbf{A}$ and $\mathbf{I}$ is the unit matrix of order n. It follows that, provided $|\mathbf{A}| \neq 0$, the matrix $\mathbf{A}^{-1}$ defined by

$$\mathbf{A}^{-1} = \frac{\mathrm{adj}\ \mathbf{A}}{|\mathbf{A}|}$$

is such that

$$\mathbf{A}\mathbf{A}^{-1} = \mathbf{I}$$

and, in this sense, it is termed the **inverse** (or **reciprocal**) **matrix** of $\mathbf{A}$. It may be verified that the multiplication of square matrices and their inverses is commutative so that

$$\mathbf{A}\mathbf{A}^{-1} = \mathbf{A}^{-1}\mathbf{A} = \mathbf{I}\,.$$

Obviously, if $|\mathbf{A}| = 0$ (that is, if the square matrix $\mathbf{A}$ is singular), then $\mathbf{A}^{-1}$ is undefined, and so only non-singular square matrices have inverses.

Again, if the inverse of a square matrix $\mathbf{A}$ exists, then $\mathbf{A}\mathbf{A}^{-1} = \mathbf{I}$. Now take the inverse $\mathbf{B}^{-1}$ of a given matrix $\mathbf{B}$ as the matrix $\mathbf{A}$, then the above relation becomes

$$\mathbf{B}^{-1}(\mathbf{B}^{-1})^{-1} = \mathbf{I}\,.$$

Premultiplying both sides by $\mathbf{B}$ yields

$$(\mathbf{B}^{-1})^{-1} = \mathbf{B}$$

that is, the inverse of the inverse is the given matrix.

The inverse of a product is given by

$$(\mathbf{A}\mathbf{B})^{-1} = \mathbf{B}^{-1}\mathbf{A}^{-1}$$

This is seen by replacing $\mathbf{A}$ by $\mathbf{A}\mathbf{B}$ in

$$\mathbf{A}\mathbf{A}^{-1} = \mathbf{I}$$

so that

$$\mathbf{A}\mathbf{B}(\mathbf{A}\mathbf{B})^{-1} = \mathbf{I}\,.$$

Premultiplying by $\mathbf{A}$ yields

$$\mathbf{B}(\mathbf{A}\mathbf{B})^{-1} = \mathbf{A}^{-1}\,.$$

Premultiplying this result by **B** yields

$$(\mathbf{AB})^{-1} = \mathbf{B}^{-1}\mathbf{A}^{-1}$$

as required.

Obviously, this result may be generalised to products of more than two matrices:

$$(\mathbf{AB} \cdots \mathbf{YZ})^{-1} = \mathbf{Z}^{-1}\mathbf{Y}^{-1} \cdots \mathbf{B}^{-1}\mathbf{A}^{-1} .$$

Example

Find the inverse of the square matrix **A** where

$$\mathbf{A} = \begin{pmatrix} 3 & 2 & -1 \\ 1 & -2 & 2 \\ 2 & 1 & 1 \end{pmatrix} .$$

Now the matrix of the cofactors of the elements of **A** is

$$\begin{pmatrix} -4 & 3 & 5 \\ -3 & 5 & 1 \\ 2 & -7 & -8 \end{pmatrix}$$

and so, the inverse of **A** is

$$-\frac{1}{11} \begin{pmatrix} -4 & -3 & 2 \\ 3 & 5 & -7 \\ 5 & 1 & -8 \end{pmatrix}$$

since $|\mathbf{A}| = -11$.

As indicated earlier, an alternative method to Cramer's rule for obtaining the solution of a system of n linear equations in n unknowns exists which involves the evaluation of the inverse of a square matrix. Consider, once more, the system of n linear equations in the n unknowns $x_1, x_2, \ldots, x_n$:

$$\sum_{k=1}^{n} a_{ik}x_k = b_k , \quad i = 1, 2, \ldots, n .$$

Now, if **x** and **b** are column matrices with elements $x_1, x_2, \ldots, x_n$ and $b_1, b_2, \ldots, b_n$ respectively, these equations may be written in matrix form as

$$\mathbf{A}\,\mathbf{x} = \mathbf{b}$$

where $\mathbf{A} = (a_{ik})$ is a square matrix of order n.

If it is assumed that $\mathbf{b} \neq \mathbf{0}$ and **A** does have an inverse $\mathbf{A}^{-1}$, then premultiplying by $\mathbf{A}^{-1}$ yields

$$\mathbf{A}^{-1}\mathbf{A}\,\mathbf{x} = \mathbf{A}^{-1}\mathbf{b}$$

or

$$\mathbf{x} = \mathbf{A}^{-1}\mathbf{b}$$

which is the matrix solution of the given system of equations. The use of this result is illustrated by the following example:

Solve the equations

$$3x_1 + 2x_2 - x_3 = -1$$

$$x_1 - 2x_2 + 2x_3 = 7$$

$$2x_1 + x_2 + x_3 = 3 .$$

For this system of equations

$$\mathbf{A} = \begin{pmatrix} 3 & 2 & -1 \\ 1 & -2 & 2 \\ 2 & 1 & 1 \end{pmatrix}$$

and, as has been shown already,

$$\mathbf{A}^{-1} = -\frac{1}{11}\begin{pmatrix} -4 & -3 & 2 \\ 3 & 5 & -7 \\ 5 & 1 & -8 \end{pmatrix} .$$

Thus,

$$\mathbf{x} = \begin{pmatrix} x_1 \\ x_2 \\ x_3 \end{pmatrix} = -\frac{1}{11}\begin{pmatrix} -4 & -3 & 2 \\ 3 & 5 & -7 \\ 5 & 1 & -8 \end{pmatrix}\begin{pmatrix} -1 \\ 7 \\ 3 \end{pmatrix} = -\frac{1}{11}\begin{pmatrix} -11 \\ 11 \\ -22 \end{pmatrix}$$

so that, $x_1 = 1$, $x_2 = -1$, $x_3 = 2$; the same result as was derived by Cramer's rule earlier.

This method of solution depends on the existence of the inverse matrix $\mathbf{A}^{-1}$. However, if the system of equations is such that $|\mathbf{A}| = 0$ then $\mathbf{A}^{-1}$ will not exist and, if further $\mathbf{b} \neq \mathbf{0}$, it is found that such a system has no finite solutions and the equations are in fact inconsistent. For example, consider the equations

$$3x - y + 2z = 1$$

$$x + 4y - 5z = -3$$

$$2x - 5y + 7z = -2 .$$

For this system of equations $|\mathbf{A}| = 0$. Also, by adding the second and third equations of the system, these three equations are seen to form an inconsistent set.

The situation which remains to be considered is that of a system of homogeneous equations ($\mathbf{b} = \mathbf{0}$). In this case, the equations may be written in matrix form as

$$\mathbf{Ax} = \mathbf{0}$$

where **0** is the zero column matrix of order n. Two cases must be considered. Firstly, if $|\mathbf{A}| \neq 0$, $\mathbf{A}^{-1}$ exists and

$$\mathbf{x} = \mathbf{A}^{-1}\, \mathbf{0} = \mathbf{0} \,.$$

This solution, in which all the x_i are equal to zero, is termed the **trivial solution** and is the only solution. However, if $|\mathbf{A}| = 0$, $\mathbf{A}^{-1}$ does not exist and the above deduction may not be made. Actually, it is fairly obvious that, under this condition,

$$\mathbf{Ax} = \mathbf{0}$$

will admit non-trivial solutions since, as has been shown, the product of two matrices may be zero with neither matrix being zero itself. Of course, such a set of equations will admit the trivial solution also.

Example

Consider the equations

$$x - (k + 1)y - kz = 0$$

$$2x + (k - 3)y + (k + 4)z = 0$$

$$x - 2ky - (3k - 2)z = 0$$

where k is a parameter.

The trivial solution, $x = y = z = 0$, exists for all values of k. However, non-trivial solutions will exist also when

$$|\mathbf{A}| = \begin{vmatrix} 1 & -(k + 1) & -k \\ 2 & (k - 3) & (k + 4) \\ 1 & -2k & -(3k - 2) \end{vmatrix} = 0$$

that is, when $k = 1$ or $k = 2$.

When $k = 1$, the equations become

$$x - 2y - z = 0$$

$$2x - 2y + 5z = 0$$

$$x - 2y - z = 0 \,,$$

that is, there are only two equations to solve for the three unknowns. Solving these two equations yields an infinity of possible solutions:

$$x = -6z \,, \quad y = -7z/2 \,.$$

A similar situation exists when $k = 2$ and, in this case, the infinity of possible solutions is

$$x = -4z \,, \quad y = -2z \,.$$

5.6 EIGENVALUES AND EIGENVECTORS

Suppose $A = (a_{ik})$ is a square matrix of order n and $\mathbf{x}$ is a column matrix with elements $x_1, x_2, \ldots, x_n$, then consider the matrix equation

$$\mathbf{Ax} = \lambda\mathbf{x}$$

where λ is a number. This equation may be written in the form

$$(\mathbf{A} - \lambda\mathbf{I})\mathbf{x} = \mathbf{0}$$

where $\mathbf{I}$ is the unit matrix of order n. If $\mathbf{x}$ is the zero column matrix, it is obviously a solution of this matrix equation which is valid for any value of λ. This is the trivial solution. However, as shown above, non-trivial solutions will exist also if

$$|A - \lambda I| = 0 \ . \tag{5.9a}$$

This equation is called the **characteristic equation** of the matrix $\mathbf{A}$. If the determinant in this equation is expanded, a polynomial in λ, of degree n, is obtained. This polynomial, which may be written as

$$|A - \lambda I| = c_0\lambda^n + c_1\lambda^{n-1} + \cdots + c_{n-1}\lambda + c_n$$

is the characteristic polynomial corresponding to the matrix $\mathbf{A}$. Hence, the characteristic equation may be written

$$c_0\lambda^n + c_1\lambda^{n-1} + \cdots + c_{n-1}\lambda + c_n = 0 \ . \tag{5.9b}$$

This is a polynomial equation of degree n, and so has n roots $\lambda_1, \lambda_2, \ldots, \lambda_n$. These n roots of the characteristic equation are called the **eigenvalues** of the matrix $\mathbf{A}$ and are the values of λ for which the original matrix equation possesses non-trivial solutions. A solution $\mathbf{x}_i$ of this matrix equation will correspond to each eigenvalue λ_i, and this solution is called the **eigenvector** corresponding to the eigenvalue λ_i. Since the above system is homogeneous, if $\mathbf{x}$ is an eigenvector of $\mathbf{A}$ then $k\mathbf{x}$, where k is any non-zero constant, is also an eigenvector of $\mathbf{A}$ corresponding to the same eigenvalue.

Since the nth order square matrix $\mathbf{A}$ has elements a_{ik} $(i, k = 1, \ldots, n)$ comparing the two forms of the characteristic equation, (5.9a) and (5.9b), shows that

$$c_0 = (-1)^n \ , \quad c_1 = (-1)^{n-1}(a_{11} + a_{22} + \cdots + a_{nn}) \ , \quad c_n = |\mathbf{A}| \ .$$

Also, if the eigenvalues are $\lambda_1, \lambda_2, \ldots, \lambda_n$,

$$c_0\lambda^n + c_1\lambda^{n-1} + \cdots + c_n = (\lambda_1 - \lambda)(\lambda_2 - \lambda) \cdots (\lambda_n - \lambda)$$

and so,

$$c_1 = (-1)^{n-1}(\lambda_1 + \lambda_2 + \cdots + \lambda_n) \ , \quad c_n = \lambda_1\lambda_2 \cdots \lambda_n \ .$$

Comparing the two sets of expressions for c_1 and c_n, it is seen that

$$\lambda_1 + \lambda_2 + \cdots + \lambda_n = a_{11} + a_{22} + \cdots + a_{nn} = \text{Tr } \mathbf{A}$$

$$\lambda_1 \lambda_2 \ldots \lambda_n = |\mathbf{A}| .$$

Example
Find the eigenvalues and eigenvectors of the matrix

$$\mathbf{A} = \begin{pmatrix} 1 & 2 \\ -8 & 11 \end{pmatrix} .$$

The characteristic equation is

$$|\mathbf{A} - \lambda \mathbf{I}| = \begin{vmatrix} 1 - \lambda & 2 \\ -8 & 11 - \lambda \end{vmatrix} = (\lambda - 3)(\lambda - 9) = 0 .$$

Therefore, the two eigenvalues are $\lambda_1 = 3$ and $\lambda_2 = 9$, and it is seen immediately that

$$\lambda_1 + \lambda_2 = 12 = \text{Tr } \mathbf{A} , \quad \lambda_1 \lambda_2 = 27 = |\mathbf{A}| .$$

To find the corresponding eigenvectors, the equation $(\mathbf{A} - \lambda \mathbf{I})\mathbf{x} = \mathbf{0}$ must be solved for $\mathbf{x}$ for each value of λ. Suppose the eigenvector corresponding to the ith eigenvalue λ_i is $\mathbf{x}_i$ and let its elements be x_i and y_i.

For $\lambda_1 = 3$, the equation is

$$\left[\begin{pmatrix} 1 & 2 \\ -8 & 11 \end{pmatrix} - 3 \begin{pmatrix} 1 & 0 \\ 0 & 1 \end{pmatrix} \right] \begin{pmatrix} x_1 \\ y_1 \end{pmatrix} = \begin{pmatrix} 0 \\ 0 \end{pmatrix}$$

that is, $x_1 = y_1 .$

Hence, the eigenvector corresponding to the eigenvalue $\lambda_1 = 3$ is

$$\mathbf{x}_1 = \begin{pmatrix} 1 \\ 1 \end{pmatrix} .$$

For $\lambda_2 = 9$ the equation is

$$\left[\begin{pmatrix} 1 & 2 \\ -8 & 11 \end{pmatrix} - 9 \begin{pmatrix} 1 & 0 \\ 0 & 1 \end{pmatrix} \right] \begin{pmatrix} x_2 \\ y_2 \end{pmatrix} = \begin{pmatrix} 0 \\ 0 \end{pmatrix}$$

that is, $4x_2 = y_2 .$

Hence, the eigenvector corresponding to the eigenvalue $\lambda_2 = 9$ is

$$\mathbf{x}_2 = \begin{pmatrix} 1 \\ 4 \end{pmatrix} .$$

If normalised eigenvectors had been required by the problem, it would have been necessary to ensure that $\mathbf{x}_1$ and $\mathbf{x}_2$ were such as to satisfy the condition

$$\sqrt{(\bar{\mathbf{x}}_i^{\mathrm{T}} \mathbf{x}_i)} = 1 .$$

Thus, the normalised eigenvectors for this problem are

$$\mathbf{x}_1 = \frac{1}{\sqrt{2}}\begin{pmatrix}1\\1\end{pmatrix}, \quad \mathbf{x}_2 = \frac{1}{\sqrt{17}}\begin{pmatrix}1\\4\end{pmatrix}.$$

It has been shown that, for a square matrix $\mathbf{A}$ of order n, the product of the n eigenvalues $\lambda_1, \ldots, \lambda_n$ is equal to $|\mathbf{A}|$. Hence, it follows that such a matrix is singular if and only if at least one of its eigenvalues is zero.

Now suppose λ to be an eigenvalue of the non-singular matrix $\mathbf{A}$ and suppose the corresponding eigenvector is $\mathbf{x}$ so that

$$\mathbf{A}\,\mathbf{x} = \lambda\mathbf{x}.$$

Since $\mathbf{A}^{-1}$ exists, premultiplying both sides of this equation by $\mathbf{A}^{-1}$ yields

$$\mathbf{A}^{-1}\,\mathbf{A}\,\mathbf{x} = \mathbf{x} = \mathbf{A}^{-1}\lambda\mathbf{x} = \lambda\mathbf{A}^{-1}\mathbf{x}.$$

Since $\mathbf{A}$ is non-singular, λ must be non-zero and so

$$\lambda\mathbf{A}^{-1}\mathbf{x} = \mathbf{x} \Rightarrow \mathbf{A}^{-1}\mathbf{x} = (1/\lambda)\mathbf{x},$$

that is, the eigenvalues of $\mathbf{A}^{-1}$ are the reciprocals of those of $\mathbf{A}$ (provided $\mathbf{A}$ is non-singular) and every eigenvector of $\mathbf{A}$ is an eigenvector of $\mathbf{A}^{-1}$ also.

Several other results concerning the eigenvalues of various special types of matrices will now be proved. Firstly, it may be noted that, if $\mathbf{A}$ is a triangular matrix, its eigenvalues are the elements of its principal diagonal. This follows since, if $\mathbf{A} = (a_{ik})$ is a triangular matrix of order n its characteristic equation is

$$(a_{11} - \lambda)(a_{22} - \lambda) \cdots (a_{nn} - \lambda) = 0,$$

whose roots are a_{ii} $(1 \leqslant i \leqslant n)$.

Secondly, the eigenvalues of a matrix $\mathbf{A}$ are the values of λ which are such that

$$\mathbf{Ax} = \lambda\mathbf{x}$$

has non-trivial solutions and the eigenvalues of the transposed matrix $\mathbf{A}^{\mathrm{T}}$ are the values of μ such that

$$\mathbf{A}^{\mathrm{T}}\mathbf{y} = \mu\mathbf{y}$$

has non-trivial solutions. These equations have non-trivial solutions when

$$|\mathbf{A} - \lambda\mathbf{I}| = 0 \quad \text{and} \quad |\mathbf{A}^{\mathrm{T}} - \mu\mathbf{I}| = 0$$

respectively.

However, since $|\mathbf{A}| = |\mathbf{A}^{\mathrm{T}}|$, it follows that the eigenvalues of $\mathbf{A}^{\mathrm{T}}$ are the same as those of $\mathbf{A}$.

Further, if λ is an eigenvalue of a matrix $\mathbf{A}$ and $\mathbf{x}$ is the corresponding eigenvector,

$$\mathbf{Ax} = \lambda\mathbf{x}$$

and so

$$\mathbf{A}^2\mathbf{x} = \mathbf{A}(\mathbf{Ax}) = \mathbf{A}(\lambda\mathbf{x}) = \lambda\mathbf{Ax} = \lambda^2\mathbf{x} .$$

Thus λ^2 is an eigenvalue of $\mathbf{A}^2$.

It follows from this result that, if p is any polynomial,

$$p(\mathbf{A})\mathbf{x} = p(\lambda)\mathbf{x}$$

for each eigenvalue λ of the matrix $\mathbf{A}$.

Another easily proved result which will be of use later is that all the eigenvalues of an Hermitian matrix are real and the eigenvectors corresponding to distinct eigenvalues are orthogonal.

To see this, suppose $\mathbf{A}$ to be an Hermitian matrix with an eigenvalue λ and corresponding eigenvector $\mathbf{x}$, so that

$$\mathbf{Ax} = \lambda\mathbf{x} .$$

If the transpose of the complex conjugate of this equation is taken then, since $(\mathbf{\bar{A}})^T = \mathbf{A}$,

$$\mathbf{\bar{x}}^T \mathbf{A} = \bar{\lambda} \, \mathbf{\bar{x}}^T .$$

If both sides of this equation are postmultiplied by $\mathbf{x}$ and both sides of the original equation are premultiplied by $\mathbf{\bar{x}}^T$ before one is subtracted from the other,

$$(\lambda - \bar{\lambda})\mathbf{\bar{x}}^T\mathbf{x} = \mathbf{0}$$

results. Now $\mathbf{\bar{x}}^T\mathbf{x}$ cannot be zero and so $\lambda = \bar{\lambda}$ showing that the eigenvalue λ is real.

Now suppose $\mathbf{x}_1$ and $\mathbf{x}_2$ are two eigenvectors of $\mathbf{A}$ corresponding to the distinct eigenvalues λ_1 and λ_2 respectively, then

$$\mathbf{Ax}_1 = \lambda_1\mathbf{x}_1 \quad \text{and} \quad \mathbf{Ax}_2 = \lambda_2\mathbf{x}_2 .$$

Taking the transpose of the complex conjugate of the first of these equation and noting that λ_1 is real, gives

$$\mathbf{\bar{x}}_1{}^T \mathbf{A} = \lambda_1\mathbf{\bar{x}}_1{}^T .$$

Now postmultiply both sides of this equation by $\mathbf{x}_2$ and premultiply the equation $\mathbf{Ax}_2 = \lambda_2\mathbf{x}_2$ by $\mathbf{\bar{x}}_1{}^T$ before one is subtracted from the other to give

$$(\lambda_1 - \lambda_2)\mathbf{\bar{x}}_1{}^T \mathbf{x}_2 = \mathbf{0} .$$

Since λ_1 and λ_2 are distinct, $\bar{\mathbf{x}}_1^T \mathbf{x}_2 = \mathbf{0}$ which means that $\mathbf{x}_1$ and $\mathbf{x}_2$ are orthogonal.

As a corollary to this result it follows that the eigenvalues of any real symmetric matrix are real and again the eigenvectors corresponding to distinct eigenvalues are orthogonal but, since, in this case, these eigenvectors are real, the condition for orthogonality is

$$\mathbf{x}_1^T \mathbf{x}_2 = \mathbf{0} \ .$$

If follows that the square matrix of order n whose columns are the eigenvectors $x_i (i = 1, \ldots, n)$ will be orthogonal if $\mathbf{A}$ is a real symmetric matrix or unitary if $\mathbf{A}$ is an Hermitian matrix.

Another result which proves of use is that the eigenvalues of a unitary matrix have magnitude unity.

To prove this, let $\mathbf{A}$ be a unitary matrix with an eigenvalue λ and corresponding eigenvector $\mathbf{x}$ then

$$\mathbf{A}\mathbf{x} = \lambda\mathbf{x} \ .$$

The transpose of the complex conjugate of this equation is

$$\bar{\mathbf{x}}^T \bar{\mathbf{A}}^T = \bar{\lambda}\bar{\mathbf{x}}^T \ .$$

If the first of these two equations is premultiplied by the second

$$\bar{\mathbf{x}}^T\bar{\mathbf{A}}^T\mathbf{A}\mathbf{x} = \lambda\bar{\lambda}\bar{\mathbf{x}}^T\mathbf{x}$$

However, $\mathbf{A}$ is unitary and so $\bar{\mathbf{A}}^T\mathbf{A} = \mathbf{I}$ and the equation reduces to

$$\bar{\mathbf{x}}^T\mathbf{x}(|\lambda|^2 - 1) = 0 \ .$$

Again $\bar{\mathbf{x}}^T\mathbf{x}$ cannot be zero, and so $|\lambda| = 1$ as required.

Obviously it follows as a corollary that each of the eigenvalues of a real orthogonal matrix has modulus unity.

There are many other results concerned with the eigenvalues and eigenvectors of matrices which could be proved. A selection has been included here of some of the more important and useful ones. Also, it is hoped that some idea has been given of the ways in which the proofs of these results proceed. If further details are required, a specialised book on matrix algebra should be consulted.

5.7 DIAGONALISATION OF MATRICES

Let $\mathbf{A} = (a_{ik})$ be a square matrix of order n and suppose its eigenvalues are λ_i and corresponding eigenvectors $\mathbf{x}_i$ where $i = 1, 2, \ldots, n$. If the eigenvectors $\mathbf{x}_i$ are written as column matrices, that is

$$\mathbf{x}_i = \begin{pmatrix} x_{1i} \\ x_{2i} \\ \cdot \\ \cdot \\ \cdot \\ x_{ni} \end{pmatrix}$$

then the eigenvalue equation $\mathbf{Ax} = \lambda\mathbf{x}$ may be written in the form

$$\begin{pmatrix} a_{11} & a_{12} & \cdots & a_{1n} \\ a_{21} & a_{22} & \cdots & a_{2n} \\ \cdot & \cdot & & \cdot \\ \cdot & \cdot & & \cdot \\ \cdot & \cdot & & \cdot \\ a_{n1} & a_{n2} & \cdots & a_{nn} \end{pmatrix} \begin{pmatrix} x_{1i} \\ x_{2i} \\ \cdot \\ \cdot \\ \cdot \\ x_{ni} \end{pmatrix} = \lambda_i \begin{pmatrix} x_{1i} \\ x_{2i} \\ \cdot \\ \cdot \\ \cdot \\ x_{ni} \end{pmatrix} .$$

The jth equation from this set of equations is

$$\sum_{k=1}^{n} a_{jk} x_{ki} = \lambda_i x_{ji} . \tag{a}$$

Now consider the square matrix $\mathbf{X}$ of order n whose columns are the eigen-vectors $\mathbf{x}_i$. Then, it is required to show that the matrix $\mathbf{X}^{-1}\mathbf{AX}$ is diagonal and the elements along its principal diagonal are the eigenvalues of $\mathbf{A}$, that is, if $\mathbf{X}^{-1}\mathbf{AX} = \mathbf{\Lambda}$

$$\mathbf{\Lambda} = \begin{pmatrix} \lambda_1 & 0 & \cdots & 0 \\ 0 & \lambda_2 & \cdots & 0 \\ \cdot & \cdot & & \cdot \\ \cdot & \cdot & & \cdot \\ \cdot & \cdot & & \cdot \\ 0 & 0 & \cdots & \lambda_n \end{pmatrix} .$$

Thus, it is required to prove that with $\mathbf{\Lambda}$ defined as above,

$$\mathbf{AX} = \mathbf{X\Lambda} .$$

The jith element of the left-hand side of this equation is given by

$$\sum_{k=1}^{n} (\mathbf{A})_{jk}(\mathbf{X})_{ki} = \sum_{k=1}^{n} a_{jk} x_{ki} = \lambda_i x_{ji}$$

where equation (a) has been used.

Also, the jith element of the right-hand side of the equation is given by

$$\sum_{k=1}^{n} (\mathbf{X})_{jk}(\mathbf{\Lambda})_{ki} = \sum_{k=1}^{n} x_{jk}\lambda_i\delta_{ki} = \lambda_i x_{ji} .$$

Since the jith elements of the left- and right-hand sides of the equation are seen to be equal, the original assertion has been proved; that is, with $\mathbf{X}$ defined as shown, $\mathbf{X}^{-1}\mathbf{AX}$ is a diagonal matrix and the elements along its principal diagonal are the eigenvalues of $\mathbf{A}$. This process is termed the **diagonalisation** of a matrix.

Example

Consider the square matrix of order 2

$$\mathbf{A} = \begin{pmatrix} 6 & 2 \\ 2 & 3 \end{pmatrix}.$$

The characteristic equation is

$$|A - \lambda I| = \begin{vmatrix} 6 - \lambda & 2 \\ 2 & 3 - \lambda \end{vmatrix} = (\lambda - 2)(\lambda - 7) = 0.$$

Therefore, the two eigenvalues are $\lambda_1 = 2$ and $\lambda_2 = 7$. By the procedure discussed earlier, it is found that the normalised eigenvector corresponding to the eigenvalue $\lambda_1 = 2$ is $\frac{1}{\sqrt{5}}\binom{2}{-1}$ and that corresponding to $\lambda_2 = 7$ is $\frac{1}{\sqrt{5}}\binom{2}{1}$. Hence, the matrix $\mathbf{X}$ referred to in the above theory is

$$\mathbf{X} = \frac{1}{\sqrt{5}}\begin{pmatrix} 1 & 2 \\ -2 & 1 \end{pmatrix}$$

and its inverse is

$$\mathbf{X}^{-1} = \frac{1}{\sqrt{5}}\begin{pmatrix} 1 & -2 \\ 2 & 1 \end{pmatrix}$$

It is straightforward to check that

$$\mathbf{X}^{-1}\mathbf{AX} = \frac{1}{5}\begin{pmatrix} 1 & -2 \\ 2 & 1 \end{pmatrix}\begin{pmatrix} 6 & 2 \\ 2 & 3 \end{pmatrix}\begin{pmatrix} 1 & 2 \\ -2 & 1 \end{pmatrix} = \begin{pmatrix} 2 & 0 \\ 0 & 7 \end{pmatrix}.$$

One important practical application of this process of diagonalisation of a matrix is in the study of quadric surfaces, where such surfaces are the three-dimensional analogues of the two-dimensional conic sections. However, before discussing this application, a brief discussion of bilinear, quadratic and Hermitian forms will be given.

If $x_1, \ldots, x_n$ and $y_1, \ldots, y_n$ are $2n$ variables, which may be either real or complex, the expression

$$B = \sum_{i=1}^{n} \sum_{k=1}^{n} a_{ik} x_i y_k$$

where the a_{ik} are numbers, is called a **bilinear form** in the given $2n$ variables. If $\mathbf{x}$ and $\mathbf{y}$ are two column matrices having elements $x_1, \ldots, x_n$ and $y_1, \ldots, y_n$ respectively and $\mathbf{A} = (a_{ik})$ is an nth-order square matrix, the above bilinear form may be written

$$B = \mathbf{x}^T \mathbf{A} \, \mathbf{y}$$

If $\mathbf{y}$ is replaced by $\mathbf{x}$ in this expression, the resulting expression

$$Q = \mathbf{x}^T \mathbf{A} \, \mathbf{x} = \sum_{i=1}^{n} \sum_{k=1}^{n} a_{ik} x_i x_k$$

is called a **quadratic form** in the n variables.

Writing the expression for Q out in detail gives

$$Q = a_{11} x_1^2 + (a_{12} + a_{21}) x_1 x_2 + \cdots + (a_{1n} + a_{n1}) x_1 x_n$$
$$+ a_{22} x_2^2 + \cdots + (a_{2n} + a_{n2}) x_2 x_n$$
$$+ \cdots + a_{nn} x_n^2 .$$

Now if c_{ik} is put equal to $\frac{1}{2}(a_{ik} + a_{ki})$ then $c_{ik} = c_{ki}$ and the quadratic form may be written

$$Q = \sum_{i=1}^{n} \sum_{k=1}^{n} c_{ik} \, x_i \, x_k .$$

If $\mathbf{A}$ is a real matrix then the matrix $\mathbf{C} = (c_{ik})$ is a real symmetric matrix. Hence, any real quadratic form Q in n variables may be written $Q = \mathbf{x}^T \mathbf{C} \, \mathbf{x}$ where $\mathbf{C}$ is a real symmetric matrix.

Finally, it might be noted that the value of a bilinear form or a quadratic form is a number.

If the matrix $\mathbf{A}$ is an Hermitian matrix, the form $\bar{\mathbf{x}}^T \mathbf{A} \, \mathbf{x}$ is called an **Hermitian form**. Once again, the elements of the column matrix $\mathbf{x}$ may be either real or complex. It may be shown that the value of an Hermitian form is a real number for every choice of $\mathbf{x}$. This follows since, using the definition of an Hermitian matrix, the complex conjugate of the Hermitian form

$$H = \bar{\mathbf{x}}^T \mathbf{A} \, \mathbf{x}$$

is seen to be

$$\overline{H} = \overline{(\bar{\mathbf{x}}^T \mathbf{A} \, \mathbf{x})} = \mathbf{x}^T \bar{\mathbf{A}} \, \bar{\mathbf{x}} = \mathbf{x}^T \mathbf{A}^T \bar{\mathbf{x}} .$$

The expression on the right is a scalar, and so taking its transpose leaves its value unchanged. Hence

$$\mathbf{x}^T \mathbf{A}^T \bar{\mathbf{x}} = (\mathbf{x}^T \mathbf{A}^T \bar{\mathbf{x}})^T = \bar{\mathbf{x}}^T \mathbf{A} \, \mathbf{x} = H .$$

Therefore, $H = \overline{H}$, which means that H is real.

If a matrix $\mathbf{A}$ is skew-Hermitian, the form $\bar{\mathbf{x}}^T \mathbf{A} \, \mathbf{x}$ is said to be a **skew-Hermitian** form, and for such a form it may be shown that the value is a purely imaginary number or zero for every choice of $\mathbf{x}$.

5.8 QUADRIC SURFACES

In rectangular coordinates, a quadric surface may be represented by an equation of the form

$$c = a_{11}x_1^2 + a_{22}x_2^2 + a_{33}x_3^2 + 2a_{12}x_1x_2 + 2a_{23}x_2x_3 + 2a_{31}x_3x_1$$

where the coordinates have been called x_1, x_2, x_3 and the coefficients have been labelled as shown so that this equation may be written as a matrix equation. In fact, if $\mathbf{A} = (a_{ik})$ is a symmetric matrix and $\mathbf{x}$ is the column matrix with elements x_1, x_2, x_3, the equation may be written

$$\mathbf{x}^\text{T} \mathbf{A} \mathbf{x} = c .$$

In the original equation, no terms of first order in x_1, x_2 or x_3 are included since, if they were to appear, they could be made to vanish by a simple change of origin.

Since $\mathbf{A}$ is a real symmetric matrix, it may be diagonalised by an orthogonal matrix $\mathbf{X}$ so that

$$\mathbf{X}^{-1} \mathbf{A} \mathbf{X} = \begin{pmatrix} \lambda_1 & 0 & 0 \\ 0 & \lambda_2 & 0 \\ 0 & 0 & \lambda_3 \end{pmatrix} = \Lambda$$

where $\lambda_1, \lambda_2, \lambda_3$ are the eigenvalues of $\mathbf{A}$. If new coordinates $\mathbf{y} = \mathbf{X}^{-1}\mathbf{x}$, where $\mathbf{y}$ is the column matrix with elements y_1, y_2, y_3, are defined, the matrix equation for the quadric surface becomes

$$\mathbf{x}^\text{T} \mathbf{X} \mathbf{X}^{-1} \mathbf{A} \mathbf{X} \mathbf{X}^{-1}\mathbf{x} = c$$

or

$$(\mathbf{X}^{-1} \mathbf{x})^\text{T}\Lambda(\mathbf{X}^{-1} \mathbf{x}) = c$$

that is,

$$\mathbf{y}^\text{T} \Lambda \mathbf{y} = c$$

where the fact that $\mathbf{X}$ is an orthogonal matrix has been used. If this equation is written in terms of y_i and λ_i ($i = 1, 2, 3$) it takes the form

$$\lambda_1 y_1^2 + \lambda_2 y_2^2 + \lambda_3 y_3^2 = c$$

or

$$\frac{y_1^2}{(c/\lambda_1)} + \frac{y_2^2}{(c/\lambda_2)} + \frac{y_3^2}{(c/\lambda_3)} = 1 . \tag{5.10}$$

The equation of the quadric surface has been reduced to this simple form by choosing the eigenvectors of $\mathbf{A}$ as the new coordinate axes. These axes are called the **principal axes** of the quadric, and the surface is seen to be symmetrical about each of these axes. The first principal axis meets the quadric where $y_2 = y_3 = 0$, that is, where $y_1 = \pm(c/\lambda_1)^{1/2}$. Hence, the distance along this axis from the origin to the point where it meets the quadric (known as the length of the semi-axis), is $(c/\lambda_1)^{1/2}$. Similarly, the lengths of the other semi-axes are $(c/\lambda_2)^{1/2}$ and $(c/\lambda_3)^{1/2}$.

If all three denominators are positive, equation (5.10) represents an ellipsoid; if one is negative, it represents an hyperboloid of one sheet; and if two are negative, it represents an hyperboloid of two sheets. In these, the three cases of interest, the principal axes are along y_1, y_2 and y_3 and, when the equation represents an ellipsoid, the lengths of the principal axes are $2(c/\lambda_i)^{1/2}$, $i = 1, 2, 3$.

If the original equation $\mathbf{x}^T \mathbf{A} \mathbf{x} = c$ had been describing a two-dimensional situation, the equation which would have resulted from the above process would have been

$$\frac{y_1^2}{(c/\lambda_1)} + \frac{y_2^2}{(c/\lambda_2)} = 1 \,,$$

with λ_1 and λ_2 being the eigenvalues of $\mathbf{A}$ once again. This equation represents an ellipse if c, λ_1, λ_2 have the same sign and an hyperbola if λ_1 and λ_2 have opposite signs. However, if one or more of λ_1, λ_2 and c are zero, the equation represents a pair of straight lines or a point or no real curve and, if λ_1 and λ_2 are non-zero but with the same sign while c is non-zero but of opposite sign, the equation is seen to represent an imaginary curve.

Finally, it should be pointed out that the above discussion applies to what are called **central quadrics**. Mention has been made of ellipsoids and hyperboloids but no mention has been made of paraboloids, for example. This is because the paraboloid is represented by an equation of the form

$$\alpha x_1^2 + \beta x_2^2 = \gamma x_3$$

and is a typical example of a non-central quadric.

Example

Show that the equation

$$x_1^2 + 3x_2^2 + 3x_3^2 + 2\sqrt{2}x_1x_2 - 4x_2x_3 + 2\sqrt{2}x_3x_1 = 1$$

represents an hyperboloid of one sheet.

The given equation may be written

$$\mathbf{x}^T \mathbf{A} \mathbf{x} = 1$$

where $\qquad \mathbf{x} = \begin{pmatrix} x_1 \\ x_2 \\ x_3 \end{pmatrix}$ and $\mathbf{A} = \begin{pmatrix} 1 & \sqrt{2} & \sqrt{2} \\ \sqrt{2} & 3 & -2 \\ \sqrt{2} & -2 & 3 \end{pmatrix}$.

The characteristic equation for the matrix $\mathbf{A}$ is

$$|\mathbf{A} - \lambda\mathbf{I}| = \begin{vmatrix} 1-\lambda & \sqrt{2} & \sqrt{2} \\ \sqrt{2} & 3-\lambda & -2 \\ \sqrt{2} & -2 & 3-\lambda \end{vmatrix} = (3-\lambda)(\lambda-5)(\lambda+1) = 0$$

Therefore, the three eigenvalues are $\lambda_1 = 3$, $\lambda_2 = 5$ and $\lambda_3 = -1$. If the equa-
tion $(\mathbf{A} - \lambda\mathbf{I})\boldsymbol{\omega} = \mathbf{0}$ is solved for $\boldsymbol{\omega}$ for each value of λ, the corresponding normalised eigenvectors are seen to be

$$\boldsymbol{\omega}_1 = \frac{1}{2}\begin{pmatrix} \sqrt{2} \\ 1 \\ 1 \end{pmatrix}, \quad \boldsymbol{\omega}_2 = \frac{1}{\sqrt{2}}\begin{pmatrix} 0 \\ -1 \\ 1 \end{pmatrix}, \quad \boldsymbol{\omega}_3 = \frac{1}{2}\begin{pmatrix} \sqrt{2} \\ -1 \\ -1 \end{pmatrix}.$$

Thus, the diagonalising matrix is

$$\mathbf{X} = \frac{1}{2}\begin{pmatrix} \sqrt{2} & 0 & \sqrt{2} \\ 1 & -\sqrt{2} & -1 \\ 1 & \sqrt{2} & -1 \end{pmatrix}$$

and

$$\mathbf{X}^{-1}\mathbf{A}\mathbf{X} = \begin{pmatrix} 3 & 0 & 0 \\ 0 & 5 & 0 \\ 0 & 0 & -1 \end{pmatrix}.$$

Thus, if new coordinates

$$\mathbf{y} = \begin{pmatrix} y_1 \\ y_2 \\ y_3 \end{pmatrix} = \mathbf{X}^{-1}\mathbf{x}$$

are defined, it follows that the given equation may be written, in terms of these
new coordinates, in the form

$$3y_1^2 + 5y_2^2 - y_3^2 = 1$$

which is the equation of an hyperboloid of one sheet referred to its principal
axes. Hence, the original equation also represents an hyperboloid of one sheet.

EXERCISES 5

(1) If $\qquad \mathbf{A} = \begin{pmatrix} 3 & -1 & 1 \\ 1 & 3 & -5 \end{pmatrix}$ and $\mathbf{B} = \begin{pmatrix} 2 & -7 & 0 \\ 3 & -3 & 5 \end{pmatrix}$

find $\mathbf{A} + \mathbf{B}$, $\mathbf{A} - \mathbf{B}$, $(\mathbf{A} + \mathbf{B})^{\mathrm{T}}$, $(\mathbf{A}^{\mathrm{T}})^{\mathrm{T}}$.

(2) If $\mathbf{A} = \begin{pmatrix} 1 & 2 & 6 \\ 3 & 4 & 7 \\ 5 & 8 & 9 \end{pmatrix}$, represent $\mathbf{A}$ as a sum of a symmetric and an anti-

symmetric matrix.

(3) If $\qquad \mathbf{A} = \begin{pmatrix} 3 & 1 & 2 \\ 2 & 1 & 3 \end{pmatrix}$ and $\mathbf{B} = \begin{pmatrix} 1 & 2 \\ 3 & 1 \\ 2 & 3 \end{pmatrix}$,

find $\mathbf{AB}$ and $\mathbf{BA}$.

(4) If
$$\mathbf{A} = \begin{pmatrix} 4 & 6 & -1 \\ 3 & 0 & 2 \\ 1 & -2 & 5 \end{pmatrix} \quad \text{and} \quad \mathbf{B} = \begin{pmatrix} 2 & 4 \\ 0 & 1 \\ -1 & 2 \end{pmatrix}$$

find $\mathbf{AB}$, $\mathbf{BA}$, $\mathbf{B^T A^T}$.

(5) Evaluate the determinants:

$$\begin{vmatrix} 4 & -7 & -4 \\ 6 & 1 & 2 \\ 1 & 5 & 3 \end{vmatrix}, \quad \begin{vmatrix} 5 & 1 & 8 \\ 15 & 3 & 6 \\ 10 & 4 & 2 \end{vmatrix}, \quad \begin{vmatrix} 1 & 24 & 21 & 93 \\ 2 & -37 & -1 & 194 \\ -2 & 35 & 0 & -171 \\ -3 & 177 & 63 & 234 \end{vmatrix}$$

(6) Show that

(i)
$$\begin{vmatrix} a & b & c \\ a^2 & b^2 & c^2 \\ (b+c) & (c+a) & (a+b) \end{vmatrix} = (a+b+c)(b-c)(c-a)(a-b),$$

(ii)
$$\begin{vmatrix} 1 & 1 & 1 & 1 \\ a & b & c & d \\ bcd & cda & dab & abc \\ a^2 & b^2 & c^2 & d^2 \end{vmatrix} = (a-b)(a-c)(a-d)(b-c)(b-d)(c-d).$$

(7) Use Cramer's rule to solve the equations

$$4x_1 + 2x_2 + x_3 = -8$$
$$3x_1 - x_2 + 2x_3 = 4$$
$$x_1 + x_2 + x_3 = -2.$$

(8) Use Cramer's rule to solve the equations

$$5x_1 - 2x_2 - 3x_3 = 10$$
$$2x_1 - 4x_2 + x_3 = 0$$
$$3x_1 + x_2 - 6x_3 = 0.$$

(9) Find the inverses of the following matrices:

$$\begin{pmatrix} -3 & 1 & -1 \\ 15 & -6 & 5 \\ -5 & 2 & -2 \end{pmatrix}, \quad \begin{pmatrix} 3 & 0 & 1 \\ 0 & 5 & 0 \\ -1 & 1 & -1 \end{pmatrix}, \quad \begin{pmatrix} 1 & 0 & 1 & 1 \\ -1 & 2 & 3 & 4 \\ 6 & -2 & 1 & 0 \\ 3 & 0 & 1 & -1 \end{pmatrix}$$

(10) Use matrix methods to solve the equations:

$$x_1 + 5x_2 + 2x_3 = 9$$
$$x_1 + x_2 + 7x_3 = 6$$

$$3x_2 - 4x_3 = 2 .$$

(11) Use matrix methods to solve the equations:

$$-8x_1 + 9x_2 - 3x_3 = 4$$

$$-4x_1 + 5x_2 + x_3 = 6$$

$$2x_1 - 2x_2 + 3x_3 = -2 .$$

(12) Use matrix methods to solve the equations:

$$4x_1 - 3x_2 + x_3 = 11$$

$$2x_1 + x_2 - 4x_3 = -1$$

$$x_1 + 2x_2 - 2x_3 = 1 .$$

(13) Find the eigenvalues and eigenvectors of the matrices:

$$\text{(i)} \begin{pmatrix} 2 & 2 \\ 1 & 3 \end{pmatrix}, \quad \text{(ii)} \begin{pmatrix} 4 & -2 \\ 1 & 1 \end{pmatrix}, \quad \text{(iii)} \begin{pmatrix} 4 + 2j & 3 + 3j \\ 2 + 2j & 5 + 3j \end{pmatrix},$$

$$\text{(iv)} \begin{pmatrix} 1 & 4 & 5 \\ 0 & 2 & 6 \\ 0 & 0 & 3 \end{pmatrix} .$$

(14) Diagonalise the matrix $\mathbf{A}$ where

$$\mathbf{A} = \begin{pmatrix} a & b & b \\ b & a & b \\ b & b & a \end{pmatrix} .$$

(15) Diagonalise the matrix $\mathbf{A}$ where

$$\mathbf{A} = \tfrac{1}{3} \begin{pmatrix} -7 & 2 & 10 \\ 2 & 2 & -8 \\ 10 & -8 & -4 \end{pmatrix} .$$

(16) Show that the equation

$$8x_1^2 + 2\sqrt{2}x_1x_2 + 7x_2^2 = 3$$

represents an ellipse.

(17) Find the equation of the quadric

$$11x_1^2 + 5x_2^2 + 2x_3^2 + 16x_1x_2 + 20x_2x_3 - 4x_3x_1 = 9$$

when it is referred to its principal axes. What does this equation represent?

Chapter 6
Vector Algebra

6.1 INTRODUCTION

For any given physical system, many of its physical properties may be classified as either scalars or vectors. The difference between these two classes is intuitive but, roughly speaking, a **scalar** is a quantity possessing magnitude, whereas a **vector** is a quantity possessing both magnitude and direction.

Any scalar is specified completely by a real number, and the laws of addition and multiplication obeyed by scalars are the same as those for real numbers. For real numbers $a, b, c \ldots$, these laws are:

Commutative laws.

$$a + b = b + a; \quad ab = ba.$$

Associative laws.

$$a + (b + c) = (a + b) + c; \quad a(bc) = (ab)c$$

Distributive law.

$$a(b + c) = ab + ac.$$

Also, subtraction and division may be defined in terms of addition and multiplication as follows:

$$c - a = c + (-a)$$

where $(-a)$ is defined by

$$b + a = 0 \Rightarrow b = (-a)$$

$$c/a = c \, a^{-1}$$

where a^{-1} is defined by

$$ba = 1 \Rightarrow b = a^{-1}.$$

Examples of scalars are length, speed, time, and energy, while displacement, velocity, acceleration, force, and momentum are all examples of vectors.

Consider displacement. If a particle is displaced from A to B (see Fig. 6.1), then the displacement is given not only by the length AB but also its direction.

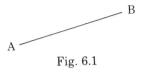

Fig. 6.1

Length is actually the magnitude of displacement.

6.2 REPRESENTATION OF A VECTOR

A vector is represented by a line of the required magnitude pointing in the required direction.

Vectors are denoted by boldface type, **a**, **b**, etc. usually. Also, the vector represented by the displacement from O to A may be denoted by $\overrightarrow{OA}$. Hence, if **a** is represented by the displacement from O to A

$$\mathbf{a} = \overrightarrow{OA} .$$

Then, if $\mathbf{a} = \overrightarrow{OA}$, the vector $-\mathbf{a}$ may be defined by

$$-\mathbf{a} = \overrightarrow{AO}$$

that is, **a** and $-\mathbf{a}$ have equal magnitude but opposite direction.

There are two general categories of vectors: fixed vectors and free vectors. A fixed vector is one which acts at a specified point in space, and so is determined by its magnitude, direction, and point of application. A typical example of such a vector is a force. A free vector is one specified by magnitude and direction only. For example, if $\mathbf{a} = \overrightarrow{OA}$ is a free vector, then $\mathbf{a} = \overrightarrow{BC}$ where OA and BC are both parallel and of equal length (see Fig. 6.2).

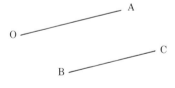

Fig. 6.2

Following this discussion of the representation of vectors, it is possible to define a vector as follows:

Any physical property of a given physical system which may be represented by the magnitude and direction of a directed line segment is defined to be a vector. The magnitude and direction of the directed line segment are defined to be the magnitude and direction of the vector.

The magnitude of the vector **a** is denoted by a or sometimes $|\mathbf{a}|$. This magnitude is a positive real number, being the length of a directed line segment, and is called the **modulus** of the vector sometimes. A vector in the same direction as **a** but of unit magnitude is denoted by **â**.

Two vectors are said to be equal if they have the same magnitude and the same direction. Symbolically,

$$\mathbf{a} = \mathbf{b} \quad \text{if and only if} \quad a = b \quad \text{and} \quad \hat{\mathbf{a}} = \hat{\mathbf{b}} \,.$$

All vectors represented by a zero directed line segment are defined equal to the zero vector and are denoted by **0**. The zero vector has zero magnitude and is associated usually with the absence of some particular physical property.

6.3 ADDITION OF VECTORS

The sum, $\overrightarrow{AB} + \overrightarrow{BC}$, of the two direct line segments $\overrightarrow{AB}$ and $\overrightarrow{BC}$ is defined to be the directed line segment $\overrightarrow{AC}$ (see Fig. 6.3).

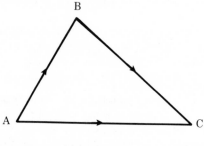

Fig. 6.3

This addition satisfies the associative law, that is

$$\overrightarrow{AB} + (\overrightarrow{BC} + \overrightarrow{CD}) = (\overrightarrow{AB} + \overrightarrow{BC}) + \overrightarrow{CD}$$

The proof follows immediately from the above definition:

$$\overrightarrow{AB} + (\overrightarrow{BC} + \overrightarrow{CD}) = \overrightarrow{AB} + \overrightarrow{BD}$$
$$= \overrightarrow{AD}$$
$$= \overrightarrow{AC} + \overrightarrow{CD}$$
$$= (\overrightarrow{AB} + \overrightarrow{BC}) + \overrightarrow{CD} \,.$$

Now, if two vectors **a** and **b** are represented by the directed line segments $\overrightarrow{AB}$ and $\overrightarrow{BC}$, then the sum **a** + **b** of the vectors is defined to be that vector represented by the directed line segment $\overrightarrow{AC}$.

Consider the parallelogram ABCD, as shown in Fig. 6.4, where the directed line segments $\overrightarrow{AB}$ and $\overrightarrow{BC}$ do represent vectors **a** and **b**.

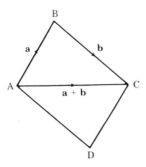

Fig. 6.4

It is seen that the vector **b** could be represented equally well by the directed line segment $\overrightarrow{AD}$, and the sum **a** + **b** is represented then by the diagonal of the parallelogram. This observation leads to the parallelogram law of addition of vectors:

If two vectors **a** and **b** are represented by directed line segments $\overrightarrow{AB}$ and $\overrightarrow{AD}$ then the sum **a** + **b** of the two vectors is represented by the directed line segment $\overrightarrow{AC}$, where ABCD are the vertices of a parallelogram taken in order.

The commutative law,

$$\mathbf{a} + \mathbf{b} = \mathbf{b} + \mathbf{a}$$

follows immediately from the symmetry of the parallelogram law of addition. The associative law,

$$\mathbf{a} + (\mathbf{b} + \mathbf{c}) = (\mathbf{a} + \mathbf{b}) + \mathbf{c}$$

is a direct consequence of the associative law for the addition of directed line segments.

Again $\mathbf{a} + \mathbf{0} = \mathbf{a}$

Also, subtraction of vectors is defined by

$$\mathbf{a} - \mathbf{b} = \mathbf{a} + (-\mathbf{b})$$

and a consequence of this definition is

$$\mathbf{b} - \mathbf{b} = \mathbf{0}.$$

Suppose **b** is represented by the directed line segment $\overrightarrow{OB}$, then −**b** is represented by $\overrightarrow{BO}$

$$\mathbf{b} - \mathbf{b} = \mathbf{b} + (-\mathbf{b})$$
$$= \overrightarrow{OB} + \overrightarrow{BO}$$
$$= \overrightarrow{OO}$$
$$= \mathbf{0} \text{ as required.}$$

6.4 MULTIPLICATION OF VECTORS BY SCALARS

If $\mathbf{a}$ is a vector and k a scalar, the product $k\mathbf{a}$ is defined to be the vector whose magnitude is $|k|$ times the magnitude of $\mathbf{a}$ and whose direction is the same as, or opposite to, that of $\mathbf{a}$ according as k is positive or negative.

A number of consequences follow from this definition:

(i) $\mathbf{a} + \mathbf{a} = 2\mathbf{a}$.

Suppose $\overrightarrow{OA} = \mathbf{a} = \overrightarrow{AB}$, then OA and AB are both of length a.

$\overrightarrow{OB}$ has length $2a$, and so represents a vector having magnitude twice that of $\mathbf{a}$ and the same direction;

$$\overrightarrow{OB} = 2\mathbf{a}$$

But $\overrightarrow{OB} = \overrightarrow{OA} + \overrightarrow{AB} = \mathbf{a} + \mathbf{a}$

and so $\mathbf{a} + \mathbf{a} = 2a$.

This result is a special case of

$$\underbrace{\mathbf{a} + \mathbf{a} + \cdots \mathbf{a}}_{n \text{ terms}} = n\mathbf{a}$$

(ii) $(p + q)\mathbf{a} = p\mathbf{a} + q\mathbf{a}$.

Suppose $\overrightarrow{OP} = p\mathbf{a}$ and $\overrightarrow{PQ} = q\mathbf{a}$ where OPQ is a straight line.

$\overrightarrow{OP}$ and $\overrightarrow{PQ}$ have the direction of $\mathbf{a}$ and magnitudes pa and qa respectively.

$\overrightarrow{OQ}$ has the direction of $\mathbf{a}$ and magnitude $(p + q)\mathbf{a}$, and so

$$\overrightarrow{OQ} = (p + q)\mathbf{a}$$.

But $\overrightarrow{OQ} = \overrightarrow{OP} + \overrightarrow{PQ} = p\mathbf{a} + q\mathbf{a}$.

Thus, $(p + q)\mathbf{a} = p\mathbf{a} + q\mathbf{a}$.

(iii) Similarly,

$$(pq)\mathbf{a} = p(q\mathbf{a})$$

(iv) $k(\mathbf{a} + \mathbf{b}) = k\mathbf{a} + k\mathbf{b}$.

Consider the situation depicted in Fig. 6.5. The directed line segments $\overrightarrow{OA}$ and $\overrightarrow{OB}$ represent the vectors $\mathbf{a}$ and $\mathbf{b}$ respectively, while the vectors $k\mathbf{a}$ and $k\mathbf{b}$ are represented by the directed line segments $\overrightarrow{OA}'$ and $\overrightarrow{OB}'$ respectively.

Since $OA' = kOA$ and $OB' = kOB$, the completed parallelograms OACB and OA'C'B' are similar and so

$$OC' = kOC$$

Thus, $\overrightarrow{OC}'$ has magnitude kOC and the same direction as $\overrightarrow{OC}$, and so

$$\overrightarrow{OC}' = k\overrightarrow{OC}$$.

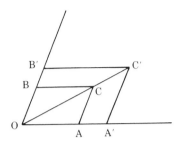

Fig. 6.5

However, $\overrightarrow{OC}$ = **a** + **b**

and $\overrightarrow{OC}'$ = $\overrightarrow{OA}'$ + $\overrightarrow{OB}'$

$$= k\mathbf{a} + k\mathbf{b} \, .$$

Finally, $k\mathbf{a} + k\mathbf{b} = k(\mathbf{a} + \mathbf{b})$ as required.

(v) Division of a vector by a scalar is defined by

$$\mathbf{a} \div k = k^{-1}\mathbf{a} \, .$$

It might be noted that the laws of addition and multiplication by a scalar as introduced here are the axioms used by pure mathematicians to define a real vector space. Actually, at each point P of a three-dimensional Euclidean space, the axioms define a vector space, called the **tangent vector space** at P. However, here vectors have been introduced intuitively in the hope that this approach will help with the more abstract topic of vector spaces if, and when, it is encountered.

6.5 VECTOR AND CARTESIAN DESCRIPTIONS

In the vector description of the position of some point P, a point O is chosen as origin for reference and the position of P is given by the displacement $\overrightarrow{OP}$. In the Cartesian picture, the position of P is described in terms of its distances x, y, z from three orthogonal plane surfaces through O; −a frame of reference $Oxyz$ is chosen and x, y, z are the distances of P from the planes Oyz, Ozx, Oxy respectively.

The solid figure shown in Fig. 6.6 is a parallelepiped. Suppose the Cartesian coordinates of the point P are (x, y, z), so that x is the perpendicular distance of P from the plane Oyz

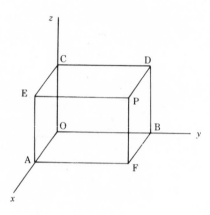

Fig. 6.6

$$x = PD = EC = FB = AO .$$

Also,
$$y = PE = DC = FA = BO$$

and
$$z = PF = EA = DB = CO .$$

Now introduce the vector coordinate of P,

$$\mathbf{r} = \overrightarrow{OP}$$

then

$$\mathbf{r} = \overrightarrow{OP} = \overrightarrow{OA} + \overrightarrow{AF} + \overrightarrow{FP}$$
$$= \overrightarrow{OA} + \overrightarrow{OB} + \overrightarrow{OC} .$$

Let $\mathbf{i}, \mathbf{j}, \mathbf{k}$ be unit vectors in the directions Ox, Oy, Oz respectively, so that

$\overrightarrow{OA}$ = vector of magnitude x in the same direction as $\mathbf{i}$
$= x\,\mathbf{i} .$

Similarly,

$$\overrightarrow{OB} = y\mathbf{j} \quad \text{and} \quad \overrightarrow{OC} = z\mathbf{k}$$

$$\mathbf{r} = x\mathbf{i} + y\mathbf{j} + z\mathbf{k} .$$

Here $\mathbf{r}$ is said to be the **position vector** of the point P.
Uniqueness Theorem

If
$$\mathbf{r} = x\mathbf{i} + y\mathbf{j} + z\mathbf{k}$$
$$= x'\mathbf{i} + y'\mathbf{j} + z'\mathbf{k}$$

then

$$x = x', \quad y = y', \quad z = z'$$

Proof

Suppose

$$\mathbf{r} = x\mathbf{i} + y\mathbf{j} + z\mathbf{k}$$

and

$$\mathbf{r} = x'\mathbf{i} + y'\mathbf{j} + z'\mathbf{k}$$

then

$$(x - x')\mathbf{i} + (y - y')\mathbf{j} + (z - z')\mathbf{k} = \mathbf{0}$$

that is

$$a\mathbf{i} + b\mathbf{j} + c\mathbf{k} = 0 , \tag{i}$$

with

$$a = x - x' , \quad b = y - y' , \quad c = z - z'$$

Now suppose $a \neq 0$, then by (i)

$$\mathbf{i} = \alpha\mathbf{j} + \beta\mathbf{k} \tag{ii}$$

with

$$\alpha = -b/a , \quad \beta = -c/a$$

both being finite.

In equation (ii), the right-hand side is a vector lying in the plane Oyz, but the left-hand side is a vector lying along Ox and certainly *not* in the plane Oyz. Hence, the assumption $a \neq 0$ leads to a contradiction, and so $a = 0$.

Similarly, it may be shown that $b = 0$ and $c = 0$.

Hence, the uniqueness theorem has been proved.

In the Cartesian description x, y, z are called the **components** of the vector $\mathbf{r}$ along Ox, Oy, Oz respectively. Again, an alternative notation for

$$\mathbf{r} = x\mathbf{i} + y\mathbf{j} + z\mathbf{k}$$

is

$$\mathbf{r} = (x, y, z) ,$$

To obtain the component of a vector $\mathbf{r} = \overrightarrow{OP}$ in the direction of some given line L, draw a line L′ through O and parallel to L (see Fig. 6.7). Next draw the perpendicular, PN, from P onto L′.

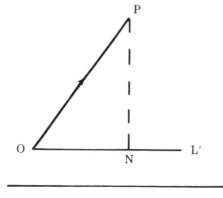

Fig. 6.7

Then

$$ON = \text{component of } \overrightarrow{OP} \text{ in the direction of } L'$$

$$= \text{component of } \overrightarrow{OP} \text{ in the direction of } L .$$

Now write

$$\overrightarrow{OP} = \mathbf{r} = r\hat{\mathbf{u}}$$

where r is the magnitude of $\overrightarrow{OP}$ and $\hat{\mathbf{u}}$ denotes a unit vector in the direction of $\overrightarrow{OP}$.

Therefore

$$\hat{\mathbf{u}} = \frac{\mathbf{r}}{r} = \frac{1}{r}(x\mathbf{i} + y\mathbf{j} + z\mathbf{k})$$

$$= l\mathbf{i} + m\mathbf{j} + n\mathbf{k}$$

where $l = x/r$, $m = y/r$, $n = z/r$.

The picture for l is as shown in Fig. 6.8, from which it is seen that

$$l = x/r = \cos\theta .$$

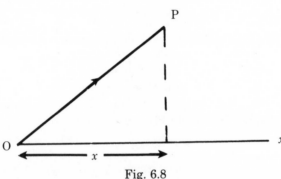

Fig. 6.8

A similar situation exists for m and n.

Hence, it is seen that l, m, n are the **direction cosines** of OP.

6.6 VECTOR MULTIPLICATION

Now that the addition of vectors and the multiplication of vectors by scalars have been discussed, two further important operations will be defined:

(i) *Scalar Products*

The **scalar product** between two vectors **a** and **b** is denoted by $\mathbf{a} \cdot \mathbf{b}$. The alternative names of **dot product** and **inner product** are used occasionally.

(ii) *Vector Products*

The **vector product** between two vectors **a** and **b** is denoted by $\mathbf{a} \times \mathbf{b}$, or sometimes $\mathbf{a} \wedge \mathbf{b}$. In this case, the alternative names employed are **cross product** and **outer product**.

6.6.1 Scalar Products

If **a** and **b** are represented by the directed line segments $\overrightarrow{OA}$ and $\overrightarrow{OB}$ respectively, then

$$\mathbf{a \cdot b} = ab\cos\theta$$

where a and b are the magnitudes of $\mathbf{a}$ and $\mathbf{b}$ respectively and θ is the angle AOB; that is, θ is the angle through which OA must be rotated to coincide with OB (see Fig. 6.9).

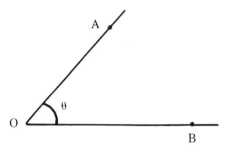

Fig. 6.9

It is important to note the following points about this definition:

    (a) by definition, the scalar product is indeed a scalar!

    (b) if θ is obtuse, $\mathbf{a} \cdot \mathbf{b}$ is negative.

    (c) $\mathbf{a} \cdot \mathbf{b} = 0$ if $a = 0$ or $b = 0$ or $\cos\theta = 0$;

that is,

$$\mathbf{a \cdot b} = 0 \quad \text{if} \quad \mathbf{a} = \mathbf{0} \quad \text{or} \quad \mathbf{b} = \mathbf{0}$$

or **a** and **b** are
perpendicular to one another.

Commutative law

$$\mathbf{a \cdot b} = ab\cos\theta$$

and

$$\mathbf{b \cdot a} = ba\cos(-\theta)\,.$$

But

$$\cos\theta = \cos(-\theta)$$

and so

$$\mathbf{a \cdot b} = \mathbf{b \cdot a}\,.$$

Associative law

The associative law

$$\mathbf{a \cdot (b \cdot c)} = \mathbf{(a \cdot b) \cdot c}$$

has no meaning. The scalar product is, by definition, a product of two vectors and, since $\mathbf{(b \cdot c)}$ is a scalar, the product $\mathbf{a \cdot (b \cdot c)}$ is not even defined. Obviously, the product $\mathbf{(a \cdot b) \cdot c}$ is not defined either.

Distributive law

The distributive law

$$\mathbf{a \cdot (b + c)} = \mathbf{a \cdot b} + \mathbf{a \cdot c}$$

may be deduced as follows from Fig. 6.10.

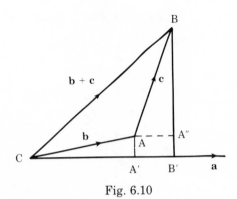

Fig. 6.10

It is seen from the figure that

$$\mathbf{a}\cdot(\mathbf{b} + \mathbf{c}) = a\,CB\cos\angle BCB'$$

$$= a\,CB'$$

$$= a\,(CA' + A'B')$$

$$= a\,(CA' + AA'')$$

$$= a\,(CA\cos\angle ACA' + BA\cos\angle BAA'')$$

$$= \mathbf{a}\cdot\mathbf{b} + \mathbf{a}\cdot\mathbf{c}$$

as required.

Also, for any scalar m,

$$\mathbf{a}\cdot(m\mathbf{b}) = m(\mathbf{a}\cdot\mathbf{b}) = (m\mathbf{a})\cdot\mathbf{b}$$

since all three expressions equal $|m|ab\cos\theta$.

Again, the scalar product of a vector with itself is the square of the magnitude of the vector:

$$\mathbf{a}^2 = \mathbf{a}\cdot\mathbf{a} = a^2\cos\theta$$

where $\theta = 0$, and so

$$\mathbf{a}^2 = a^2 .$$

Scalar product in terms of Cartesian components
Consider two vectors $\mathbf{a}$ and $\mathbf{b}$ and suppose that

$$\mathbf{a} = a_1\mathbf{i} + a_2\mathbf{j} + a_3\mathbf{k}$$

and

$$\mathbf{b} = b_1\mathbf{i} + b_2\mathbf{j} + b_3\mathbf{k}$$

then

$$\mathbf{a}\cdot\mathbf{b} = a_1b_1\mathbf{i}\cdot\mathbf{i} + a_1b_2\mathbf{i}\cdot\mathbf{j} + a_1b_3\mathbf{i}\cdot\mathbf{k}$$

$$+ a_2b_1\mathbf{j}\cdot\mathbf{i} + a_2b_2\mathbf{j}\cdot\mathbf{j} + a_2b_3\mathbf{j}\cdot\mathbf{k}$$

$$+ a_3b_1\mathbf{k}\cdot\mathbf{i} + a_3b_2\mathbf{k}\cdot\mathbf{j} + a_3b_3\mathbf{k}\cdot\mathbf{k}\;.$$

However, $\mathbf{i}$, $\mathbf{j}$, $\mathbf{k}$ are unit vectors and so

$$\mathbf{i}\cdot\mathbf{i} = \mathbf{i}^2 = 1$$

and similarly

$$\mathbf{j}\cdot\mathbf{j} = 1\;,\quad \mathbf{k}\cdot\mathbf{k} = 1\;.$$

Also, the three unit vectors $\mathbf{i}$, $\mathbf{j}$ and $\mathbf{k}$ are mutually perpendicular and so

$$\mathbf{i}\cdot\mathbf{j} = \mathbf{j}\cdot\mathbf{k} = \mathbf{k}\cdot\mathbf{i} = 0$$

Hence, $\qquad\qquad\quad \mathbf{a}\cdot\mathbf{b} = a_1b_1 + a_2b_2 + a_3b_3\;.$

A special case of this result is

$$\mathbf{a}\cdot\mathbf{a} = a_1^2 + a_2^2 + a_3^2\;.$$

Although vectors and vector methods are usually associated with physical problems and, in particular, with problems occurring in mechanics, they prove extremely useful for tackling some problems in geometry. This seemingly unlikely application will be illustrated now by considering a number of examples.

Example 1

To show that the diagonals of a rhombus intersect at right angles.

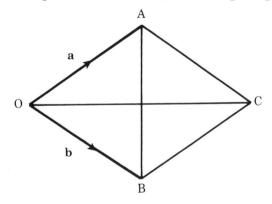

Fig. 6.11

Suppose $\mathbf{a}$ and $\mathbf{b}$ are represented by $\overrightarrow{OA}$ and $\overrightarrow{OB}$ respectively as shown in Fig. 6.11, then

$$\overrightarrow{OC} = \mathbf{c} = \mathbf{a} + \mathbf{b}$$

and $\qquad\qquad\qquad \overrightarrow{BA} = \overrightarrow{BO} + \overrightarrow{OA}$

$$= -\overrightarrow{OB} + \overrightarrow{OA}$$

$$= -\mathbf{b} + \mathbf{a}.$$

Now $$\overrightarrow{OC}\cdot\overrightarrow{BA} = (\mathbf{a} + \mathbf{b})\cdot(\mathbf{a} - \mathbf{b})$$

$$= \mathbf{a}^2 - \mathbf{b}^2$$

$$= 0,$$

since, for a rhombus, OA = OB. Thus, OC is perpendicular to AB, or, in other words, the diagonals of a rhombus do intersect at right angles.

Example 2

To derive the cosine rule.

Adopting the same notation as that used in the previous example,

$$\overrightarrow{BA} = \mathbf{a} - \mathbf{b}$$

Then $$(BA)^2 = (\overrightarrow{BA})^2 = (\mathbf{a} - \mathbf{b})^2$$

$$= \mathbf{a}^2 + \mathbf{b}^2 - 2\mathbf{a}\cdot\mathbf{b}$$

$$= a^2 + b^2 - 2ab\cos\theta$$

where $\theta = A\hat{O}B$, the angle between $\mathbf{a}$ and $\mathbf{b}$.

Hence the well-known cosine rule.

Example 3

Consider the angle θ between the two lines L_1 and L_2. Suppose that $\hat{\mathbf{u}}_1 = (l_1,m_1,n_1)$ is a unit vector along L_1 and $\hat{\mathbf{u}}_2 = (l_2,m_2,n_2)$ is a unit vector along L_2.

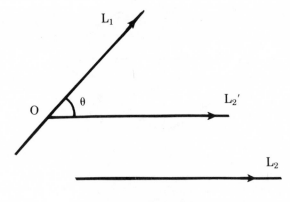

Fig. 6.12

As a first step, draw a line L_2' parallel to L_2 and cutting the line L_1 at O, as shown in Fig. 6.12. The angle between L_1 and L_2 is defined to be the same as that between L_1 and L_2'. The unit vectors along L_2 and L_2' are the same since the two lines are parallel.

Note that this construction is necessary since, in general, the original two lines L_1 and L_2 may not intersect.

Now with the angle θ defined as above,

$$\cos\theta = \hat{\mathbf{u}}_1 \cdot \hat{\mathbf{u}}_2$$

$$= (l_1, m_1, n_1) \cdot (l_2, m_2, n_2)$$

$$= l_1 l_2 + m_1 m_2 + n_1 n_2 \ .$$

A special case of this result occurs when

$$\hat{\mathbf{u}}_1 = \hat{\mathbf{u}}_2 = \hat{\mathbf{u}} \ .$$

In this case

$$\hat{\mathbf{u}}^2 = \hat{\mathbf{u}} \cdot \hat{\mathbf{u}} = l^2 + m^2 + n^2 = 1 \ .$$

Example 4

To find the distance between two points.

Consider the two points P_1 and P_2 with position vectors

$$\mathbf{r}_1 = (x_1, y_1, z_1) \ , \quad \mathbf{r}_2 = (x_2, y_2, z_2)$$

Now
$$\overrightarrow{P_1 P_2} = \overrightarrow{OP_2} - \overrightarrow{OP_1}$$

$$= \mathbf{r}_2 - \mathbf{r}_1$$

$$= (x_2 - x_1, \ y_2 - y_1, \ z_2 - z_1) \ .$$

The square of the distance between the two points is given by

$$(P_1 P_2)^2 = (\mathbf{r}_2 - \mathbf{r}_1)^2 = (x_2 - x_1)^2 + (y_2 - y_1)^2 + (z_2 - z_1)^2 \ .$$

If P is the point with position vector

$$\mathbf{r} = (x, y, z)$$

a special case of the above result is

$$(OP)^2 = \mathbf{r}^2 = x^2 + y^2 + z^2 \ .$$

Example 5

To find the equation of a straight line.

The precise form of the equation of a straight line depends on the information given. Consequently, in this example, several cases will be examined—cases differing in the way in which the line is specified.

(i) Suppose the line is specified in terms of one point on it, together with its direction.

Let the point on the line be A, having position vector $\mathbf{a}$, and suppose $\hat{\mathbf{u}}$ is a unit vector along the direction of the line. Also suppose that P is a typical point on the line, having position vector **r**, such that the distance AP equals s. The situation is as pictured in Fig. 6.13

Since **û** is a unit vector along the direction of the line

$$\overrightarrow{AP} = s\hat{u}$$

and so
$$\overrightarrow{OP} = \overrightarrow{OA} + \overrightarrow{AP}$$

may be written

$$\mathbf{r} = \mathbf{a} + s\hat{u}$$

which is the required equation of the line.

(ii) Suppose the line is specified in terms of one point on it and some vector **v** (not necessarily a unit vector) along the direction of the line.

Let the given point be A once more and suppose **û** is a unit vector along the direction of the line, then

$$\mathbf{v} = k\hat{u} \qquad \text{where } k \neq 1 .$$

From (i), the equation of the line is

$$\mathbf{r} = \mathbf{a} + s\hat{u} = \mathbf{a} + t\mathbf{v}$$

where $t = s/k$.

(iii) Suppose the line is specified in terms of two points on it.

Let the two points be A and B, having position vectors **a** and **b** respectively. Then

$$\overrightarrow{AB} = \overrightarrow{OB} - \overrightarrow{OA} = \mathbf{b} - \mathbf{a} .$$

But $\overrightarrow{AB}$ is a vector along the direction of the line and so, by (ii), the equation of the line is

$$\mathbf{r} = \mathbf{a} + t(\mathbf{b} - \mathbf{a}) = (1 - t)\mathbf{a} + t\mathbf{b} .$$

(iv) Suppose the line is specified again by two points A and B on it as in (iii) but suppose also that P is the point having position vector **r** and dividing AB in the ratio $\lambda : \mu$.

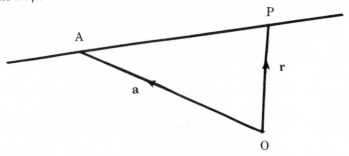

Fig. 6.13

In this case,

$$AP : PB = \lambda : \mu$$

and so

$$\mu AP - \lambda PB = 0 \ .$$

However, AP and PB are in the same direction and so

$$\mu \overrightarrow{AP} - \lambda \overrightarrow{PB} = 0$$

that is,

$$\mu(\mathbf{r} - \mathbf{a}) - \lambda(\mathbf{b} - \mathbf{r}) = 0 \ .$$

Thus

$$\mathbf{r} = \frac{\mu \mathbf{a} + \lambda \mathbf{b}}{\mu + \lambda} = (1 - t)\mathbf{a} + t\mathbf{b}$$

where $t = \lambda/(\mu + \lambda)$.

Example 6

To find the equation of a plane.

Suppose the position is as illustrated in Fig. 6.14. Let ON be the perpendicular distance of the point O from the given plane. Also, suppose that $\hat{\mathbf{u}}$ is the unit vector in the direction $\overrightarrow{ON}$ and that the distance ON equals p.

If P is any point in the plane, ON and NP will be perpendicular to one another. Therefore ON, which equals p, is the component of $\overrightarrow{OP}$ along $\overrightarrow{ON}$, and so

$$ON = OP \cos\theta$$

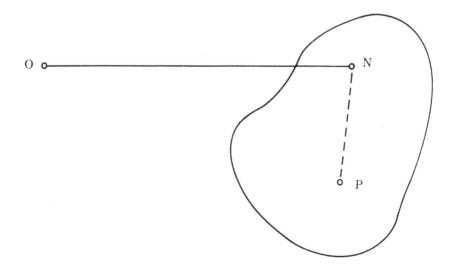

Fig. 6.14

where $\theta = \angle PON$.

In other words

$$p = \mathbf{r} \cdot \hat{\mathbf{u}}$$

if $\overrightarrow{OP} = \mathbf{r}$.

This is the vector equation of the plane.

Example 7

To find the equation of a sphere.

Suppose the sphere is of radius R and has its centre at the point A which has position vector $\mathbf{a}$. If P is some point on the sphere having position vector $\mathbf{r}$, the magnitude of $\overrightarrow{AP}$ equals R and so

$$(\overrightarrow{AP})^2 = R^2$$

But $$\overrightarrow{AP} = \overrightarrow{OP} - \overrightarrow{OA} = \mathbf{r} - \mathbf{a}$$

and so, the required equation is

$$(\mathbf{r} - \mathbf{a})^2 = R^2 \, .$$

It might be noted that if

$$\mathbf{r} = (x, y, z) \quad \text{and} \quad \mathbf{a} = (a, b, c)$$

the equation may be written

$$(x - a)^2 + (y - b)^2 + (z - c)^2 = R^2 \, .$$

The derivation of these various equations by vector methods is an illuminating exercise in its own right, but the vector equations may be used further to examine geometrical problems. This will be illustrated by considering the problem of proving that the medians of a triangle are concurrent.

Consider the triangle ABC as shown in Fig. 6.15 and suppose its vertices have position vectors $\mathbf{a}$, $\mathbf{b}$ and $\mathbf{c}$ respectively. Also suppose the mid-point of the sides are D, E and F as shown.

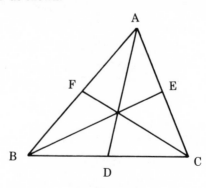

Fig. 6.15

If the point D has position vector **d**,

$$\mathbf{d} = \tfrac{1}{2}(\mathbf{b} + \mathbf{c}).$$

The equation of AD is

$$\mathbf{r} = t\mathbf{a} + (1 - t)\mathbf{d} = t\mathbf{a} + \tfrac{1}{2}(1 - t)(\mathbf{b} + \mathbf{c}).$$

In this equation, the coefficients of **a**, **b** and **c** are equal when $t = \tfrac{1}{2}(1 - t)$
and, at this point, $\mathbf{r} = \tfrac{1}{3}(\mathbf{a} + \mathbf{b} + \mathbf{c})$.
This point lies on AD and, by symmetry, it lies on the other medians. Therefore, the medians of a triangle are concurrent.

Before leaving the subject of scalar products temporarily, there is one
further important result to be considered. This is the result that any vector
may be resolved into two components, one along a given direction, the other
perpendicular to it.

To prove this, suppose $\overrightarrow{OA}$ = **a** is the vector in question and L is some line
through O. Complete the rectangle ONAM as shown in Fig. 6.16.

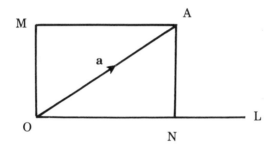

Fig. 6.16

Now
$$\mathbf{a} = \overrightarrow{OA} = \overrightarrow{ON} + \overrightarrow{NA}$$
$$= \overrightarrow{ON} + \overrightarrow{OM}$$
$$= \mathbf{a}_{\parallel} + \mathbf{a}_{\perp}.$$

where
$$\mathbf{a}_{\parallel} = \overrightarrow{ON} = \text{a vector along the direction of L.}$$
$$\mathbf{a}_{\perp} = \overrightarrow{OM} \quad \text{a vector perpendicular to the direction of L.}$$

Hence, the required result.

It might be noted that, if **û** is a unit vector in the direction of L,

$$ON = \overrightarrow{OA} \cdot \mathbf{\hat{u}} = \mathbf{a} \cdot \mathbf{\hat{u}}$$

and so
$$\overrightarrow{ON} = (\mathbf{a} \cdot \mathbf{\hat{u}})\mathbf{\hat{u}}.$$

Rotations

Consider the rotation of an area A about a line L, where the line L is perpendicular to the area A. One vectorial direction perpendicular to the plane may be associated with a clockwise rotation, and the opposite direction with an anticlockwise rotation. The convention used is to associate the sense of rotation with the direction perpendicular to the plane that corresponds to a right-handed screw motion.

Therefore, for a right-handed set of axes $Oxyz$, rotation of Oy to Oz in the plane $x = 0$ corresponds to a vector along Ox; rotation from Oz to Ox corresponds to a vector along Oy and a rotation from Ox to Oy corresponds to a vector along Oz.

6.6.2 Vector Products

If **a** and **b** are represented by the directed line segments $\overrightarrow{OA}$ and $\overrightarrow{OB}$ respectively, then

$$\mathbf{a} \times \mathbf{b} = ab\sin\theta\hat{\mathbf{n}}$$

$$= \text{OA OB } \sin\theta\hat{\mathbf{n}}$$

where $\hat{\mathbf{n}}$ is a unit vector perpendicular to the plane OAB and corresponding to a rotation from OA to OB (see Fig. 6.17).

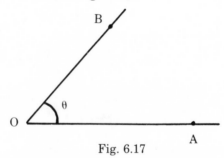

Fig. 6.17

It might be noted that the area of the triangle OAB is given by

$$\Delta\text{OAB} = \tfrac{1}{2}\text{OA OB }\sin\theta = \tfrac{1}{2}|\mathbf{a} \times \mathbf{b}|$$

that is

$$\tfrac{1}{2}(\mathbf{a} \times \mathbf{b}) = (\Delta\text{OAB})\hat{\mathbf{n}} = \text{vector area of the triangle.}$$

It is important to note the following points concerning vector products which follow immediately from this definition:

(a) by definition, the vector product is indeed a vector!

(b) $\mathbf{a} \times \mathbf{b} = \mathbf{0}$ if $a = 0$ or $b = 0$ or $\sin\theta = 0$ that is, if $\mathbf{a} = \mathbf{0}$ or $\mathbf{b} = \mathbf{0}$ or $\theta = 0$ or π.

$\mathbf{a} \times \mathbf{b} = \mathbf{0}$ if $\mathbf{a} = \mathbf{0}$ or $\mathbf{b} = \mathbf{0}$ or if $\mathbf{a}$ and $\mathbf{b}$ are either parallel or anti-parallel to one another.

(c) $\mathbf{a} \times \mathbf{b} = ab\sin\theta\hat{\mathbf{n}}$

and so

$$\mathbf{b} \times \mathbf{a} = ba\sin(2\pi - \theta)\hat{\mathbf{n}}$$

$$= -ab\sin\theta \, \hat{\mathbf{n}} = -\mathbf{a} \times \mathbf{b}.$$

The vector product is *not* commutative; it obeys an anti-commutative law.

Before proceeding further, two important theorems concerning vector products will be proved:

Theorem

If $\mathbf{b}'$ is the component of $\mathbf{b}$ perpendicular to $\mathbf{a}$ then

$$\mathbf{a} \times \mathbf{b} = \mathbf{a} \times \mathbf{b}'.$$

Proof

Suppose the situation is as shown in Fig. 6.18, with the directed line segments $\overrightarrow{OA}$ and $\overrightarrow{OB}$ representing the vectors $\mathbf{a}$ and $\mathbf{b}$ respectively. Then $\mathbf{b}'$ is represented by the directed line segment $\overrightarrow{OD}$

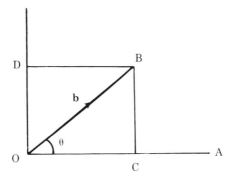

Fig. 6.18

Now $\mathbf{a} \times \mathbf{b} = OA \, OB \sin\theta \, \hat{\mathbf{n}}$

and $\mathbf{a} \times \mathbf{b}' = OA \, OD \sin \pi/2 \, \hat{\mathbf{n}}$

                                 $= OA \, OD \, \hat{\mathbf{n}}$

But $OD = OB \sin\theta$

and so $\mathbf{a} \times \mathbf{b}' = OA \, OB \sin\theta \, \hat{\mathbf{n}}$

                                 $= \mathbf{a} \times \mathbf{b}$

Theorem

$$\mathbf{a} \times (\mathbf{b} + \mathbf{c}) = \mathbf{a} \times \mathbf{b} + \mathbf{a} \times \mathbf{c}.$$

Proof

Let **b′**, **c′** and (**b′** + **c′**) be the components of **b**, **c** and (**b** + **c**) respectively which are perpendicular to **a**. Then,

$$\mathbf{a} \times \mathbf{b} = \mathbf{a} \times \mathbf{b}'$$

$$\mathbf{a} \times \mathbf{c} = \mathbf{a} \times \mathbf{c}'$$

$$\mathbf{a} \times (\mathbf{b} + \mathbf{c}) = \mathbf{a} \times (\mathbf{b}' + \mathbf{c}')$$

and it is sufficient to show that

$$\mathbf{a} \times (\mathbf{b}' + \mathbf{c}') = \mathbf{a} \times \mathbf{b}' + \mathbf{a} \times \mathbf{c}' .$$

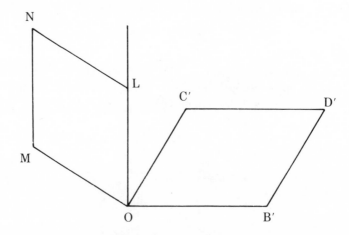

Fig. 6.19

Suppose **b′**, **c′** and (**b′** + **c′**) are represented by $\overrightarrow{OB}'$ $\overrightarrow{OC}'$ and $\overrightarrow{OD}'$ respectively. Then, the parallelogram OB′D′C′ is in the plane perpendicular to **a**.

Now, **a** × **b′** is a vector of magnitude aOB′ in a direction perpendicular to both **a** and **b′**. Since perpendicular to **a** it must lie in the plane of parallelogram OB′D′C′. Therefore, its direction is perpendicular to OB′ in that plane.

Hence **a** × **b′** may be represented by $\overrightarrow{OL}$ where

$$OL = a\text{OB}' \tag{i}$$

(see Fig. 6.19)

Similarly, **a** × **c′** may be represented by $\overrightarrow{OM}$, where OM is in the plane of the parallelogram OB′D′C′, is perpendicular to OC′, and

$$OM = a\text{OC}' . \tag{ii}$$

Now complete the parallelogram OLNM as shown in Fig. 6.19

$$\overrightarrow{ON} = \overrightarrow{OL} + \overrightarrow{OM}$$

$$= \mathbf{a} \times \mathbf{b}' + \mathbf{a} \times \mathbf{c}' \,.$$

Also, by (i) and (ii)

$$OB'/OC' = OL/OM$$

Parallelograms OB′D′C′ and OLNM are similar, therefore, and so

$$ON/OD' = OL/OB' = a$$

$$ON = aOD' \,.$$

Also, since the parallelograms are similar

$$\angle D'OB' = \angle NOL$$

and so $$\angle NOD' = \pi/2$$

Hence $$\overrightarrow{ON} = \mathbf{a} \times \overrightarrow{OD}' = \mathbf{a} \times (\mathbf{b}' + \mathbf{c}')$$

and $$\mathbf{a} \times (\mathbf{b} + \mathbf{c}) = \mathbf{a} \times \mathbf{b} + \mathbf{a} \times \mathbf{c}$$

as required.

Corollary

$$(\mathbf{a} + \mathbf{b}) \times \mathbf{c} = \mathbf{a} \times \mathbf{c} + \mathbf{b} \times \mathbf{c} \,.$$

Components of $\mathbf{a} \times \mathbf{b}$

From the definition of a vector product, it is seen that

$$\mathbf{i} \times \mathbf{i} = \mathbf{0} \,; \quad \mathbf{j} \times \mathbf{j} = \mathbf{0} \,; \quad \mathbf{k} \times \mathbf{k} = \mathbf{0} \,.$$

Also, $\mathbf{i} \times \mathbf{j}$ is a vector of unit magnitude whose direction is appropriate to a right-handed screw motion from Ox to Oy; that is, its direction is along Oz.

Therefore, $$\mathbf{i} \times \mathbf{j} = \mathbf{k} = -\mathbf{j} \times \mathbf{i} \,.$$

A similar argument shows that

$$\mathbf{j} \times \mathbf{k} = \mathbf{i} = -\mathbf{k} \times \mathbf{j}$$

and $$\mathbf{k} \times \mathbf{i} = \mathbf{j} = -\mathbf{i} \times \mathbf{k} \,.$$

Now consider the two vectors

$$\mathbf{a} = a_1\mathbf{i} + a_2\mathbf{j} + a_3\mathbf{k}$$

$$\mathbf{b} = b_1\mathbf{i} + b_2\mathbf{j} + b_3\mathbf{k} \,.$$

The vector product, $\mathbf{a} \times \mathbf{b}$, is given by

$$\mathbf{a} \times \mathbf{b} = \quad a_1b_2\mathbf{i} \times \mathbf{j} \quad + a_1b_3\mathbf{i} \times \mathbf{k}$$

$$+ a_2 b_1 \mathbf{j} \times \mathbf{i} + a_2 b_3 \mathbf{j} \times \mathbf{k}$$

$$+ a_3 b_1 \mathbf{k} \times \mathbf{i} + a_3 b_2 \mathbf{k} \times \mathbf{j}$$

$$= (a_2 b_3 - a_3 b_2)\mathbf{i} + (a_3 b_1 - a_1 b_3)\mathbf{j}$$

$$+ (a_1 b_2 - a_2 b_1)\mathbf{k}$$

$$= \begin{vmatrix} \mathbf{i} & \mathbf{j} & \mathbf{k} \\ a & a & a \\ b & b & b \end{vmatrix}.$$

Hence, an expression has been derived for $\mathbf{a} \times \mathbf{b}$ in terms of a 3×3 determinant, which involves the three unit vectors $\mathbf{i}$, $\mathbf{j}$ and $\mathbf{k}$ as well as the components of the two vectors, $\mathbf{a}$ and $\mathbf{b}$, referred to a right-handed set of Cartesian axes.

Geometrical application of vector products
Follow ideas introduced earlier, the area of a triangle ABC is given by

$$\tfrac{1}{2}|\overrightarrow{AB} \times \overrightarrow{AC}| = \tfrac{1}{2}|(\mathbf{b} - \mathbf{a}) \times (\mathbf{c} - \mathbf{a})|$$

$$= \tfrac{1}{2}|\mathbf{b} \times \mathbf{c} + \mathbf{c} \times \mathbf{a} + \mathbf{a} \times \mathbf{b}|.$$

Example

If A, B, C are the points (1,2,3), (1,1,1) and (0,2,2) respectively, find the area of triangle ABC.

Now,
$$\mathbf{a} \times \mathbf{b} = \mathbf{i} \begin{vmatrix} 2 & 3 \\ 1 & 1 \end{vmatrix} - \mathbf{j} \begin{vmatrix} 1 & 3 \\ 1 & 1 \end{vmatrix} + \mathbf{k} \begin{vmatrix} 1 & 2 \\ 1 & 1 \end{vmatrix}$$

$$= -\mathbf{i} + 2\mathbf{j} - \mathbf{k}.$$

Also,
$$\mathbf{b} \times \mathbf{c} = \quad -2\mathbf{j} + 2\mathbf{k}$$

$$\mathbf{c} \times \mathbf{a} = 2\mathbf{i} + 2\mathbf{j} - 2\mathbf{k}.$$

The area of the triangle ABC

$$= \tfrac{1}{2}|\mathbf{i} + 2\mathbf{j} - \mathbf{k}|$$

$$= \tfrac{1}{2}\{1^2 + 2^2 + (-1)^2\}^{1/2}$$

$$= \tfrac{1}{2}\sqrt{6}$$

where the fact that

$$a = |\mathbf{a}| = (\mathbf{a \cdot a})^{1/2} = (a_1^2 + a_2^2 + a_3^2)^{1/2}$$

has been used.

The triple scalar product

The triple scalar product of three vectors **a**, **b**, **c** is $(\mathbf{a} \times \mathbf{b})\cdot\mathbf{c}$ and is sometimes written (**a**, **b**, **c**).

As before,

$$\mathbf{a} \times \mathbf{b} = \begin{vmatrix} a_2 & a_3 \\ b_2 & b_3 \end{vmatrix} \mathbf{i} - \begin{vmatrix} a_1 & a_3 \\ b_1 & b_3 \end{vmatrix} \mathbf{j} + \begin{vmatrix} a_1 & a_2 \\ b_1 & b_2 \end{vmatrix} \mathbf{k} \, .$$

Then, if

$$\mathbf{c} = c_1\mathbf{i} + c_2\mathbf{j} + c_3\mathbf{k}$$

$$(\mathbf{a} \times \mathbf{b})\cdot\mathbf{c} = \begin{vmatrix} a_2 & a_3 \\ b_2 & b_3 \end{vmatrix} c_1 - \begin{vmatrix} a_1 & a_3 \\ b_1 & b_3 \end{vmatrix} c_2 + \begin{vmatrix} a_1 & a_2 \\ b_1 & b_2 \end{vmatrix} c_3$$

$$= \begin{vmatrix} c_1 & c_2 & c_3 \\ a_1 & a_2 & a_3 \\ b_1 & b_2 & b_3 \end{vmatrix}$$

$$= \begin{vmatrix} a_1 & a_2 & a_3 \\ b_1 & b_2 & b_3 \\ c_1 & c_2 & c_3 \end{vmatrix} \, .$$

Similarly,

$$(\mathbf{b} \times \mathbf{c})\cdot\mathbf{a} = \begin{vmatrix} a_1 & a_2 & a_3 \\ b_1 & b_2 & b_3 \\ c_1 & c_2 & c_3 \end{vmatrix}$$

$$= (\mathbf{a} \times \mathbf{b})\cdot\mathbf{c} = (\mathbf{c} \times \mathbf{a})\cdot\mathbf{b} \, .$$

Also, owing to the properties of scalar and vector products,

$$\mathbf{a}\cdot(\mathbf{b} \times \mathbf{c}) = (\mathbf{b} \times \mathbf{c})\cdot\mathbf{a}$$

and

$$(\mathbf{b} \times \mathbf{a})\cdot\mathbf{c} = -(\mathbf{a} \times \mathbf{b})\cdot\mathbf{c} \, .$$

Hence,

$$(\mathbf{a},\mathbf{b},\mathbf{c}) = (\mathbf{b},\mathbf{c},\mathbf{a})$$

$$= (\mathbf{c},\mathbf{a},\mathbf{b}) = -(\mathbf{b},\mathbf{a},\mathbf{c}) \, .$$

Geometrical interpretation of the triple scalar product

First draw OL through O and perpendicular to the plane OAB, as shown in Fig.6.20. Next draw CN so that CN is perpendicular to OL. Now,

$$\mathbf{a} \times \mathbf{b} = 2(\Delta OAB)\hat{\mathbf{n}}$$

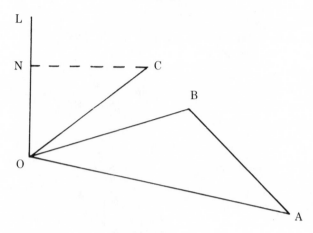

Fig. 6.20

where $\hat{\mathbf{n}}$ is the unit vector perpendicular to the plane OAB, and so

$$(\mathbf{a} \times \mathbf{b}) \cdot \mathbf{c} = 2(\Delta OAB)(\mathbf{c} \cdot \hat{\mathbf{n}}) .$$

But
$$\mathbf{c} \cdot \hat{\mathbf{n}} = \overrightarrow{OC} \cdot \hat{\mathbf{n}} = \pm ON$$

and so
$$(\mathbf{a} \times \mathbf{b}) \cdot \mathbf{c} = \pm 6 \left(\tfrac{1}{3} ON \cdot \Delta OAB\right)$$

$$= \pm 6 \text{ (volume of tetrahedron OABC).}$$

Volume of tetrahedron in general

In general, the volume of the tetrahedron ABCD is seen to be

$$\pm \tfrac{1}{6}(\overrightarrow{DA}, \overrightarrow{DB}, \overrightarrow{DC}) = \pm \tfrac{1}{6}(\mathbf{a} - \mathbf{d}, \ \mathbf{b} - \mathbf{d}, \ \mathbf{c} - \mathbf{d})$$

$$= \pm \tfrac{1}{6}\{(\mathbf{a} - \mathbf{d}) \times (\mathbf{b} - \mathbf{d})\} \cdot (\mathbf{c} - \mathbf{d})$$

$$= \pm \tfrac{1}{6}\{(\mathbf{a},\mathbf{b},\mathbf{c}) + (\mathbf{b},\mathbf{a},\mathbf{d}) + (\mathbf{d},\mathbf{a},\mathbf{c}) + (\mathbf{b},\mathbf{d},\mathbf{c})\} .$$

Here it has been assumed that A,B,C,D are the points with position vectors $\mathbf{a},\mathbf{b},\mathbf{c},\mathbf{d}$ respectively. Also, it is seen that

$$(\mathbf{d},\mathbf{a},\mathbf{d}) = (\mathbf{d},\mathbf{d},\mathbf{a}) = (\mathbf{d} \times \mathbf{d}) \cdot \mathbf{a} = 0$$

and similarly
$$(\mathbf{b},\mathbf{d},\mathbf{d}) = 0 .$$

Example

Find the volume of the tetrahedron whose vertices are (1,1,1), (1,3,4), (0,1,2) and (3,0,1).

Suppose $\mathbf{a}, \mathbf{b}, \mathbf{c}, \mathbf{d}$ are (1,1,1), (1,3,4), (0,1,2) and (3,0,1) respectively. Then

$$\overrightarrow{DA} = (-2,1,0)$$

$$\overrightarrow{DB} = (-2,3,3)$$

$$\overrightarrow{DC} = (-3,1,1) \ .$$

Therefore $\overrightarrow{DA} \times \overrightarrow{DB} = (3,6,-4)$

$$(\overrightarrow{DA} \times \overrightarrow{DB}) \cdot \overrightarrow{DC} = 3 \cdot (-3) + 6.1 + (-4) \cdot 1 = -7 \ .$$

The required volume $= \pm \frac{1}{6} (\overrightarrow{DA} \times \overrightarrow{DB}) \cdot \overrightarrow{DC}$

$$= \pm \frac{1}{6} (-7) = 7/6 \ .$$

6.7 LINEAR DEPENDENCE

The concept of linear dependence of a set of vectors, which is of such fundamental importance, will be introduced through the following theorem:

Theorem

If **a**, **b**, **c** are represented by $\overrightarrow{OA}, \overrightarrow{OB}, \overrightarrow{OC}$ respectively and if the points O,A,B,C lie in a plane, then there exist λ, μ, ν, not all zero, such that

$$\lambda \mathbf{a} + \mu \mathbf{b} + \nu \mathbf{c} = \mathbf{0} \ .$$

In this case, the vectors **a**, **b**, **c** are said to be **linearly dependent** on one another.

Proof

Case (1): suppose $\mathbf{a} \times \mathbf{b} = \mathbf{0}$.

In this case, there exist λ, μ not both zero, for which

$$\lambda \mathbf{a} + \mu \mathbf{b} = \mathbf{0}$$

since

if $\lambda \neq 0$, $\mu = 0$ then $\mathbf{a} = \mathbf{0}$,

if $\lambda = 0$, $\mu \neq 0$ then $\mathbf{b} = \mathbf{0}$,

if λ, μ are both non-zero, then

$$\mathbf{a} = -\frac{\mu}{\lambda} \mathbf{b} = k\mathbf{b}$$

which implies that **a** is either parallel ($k > 0$) or anti-parallel ($k < 0$) to **b**. These are the three circumstances under which $\mathbf{a} \times \mathbf{b}$ is zero.

Hence, case (1) covers the situation where the ν equals zero.

Case (2): $\mathbf{a} \times \mathbf{b} \neq \mathbf{0}$.

In this case, OA and OB are both non-zero and do not coincide with one another. Now suppose OA and OB are as shown in Fig. 6.21 and construct CA′ and CB′ parallel to OB and OA respectively to intersect OA and OB at A′ and B′. This construction is possible since the points O,A,B,C all lie in a plane.

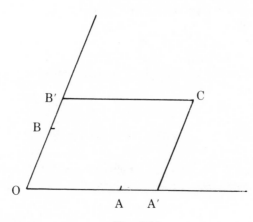

Fig. 6.21

Now $\overrightarrow{OA}' = \alpha\overrightarrow{OA}$, $\overrightarrow{OB}' = \beta\overrightarrow{OB}$.

Therefore $\overrightarrow{OC} = \overrightarrow{OA}' + \overrightarrow{OB}' = \alpha\overrightarrow{OA} + \beta\overrightarrow{OB}$

that is $\mathbf{c} = \alpha\mathbf{a} + \beta\mathbf{b}$

or in other words, the vectors **a**, **b**, **c** are linearly dependent.

    Case (2) covers the situation where λ, μ, ν are all non-zero.

Corollary

If **a**, **b**, **c** are linearly dependent, then O,A,B,C are coplanar.

Proof

Since the vectors **a**, **b**, **c** are linearly dependent

$$\lambda\mathbf{a} + \mu\mathbf{b} + \nu\mathbf{c} = \mathbf{0}$$

with λ, μ, ν not all zero.

Suppose $\nu \neq 0$, then

$$\mathbf{c} = -\frac{\lambda}{\nu}\mathbf{a} - \frac{\mu}{\nu}\mathbf{b} = \alpha\mathbf{a} + \beta\mathbf{b}$$

and the diagram (see Fig. 6.21) may be drawn as before with C in the plane of O,A,B.

Theorem

If $\overrightarrow{OA}$, $\overrightarrow{OB}$, $\overrightarrow{OC}$ are coplanar, that is if they are linearly dependent, then their triple scalar product is zero.

Proof

As usual suppose $\overrightarrow{OA}$, $\overrightarrow{OB}$, $\overrightarrow{OC}$ represent **a**, **b**, **c** then

$$\text{Volume of tetrahedron OABC} = \pm\tfrac{1}{6}(\mathbf{a}, \mathbf{b}, \mathbf{c}).$$

If $\overrightarrow{OA}$, $\overrightarrow{OB}$, $\overrightarrow{OC}$ are coplanar, this volume is zero.

   Hence required result.

   An alternative proof of this theorem, which does not depend on the idea of the volume of a tetrahedron, is as follows:

Since the three given vectors are linearly dependent then there exist λ,μ,ν not all zero, such that

$$\lambda\mathbf{a} + \mu\mathbf{b} + \nu\mathbf{c} = \mathbf{0} .$$

Suppose $\lambda \neq 0$ and multiply scalarly throughout by $\mathbf{b} \times \mathbf{c}$ then

$$\lambda(\mathbf{a}, \mathbf{b}, \mathbf{c}) + \mu(\mathbf{b}, \mathbf{b}, \mathbf{c}) + \nu(\mathbf{c}, \mathbf{b}, \mathbf{c}) = 0 .$$

The second and third terms are zero and so

$$(\mathbf{a}, \mathbf{b}, \mathbf{c}) = 0 \quad \text{since } \lambda \neq 0 .$$

Converse

If $(\mathbf{a}, \mathbf{b}, \mathbf{c}) = 0$, then $\mathbf{a}, \mathbf{b}, \mathbf{c}$ are linearly dependent.

Proof

Volume of tetrahedron OABC $= \pm \frac{1}{6} (\mathbf{a}, \mathbf{b}, \mathbf{c})$

This volume equals zero if $(\mathbf{a}, \mathbf{b}, \mathbf{c})$ equals zero.

   Hence required result.

Applications of Geometry

(1) The condition that two lines intersect.

Suppose the lines are

$$\mathbf{r} = \mathbf{a}_1 + t_1\mathbf{d}_1 , \quad \mathbf{r} = \mathbf{a}_2 + t_2\mathbf{d}_2 .$$

These lines intersect if there exist values of t_1 and t_2 for which

$$\mathbf{a}_1 + t_1\mathbf{d}_1 = \mathbf{a}_2 + t_2\mathbf{d}_2$$

$$(\mathbf{a}_1 - \mathbf{a}_2) + t_1\mathbf{d}_1 - t_2\mathbf{d}_2 = \mathbf{0} ,$$

that is, if the vectors

$$(\mathbf{a}_1 - \mathbf{a}_2) , \quad \mathbf{d}_1 , \quad \mathbf{d}_2$$

are linearly dependent.

   The required condition is

$$(\mathbf{a}_1 - \mathbf{a}_2 , \quad \mathbf{d}_1 , \quad \mathbf{d}_2) = 0 .$$

(2) Equation of the plane through the points, A,B,C.

Suppose A,B,C are the points with position vectors $\mathbf{a}, \mathbf{b}, \mathbf{c}$ respectively. If the point P, with position vector $\mathbf{r}$, also lies in the plane, then AP, BP, CP are coplanar.

Hence $\overrightarrow{AP}$, $\overrightarrow{BP}$, $\overrightarrow{CP}$ are linearly dependent.

Therefore, $\mathbf{r} - \mathbf{a}, \mathbf{r} - \mathbf{b}, \mathbf{r} - \mathbf{c}$ are linearly dependent, and so $(\mathbf{r} - \mathbf{a}, \mathbf{r} - \mathbf{b}, \mathbf{r} - \mathbf{c}) = 0$.

6.8 RECIPROCAL VECTORS

Define the vectors $\mathbf{a}^*$, $\mathbf{b}^*$, $\mathbf{c}^*$ to be reciprocal, as a set, to the vectors $\mathbf{a}$, $\mathbf{b}$, $\mathbf{c}$ if

$$\mathbf{a}^* = \frac{\mathbf{b} \times \mathbf{c}}{(\mathbf{a}, \mathbf{b}, \mathbf{c})}, \quad \mathbf{b}^* = \frac{\mathbf{c} \times \mathbf{a}}{(\mathbf{a}, \mathbf{b}, \mathbf{c})}, \quad \mathbf{c}^* = \frac{\mathbf{a} \times \mathbf{b}}{(\mathbf{a}, \mathbf{b}, \mathbf{c})} .$$

Hence, by using the properties of the triple scalar product, it follows that

$$\mathbf{a}^* \cdot \mathbf{a} = \mathbf{b}^* \cdot \mathbf{b} = \mathbf{c}^* \cdot \mathbf{c} = 1$$

and

$$\mathbf{a}^* \cdot \mathbf{b} = \mathbf{a}^* \cdot \mathbf{c} = 0 , \quad \mathbf{b}^* \cdot \mathbf{a} = \mathbf{b}^* \cdot \mathbf{c} = 0$$

$$\mathbf{c}^* \cdot \mathbf{a} = \mathbf{c}^* \cdot \mathbf{b} = 0 .$$

It should be noted that there is *no* division of one vector by another; that is, $\mathbf{a}/\mathbf{b}$ is meaningless.

Referring to the important unit vectors $\mathbf{i}$, $\mathbf{j}$, $\mathbf{k}$ it is seen that

$$\mathbf{i}^* = \frac{\mathbf{j} \times \mathbf{k}}{(\mathbf{i}, \mathbf{j}, \mathbf{k})} = \frac{\mathbf{i}}{\mathbf{i} \cdot \mathbf{i}} = \mathbf{i} .$$

Similarly, $\mathbf{j} = \mathbf{j}^*$ and $\mathbf{k} = \mathbf{k}^*$.

The unit vectors $\mathbf{i}$, $\mathbf{j}$, $\mathbf{k}$ are their own reciprocal vectors.

Now that these definitions have been introduced, a position has been reached where several more important theorems may be proved.

Theorem I.

If OA, OB, OC are non-coplanar then any vector $\mathbf{r}$ may be resolved into the form $\mathbf{r} = \lambda\mathbf{a} + \mu\mathbf{b} + \nu\mathbf{c}$ where $\mathbf{a}$, $\mathbf{b}$, $\mathbf{c}$ are the vectors represented by $\overrightarrow{OA}$, $\overrightarrow{OB}$, $\overrightarrow{OC}$ respectively.

Proof

Suppose P is the point with position vector $\mathbf{r}$. Construct a parallelepiped, as shown in Fig. 6.22, with O diagonally opposite P and the points A,B,C on the edges OX, OY, OZ meeting at O.

Now $\mathbf{r} = \overrightarrow{OP} = \overrightarrow{OX} + \overrightarrow{XL} + \overrightarrow{LP}$

$$= \overrightarrow{OX} + \overrightarrow{OY} + \overrightarrow{OZ} .$$

But, for some scalar λ,

$$\overrightarrow{OX} = \lambda\mathbf{a} .$$

Also, for scalars μ and ν,

$$\overrightarrow{OY} = \mu\mathbf{b} , \quad \overrightarrow{OZ} = \nu\mathbf{c} .$$

Therefore, $\mathbf{r} = \lambda a + \mu\mathbf{b} + \nu\mathbf{c}$.   (i)

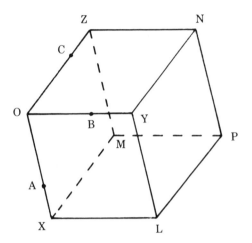

Fig. 6.22

Expressions may be found for λ, μ and ν as follows:
  Multiply equation (i) scalarly by $\mathbf{b} \times \mathbf{c}$ to give

$$\mathbf{r}\cdot(\mathbf{b} \times \mathbf{c}) = \lambda(\mathbf{a}, \mathbf{b}, \mathbf{c})$$

$$\lambda = \frac{\mathbf{r}\cdot(\mathbf{b} \times \mathbf{c})}{(\mathbf{a}, \mathbf{b}, \mathbf{c})} = \mathbf{r}\cdot\mathbf{a^*} \ .$$

Similarly, it may be shown that

$$\mu = \mathbf{r}\cdot\mathbf{b^*}, \quad \nu = \mathbf{r}\cdot\mathbf{c^*}$$

Corollary

$$\mathbf{r} = 0 \quad \text{if} \quad \mathbf{r}\cdot\mathbf{a^*} = \mathbf{r}\cdot\mathbf{b^*} = \mathbf{r}\cdot\mathbf{c^*} = 0 \ .$$

Theorem
Suppose $\mathbf{r}\cdot\mathbf{a} = \mathbf{r}\cdot\mathbf{b} = \mathbf{r}\cdot\mathbf{c} = 0$, then provided $(\mathbf{a},\mathbf{b},\mathbf{c}) \neq 0$, $\mathbf{r} = \mathbf{0}$.
Proof
If $\mathbf{r}\cdot\mathbf{b} = \mathbf{r}\cdot\mathbf{c} = 0$, either $\mathbf{r} = \mathbf{0}$ or $\mathbf{r}$ is perpendicular to both $\mathbf{b}$ and $\mathbf{c}$.
Either $\mathbf{r} = \mathbf{0}$ or $\mathbf{r}$ is in the direction of $\mathbf{b} \times \mathbf{c}$; that is

$$\mathbf{r} = k(\mathbf{b} \times \mathbf{c}) \ .$$

However,

$$\mathbf{r}\cdot\mathbf{a} = 0$$

also, and so $k(\mathbf{a},\mathbf{b},\mathbf{c}) = 0$
But, it is given that $(\mathbf{a},\mathbf{b},\mathbf{c}) \neq 0$,
and so k must equal zero.
  Hence $\mathbf{r} = \mathbf{0}$.

Theorem

If $\mathbf{r} \cdot \mathbf{a} = 0$, then $\mathbf{r} = \mathbf{F} \times \mathbf{a}$ for some $\mathbf{F}$.

Proof

Let $\overrightarrow{OP}$ and $\overrightarrow{OA}$ represent $\mathbf{r}$ and $\mathbf{a}$ respectively. Since $\mathbf{r} \cdot \mathbf{a} = 0$, P lies in the plane through O and perpendicular to OA. Draw the line OQ in this plane, as shown in Fig. 6.23, so that $\overrightarrow{OP}$, $\overrightarrow{OQ}$, $\overrightarrow{OA}$ form a right-handed set of orthogonal axes and suppose $\overrightarrow{OQ}$ to be a unit vector.

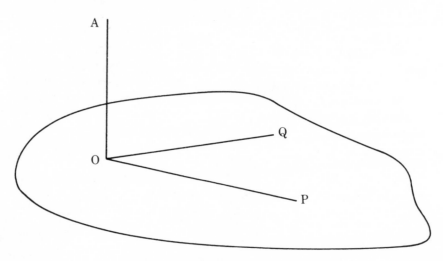

Fig. 6.23

Then,
$$\overrightarrow{OQ} \times \overrightarrow{OA} = \overrightarrow{OQ} \times \mathbf{a} = 1a \sin \pi/2 \,\hat{\mathbf{u}}$$

where $\hat{\mathbf{u}}$ is a unit vector along OP.

Therefore
$$\hat{\mathbf{u}} = \frac{1}{a} \overrightarrow{OQ} \times \mathbf{a}$$

and so
$$\mathbf{r} = r\hat{\mathbf{u}} = \frac{r}{a} \overrightarrow{OQ} \times \mathbf{a} = \mathbf{F} \times \mathbf{a}$$

where
$$\mathbf{F} = \frac{r}{a} \overrightarrow{OQ} \, .$$

It is important to realise, however, that this vector $\mathbf{F}$ is *not* unique. It may be shown that, for $\mathbf{F} \neq \mathbf{F}_1$,

$$\mathbf{r} = \mathbf{F}_1 \times \mathbf{a} \, .$$

Suppose
$$\mathbf{r} = \mathbf{F} \times \mathbf{a} = \mathbf{F}_1 \times \mathbf{a}$$

then
$$(\mathbf{F}_1 - \mathbf{F}) \times \mathbf{a} = 0$$

and so $$F_1 - F = \lambda a .$$

If F satisfies the original equation, so does $F + \lambda a$.

The result of theorem I (see page 182) is of tremendous importance since it implies that, once three linearly independent vectors are given, any other vector may be specified completely by the three scalar coefficients appearing in the expansion of that vector in terms of the three given vectors. The set of linearly independent vectors is called a **basis**, and the vectors themselves are **basis vectors**. The scalar coefficients are referred to as the components of the vector relative to the given basis.

One basis has been encountered already when discussing the relation between the vector and Cartesian descriptions. In that case, the basis vectors were i, j, k—the unit vectors in the x, y and z directions respectively. This is the natural set of basis vectors in three-dimensional Euclidean space and is composed of three mutually orthogonal unit vectors. Hence, it is an orthonormal basis. Such a basis is denoted sometimes by $\hat{O}_i$, where the index i may take the values 1,2,3 and

$$\hat{O}_1 = i , \quad \hat{O}_2 = j , \quad \hat{O}_3 = k .$$

Then, earlier results may be written in the form:

$$\hat{O}_1 \cdot \hat{O}_1 = \hat{O}_2 \cdot \hat{O}_2 = \hat{O}_3 \cdot \hat{O}_3 = 1$$

$$\hat{O}_1 \cdot \hat{O}_2 = \hat{O}_2 \cdot \hat{O}_3 = \hat{O}_3 \cdot \hat{O}_1 = 0$$

and

$$\hat{O}_1 \times \hat{O}_1 = \hat{O}_2 \times \hat{O}_2 = \hat{O}_3 \times \hat{O}_3 = 0$$

$$\hat{O}_1 \times \hat{O}_2 = \hat{O}_3 = - \hat{O}_2 \times \hat{O}_1$$

$$\hat{O}_2 \times \hat{O}_3 = \hat{O}_1 = - \hat{O}_3 \times \hat{O}_2$$

$$\hat{O}_3 \times \hat{O}_1 = \hat{O}_2 = - \hat{O}_1 \times \hat{O}_3 .$$

6.9 THE INDEX NOTATION

On some occasions it proves useful to denote the basis vectors by e_1, e_2, e_3 instead of a, b, c since they may be written as e_i where the index i may take the values 1,2,3. Relative to such a basis, the components of a vector r may be denoted by r_1, r_2, r_3 or alternatively by r_i where, once again i may take the values 1,2,3. Then

$$r = r_1 e_1 + r_2 e_2 + r_3 e_3 = \sum_{i=1}^{3} r_i e_i .$$

The following two conventions may be introduced:
(i) An index which appears only once in any term or product of terms may take the values 1, 2, and 3.

(ii) An index which is repeated in any term or product of terms is summed from 1 to 3.

This second convention is **Einstein's summation convention**.

In the index notation, single indices are called **free indices**, whereas repeated indices are referred to as **dummy indices** since they do not play an intrinsic role; for example $v_i e_i$ and $v_j e_j$ both represent the vector

$$\mathbf{v} = v_1 \mathbf{e}_1 + v_2 \mathbf{e}_2 + v_3 \mathbf{e}_3$$

since, in each case, the index is repeated and by the Einstein summation convention, that means that the index must be summed from 1 to 3.

According to the conventions, the components of a vector $\mathbf{r}$ are denoted by r_i without specifying the values taken by the index i, and the vector $\mathbf{r}$ is written explicitly as $\mathbf{r} = r_i \mathbf{e}_i$.

It is important to realise from the outset that the same letter must not be used for two different purposes. For example, the quantities

$$u_1(v_1 w_1 + v_2 w_2 + v_3 w_3), \quad u_2(v_1 w_1 + v_2 w_2 + v_3 w_3),$$

$$u_3(v_1 w_1 + v_2 w_2 + v_3 w_3)$$

may be written $u_1 v_i w_i, \quad u_2 v_i w_i, \quad u_3 v_i w_i$

or simply $u_j v_i w_i$.

However, the same letter must not be used for the free index on u as is used for the dummy index on v and w, since, according to the summation convention

$$u_i v_i w_i = u_1 v_1 w_1 + u_2 v_2 w_2 + u_3 v_3 w_3.$$

Normally, the summation convention applies to an index which appears *twice* only; usually a mistake is indicated if the same index appears more than twice.

A vector $\mathbf{v}$ is specified completely by its components relative to a given basis, and so it is usual to talk of the vector v_i and to specify a vector by three numbers as (v_1, v_2, v_3).

The Gram—Schmidt Orthonormalisation Process

This is a method for constructing an orthonormal basis from a general basis. Suppose $\mathbf{e}_i$ is some given general basis, then put

$$\mathbf{O}_1 = \mathbf{e}_1$$

$$\mathbf{O}_2 = \mathbf{e}_2 + \lambda \mathbf{O}_1$$

where λ is some scalar.

λ may be chosen so that $\mathbf{O}_1$ and $\mathbf{O}_2$ are perpendicular. The condition is

$$\mathbf{O}_2 \cdot \mathbf{O}_1 = 0$$

that is

$$\mathbf{e}_2 \cdot \mathbf{O}_1 + \lambda \mathbf{O}_1 \cdot \mathbf{O}_1 = 0$$

and so

$$\lambda = -\mathbf{e}_2 \cdot \mathbf{O}_1 / \mathbf{O}_1 \cdot \mathbf{O}_1 .$$

Now put

$$\mathbf{O}_3 = \mathbf{e}_3 + \mu \mathbf{O}_2 + \nu \mathbf{O}_1$$

where μ and ν are scalars which may be chosen so that $\mathbf{O}_3$ is perpendicular to both $\mathbf{O}_2$ and $\mathbf{O}_1$. The conditions are

$$\mathbf{O}_3 \cdot \mathbf{O}_2 = 0 , \quad \mathbf{O}_3 \cdot \mathbf{O}_1 = 0 \qquad \text{respectively.}$$

These conditions may be written

$$\mathbf{e}_3 \cdot \mathbf{O}_2 + \mu \mathbf{O}_2 \cdot \mathbf{O}_2 = 0$$

$$\mathbf{e}_3 \cdot \mathbf{O}_1 + \nu \mathbf{O}_1 \cdot \mathbf{O}_1 = 0$$

from which it follows that

$$\mu = - \mathbf{e}_3 \cdot \mathbf{O}_2 / \mathbf{O}_2 \cdot \mathbf{O}_2 , \quad \nu = - \mathbf{e}_3 \cdot \mathbf{O}_1 / \mathbf{O}_1 \cdot \mathbf{O}_1 .$$

Since the vectors $\mathbf{e}_i$ are linearly independent, the vectors $\mathbf{O}_i$ must be non-zero and linearly independent. The vectors $\hat{\mathbf{O}}_i$ defined by

$$\hat{\mathbf{O}}_i = \mathbf{O}_i / |\mathbf{O}_i|$$

then form an orthonormal basis.

The requirement that $\hat{\mathbf{O}}_3$ be perpendicular to both $\hat{\mathbf{O}}_1$ and $\hat{\mathbf{O}}_2$ does not determine the direction of $\hat{\mathbf{O}}_3$ uniquely. However, the orientation of $\hat{\mathbf{O}}_3$ relative to $\hat{\mathbf{O}}_1$ and $\hat{\mathbf{O}}_2$ may be fixed by the requirement that $\hat{\mathbf{O}}_3 = \hat{\mathbf{O}}_1 \times \hat{\mathbf{O}}_2$. With this added requirement, the orthonormal basis is right-handed.

The Kronecker Delta

This is defined by

$$\delta_{ij} = \begin{cases} 1 \text{ if } i = j \\ 0 \text{ if } i \neq j . \end{cases}$$

These indices are free indices, and so both range from 1 to 3. Therefore,

$$\delta_{11} = \delta_{22} = \delta_{33} = 1$$

$$\delta_{12} = \delta_{13} = \delta_{21} = 0$$

$$\delta_{31} = \delta_{23} = \delta_{32} = 0 .$$

It should be noted that δ_{ij} symmetric in its indices and so $\delta_{ij} = \delta_{ji}$. Also, according to the definition

$$\delta_{ij} = 1 \quad \text{if } i = j$$

but note that

$$\delta_{ii} \neq 1$$

since, owing to the summation convention

$$\delta_{ii} = \delta_{11} + \delta_{22} + \delta_{33} = 3 .$$

Frequently, the Kronecker delta may be manipulated as a 'substitution operator' which substitutes a free index for a dummy index. For example, consider

$$v_i \delta_{i1}$$

Since the index i is repeated

$$v_i \delta_{i1} = v_1 \delta_{11} + v_2 \delta_{21} + v_3 \delta_{31} = v_1 .$$

as $\delta_{21} = \delta_{31} = 0$
+ $\delta_{11} = 1$

More generally

$$v_i \delta_{ij} = v_j ,$$

and the Kronecker delta has the effect of substituting the free index j on v in place of the dummy index i.

The permutation symbol

This is defined by

$$\varepsilon_{ijk} = \begin{cases} +1 \text{ if } ijk \text{ is a cyclic permutation of 1 2 3,} \\ -1 \text{ if } ijk \text{ is any other permutation of 1 2 3,} \\ 0 \text{ otherwise.} \end{cases}$$

$(123123)\cdots$

The permutation symbol is zero when any two indices are equal; for example

$$\varepsilon_{112} = \varepsilon_{232} = \varepsilon_{133} = 0 .$$

Otherwise, it is non-zero with

$$\varepsilon_{123} = \varepsilon_{231} = \varepsilon_{312} = +1$$

and

$$\varepsilon_{132} = \varepsilon_{321} = \varepsilon_{213} = -1 .$$

Accordingly, ε_{ijk} is unchanged if its indices are permuted cyclically

$$\varepsilon_{ijk} = \varepsilon_{jki} = \varepsilon_{kij} ,$$

but changes sign if two if its indices are interchanged

$$\varepsilon_{ijk} = -\varepsilon_{jik} = -\varepsilon_{ikj} = -\varepsilon_{kji} .$$

Products of permutation symbols appear frequently in manipulations employing the index notation, and consequently the following theorem proves to be extremely useful:

Theorem

$$\varepsilon_{ijk} \, \varepsilon_{ilm} = \delta_{jl} \delta_{km} - \delta_{jm} \, \delta_{kl} .$$

Proof

This identity may be proved by inspection provided it is remembered that j, k, l, m are free indices and take the values 1, 2, 3.

Firstly consider the situation when l and m have the same value. Suppose $l = m = 1$. The left-hand side of the identity is then zero since $\varepsilon_{i11} = 0$. Also the right-hand side is zero since

$$\delta_{j1}\,\delta_{k1} - \delta_{j1}\,\delta_{k1} = 0 \ .$$

Now suppose l and m to have different values. Let $l = 1$ and $m = 2$. Then, the left-hand side of the identity is

$$\varepsilon_{ijk}\,\varepsilon_{i12} = \varepsilon_{1jk}\,\varepsilon_{112} + \varepsilon_{2jk}\,\varepsilon_{212} + \varepsilon_{3jk}\,\varepsilon_{312}$$

$$= \varepsilon_{3jk} = \begin{cases} +1 & \text{if } j = 1\,, k = 2 \\ -1 & \text{if } j = 2\,, k = 1 \\ 0 & \text{otherwise} \ . \end{cases}$$

Also, the right-hand side is

$$\delta_{j1}\delta_{k2} - \delta_{j2}\delta_{k1} = \begin{cases} +1 & \text{if } j = 1\,, \quad k = 2 \\ -1 & \text{if } j = 2\,, \quad k = 1 \\ 0 & \text{otherwise.} \end{cases}$$

This exhausts all the possibilities, and so the theorem is proved.

A second useful identity may be obtained from the above result by putting the indices j and l equal, then summing to give

$$\varepsilon_{ijk}\,\varepsilon_{ijm} = \delta_{jj}\,\delta_{km} - \delta_{jm}\,\delta_{kj} \qquad (\text{as } \delta_{jj} = 3$$

$$= 3\delta_{km} - \delta_{km} = 2\delta_{km} \ .$$

Now that the Kronecker delta and the permutation symbol have been introduced, the conditions satisfied by an orthonormal basis—as discussed earlier—may be written in the form

$$\hat{\mathbf{O}}_i \cdot \hat{\mathbf{O}}_j = \delta_{ij} \ ,$$

the orthonormality conditions, and

$$\hat{\mathbf{O}}_i \times \hat{\mathbf{O}}_j = \varepsilon_{ijk}\,\hat{\mathbf{O}}_k \ ,$$

the condition satisfied by a right-handed orthonormal basis.

Multiplying the last equation by ε_{ijm} gives

$$\varepsilon_{ijm}\,\hat{\mathbf{O}}_i \times \hat{\mathbf{O}}_j = \varepsilon_{ijm}\,\varepsilon_{ijk}\,\hat{\mathbf{O}}_k = 2\delta_{km}\hat{\mathbf{O}}_k = 2\hat{\mathbf{O}}_m \ .$$

The index notation as developed here may be used to formulate operations in terms of components relative to a given right-handed orthonormal basis $\hat{\mathbf{O}}_i$ in an extremely concise manner. Some typical vector forms, together with their corresponding component forms, are shown in the table.

Vector form	Component form
$\mathbf{v}$	v_i
$\mathbf{u} + \mathbf{v}$	$u_i + v_i$
$m\mathbf{v}$	$m v_i$
$\mathbf{u}\cdot\mathbf{v}$	$u_i v_i$
$\mathbf{u} \times \mathbf{v}$	$\varepsilon_{ijk}\, u_j\, v_k$
$\mathbf{u}\cdot(\mathbf{v} \times \mathbf{w})$	$\varepsilon_{ijk}\, u_i\, v_j\, w_k$

As an example of the derivation of the given component forms, consider $\mathbf{z} = \mathbf{u} + \mathbf{v}$.

Relative to the basis $\hat{\mathbf{O}}_i$,

$$z_i \hat{\mathbf{O}}_i = u_i \hat{\mathbf{O}}_i + v_i \hat{\mathbf{O}}_i \,,$$

that is,

$$(z_i - u_i - v_i)\hat{\mathbf{O}}_i = \mathbf{0}.$$

Since the vectors $\hat{\mathbf{O}}_i$ are linearly independent,

$$z_i = u_i + v_i \,.$$

This result may be stated as the component of the sum of two vectors is the sum of the components of the two vectors.

As a second example, consider

$$\mathbf{z} = \mathbf{u} \times \mathbf{v}$$

Relative to the basis $\hat{\mathbf{O}}_i$,

$$z_i \hat{\mathbf{O}}_i = (u_j\, \hat{\mathbf{O}}_j) \times (v_k\, \hat{\mathbf{O}}_k)$$

$$= u_j v_k\, \hat{\mathbf{O}}_j \times \hat{\mathbf{O}}_k$$

$$= u_j v_k\, \varepsilon_{jki}\, \hat{\mathbf{O}}_i \,.$$

Since the vectors $\hat{\mathbf{O}}_i$ are linearly independent,

$$z_i = u_j v_k\, \varepsilon_{jki} = \varepsilon_{ijk}\, u_j v_k \,,$$

where the properties of the permutation symbol have been used.

The component forms corresponding to the remaining vector forms, in the table may be found in a similar manner.

So far, three forms of products of vectors have been discussed:

(i) the scalar product $\mathbf{u}\cdot\mathbf{v}$, which is a *scalar*,
(ii) the vector product $\mathbf{u} \times \mathbf{v}$, which is a *vector*
(iii) the triple scalar product $\mathbf{u}\cdot(\mathbf{v} \times \mathbf{w})$, which is a *scalar*.

It remains to consider the triple vector product $\mathbf{u} \times (\mathbf{v} \times \mathbf{w})$, which is a *vector*, and the important identity associated with this product is proved most easily by using the index notation.

Theorem

$$\mathbf{u} \times (\mathbf{v} \times \mathbf{w}) = (\mathbf{u}\cdot\mathbf{w})\mathbf{v} - (\mathbf{u}\cdot\mathbf{v})\mathbf{w}$$

Proof

Consider the ith component of $\mathbf{u} \times (\mathbf{v} \times \mathbf{w})$ and let this ith component be represented by $[\mathbf{u} \times (\mathbf{v} \times \mathbf{w})]_i$, then

$$[\mathbf{u} \times (\mathbf{v} \times \mathbf{w})]_i = \varepsilon_{ijk}\, u_j\, (\mathbf{v} \times \mathbf{w})_k$$

$$= \varepsilon_{ijk}\, u_j\, \varepsilon_{klm}\, v_l\, w_m$$

$$= \varepsilon_{ijk}\, \varepsilon_{klm}\, u_j\, v_l\, w_m$$

$$= \varepsilon_{kij}\, \varepsilon_{klm}\, u_j\, v_l\, w_m$$

$$= (\delta_{il}\delta_{jm} - \delta_{im}\delta_{jl})u_j v_l w_m$$

$$= u_j v_i w_j - u_j v_j w_i$$

$$= (\mathbf{u}\cdot\mathbf{w})v_i - (\mathbf{u}\cdot\mathbf{v})w_i \ ,$$

and so, $$\mathbf{u} \times (\mathbf{v} \times \mathbf{w}) = (\mathbf{u}\cdot\mathbf{w})\mathbf{v} - (\mathbf{u}\cdot\mathbf{v})\mathbf{w} \ .$$

This identity, together with the alternative form

$$(\mathbf{u} \times \mathbf{v}) \times \mathbf{w} = (\mathbf{u}\cdot\mathbf{w})\mathbf{v} - (\mathbf{v}\cdot\mathbf{w})\mathbf{u}$$

occur fairly often and might usefully be known. However, one of the beauties of the index notation is that, once the technique of using it has been mastered and the user feels confident in its use, there is little point in committing identities, such as these, to memory since they may be derived very quickly when required.

To complete this discussion of the index notation, some further examples will be considered:

(1) If the components of the vectors $\mathbf{a}, \mathbf{b}, \mathbf{c}, \mathbf{d}$ relative to a right-handed orthonormal basis are a_i, b_i, c_i, d_i, simplify and identify

$$\varepsilon_{ijk}\, \varepsilon_{ilm}\, a_j b_l c_k d_m \ .$$

Now $$\varepsilon_{ijk}\, \varepsilon_{ilm}\, a_j b_l c_k d_m = (\delta_{jl}\delta_{km} - \delta_{jm}\delta_{kl})a_j b_l c_k d_m$$

$$= a_j b_j c_k d_k - a_j b_k c_k d_j$$

$$= (\mathbf{a}\cdot\mathbf{b})(\mathbf{c}\cdot\mathbf{d}) - (\mathbf{a}\cdot\mathbf{d})(\mathbf{b}\cdot\mathbf{c}) \ .$$

(2) Prove that

$$(\mathbf{a} \times \mathbf{b})\cdot(\mathbf{c} \times \mathbf{d}) = (\mathbf{a}\cdot\mathbf{c})(\mathbf{b}\cdot\mathbf{d}) - (\mathbf{b}\cdot\mathbf{c})(\mathbf{a}\cdot\mathbf{d})$$

Now $$(\mathbf{a} \times \mathbf{b})\cdot(\mathbf{c} \times \mathbf{d}) = [\mathbf{b} \times (\mathbf{c} \times \mathbf{d})]\cdot\mathbf{a}$$

$$= [(\mathbf{b}\cdot\mathbf{d})\mathbf{c} - (\mathbf{b}\cdot\mathbf{c})\mathbf{d}]\cdot\mathbf{a}$$

$$= (\mathbf{a}\cdot\mathbf{c})\,(\mathbf{b}\cdot\mathbf{d}) - (\mathbf{b}\cdot\mathbf{c})\,(\mathbf{a}\cdot\mathbf{d})$$

where the properties of triple scalar products together with the above theorem on triple vector products have been used.

6.10 DIFFERENTIATION OF VECTORS WITH RESPECT TO SCALARS

The fact that a vector varies, for example, from one point of a curve to another, or from one time to another, leads to a consideration of the rate of change of the vector at a point on a curve or at a particular time. Suppose a vector $\mathbf{v}$ is given as a function of a scalar parameter u by $\mathbf{v} \equiv \mathbf{v}(u)$.

Let $\mathbf{v}(u)$, $\mathbf{v}(u + \delta u)$ represent the vector functions corresponding to the values $u, u + \delta u$ of the independent variable parameter. Now, from an origin O, draw the two vectors $\overrightarrow{OP}$, $\overrightarrow{OP}'$ such that

$$\overrightarrow{OP} = \mathbf{v}(u) ; \quad \overrightarrow{OP}' = \mathbf{v}(u + \delta u) .$$

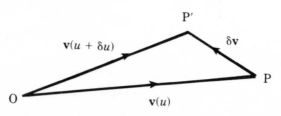

Fig. 6.24

These define a further vector $\overrightarrow{PP}'$ given by

$$\overrightarrow{PP}' = \overrightarrow{OP}' - \overrightarrow{OP} = \mathbf{v}(u + \delta u) - v(u)$$

and which represents the change of $\mathbf{v}$ as u changes to $u + \delta u$. Calling this change in the value of $\mathbf{v}$ the vector $\delta\mathbf{v}$, another vector parallel to $\overrightarrow{PP}'$ of magnitude $PP'/\delta u$ may be formed and represented by

$$\frac{\delta\mathbf{v}}{\delta u} = \frac{\mathbf{v}(u + \delta u) - \mathbf{v}(u)}{\delta u} .$$

This is the average rate of change of the vector $\mathbf{v}$ over the interval δu of the parameter u. Then, defining the limit of this ratio as $\delta u \to 0$, as for scalar rates of change, the vector

$$\frac{d\mathbf{v}}{du} = \lim_{\delta u \to 0} \frac{\delta\mathbf{v}}{\delta u} = \lim_{\delta u \to 0} \frac{\mathbf{v}(u + \delta u) - \mathbf{v}(u)}{\delta u}$$

is obtained. Provided the limit exists, this defines the instantaneous rate of change of the vector $\mathbf{v}$. This introduces the concept of the derivative of a vector with respect to a scalar.

Now consider a vector whose magnitude and direction depend upon several scalar variables.

Definition

If v_i are the Cartesian components of a vector, $\mathbf{v} = \mathbf{v}(r,s, \cdots)$ the partial derivatives of $\mathbf{v}$ are defined to be the vectors whose components are the partial derivatives of v_i.

If $\mathbf{v}$ and $\mathbf{w}$ are two vector functions of a scalar parameter u, and m is a scalar function of u, then

$$\frac{d}{du}(\mathbf{v} + \mathbf{w}) = \frac{d\mathbf{v}}{du} + \frac{d\mathbf{w}}{du} \qquad \text{(i)}$$

$$\frac{d}{du}(m\mathbf{v}) = \frac{dm}{du}\mathbf{v} + m\frac{d\mathbf{v}}{du} \qquad \text{(ii)}$$

$$\frac{d}{du}(\mathbf{v}\cdot\mathbf{w}) = \frac{d\mathbf{v}}{du}\cdot\mathbf{w} + \mathbf{v}\cdot\frac{d\mathbf{w}}{du} \qquad \text{(iii)}$$

$$\frac{d}{du}(\mathbf{v} \times \mathbf{w}) = \frac{d\mathbf{v}}{du}\times\mathbf{w} + \mathbf{v} \times \frac{d\mathbf{w}}{du} \qquad \text{(iv)}$$

These identities may be generalised if $\mathbf{v}$ and $\mathbf{w}$ are functions of more than one scalar parameter. In this case, (iii) and (iv) become

$$\frac{\partial}{\partial s}(\mathbf{v}\cdot\mathbf{w}) = \mathbf{v}\cdot\frac{\partial\mathbf{w}}{\partial s} + \frac{\partial\mathbf{v}}{\partial s}\cdot\mathbf{w}$$

$$\frac{\partial}{\partial s}(\mathbf{v} \times \mathbf{w}) = \mathbf{v} \times \frac{\partial\mathbf{w}}{\partial s} + \frac{\partial\mathbf{v}}{\partial s} \times \mathbf{w} \ .$$

The proof is quite straightforward. In terms of a (rectangular) Cartesian basis

$$\frac{\partial}{\partial s}(\mathbf{v}\cdot\mathbf{w}) = \frac{\partial}{\partial s}(v_i w_i) = v_i\frac{\partial w_i}{\partial s} + \frac{\partial v_i}{\partial s}w_i$$

$$= v_i\left(\frac{\partial\mathbf{w}}{\partial s}\right)_i + \left(\frac{\partial\mathbf{v}}{\partial s}\right)_i w_i = \mathbf{v}\cdot\frac{\partial\mathbf{w}}{\partial s} + \frac{\partial\mathbf{v}}{\partial s}\cdot\mathbf{w} \ .$$

Similarly, remembering that ε_{ijk} is a constant for all choices of indices,

$$\left[\frac{\partial}{\partial s}(\mathbf{v} \times \mathbf{w})\right]_i = \frac{\partial}{\partial s}(\mathbf{v} \times \mathbf{w})_i = \frac{\partial}{\partial s}(\varepsilon_{ijk}\, v_j\, w_k)$$

$$= \varepsilon_{ijk}\frac{\partial}{\partial s}(v_j\, w_k)$$

$$= \varepsilon_{ijk}\, v_j\, \frac{\partial w_k}{\partial s} + \varepsilon_{ijk}\, \frac{\partial v_j}{\partial s}\, w_k$$

$$= \varepsilon_{ijk}\, v_j\!\left(\frac{\partial \mathbf{w}}{\partial s}\right)_{\!k} + \varepsilon_{ijk}\!\left(\frac{\partial \mathbf{v}}{\partial s}\right)_{\!j} w_k$$

$$= \mathbf{v} \times \frac{\partial \mathbf{w}}{\partial s} + \frac{\partial \mathbf{v}}{\partial s} \times \mathbf{w}\,.$$

Suppose the position vector **r** of the point P is a function of a single variable λ,

$$\mathbf{r} \equiv \mathbf{r}(\lambda)\,.$$

The locus of P is a curve, λ being a parameter along the curve.

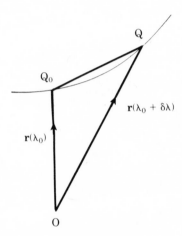

Fig. 6.25

Let Q_0 and Q be two neighbouring points on the curve. The position vector $\overrightarrow{Q_0 Q}$ of Q relative to Q_0 is

$$\mathbf{r}(\lambda_0 + \delta\lambda) - \mathbf{r}(\lambda_0)\,.$$

As Q approaches Q_0, the direction of $\overrightarrow{Q_0 Q}$ becomes the direction of the tangent to the curve at Q_0. As Q tends to Q_0, δλ tends to zero and so the direction of $\overrightarrow{Q_0 Q}$ tends to d**r**/dλ. Hence, d**r**/dλ is a tangent vector to the curve.

Now consider a moving particle. The particle describes a curve in time, and so it is natural to use time as the parameter along this path:

$$\mathbf{r} \equiv \mathbf{r}(t)$$

v = d**r**/dt is the velocity of the particle, and its direction is seen to be tangent to the path of the particle. The magnitude of the velocity is

$$v^2 = \frac{d\mathbf{r}}{dt} \cdot \frac{d\mathbf{r}}{dt} = \left(\frac{ds}{dt}\right)^2$$

where s is simply the scalar arc length. ds/dt is the speed.

Also, $\dfrac{d\mathbf{v}}{dt} = \dfrac{d^2\mathbf{r}}{dt^2}$ = rate of change of velocity = acceleration.

Sometimes these are written

$$\mathbf{v} = \dot{\mathbf{r}} = d\mathbf{r}/dt$$

$$\mathbf{a} = \ddot{\mathbf{r}} = d\mathbf{v}/dt = d^2\mathbf{r}/dt^2 .$$

Example

$$\mathbf{v} = \mathbf{i} + 2\lambda\mathbf{j} + 3\lambda^2\mathbf{k} , \quad \mathbf{w} = 3\lambda^2\mathbf{i} + 2\lambda\mathbf{j} + \mathbf{k}$$

Find $d(\mathbf{v}\cdot\mathbf{w})/d\lambda$.

(a) $\mathbf{v}\cdot\mathbf{w} = 3\lambda^2 + 4\lambda^2 + 3\lambda^2 = 10\lambda^2$

and so $\dfrac{d(\mathbf{v}\cdot\mathbf{w})}{d\lambda} = 20\lambda .$

(b) $\dfrac{d}{d\lambda}(\mathbf{v}\cdot\mathbf{w}) = \mathbf{v}\cdot\dfrac{d\mathbf{w}}{d\lambda} + \dfrac{d\mathbf{v}}{d\lambda}\cdot\mathbf{w}$

$$= (1, 2\lambda, 3\lambda^2)\cdot(6\lambda, 2, 0) + (0, 2, 6\lambda)\cdot(3\lambda^2, 2\lambda, 1)$$

$$= 6\lambda + 4\lambda + 4\lambda + 6\lambda = 20\lambda .$$

EXERCISES 6

(1) Verify that, for all vectors $\mathbf{a}$ and $\mathbf{b}$,

$$|\mathbf{a} + \mathbf{b}| \leqslant |\mathbf{a}| + |\mathbf{b}| ; \quad |\mathbf{a} - \mathbf{b}| \geqslant |\mathbf{a}| - |\mathbf{b}| .$$

(2) ABCD is a parallelogram and E is the mid-point of AB. Prove, by vector methods, that DE and AC trisect one another.

(3) ABC and A'B'C' are two triangles with centroids G and G' respectively. Show that

$$3\,\overrightarrow{GG}' = \overrightarrow{AA}' + \overrightarrow{BB}' + \overrightarrow{CC}' .$$

[Note that the position vector of G is $\frac{1}{3}(\mathbf{a} + \mathbf{b} + \mathbf{c})$.]

(4) Find the perpendicular distance of the point with position vector $\mathbf{a}$ from the plane $\mathbf{r}\cdot\hat{\mathbf{u}} = p$.

(5) If $\mathbf{a}$ and $\mathbf{b}$ are perpendicular vectors, show that

$$|(\mathbf{a} \times \mathbf{b}) \times \mathbf{b}| = ab^2 .$$

(6) Prove that, for all vectors **a** and **b**,

$$|\mathbf{a} \times \mathbf{b}| = a^2 b^2 - (\mathbf{a} \cdot \mathbf{b})^2 .$$

(7) Show that the points A, B, C, D are coplanar if

$$(\mathbf{a},\mathbf{b},\mathbf{c}) + (\mathbf{c},\mathbf{d},\mathbf{a}) + (\mathbf{b},\mathbf{a},\mathbf{d}) + (\mathbf{d},\mathbf{c},\mathbf{b}) = 0 .$$

(8) Show that the lines joining the vertices of any tetrahedron to the centroids of the opposite faces intersect one another.

(9) Given the vectors $\mathbf{a} = (1,2,3)$, $\mathbf{b} = (0,-1,7)$, $\mathbf{c} = (1,3,-2)$ evaluate
(i) $\mathbf{a} + \mathbf{b} + \mathbf{c}$; (ii) $\mathbf{a} - \mathbf{b} - 9\mathbf{c}$; (iii) $\mathbf{a} \cdot \mathbf{b}$; (iv) $\mathbf{b} \cdot \mathbf{a}$; (v) $\mathbf{a} \cdot \mathbf{c}$.

(10) Find the angle between the vectors $(1,2,3)$ and $(3,4,5)$.

(11) Find a vector perpendicular to both the vector $(1,1,0)$ and the vector $(2,-3,0)$ using
(i) geometrical reasoning,
(ii) the idea of the scalar product,
(iii) the idea of the vector product.

(12) Given the vectors $\mathbf{a} = (2,2,-3)$, $\mathbf{b} = (3,-2,3)$, $\mathbf{c} = (1,6,-9)$, evaluate
(i) $\mathbf{a} \cdot \mathbf{c}$; (ii) $\mathbf{b} \cdot \mathbf{c}$; (iii) $\mathbf{a} \times \mathbf{b}$; (iv) $(\mathbf{a} \times \mathbf{b}) \times \mathbf{c}$; (v) $(\mathbf{a} \times \mathbf{b}) \cdot \mathbf{c}$.
Also, find the angles between the vectors **a** and **b** and between the vectors **a** and $(\mathbf{b} \times \mathbf{c})$.

(13) Find the area of the triangle with vertices A, B, C where $\overrightarrow{OA} = (1,1,1)$, $\overrightarrow{OB} = (3,7,-2)$, $\overrightarrow{OC} = (2,0,1)$.

(14) Find the volume of the tetrahedron ABCD where

$$\overrightarrow{OA} = (1,1,1) , \quad \overrightarrow{OB} = (1,3,1) , \quad \overrightarrow{OC} = (3,1,1) , \quad \overrightarrow{OD} = (1,1,3).$$

(15) Two lines through a point with position vector **a** are

$$\mathbf{r} = \mathbf{a} + \mathbf{d}_1 t , \quad \mathbf{r} = \mathbf{a} + \mathbf{d}_2 t .$$

Show that the plane through these lines is

$$(\mathbf{r} - \mathbf{a} , \quad \mathbf{d}_1 , \quad \mathbf{d}_2) = 0 .$$

(16) If **a**, **b**, **c** are non-zero and

$$(\mathbf{a} \times \mathbf{b}) \times \mathbf{c} = \mathbf{a} \times (\mathbf{b} \times \mathbf{c}) ,$$

show that either **b** is perpendicular to both **a** and **c**, or **a** and **c** lie in the same or opposite directions.

(17) Relative to a right-handed orthonormal basis, obtain the component forms of

$$m\mathbf{v} ; \quad \mathbf{u} \cdot \mathbf{v} ; \quad \mathbf{u} \cdot (\mathbf{v} \times \mathbf{w}) .$$

(18) The components of the vectors **a**, **b**, **c**, **d** relative to a right-handed orthonormal basis are a_i, b_i, c_i, d_i. Simplify and identify the following expressions:

(i) $a_k \, \delta_{ki} \, b_i \, \delta_{lj} \, c_j \, d_l$

(ii) $\varepsilon_{ijk} \, a_i \, \delta_{jk}$

(iii) $\delta_{ij} \, a_j \, \delta_{ik} \, b_l \, \varepsilon_{mlk}$

(iv) $\varepsilon_{ijk} \, \varepsilon_{lmn} \, \varepsilon_{lmp} \, b_k \, c_n \, a_j \, d_p$.

(19) Prove the following identities:

(i) $(\mathbf{a} \times \mathbf{b}) \cdot [(\mathbf{b} \times \mathbf{c}) \times (\mathbf{c} \times \mathbf{a})] = (\mathbf{a}, \mathbf{b}, \mathbf{c})^2$

(ii) $\mathbf{a} \times (\mathbf{b} \times \mathbf{c}) + \mathbf{b} \times (\mathbf{c} \times \mathbf{a}) + \mathbf{c} \times (\mathbf{a} \times \mathbf{b}) = 0$

(iii) $(\mathbf{a} + \mathbf{b}, \mathbf{b} + \mathbf{c}, \mathbf{c} + \mathbf{a}) = 2(\mathbf{a}, \mathbf{b}, \mathbf{c})$

(20) Express any vector **v** as a linear combination of the vectors **a**, **b** and $(\mathbf{a} \times \mathbf{b})$.

(21) Consider the vectors $(2,0,0)$, $(1,5,2)$ and $(3,-2,7)$. Show that they form a basis but not an orthogonal set. Use the Gram-Schmidt orthonormalisation process to derive an orthonormal basis.

(22) Given $\mathbf{r} = \sin\theta\mathbf{i} + \cos\theta\mathbf{j} + 4\mathbf{k}$, show that $d\mathbf{r}/d\theta$ is perpendicular to **r**.

(23) Evaluate

$$\frac{d}{dt}\left[\mathbf{v} \cdot \frac{d\mathbf{v}}{dt} \times \frac{d^2\mathbf{v}}{dt^2}\right] .$$

Chapter 7
Functions of Severable Variables

7.1 INTRODUCTION

In previous chapters, attention has been restricted to functions depending on a single variable. However, in the present chapter, it is intended to develop the theory of functions of more than one variable. It should be noted at the outset that this type of function is particularly common in the physical sciences and engineering; for example, the pressure p of a dilute gas is related to its volume V and temperature T by $p = RT/V$ where R is a constant. Hence, p is a function of the two variables T and V.

In general, if a variable quantity z depends on the values of two other variable quantities x and y, z will be some function of x and y: $z = f(x,y)$. If x and y may vary independently of one another, they are said to be **independent variables** while z is said to be the **dependent variable**.

7.2 PARTIAL DERIVATIVES

If z depends on x and y as indicated above, and x is changed by an increment δx while y is kept constant, then z will change by an increment

$$\delta z = f(x + \delta x, y) - f(x,y) \, .$$

The partial derivative of z with respect to x is defined as

$$\lim_{\delta x \to 0} \frac{\delta z}{\delta x} = \lim_{\delta x \to 0} \frac{f(x + \delta x, y) - f(x,y)}{\delta x}$$

by analogy with the definition of the derivative of a function of one variable. The limit on the right-hand side is the partial derivative of the function $z = f(x,y)$ with respect to x and is denoted by $\partial z/\partial x$ or f_x. Clearly the partial derivative is calculated using the same rules as are employed for ordinary derivatives, provided y is treated as a constant throughout.

Similarly for the partial derivatives with respect to y.

Obviously the idea may be extended easily to functions of more than two variables.

Example
Let (x,y) be the rectangular coordinates of a point in a plane, and (r,θ) the polar coordinates so that

$$x = r\cos\theta \quad y = r\sin\theta . \tag{a}$$

Here x and y are given in terms of the independent variables r and θ. Hence,

$$\partial x/\partial r = \cos\theta , \quad \partial y/\partial r = \sin\theta$$

$$\partial x/\partial\theta = -r\sin\theta , \quad \partial y/\partial\theta = r\cos\theta .$$

Again, equations (a) may be solved for (r,θ) in terms of (x,y) to give

$$r = (x^2 + y^2)^{\frac{1}{2}} , \quad \theta = \tan^{-1}(y/x) .$$

In these equations the independent variables are x and y and so

$$\partial r/\partial x = x/[(x^2 + y^2)^{\frac{1}{2}}] = x/r = \cos\theta$$

$$\partial r/\partial y = \sin\theta$$

$$\partial\theta/\partial x = -y/(x^2 + y^2) = -y/r^2 = -\sin\theta/r$$

$$\partial\theta/\partial y = \cos\theta/r .$$

If $z = f(x,y)$, then in general the first partial derivatives will be functions of x and y also and may be differentiated partially again with respect to either of the variables. The four second partial derivatives of z are

$$\frac{\partial}{\partial x}\left(\frac{\partial z}{\partial x}\right) = \frac{\partial^2 z}{\partial x^2} , \quad \frac{\partial}{\partial x}\left(\frac{\partial z}{\partial y}\right) = \frac{\partial^2 z}{\partial x\,\partial y} ,$$

$$\frac{\partial}{\partial y}\left(\frac{\partial z}{\partial x}\right) = \frac{\partial^2 z}{\partial y\,\partial x} , \quad \frac{\partial}{\partial y}\left(\frac{\partial z}{\partial y}\right) = \frac{\partial^2 z}{\partial y^2} .$$

Here the order of the symbols ∂x, ∂y from right to left indicates the order of differentiation.

If $z = f(x,y)$, these partial derivatives may be written f_{xx}, f_{xy}, f_{yx}, f_{yy} respectively. In this notation, the order of the suffices from right to left indicates the order of differentiation.

It should be noted that in general $f_{xy} \neq f_{yx}$. However, it may be shown that, if f_x and f_y exist in the neighbourhood of a point (a,b) and if f_x and f_y are differentiable at (a,b) then, at the point (a,b), $f_{xy} = f_{yx}$. These conditions are *usually* satisfied in practice, and so, it is even more important to realise that in general $f_{xy} \neq f_{yx}$.

7.3 THE CHAIN RULE
Suppose $z = f(x,y)$ and let δz be the small change in z corresponding to the small independent changes δx in x and δy in y, then

$$\delta z = f(x + \delta x, y + \delta y) - f(x,y)$$

$$= \frac{\{f(x + \delta x, y + \delta y) - f(x, y + \delta y)\}\delta x}{\alpha x} + \frac{\{f(x, y + \delta y) - f(x,y)\}\delta y}{\delta y}.$$

But
$$\lim_{\delta x \to 0} \frac{f(x + \delta x, y + \delta y) - f(x, y + \delta y)}{\delta x} = \frac{\partial}{\partial x} f(x, y + \delta y)$$

and, as $\delta y \to 0$ also, this becomes

$$\frac{\partial}{\partial x} f(x,y) = \frac{\partial z}{\partial x}.$$

Similarly,
$$\lim_{\delta y \to 0} \frac{f(x,y + \delta y) - f(x,y)}{\delta y} = \frac{\partial z}{\partial y}.$$

Thus, in the limit as $\delta x \to 0$ and $\delta y \to 0$,

$$dz = \frac{\partial z}{\partial x} dx + \frac{\partial z}{\partial y} dy \qquad (7.1)$$

gives the differential of z. This definition follows in the same way as for a function of one variable.

Now suppose $z = f(x,y)$ but x and y, instead of being independent variables, are both functions of a single variable t. Corresponding to a given increment δt in t, there will be increments δx and δy in x and y and an increment δz in z. In this case, it is seen that

$$\frac{dz}{dt} = \frac{\partial z}{\partial x} \frac{dx}{dt} + \frac{\partial z}{\partial y} \frac{dy}{dt}. \qquad (7.2)$$

Results (7.1) and (7.2) may be generalised further:

When z is given as a function of the variables $x_1, x_2, \ldots, x_n$, equation (7.1) generalises to

$$dz = \frac{\partial z}{\partial x_1} dx_1 + \frac{\partial z}{\partial x_2} dx_2 + \cdots + \frac{\partial z}{\partial x_n} dx_n,$$

and if $x_1, x_2, \ldots, x_n$ are each given as functions of $t_1, t_2, t_3, \ldots$, then

$$\frac{\partial z}{\partial t_i} = \frac{\partial z}{\partial x_1} \frac{\partial x_1}{\partial t_i} + \frac{\partial z}{\partial x_2} \frac{\partial x_2}{\partial t_i} + \cdots + \frac{\partial z}{\partial x_n} \frac{\partial x_n}{\partial t_i}$$

for $i = 1,2,3, \ldots$.

These results are referred to as the **chain rule**.

Example

If $z = f(x,y)$ where $2x = e^u + e^v$ and $2y = e^u - e^v$, show that

$$\frac{\partial z}{\partial u} + \frac{\partial z}{\partial v} = x \frac{\partial z}{\partial x} + y \frac{\partial z}{\partial y}.$$

Now
$$\frac{\partial z}{\partial u} = \frac{\partial z}{\partial x}\frac{\partial x}{\partial u} + \frac{\partial z}{\partial y}\frac{\partial y}{\partial u} = \frac{1}{2}e^u\left(\frac{\partial z}{\partial x} + \frac{\partial z}{\partial y}\right).$$

Similarly
$$\frac{\partial z}{\partial v} = \frac{1}{2}e^v\left(\frac{\partial z}{\partial x} - \frac{\partial z}{\partial y}\right).$$

Therefore
$$\frac{\partial z}{\partial u} + \frac{\partial z}{\partial v} = \frac{1}{2}\frac{\partial z}{\partial x}(e^u + e^v) + \frac{1}{2}\frac{\partial z}{\partial y}(e^u - e^v)$$

$$= x\frac{\partial z}{\partial x} + y\frac{\partial z}{\partial y}.$$

It might be noted that, if z is a function of x and y where y itself is a function of x, z becomes a function of x alone when y is expressed in terms of x. This case is covered by (7.2) with $t = x$, and so

$$\frac{dz}{dx} = \frac{\partial z}{\partial x} + \frac{\partial z}{\partial y}\frac{dy}{dx}.$$

Here dz/dx is the total derivative of z with respect to x; that is, the derivative with respect to x of the function obtained by substituting for y in z its expression as a function of x. $\partial z/\partial x$ is the partial derivative of z with respect to x when y is kept constant.

When y is defined as a function of x by an equation $f(x,y) = 0$, y is said to be an **implicit function** of x. In such a case, dy/dx may be found as follows:

By definition, y is a function of x such that, when substituted in $f(x,y)$ the identity

$$f\{x,y(x)\} = 0$$

results. Since f is identically zero, its total derivative is zero, and so

$$\frac{df}{dx} = \frac{\partial f}{\partial x} + \frac{\partial f}{\partial y}\frac{dy}{dx} = 0$$

or
$$f_x + f_y\frac{dy}{dx} = 0,$$

that is
$$dy/dx = -f_x/f_y.$$

Example
Consider the function

$$f(x,y) = \frac{x^2}{a^2} + \frac{y^2}{b^2} - 1 = 0,$$

$$f_x = 2x/a^2, \quad f_y = 2y/b^2$$

and so
$$dy/dx = -xb^2/ya^2.$$

7.4 HOMOGENEOUS FUNCTIONS

A function $f(x_1,x_2,\ldots,x_m)$ is said to be **homogeneous** of degree n in the variable $x_1,x_2,\ldots,x_m$ if

$$f(x_1t,x_2t,\ldots,x_mt) = t^n f(x_1,x_2,\ldots,x_m) .$$

For example, $(x^2 + y^2 + z^2)$ is homogeneous of degree 2, and $(x + y)/(x^4 + z^4)$ is homogeneous of degree -3.

Theorem

If $f(x_1,x_2,\ldots,x_m)$ is a homogeneous function of degree n in $x_1,x_2,\ldots,x_m$, then

$$x_1 \frac{\partial f}{\partial x_1} + x_2 \frac{\partial f}{\partial x_2} + \cdots + x_m \frac{\partial f}{\partial x_m} = nf .$$

(This theorem is due to Euler.)

Proof

Let $x_1 = \alpha_1 t,\ x_2 = \alpha_2 t,\ \ldots,\ x_m = \alpha_m t$ so that

$$u = f(x_1,x_2,\ldots,x_m) = f(\alpha_1 t,\alpha_2 t,\ldots,\alpha_m t) = t^n f(\alpha_1\alpha_2,\ldots,\alpha_m).$$

The function u is a function of the variable t and, by differentiating the two equivalent forms $f(\alpha_1 t,a_2 t,\ldots,\alpha_m t)$ and $t^n f(\alpha_1,\alpha_2,\ldots,\alpha_m)$, two forms of the derivative du/dt are obtained.

$$\frac{du}{dt} = \frac{\partial u}{\partial x_1}\frac{dx_1}{dt} + \frac{\partial u}{\partial x_2}\frac{dx_2}{dt} + \cdots + \frac{\partial u}{\partial x_m}\frac{dx_m}{dt}$$

$$= \alpha_1 u_{x_1} + \alpha_2 u_{x_2} + \cdots + \alpha_m u_{x_m} .$$

Also $\qquad\qquad du/dt = nt^{n-1} f(\alpha_1,\alpha_2,\ldots,\alpha_m) .$

On multiplying by t,

$$\alpha_1 t u_{x_1} + \alpha_2 t u_{x_2} + \cdots + \alpha_m t u_{x_m} = nt^n f(\alpha_1,\alpha_2,\ldots,\alpha_m)$$

$$= nf(\alpha_1 t,\alpha_2 t,\ldots,\alpha_m t) .$$

Hence the required result.

The kinetic energy, T, of a particle is a homogeneous function of degree 2 in the velocity components,

$$T = \tfrac{1}{2} m(\dot{x}^2 + \dot{y}^2 + \dot{z}^2) .$$

For this reason, such functions are of interest to applied mathematicians, physical scientists, and engineers. In this case, Euler's theorem gives

$$\dot{x}\frac{\partial T}{\partial \dot{x}} + \dot{y}\frac{\partial T}{\partial \dot{y}} + \dot{z}\frac{\partial T}{\partial \dot{z}} = 2T .$$

7.5 TAYLOR'S THEOREM FOR A FUNCTION OF SEVERAL VARIABLES

This theorem for a function of one variable has been discussed already in Chapters 1 and 4. Now consider a function $f(t)$ of the single variable t. The Taylor series expansion of $f(t)$ about the point $t = 0$ is

$$f(t) = f(0) + \left.\frac{df}{dt}\right|_{t=0} t + \frac{1}{2!} \left.\frac{d^2 f}{dt^2}\right|_{t=0} t^2 + \cdots$$

$$= \sum_n \frac{1}{n!} f^n(0) \, t^n$$

where $f^n(0)$ is the nth derivative of $f(t)$ evaluated at $t = 0$.

The Taylor series expansion for a function of several variables may be deduced from the above as follows: Suppose the function is $u(\mathbf{x})$ and that the variables $\mathbf{x}$ are given as functions of the single variable t by

$$\mathbf{x} = \mathbf{x}_0 + t\mathbf{h} \tag{7.3}$$

where $\mathbf{x}_0$ and $\mathbf{h}$ are fixed. Then $u(\mathbf{x})$ becomes a function of the single variable t, so that

$$u(t) = u(0) + \left.\frac{du}{dt}\right|_{t=0} t + \frac{1}{2!} \left.\frac{d^2 u}{dt^2}\right|_{t=0} t^2 + \cdots . \tag{7.4}$$

In index notation, (7.3) becomes

$$x_i = (x_0)_i + t h_i$$

and so

$$dx_i/dt = h_i .$$

Using the chain rule gives

$$\frac{du}{dt} = \frac{\partial u}{\partial x_i} \frac{dx_i}{dt} = \frac{\partial u}{\partial x_i} h_i$$

$$\frac{d^2 u}{dt^2} = \frac{d}{dt}\left(\frac{\partial u}{\partial x_i} h_i\right) = \frac{\partial}{\partial x_j}\left(\frac{\partial u}{\partial x_i} h_i\right) h_j = \frac{\partial^2 u}{\partial x_j \partial x_i} h_i h_j .$$

Similarly,

$$\frac{d^3 u}{dt^3} = \frac{\partial^3 u}{\partial x_k \partial x_j \partial x_i} h_i h_j h_k , \quad \text{etc.}$$

In (7.4) these differentials are evaluated at $t = 0$; that is, when $\mathbf{x} = \mathbf{x}_0$. Substituting into (7.4) and putting $t = 1$ yields

$$u(\mathbf{x}_0 + \mathbf{h}) = u(\mathbf{x}_0) + \left.\frac{\partial u}{\partial x_i}\right|_{\mathbf{x}=\mathbf{x}_0} h_i + \frac{1}{2!} \left.\frac{\partial^2 u}{\partial x_i \partial x_j}\right|_{\mathbf{x}=\mathbf{x}_0} h_i h_j + \cdots \tag{7.5}$$

This is the Taylor series expansion for a function of n variables $\mathbf{x}$ about the point $\mathbf{x}_0$. The expansion for the function $u(\mathbf{x})$ as a power series in $\mathbf{x}$ is obtained by putting $\mathbf{x}_0 = \mathbf{0}$ and $\mathbf{h} = \mathbf{x}$ in (7.5). Hence,

$$u(\mathbf{x}) = u(\mathbf{0}) = \left.\frac{\partial u}{\partial x_i}\right|_{\mathbf{x}=0} x_i + \frac{1}{2!} \left.\frac{\partial^2 u}{\partial x_i \partial x_j}\right|_{\mathbf{x}=0} x_i x_j + \cdots . \tag{7.6}$$

Example

Find $u(x,y) = y^2/x^3$ as a power series in $(x - 1)$ and $(y + 1)$ up to and including second-order terms.

Since (7.5) is a power series expansion or $u(\mathbf{x}_0 + \mathbf{h})$ in powers of h the problem is solved by putting

$$\mathbf{x}_0 + \mathbf{h} = (x,y) \quad \text{and} \quad \mathbf{h} = (x - 1, y + 1) .$$

Therefore,
$$\mathbf{x}_0 = (1,-1) .$$

Now
$$u(\mathbf{x}_0) = u(1,-1) = 1$$

$$\left.\frac{\partial u}{\partial x_i}\right|_{\mathbf{x}=\mathbf{x}_0} h_i = \left.\frac{\partial u}{\partial x}\right|_{(1,-1)} (x - 1) + \left.\frac{\partial u}{\partial y}\right|_{(1,-1)} (y + 1)$$

$$= -3(x - 1) - 2(y + 1)$$

$$\frac{1}{2!} \left.\frac{\partial^2 u}{\partial x_i \partial x_j}\right|_{\mathbf{x}=\mathbf{x}_0} h_i h_j = \frac{1}{2!} \left\{ \left.\frac{\partial^2 u}{\partial x^2}\right|_{(1,-1)} (x - 1)^2 + \left.\frac{\partial^2 u}{\partial y^2}\right|_{(1,-1)} (y + 1)^2 \right.$$

$$\left. + \left.\frac{\partial^2 u}{\partial x \partial y}\right|_{(1,-1)} 2(x - 1)(y + 1) \right\}$$

$$= 6(x - 1)^2 + (y + 1)^2 + 6(x - 1)(y + 1) .$$

The required expansion, up to and including second-order terms, is

$$u(\mathbf{x}) = 1 - 3(x - 1) - 2(y + 1) + 6(x - 1)^2$$
$$+ (y + 1)^2 + 6(x - 1)(y + 1) .$$

7.6 EXTREME VALUES OF FUNCTIONS OF SEVERAL VARIABLES

The theory of extreme values for functions of one variable has been considered already in Chapter 1. It remains to extend the ideas to cover functions of several variables. To fix ideas, consider $f(x,y)$ which is a function of the two independent variables x and y. However, it should be noted that the theory is applicable regardless of the number of independent variables.

The function $f(x,y)$ is said to have a maximum value at the point (a,b) if

$$f(a + h, \ b + k) - f(a,b) < 0$$

for all sufficiently small positive or negative values of h and k. A minimum is defined with the inequality reversed.

Now applying Taylor's theorem, equation (7.5), it is seen that

$$f(a + h, b + k) = f(a,b) + \left(h \frac{\partial f}{\partial x} + k \frac{\partial f}{\partial y} \right)_{\substack{x=a \\ y=b}}$$

$$+ \frac{1}{2}\left(h^2 \frac{\partial^2 f}{\partial x^2} + 2hk \frac{\partial^2 f}{\partial x \partial y} + k^2 \frac{\partial^2 f}{\partial y^2} \right)_{\substack{x=a \\ y=b}} + \cdots .$$

For convenience write

$$\left(\frac{\partial f}{\partial x} \right)_{\substack{x=a \\ y=b}} = (f_x)_{\substack{x=a \\ y=b}} = f_a ; \left(\frac{\partial f}{\partial y} \right)_{\substack{x=a \\ y=b}} = (f_y)_{\substack{x=a \\ y=b}} = f_b ,$$

and similarly

$$\left(\frac{\partial^2 f}{\partial x^2} \right)_{\substack{x=a \\ y=b}} = f_{aa} , \left(\frac{\partial^2 f}{\partial x \partial y} \right)_{\substack{x=a \\ y=b}} = f_{ab} , \left(\frac{\partial^2 f}{\partial y^2} \right)_{\substack{x=a \\ y=b}} = f_{bb} ,$$

then

$$f(a + h, b + k) = f(a,b) + (hf_a + kf_b) + \tfrac{1}{2}(h^2 f_{aa} + 2hk f_{ab} + k^2 f_{bb}) + \cdots \quad (7.7)$$

Hence, for sufficiently small values of h and k, the sign of
$[f(a + h, b + k) - f(a,b)]$ is the sign of $(hf_a + kf_b)$. However, for a maximum
(or minimum) value of $f(x,y)$ at (a,b), the sign of this term must be negative (or
positive) for all independent positive or negative values of h and k. If $k = 0$,
changing the sign of h would change the sign of $(hf_a + kf_b)$ unless $f_a = 0$.
Similarly, if $h = 0$, f_b would need to equal zero.

Thus, a necessary condition for $f(x,y)$ to possess an extreme value—a maximum or a minimum—at the point (a,b) is

$$f_a = 0 \quad \text{and} \quad f_b = 0 ;$$

that is, both f_x and f_y should be zero at the point (a,b).

If these conditions are satisfied,

$$f(a + h, b + k) - f(a,b) = \tfrac{1}{2}(h^2 f_{aa} + 2hk f_{ab} + k^2 f_{bb}) + \cdots$$

and again for sufficiently small h and k, the sign of the right-hand side depends
on the sign of $(h^2 f_{aa} + 2hk f_{ab} + k^2 f_{bb})$.

Now put

$$h = \rho \cos\theta , \quad k = \rho \sin\theta$$

where ρ is positive. The signs of h and k depend now on the value of θ. Also

$$h^2 f_{aa} + 2hk f_{ab} + k^2 f_{bb} = \rho^2 (f_{aa} \cos^2\theta + 2f_{ab} \cos\theta \sin\theta + f_{bb} \sin^2\theta). \quad (7.8)$$

Before proceeding, suppose that not all of f_{aa}, f_{ab}, f_{bb} are zero since, if they were,
the above term would vanish and it would be necessary to consider the next term

in the Taylor series (7.7). If $f_{aa} = f_{bb} = 0$ but $f_{ab} \neq 0$ the sign of (7.8) is determined by the sign of $f_{ab}\cos\theta\sin\theta$, and this changes sign if θ (and therefore k) changes sign. Under these conditions the function may have neither a maximum nor a minimum value at the point (a,b). In fact, $f(x,y)$ is said to have a **saddle point** at (a,b).

If $f_{aa} \neq 0$, the expression on the right-hand side of (7.8) may be written

$$\rho^2\{(f_{aa}\cos\theta + f_{ab}\sin\theta)^2 + (f_{aa}f_{bb} - f_{ab}{}^2)\sin^2\theta\}/f_{aa} \qquad (7.9a)$$

or, if $f_{bb} \neq 0$, it may be written

$$\rho^2\{(f_{bb}\sin\theta + f_{ab}\cos\theta)^2 + (f_{aa}f_{bb} - f_{ab}{}^2)\cos^2\theta\}/f_{bb} . \qquad (7.9b)$$

There are now three cases to consider:

(a) $$f_{aa}f_{bb} - f_{ab}{}^2 > 0 .$$

If this condition is satisfied

$$f_{aa}f_{bb} > f_{ab}{}^2 > 0$$

and so, f_{aa} and f_{bb} are of the same sign. Also, the sign of expressions (7.9a) and (7.9b) is seen to be the same as the sign of f_{aa} (or f_{bb}). Hence, there is a maximum value if $f_{aa} < 0$ and a minimum value if $f_{aa} > 0$.

(b) $$f_{aa}f_{bb} - f_{ab}{}^2 < 0 .$$

If this condition is satisfied, the expression (7.9a) is not of invariable sign. When $\theta = 0$ it is positive but, when $\theta = \tan^{-1}(-f_{aa}/f_{ab})$, it is negative. Hence, once more the function has a stationary value which is neither a maximum nor a minimum; that is, a saddle point. It might be noted that the situation $f_{aa} = f_{bb} = 0$, $f_{ab} \neq 0$ is covered by this case.

(c) $$f_{aa}f_{bb} - f_{ab}{}^2 = 0 .$$

In this case, the expression (7.9a) has the same sign as f_{aa} except possibly for $\theta = \tan^{-1}(-f_{aa}/f_{ab})$. Further investigation is necessary to determine the nature of the stationary value under these conditions. In general, this is not easy and it will not be considered here.

Example

Determine the nature of the stationary points of the function

$$f(x,y) = x^4 + 4x^2y^2 - 2x^2 + 2y^2 - 1 .$$

The points where $f(x,y)$ has stationary values are the roots of the simultaneous equations

$$f_x = 4x(x^2 + 2y^2 - 1) = 0 ; f_y = 4y(2x^2 + 1) = 0 .$$

Solving these yields

$$x = 0 , \pm 1 ; y = 0 ,$$

giving the stationary points of the given function as (0,0), (1,0) and (−1,0). It now remains to determine the nature of these stationary points. Firstly, note that

$$f_{xx} = 12x^2 + 8y^2 - 4 \ , f_{yy} = 8x^2 + 4 \ , f_{xy} = 16xy \ .$$

For the point (0,0)

$$f_{xx}(0,0) = -4 \ , f_{yy}(0,0) = 4 \ , f_{xy}(0,0) = 0$$

and so

$$f_{xx}(0,0)f_{yy}(0,0) - f_{xy}{}^2(0,0) = -16 < 0 \ .$$

Hence, this point is a saddle point.
   For the point (1,0),

$$f_{xx}(1,0) = 8 \ , f_{yy}(1,0) = 12 \ , f_{xy}(1,0) = 0$$

and so

$$f_{xx}(1,0)f_{yy}(1,0) - f_{xy}{}^2(1,0) = 96 > 0 \ .$$

Hence, this point is a minimum.
   For the point (−1,0),

$$f_{xx}(-1,0) = 8 \ , f_{yy}(-1,0) = 12 \ , f_{xy}(-1,0) = 0$$

and so

$$f_{xx}(-1,0)f_{yy}(-1,0) - f_{xy}{}^2(-1,0) = 96 > 0 \ .$$

Hence, this point is a minimum also.
   Therefore, the given function $f(x,y)$ has two minima (at (1,0) and (−1,0)) and one saddle point at (0,0). Finally it might be noted that, at both minima, $f(x,y) = -2$ and at the saddle point $f(x,y) = -1$.

7.6.1 Lagrange multipliers

In the previous section, the problem of finding the extreme values of a function of several independent variables has been solved successfully. Although a function of *two* independent variables was discussed in detail, the extension to functions of more than two independent variables is straightforward. However, it remains to consider the problem of determining the extreme values of a function of several variables which are not all independent but may be connected by one or more relations.

   Suppose it is required to find the extremum (maximum or minimum) of the function $f(x_1,x_2, \ldots ,x_n)$, where the n variables $x_1,x_2, \ldots ,x_n$ satisfy the equation of constraint

$$g(x_1,x_2, \ldots ,x_n) = 0 \ . \tag{7.10}$$

If f is to have an extremum for a given set of values $(x_1^0, x_2^0, \ldots, x_n^0)$ then

$$df = \frac{\partial f}{\partial x_1}\, dx_1 + \frac{\partial f}{\partial x_2}\, dx_2 + \cdots + \frac{\partial f}{\partial x_n}\, dx_n = 0 \qquad (7.11)$$

where the derivatives are to be evaluated at $(x_1^0, x_2^0, \ldots, x_n^0)$.

Also, since (7.10) is to be satisfied always, for any small departure from the extremum

$$dg = \frac{\partial g}{\partial x_1}\, dx_1 + \frac{\partial g}{\partial x_2}\, dx_2 + \cdots + \frac{\partial g}{\partial x_n}\, dx_n = 0 \qquad (7.12)$$

with the derivatives again evaluated at $(x_1^0, x_2^0, \ldots, x_n^0)$.

If all the variables $x_1, x_2, \ldots, x_n$ were completely independent, it would be possible to choose each dx_i in (7.11) to be zero except for dx_k say. Then it could be concluded that $\partial f/\partial x_k = 0$ for all k. However, the variables $x_1, x_2, \ldots, x_n$ are *not* independent; they are related via (7.10). In the method under discussion, a parameter λ, which is to be determined later, is introduced and the restrictive condition (7.12) is multiplied by it. The result is added to (7.11) to give

$$\left(\frac{\partial f}{\partial x_1} + \lambda\,\frac{\partial g}{\partial x_1}\right) dx_1 + \left(\frac{\partial f}{\partial x_2} + \lambda\,\frac{\partial g}{\partial x_2}\right) dx_2 + \cdots + \left(\frac{\partial f}{\partial x_n} + \lambda\,\frac{\partial g}{\partial x_n}\right) dx_n = 0\,.$$
$$(7.13)$$

Here only $(n-1)$ of the dx_i are independent, but the value of λ is still to be determined. Choose λ to eliminate the coefficient of dx_n; that is, so that

$$\frac{\partial f}{\partial x_n} + \lambda\,\frac{\partial g}{\partial x_n} = 0\,.$$

λ is a constant characteristic of the extremum $(x_1^0, x_2^0, \ldots, x_n^0)$.

With this one term in (7.13) eliminated, the remaining dx_i are independent, and so it may be concluded that

$$\frac{\partial f}{\partial x_k} + \lambda\,\frac{\partial g}{\partial x_k} = 0 \quad \text{for} \quad k = 1, 2, \ldots, n-1\,.$$

The end result is

$$\frac{\partial f}{\partial x_k} + \lambda\,\frac{\partial g}{\partial x_k} = 0 \quad \text{for} \quad k = 1, 2, \ldots, n\,. \qquad (7.14)$$

Therefore, after λ is introduced, (7.13) may be treated as if all the dx_i are mutually independent. Thus, the awkward constraining condition (7.12) has been handled quite elegantly. The constraint has not disappeared but complications introduced by it have been postponed to a later stage of the problem where they are handled more easily. Equations (7.14), together with (7.10), may be solved to find the values of $x_1^0, x_2^0, \ldots, x_n^0$ and λ. The value of λ is not required necessarily, and λ is referred to as a **Lagrange undetermined multiplier**—the method being due to Lagrange. Finally, note that the method may be generalised easily to the case of more than one constraint.

Examples

(1) Show that the function $x^2 + y^2 + z^2$ has four stationary values on the surface $xyz = a^3$.

Consider $f = (x^2 + y^2 + z^2) + \lambda(xyz - a^3)$, where λ is a Lagrange undetermined multiplier. Then

$$\partial f/\partial x = 2x + \lambda yz = 0$$

$$\partial f/\partial y = 2y + \lambda zx = 0$$

$$\partial f/\partial z = 2z + \lambda xy = 0 .$$

It follows from these three equations that

$$x^2 = y^2 = z^2 ,$$

and so the required stationary points are

$$(a,a,a) , (a,-a,-a) , (-a,a,-a) , (-a,-a,a) .$$

(2) If $x + y + z = 1$ and $xyz = -1$, show that $x^2 + y^2 + z^2$ has three equal stationary points.

Consider $f = (x^2 + y^2 + z^2) + \lambda(x + y + z - 1) + \mu(xyz + 1)$, where λ and μ are Lagrange undetermined multipliers. Then

$$\partial f/\partial x = 2x + \lambda + \mu yz = 0$$

$$\partial f/\partial y = 2y + \lambda + \mu zx = 0$$

$$\partial f/\partial z = 2z + \lambda + \mu xy = 0 .$$

Elimination of λ and μ between these equations yields

$$(x - y)(y - z)(z - x) = 0$$

so that either $x = y$ or $y = z$ or $z = x$.

When $x = y$, the two constraint equations become

$$2x + z = 1 , \quad x^2 z = -1 ,$$

and eliminating z between these gives

$$(x - 1)(2x^2 + x + 1) = 0$$

which has one real solution $x = 1$. Thus $(1,1,-1)$ is a stationary point.

Similarly, $(1,-1,1)$ and $(-1,1,1)$ are also stationary points, and all three stationary points are seen to yield the same stationary value of $x^2 + y^2 + z^2$.

EXERCISES 7

(1) Given $u = x^2 + 2x - 1$ and $x = t^2 - 1$ find du/dt by
  (a) substituting t for x,
  (b) using the chain rule.

(2) Given $u(x,y) = (x + 1)^2 - 3xy^2 + 4y$ find
  (a) $u(2, -1)$,   (b) $u(1/x , x/y)$.

(3) Find all the first partial derivatives of
  (a) $u(x,y) = \tan(x/y)$

  (b) $f(r,\theta) = r^2 \sin^2\theta + r^3$

  (c) $u(r,s,t) = r^3 + s^2t + (t - 1)(r - 3)$

  (d) $\phi(p,q) = \exp(p^2\log q)$.

(4) Verify that $\dfrac{\partial^2 f}{\partial x \partial y} = \dfrac{\partial^2 f}{\partial y \partial x}$ for

  (a) $f(x,y) = \sin^2(x + y) + x^2\cos y$,

  (b) $f(x,y,z) = x^3y^2z$.

(5) Show that the function $V(x,y,z) = (x^2 + y^2 + z^2)^{-\frac{1}{2}}$ satisfies Laplace's equation

$$\frac{\partial^2 V}{\partial x^2} + \frac{\partial^2 V}{\partial y^2} + \frac{\partial^2 V}{\partial z^2} = 0 .$$

(6) Show that, if $z = f(x^ny)$ where $n \neq 0$, then

$$x\frac{\partial z}{\partial x} = ny\frac{\partial z}{\partial y} .$$

(7) Prove that $y = f(x + ct) + g(x - ct)$ satisfies the equation

$$\frac{\partial^2 y}{\partial t^2} = c^2 \frac{\partial^2 y}{\partial x^2}$$

where c is a constant and the functions f and g are twice differentiable.

(8) Suppose $u(x \; y) = x^2 + y^4 + 2xy^2$. If $x = t^2\sin\theta$ and $y = t\cos\theta$, find $\partial u/\partial t$ and $\partial u/\partial\theta$.

(9) Given $x = r + 3s$ and $y = r - s$, obtain $\partial^2 u/\partial x \partial y$ in terms of derivatives with respect to r and s.

(10) If $f(x,y) = 0$, show that

$$\frac{dy}{dx} = -\frac{f_x}{f_y} \quad \text{and} \quad \frac{d^2y}{dx^2} = \frac{2f_xf_yf_{xy} - f_y^2f_{xx} - f_x^2f_{yy}}{f_y^3} .$$

(11) The kinetic energy of a particle of mass m is given by

$$T = \tfrac{1}{2}m(v_x^2 + v_y^2).$$

Show that the components of momentum are given by $M_x = \partial T/\partial V_x$ and $M_y = \partial T/\partial V_y$. Also deduce that

$$2T = v_x M_x + v_y M_y.$$

(12) Expand $\sin x^2 y$ as a power series in $(x - \pi)$ and y up to and including the second-order terms.

(13) Expand, by a Taylor series, $x^2 y + y^2 + 3$ in powers of $x + 1$ and $y + 3$.

(14) Using Taylor's series for a function of two variables, write out the complete expansion of $x^4 + y^4 - 3x^2 y + 6$ about the point $x = 3$, $y = 3$.

(15) Find the stationary values of the function $f(x,y) = e^{x+y}(x^2 - xy + y^2)$. Show that it has no maxima and one minimum value.

(16) Show that the function $f(x,y) = x^2 y - 4x^2 - y^2$ has three stationary points, one of which is a maximum.

(17) Determine and examine the stationary values of the function $f(x,y) = x^3 + y^3 - 3axy$.

(18) Show that the function $f(x,y) = x^3 + y^3 - 2(x^2 + y^2) + 3xy$ has stationary values at the points $(0,0)$ and $(\tfrac{1}{3},\tfrac{1}{3})$, and investigate their nature.

(19) Find the maximum of the function $f(x,y,z) = x^2 y^2 z^2$ subject to the subsidiary condition $x^2 + y^2 + z^2 = c^2$. Deduce that the geometric mean of three positive numbers $(x^2, y^2$ and $z^2)$ is never greater than their arithmetic mean.

(20) Find the triangle (with sides x,y,z) of given perimeter $2s$ and the greatest possible area.

(21) Find the stationary points of the function $f(x,y) = x^3 y^2$ subject to the subsidiary condition $x^2 - xy = a^2$, where $a > 0$.

Chapter 8
Ordinary Differential Equations

8.1 INTRODUCTION
Equations such as

$$d^2y/dx^2 = -p^2y$$

involving one or more derivatives are called **differential equations**. An ordinary differential equation for a variable y as a function of a real variable x is an equality involving y and its derivatives with respect to x;—it is an equation which has only one independent variable. In the example cited, y is the dependent variable, x the independent one.

Probably the simplest type of differential equation is

$$dy/dx = g(x) \tag{8.1}$$

where $g(x)$ is a given function of x. A solution is

$$y = \int_a^x g(t)dt ,$$

and this solution contains one arbitrary constant which appears as the lower limit of integration.

Equation (8.1) contains only the first derivative of y and is called a **first-order** differential equation. An **nth-order** differential equation contains terms involving the nth derivative d^ny/dx^n but no higher derivatives.

The **degree** of a differential equation is the degree or power of the highest derivative when the equation has been made rational and integral as far as the derivatives are concerned. Therefore, an equation such as

$$(dy/dx)^2 + dy/dx - 3 = 0$$

is of the first order and second degree. However, to determine the degree of

$$\left\{ 1 + \left(\frac{dy}{dx}\right)^2 \right\}^{3/2} = \frac{d^2y}{dx^2}$$

the equation must be squared first to rationalise it. Then it is seen to be of the second order and second degree since the highest derivative occurs squared.

Differential equations arise in a variety of ways; from geometrical problems, from physical problems, and some also from primitives, that is, from relations between the variables which involve essential arbitrary constants, where constants are termed essential if they cannot be replaced by a smaller number of constants. In general, an equation involving n essential arbitrary constants gives rise to an nth-order differential equation. For example, consider $x = A \cos (pt - a)$. The essential arbitrary constants A and a may be eliminated by differentiating twice to give

$$d^2x/dt^2 = -p^2A \cos (pt - a) = -p^2x .$$

Therefore, in general, for an equation with n essential arbitrary constants, differentiating n times gives $(n + 1)$ equations from which the n constants may be eliminated. The resulting equation contains an nth derivative, and so is of the nth order. Conversely, it may be shown that the most general solution of an nth-order ordinary differential equation contains n arbitrary constants.

When it is known that a physical quantity y obeys a certain differential equation, these n constants may be fixed by knowledge of certain particular values of y and its derivatives. For example, consider the equation of simple harmonic motion

$$d^2y/dt^2 + p^2y = 0 .$$

To obtain a solution without arbitrary constants, two conditions—such as the values of y and dy/dt when $t = 0$ (initial displacement and velocity)—are needed.

Referring back to equation (8.1), this is said to be a **linear** equation for y. This means that each term in the equation involves y through, at most, a single factor y or dy/dx or d^2y/dx^2 or $\cdots$. Equations containing such terms as y^3, $y(dy/dx)$, $(1 + y)^{-1}$ are **non-linear**.

Solutions to differential equations may be either real or complex. If a complex solution is obtained, the real and imaginary parts are seen to form further solutions. ($j = \sqrt{-1}$ is merely a constant). This is a special case of the principle of superposition which states that, if y_1 and y_2 are both solutions of a linear equation, and c_1, c_2 are arbitrary constants, then $(c_1y_1 + c_2y_2)$ is also a solution. More generally, any number of known solutions $y_1, y_2 \cdots$ with constants $c_1, c_2 \cdots$ may be combined to obtain a new solution.

Again, a **homogeneous** equation is defined as one in which all the terms are of the same dimensions. It should be noted that if x and y are regarded as being of dimension one, dy/dx is of dimension 0, d^2y/dx^2 of dimension -1, d^3y/dx^3 of dimension -2, etc. Equations which are not homogeneous are said to be **inhomogeneous**.

8.2 DIFFERENTIAL EQUATIONS OF THE FIRST ORDER AND FIRST DEGREE

The equations to be considered are of the form

$$M(x,y) + N(x,y)\frac{dy}{dx} = 0 \tag{8.2}$$

where M and N are functions of both x and y.

This equation is written in the form

$$M(x,y)\,dx + N(x,y)\,dy = 0$$

frequently, and the use of differentials in this way may be justified rigorously. It is not possible to solve the general equation of this form in terms of a finite number of known functions, but various special cases for which a solution may be found, will be discussed.

Note that equation (8.2) could have been written

$$dy/dx = F(x,y) \, .$$

Now consider the class of equations of the form

$$dy/dx = \beta(x)\,\gamma(y) \tag{8.3}$$

where $\beta(x)$ is a function of x only and $\gamma(y)$ is a function of y only.

In general, this equation is non-linear since $\gamma(y)$ is not necessarily a linear function of y. However, the equation is linear in dy/dx, and so is of the first order. Also, owing to the form of the right-hand side of (8.3), the equation is of a particularly simple type known as a **separable** equation and may be written

$$dy/\gamma(y) = \beta(x)dx \, .$$

This equation connects the differentials dx and dy over some range of values of x, and so both sides may be integrated over any part of this range giving

$$\int_{a}^{y} \frac{du}{\gamma(u)} = \int_{b}^{x}\beta(t)dt \, .$$

This solution contains an arbitrary constant of integration arising from the choice of lower limits a and b. If the boundary condition, $y = y_0$ when $x = x_0$ is given, the constant is fixed and the solution is

$$\int_{y_0}^{y} \frac{du}{\gamma(u)} = \int_{x_0}^{x}\beta(t)dt \, .$$

Example

Consider $$dy/dx = x^2y^4 ,$$

that is, $$dy/y^4 = x^2 dx$$

or $$-y^{-3} = x^3 + c$$

where c is an arbitrary constant which may be determined by specifying boundary conditions such as $y = 1$ when $x = 2$, in which case, $c = -9$.

Occasionally, a very simple form of this type of differential equation is met in which either $\beta(x)$ or $\gamma(y)$ is a constant.

Also, a situation arises sometimes in which equation (8.2) is said to be **exact**. This is the case when the left-hand side is the derivative of some function $f(x,y)$ with respect to x. The integral is then $f(x,y)$ = constant. Often it is easy to see by inspection whether an equation is exact or not. Again, in some cases, an integrating factor may be found by inspection which renders an equation exact. Such a factor always exists but they can be difficult to find.

Examples

(1) Consider $$ydx + xdy = 0 .$$

This is exact and gives $$d(xy) = 0$$

that is, xy = constant.

(2) Consider $$x\frac{dy}{dx} - y = 2x^2y\frac{dy}{dx} .$$

This is inexact but may be made exact by multiplying by x^{-2}; that is

$$\frac{1}{x}\frac{dy}{dx} - \frac{y}{x^2} = 2y\frac{dy}{dx} .$$

The left-hand side is now the derivative of y/x with respect to x, and so the equation may be integrated to give

$$y/x = y^2 + \text{constant.}$$

The actual condition to be satisfied by a first-order, first-degree differential equation if it is to be exact is fairly simple to obtain and will be discussed now. Consider equation (8.2),

(i) Suppose the equation is exact, then $Mdx + Ndy \equiv$ perfect differential df, say.

Also, $$df = \frac{\partial f}{\partial x}dx + \frac{\partial f}{\partial y}dy$$

since f is a function of x and y.

From the two expressions for df, it follows that

$$M = \partial f/\partial x , N = \partial f/\partial y .$$

Then

$$\frac{\partial N}{\partial x} = \frac{\partial^2 f}{\partial x \partial y} = \frac{\partial M}{\partial y}$$

provided f satisfies the conditions given in Chapter 7, so that

$$\frac{\partial^2 f}{\partial x \partial y} = \frac{\partial^2 f}{\partial y \partial x}.$$

(ii) Now suppose $\partial N/\partial x = \partial M/\partial y$ and let $F = \int M dx$, where the integration is performed on the assumption that y is constant. Then

$$\partial F/\partial x = M$$

and, provided F satisfies the conditions given in Chapter 7,

$$\frac{\partial^2 F}{\partial x \partial y} = \frac{\partial^2 F}{\partial y \partial x} = \frac{\partial M}{\partial y} = \frac{\partial N}{\partial x},$$

that is,

$$\frac{\partial}{\partial x}(N - \partial F/\partial y) = 0,$$

or

$$N - \partial F/\partial y = \phi(y).$$

Now put

$$N = \frac{\partial F}{\partial y} + \phi(y), f = F + \int \phi dy, \text{ then } N = \partial f/\partial y.$$

Also, by definition of F, $M = \partial F/\partial x = \partial f/\partial x$.

Therefore,

$$M dx + N dy = \frac{\partial f}{\partial x} dx + \frac{\partial f}{\partial y} dy.$$

$$= df, \text{ a perfect differential.}$$

Thus, the necessary and sufficient condition for equation (8.2) to be exact is

$$\partial N/\partial x = \partial M/\partial y.$$

Example

Consider $(2x^3 + 3y)dx + (3x + y - 1)dy = 0$.

In this equation $\partial M/\partial y = \partial N/\partial x = 3$, and so the equation is exact. Also,

$$\partial f/\partial x = 2x^3 + 3y$$

and so

$$f = \tfrac{1}{2}x^4 + 3xy + \phi(y).$$

Then

$$\partial f/\partial y = 3x + d\phi/dy = 3x + y - 1.$$

Therefore

$$d\phi/dy = y - 1, \quad \phi = \tfrac{1}{2}y^2 - y + c.$$

Hence, the solution $(\tfrac{1}{2}x^4 + 3xy + \tfrac{1}{2}y^2 - y + c)$, where c is a constant of integration.

A further type of differential equation of the first order and first degree which may be solved easily is the so-called homogeneous equation of the first order and first degree. This is one which may be written in the form

$$dy/dx = f(y/x) .$$

To test whether a function of x and y may be written in the form on the right-hand side of this equation, put $y = vx$. If the result is of the form $f(v)$, the test is satisfied.

Example

(i) $$dy/dx = (x^2 + y^2)/2x^2 \rightarrow (1 + v^2)/2 .$$

Therefore, homogeneous.

(ii) $$dy/dx = y^4/x^3 \rightarrow xv^4 .$$

Therefore, inhomogeneous.

To illustrate the method of solution of such equations, consider example (i). First put $y = vx$ so that

$$\frac{dy}{dx} = v + x\frac{dv}{dx}$$

and (i) becomes

$$v + x\frac{dv}{dx} = \frac{1}{2}(1 + v^2) ,$$

that is

$$2x\frac{dv}{dx} = (1 - v)^2$$

which is separable and may be integrated to give

$$\frac{2}{1 - v} = \log x + c ,$$

that is

$$\frac{2x}{x - y} = \log x + c$$

where c is a constant of integration.

Now consider the equation

$$dy/dx = (y - x + 1)/(y + x + 5) .$$

This equation is not homogeneous, although it would have been if the right-hand side had been of the form $(y - x)/(y + x)$. Now $y - x = 0$ and $y + x = 0$ represent a pair of straight lines through the origin. The intersection of the straight lines $y - x + 1 = 0$ and $y + x + 5 = 0$ is the point $(-2, -3)$. Hence, if the origin is altered to the point $(-2, -3)$ then

$$x = X - 2 , y = Y - 3$$

and the equation becomes

$$dY/dX = (Y - X)/(Y + X)$$

which is homogeneous and may be solved as before.

In the special case

$$\frac{dy}{dx} = \frac{\alpha y + \beta x + \gamma_1}{\alpha y + \beta x + \gamma_2}$$

put $z = \alpha y + \beta x$ so that $dz/dx = \alpha(dy/dx) + \beta$ and solve by separation of variables.

8.3 LINEAR EQUATIONS OF THE FIRST ORDER

The general linear equation of the first order may be written in the form

$$dy/dx + P(x)y = Q(x) \tag{8.4}$$

where $P(x)$ and $Q(x)$ are functions of x but not of y. Note that the coefficient of dy/dx may be made unity always by division.

A simple example of such an equation is

$$dy/dx + 2y/x = x .$$

This becomes exact if multiplied by x^2,

$$x^2 \frac{dy}{dx} + 2xy = x^3$$

which may be integrated to give

$$x^2 y = \tfrac{1}{4} x^4 + \text{constant.}$$

Hence, this example is solved easily by using a reasonably obvious integrating factor.

Now consider equation (8.4) and suppose it has an integrating factor R. Then, the left-hand side of

$$R \frac{dy}{dx} + RP(x)y = RQ(x)$$

is the derivative of some product or quotient and the term $R\,dy/dx$ shows that this product must be Ry.

Hence put

$$R \frac{dy}{dx} + RP(x)y = \frac{d}{dx}(Ry) = R \frac{dy}{dx} + y \frac{dR}{dx}$$

which gives

$$RP(x) = dR/dx$$

or

$$R = \exp\{\textstyle\int P(x)dx\} . \tag{8.5}$$

Therefore, to solve an equation of type (8.4), multiply throughout by an integrating factor R as given in equation (8.5).

Example

Consider

$$(1 + x^2)\frac{dy}{dx} + xy = x,$$

that is

$$\frac{dy}{dx} + \frac{x}{1 + x^2}y = \frac{x}{1 + x^2}. \qquad (a)$$

Here

$$P(x) = x(1 + x^2)^{-1} \quad \text{and so}$$

$$\int P(x)dx = \int x(1 + x^2)^{-1}dx = \tfrac{1}{2}\int 2x(1 + x^2)^{-1}dx$$

$$= \tfrac{1}{2}\log(1 + x^2) = \log\sqrt{(1 + x^2)}.$$

Hence

$$R = \sqrt{(1 + x^2)}.$$

Multiplying throughout by R in (a) yields

$$\sqrt{(1 + x^2)}\frac{dy}{dx} + \frac{x}{\sqrt{(1 + x^2)}}y = \frac{x}{\sqrt{(1 + x^2)}},$$

that is

$$y\sqrt{(1 + x^2)} = \sqrt{(1 + x^2)} + \text{constant}.$$

It might be noted that, in this example, the variables are separable and the method discussed earlier might have been used as an alternative.

Also, the so-called **Bernoulli equation**

$$dy/dx + P(x)y = y^n Q(x)$$

may be reduced to the form (8.4) by using the transformation

$$v = y^{-n+1}, y^{-n} \, dy/dx = (1 - n)^{-1} \, dv/dx$$

so that the equation becomes

$$\frac{1}{(1 - n)}\frac{dv}{dx} + vP(x) = Q(x)$$

as required.

Again, the apparently more general equation

$$f'(y)\frac{dy}{dx} + f(y)P(x) = Q(x)$$

is also a linear equation as is seen by introducing the new variable

$$v = f(y), \, dv/dx = f'(y)dy/dx$$

to give

$$dv/dx + vP(x) = Q(x)$$

as required.

8.4 LINEAR EQUATIONS WITH CONSTANT COEFFICIENTS

The general equation in this class is of the form

$$p_0 \frac{d^n y}{dx^n} + p_1 \frac{d^{n-1} y}{dx^{n-1}} + \cdots + p_n y = f(x) \tag{8.6}$$

where $f(x)$ is a function of x but $p_0, p_1, \ldots, p_n$ are all constants. These equations are important in the study of vibrations of all kinds; mechanical, acoustical, electrical.

(a) The simplest case of equation (8.6) which can be encountered is when $n = 1$ and $f(x) = 0$. In this case, the equation becomes

$$p_0 \frac{dy}{dx} + p_1 y = 0 , \tag{8.7}$$

that is

$$p_0 \frac{dy}{y} + p_1 dx = 0$$

$$p_0 \log y + p_1 x = \text{const.} = \log A, \text{ say.}$$

Hence, $\quad\quad y = A\exp(-p_1 x/p_0) .$

(b) Equations of the second order

Take $n = 2$ and $f(x) = 0$, then (8.6) becomes

$$p_0 \frac{d^2 y}{dx^2} + p_1 \frac{dy}{dx} + p_2 y = 0 . \tag{8.8}$$

The solution of (8.7) suggests that $y = Ae^{mx}$, where m is a constant, may satisfy (8.8). With this value of y (8.8) reduces to

$$Ae^{mx} (p_0 m^2 + p_1 m + p_2) = 0 .$$

Thus, if m is a root of the equation

$$p_0 m^2 + p_1 m + p_2 = 0 \tag{8.9}$$

then $y = Ae^{mx}$ is a solution of (8.8), whatever the value of A.

Let α and β be the roots of (8.9), then provided the roots are unequal we have two solutions

$$y = Ae^{\alpha x} \quad \text{and} \quad y = Be^{\beta x} .$$

Thus, the solution of (8.8) may be written

$$y = Ae^{\alpha x} + Be^{\beta x} . \tag{8.10}$$

It is trivial to check that (8.10) is a solution of (8.8) merely by substituting back. Equation (8.9) is called the **auxiliary equation**. Since it contains two arbitrary constants, (8.10) is regarded as being the most general solution of (8.8).

(c) When the auxiliary equation (8.9) has complex roots of the form $p + jq$ and $p - jq$, it is best to modify the solution

$$y = Ae^{(p+jq)x} + Be^{(p-jq)x} \tag{8.11}$$

so as to present it without imaginary quantities.

To do this we use

$$e^{jqx} = \cos qx + j \sin qx$$

$$e^{-jqx} = \cos qx - j \sin qx .$$

Equation (8.11) then becomes

$$y = Ae^{px}(\cos qx + j \sin qx) + Be^{px}(\cos qx - j \sin qx)$$

$$= e^{px}(E \cos qx + F \sin qx)$$

where $E = A + B$, $F = j(A - B)$.
It does not follow that F is always imaginary. For example

$$\left. \begin{array}{l} A = 1 + 2j \\ B = 1 - 2j \end{array} \right\} \rightarrow \left\{ \begin{array}{l} E = 2 \\ F = -4 . \end{array} \right.$$

Example

Solve

$$\frac{d^2y}{dx^2} + 4y = 0 .$$

The auxiliary equation is

$$m^2 + 4 = 0 \Rightarrow m = \pm 2j$$

and so

$$y = Ae^{2jx} + Be^{-2jx}$$

$$= E \cos 2x + F \sin 2x .$$

(d) When the auxiliary equation has equal roots $\alpha = \beta$, the

solution

$$y = Ae^{\alpha x} + Be^{\beta x}$$

reduces to

$$y = Ce^{\alpha x} .$$

Since it involves only *one* arbitrary constant, this solution cannot be regarded as being the most general one.

Consider the equation

$$\frac{d^2y}{dx^2} - 2\alpha \frac{dy}{dx} + \alpha^2 y = 0 .$$

The auxiliary equation is

$$m^2 - 2\alpha m + \alpha^2 = (m - \alpha)^2 = 0$$

which obviously has equal roots.

Now $y = Ae^{\alpha x}$ is one solution. Suppose the general solution is $y = e^{\alpha x}V$ where V is a function of x; then

$$\frac{d^2y}{dx^2} - 2\alpha\frac{dy}{dx} + \alpha^2 y = e^{\alpha x}\frac{d^2V}{dx^2} = 0$$

$$\Rightarrow V = A + Bx$$

so that
$$y = (A + Bx)e^{\alpha x}.$$

Similarly, for an equation with p equal roots, it is found that

$$y = (A_1 + A_2 x + \cdots + A_p x^{p-1})e^{\alpha x}.$$

All these methods apply to higher-order equations provided $f(x) = 0$. Suppose V to be the set of infinitely differentiable functions y with fixed domain which is normally R, the line of real numbers. Then a function $T : V \rightarrow V$ is a **linear operator** if, for all $c_1, c_2 \in R$ and $y_1, y_2 \in V$,

$$T(c_1 y_1 + c_2 y_2) = c_1 T(y_1) + c_2 T(y_2).$$

The nth derivative $d^n y/dx^n$ defines a linear operator $D^n : V \rightarrow V$; if p and q are real numbers

$$\frac{d^2y}{dx^2} + q\frac{dy}{dx} + py$$

defines a linear operator $(D^2 + qD + p):V \rightarrow V$; and so on.

The words **linear equation** are often applied to an equation of the form

$$T(y) = h$$

where $T : V \rightarrow V$ is a linear operator and h a fixed element of V.

Lemma

Let $T : V \rightarrow V$ be a linear operator and $y_1 \in V$ a particular solution of the equation $T(y) = h$. Then, every solution of $T(y) = h$ has the form $y_0 + y_1$, where y_0 is a solution of the equation $T(y) = 0$.

Proof

The definition of linear operator implies that

$$T(y_0 + y_1) = T(y_0) + T(y_1) = h$$

and so $y_0 + y_1$ is a solution of $T(y) = h$.

Similarly, if z is an arbitrary solution of $T(y) = h$ then

$$T(z - y_1) = T(z) - T(y_1) = h - h = 0$$

and so $z - y_1 = y_0$ for some solution y_0 of $T(y) = 0$. In other words, every solution z of $T(y) = h$ has the form $y_0 + y_1$.

Corollary

Let $y_1, \ldots, y_n \in V$ be functions with the property that every solution y_0 of $T(y) = 0$ has the form

$$y_0 = c_1 y_1 + \cdots + c_n y_n$$

where $c_1, \ldots, c_n$ are real numbers. If $z \in V$ is a particular solution of $T(y) = h$ then every solution of $T(y) = h$ has the form $(c_1 y_1 + \cdots + c_n y_n + z)$.

Here z is a **particular integral** of $T(y) = h$; the expression $c_1 y_1 + \cdots + c_n y_n$ is the **complementary function**, and the real numbers $c_1, \ldots, c_n$ are arbitrary constants.

Now consider the equation

$$\frac{d^n y}{dx^n} + a_1 \frac{d^{n-1} y}{dx^{n-1}} + \cdots + a_n y = h(x) .$$

This may be written in the form

$$T(y) = h$$

where $T : V \to V$ is the linear operator $D^n + a_1 D^{n-1} + \cdots + a_n$.

By the above lemma, it is possible to find all solutions of $T(y) = h$ in two steps:

    (i) find all solutions of $T(y) = 0$

and (ii) find a particular solution of $T(y) = h$.

Methods for carrying out step (i) have been discussed already. A method for dealing with step (ii) will be discussed shortly. However, in practice, it is often possible to 'guess' a particular solution as will be illustrated now.

Examples

(1) Consider

$$\frac{d^2 y}{dx^2} - \frac{dy}{dx} - 2y = 44 - 76x - 48x^2 .$$

The auxiliary equation is

$$m^2 - m - 2 = (m - 2)(m + 1) = 0 .$$

Therefore, the complementary function is

$$Ae^{2x} + Be^{-x} .$$

To find a particular integral, since $h(x) = 44 - 76x - 48x^2$, it is reasonable to try a polynomial in x;

$$ax^2 + bx + c .$$

Substituting into the original equation and comparing coefficients gives $a = 24$, $b = 14$, $c = -5$.

Therefore, the solution is

$$y = Ae^{2x} + Be^{-x} + 24x^2 + 14x - 5 .$$

(2) Consider

$$\frac{d^3y}{dx^3} - 6\frac{d^2y}{dx^2} + 11\frac{dy}{dx} - 6y = 20\cos x .$$

The auxiliary equation is

$$m^3 - 6m^2 + 11m - 6 = (m-1)(m-2)(m-3) = 0 .$$

The complementary function is

$$Ae^x + Be^{2x} + Ce^{3x} .$$

To find a particular integral, since $h(x) = 20\cos x$, it is reasonable to try linear combinations of $\cos x$ and $\sin x$:

$$a\cos x + b\sin x .$$

Substituting into the original equation and comparing coefficients gives $a = 0$, $b = 2$.
Therefore, the solution is

$$y = Ae^x + Be^{2x} + Ce^{3x} + 2\sin x$$

(3) Consider

$$\frac{d^3y}{dx^3} - 2\frac{d^2y}{dx^2} + \frac{dy}{dx} - 2y = 4e^x .$$

The auxiliary equation is

$$m^3 - 2m^2 + m - 2 = (m-2)(m^2+1) = 0 .$$

The complementary function is

$$Ae^{2x} + B\cos x + C\sin x .$$

To find a particular integral, since $h(x) = 4e^x$, it is reasonable to try multiples of e^x: ae^x.
Substituting into the original equation and comparing coefficients gives $a = -2$.
Hence, the solution is

$$y = Ae^{2x} + B\cos x + C\sin x - 2e^x .$$

Now consider the second-order equation

$$T(y) = \frac{d^2y}{dx^2} + q\frac{dy}{dx} + py = h ,$$

where p, q are real numbers and h is a function of x. The aim is to find a particular integral for equations such as this. In practice the method outlined already—which might be termed inspired guesswork—is often best. However, here a general method will be discussed which is surer but often slower. The method has the merit that it may be extended to higher order equations and to the case when p, q are non-constant functions. It is called the method of **variation of parameters**.

Suppose that solutions of

$$T(y) = 0$$

have been found in the form

$$y_0 = c_1 y_1 + c_2 y_2$$

where c_1, c_2 are arbitrary real numbers. Consider functions of the form

$$y = v_1 y_1 + v_2 y_2$$

where v_1, v_2 are non-constant functions. Then,

$$\frac{dy}{dx} = \left(\frac{dv_1}{dx} y_1 + \frac{dv_2}{dx} y_2 \right) + \left(v_1 \frac{dy_1}{dx} + v_2 \frac{dy_2}{dx} \right).$$

Suppose that

$$\frac{dv_1}{dx} y_1 + \frac{dv_2}{dx} y_2 = 0,$$

then

$$\frac{d^2 y}{dx^2} = \left(\frac{dv_1}{dx} \frac{dy_1}{dx} + \frac{dv_2}{dx} \frac{dy_2}{dx} \right) + \left(v_1 \frac{d^2 y_1}{dx^2} + v_2 \frac{d^2 y_2}{dx^2} \right).$$

Hence

$$\frac{d^2 y}{dx^2} + q \frac{dy}{dx} + py = \left(\frac{dv_1}{dx} \frac{dy_1}{dx} + \frac{dv_2}{dx} \frac{dy_2}{dx} \right)$$

$$+ v_1 \left(\frac{d^2 y_1}{dx^2} + q \frac{dy_1}{dx} + py_1 \right)$$

$$+ v_2 \left(\frac{d^2 y_2}{dx^2} + q \frac{dy_2}{dx} + py_2 \right)$$

$$= \frac{dv_1}{dx} \frac{dy_1}{dx} + \frac{dv_2}{dx} \frac{dy_2}{dx}.$$

It follows that y will be a solution of

$$T(y) = h$$

if v_1, v_2 satisfy the equations

$$\frac{dv_1}{dx} y_1 + \frac{dv_2}{dx} y_2 = 0$$

and

$$\frac{dv_1}{dx} \frac{dy_1}{dx} + \frac{dv_2}{dx} \frac{dy_2}{dx} = h.$$

From these equations, it is seen that

$$\frac{dv_1}{dx}\left(y_1 \frac{dy_2}{dx} - y_2 \frac{dy_1}{dx}\right) = -y_2 h$$

and

$$\frac{dv_2}{dx}\left(y_1 \frac{dy_2}{dx} - y_2 \frac{dy_1}{dx}\right) = y_1 h$$

which may be solved to give dv_1/dx and dv_2/dx. The resulting expressions may be integrated to give the functions v_1 and v_2—although in a specific example it may not be possible to perform the integration explicitly.

The result of the lemma proved earlier shows that every solution of $T(y) = h$ has the form $y_0 + y$.

Examples

(1) Consider the equation

$$d^2y/dx^2 + y = 2\cos x.$$

The complementary function is $A\cos x + B\sin x = Ay_1 + By_2$. The equations for v_1 and v_2 become

$$\frac{dv_1}{dx}(\cos x \cos x + \sin x \sin x) = -2 \sin x \cos x$$

and so

$$v_1 = -2\int \sin x \cos x \, dx = \tfrac{1}{2}\cos 2x$$

$$dv_2/dx = 2\cos^2 x$$

$$v_2 = x + \tfrac{1}{2}\sin 2x.$$

The solution is

$$y = A\cos x + B\sin x + v_1\cos x + v_2\sin x$$

$$= A\cos x + B\sin x + x\sin x.$$

(2) Consider the equation

$$\frac{d^2y}{dx^2} + \frac{dy}{dx} - 2y = e^x + \sin x - 4x.$$

The complementary function is $Ae^{-2x} + Be^x = Ay_1 + By_2$. Also

$$y_1 \frac{dy_2}{dx} - y_2 \frac{dy_1}{dx} = 3e^{-x} .$$

The equations for v_1 and v_2 become

$$3 \frac{dv_1}{dx} = -e^{2x}(e^x + \sin x - 4x)$$

$$3 \frac{dv_2}{dx} = e^{-x}(e^x + \sin x - 4x) .$$

These may be integrated to give

$$3v_1 = -\tfrac{1}{3}e^{3x} + \tfrac{1}{5}e^{2x}(-2\sin x + \cos x) + 2xe^{2x} - e^{2x}$$

$$3v_2 = x - \tfrac{1}{2}e^{-x}(\sin x + \cos x) + 4xe^{-x} + 4e^{-x} .$$

Thus, the particular integral obtained is

$$v_1 y_1 + v_2 y_2 = -\tfrac{1}{9}e^x + 2x + 1 + \tfrac{1}{3}xe^x$$

$$-\tfrac{1}{10}\cos x - \tfrac{3}{10}\sin x .$$

The complete solution is

$$y = Ae^{-2x} + Ce^x + 2x + 1 + \tfrac{1}{3}xe^x - \tfrac{1}{10}\cos x - \tfrac{3}{10}\sin x$$

(where $C = B - \tfrac{1}{9}$).

8.5 MISCELLANEOUS EQUATIONS
Firstly, it may be noted that the homogeneous linear equation

$$p_0 x^n \frac{d^n y}{dx^n} + p_1 x^{n-1} \frac{d^{n-1}y}{dx^{n-1}} + \cdots + p_n y = f(x)$$

reduces to the constant coefficient type if the substitution $x = e^t$ is used. If $x = e^t$, $dx/dt = e^t = x$ and

$$\frac{d}{dx} = \frac{dt}{dx}\frac{d}{dt} = \frac{1}{x}\frac{d}{dt} ,$$

$$\frac{d^2}{dx^2} = \frac{d}{dx}\left(\frac{1}{x}\frac{d}{dt}\right) = -\frac{1}{x^2}\frac{d}{dt} + \frac{1}{x^2}\frac{d^2}{dt^2} ,$$

and so on.

Again, some second-order equations may be reduced to equations of the first order. This may be done always if the equation (i) does not contain y explicitly, (ii) does not contain x explicitly, or (iii) is homogeneous.

(i) *The case of y absent*
In this case, write p for dy/dx and dp/dx for d^2y/dx^2.
Example
Consider

$$x\frac{d^2y}{dx^2} + \frac{dy}{dx} = 4x \ .$$

This transforms into

$$x\frac{dp}{dx} + p = 4x$$

which may be integrated to give

$$xp = 2x^2 + a$$

that is,
$$\frac{dy}{dx} = p = 2x + \frac{a}{x}$$

or
$$y = x^2 + a\log x + b$$

where a and b are constants of integration.
(ii) *The case of x absent*
In this case write p for dy/dx and pdp/dy for d^2y/dx^2.
Example

Consider
$$y\frac{d^2y}{dx^2} = \left(\frac{dy}{dx}\right)^2 .$$

This transforms into

$$yp\frac{dp}{dy} = p^2$$

which may be integrated to give

$$\begin{array}{ll} & p = by \\ \text{or} & y = ae^{bx} \end{array}$$

where a and b are constants of integration.
(iii) *The homogeneous case*
The homogeneous equation

$$xy\frac{d^2y}{dx^2} + x\left(\frac{dy}{dx}\right)^2 = 3y\frac{dy}{dx}$$

may be solved by substituting $x = e^t$ as in an earlier example. However, for a homogeneous equation of the form

$$(x^2 + y^2)\left(y - x\frac{dy}{dx}\right) + x^2y^2\frac{d^2y}{dx^2} = 0 \, ,$$

it is necessary first to use the substitution $y = vx$.

8.6 SERIES SOLUTIONS OF ORDINARY DIFFERENTIAL EQUATIONS

Here attention will be focused on differential equations of the form

$$\frac{d^2y}{dx^2} + P(x)\frac{dy}{dx} + Q(x)\,y = 0$$

where $P(x)$ and $Q(x)$ are functions of x alone. Following F. G. Fröbenius, a trial solution of the form

$$y = x^c(a_0 + a_1x + a_2x^2 + \cdots) = x^c\sum_{i=0}^{\infty}a_ix^i$$

where the a_i are constants, will be assumed. The index c will be determined by a quadratic equation, the so-called **indicial equation**. This equation may have equal roots, roots which are different and differ by an integer, or roots which are different and differ by a quantity not an integer. It proves necessary to discuss these cases separately.

From the outset it should be noted that this method fails under certain circumstances. For example, a function like $e^{1/x}$ cannot be expanded in ascending powers of x, and so the method would be expected to fail for differential equations having solutions of this type. However, more of this later. There are, in fact, four separate cases to be considered and these will be examined now by discussing a particular example of each type rather than by proving various existence theorems. Details of the various relevant existence theorems may be found in books devoted solely to the study of differential equations:—for example, the book by Piaggio.

Case 1 Roots of the indicial equation different and differing by a quantity not an integer.

Consider

$$4x\frac{d^2y}{dx^2} + 2\frac{dy}{dx} + y = 0 \, .$$

Put

$$y = \sum_{i=0}^{\infty}a_ix^{c+i} \, , \quad \text{where } a_0 \neq 0 \, .$$

then

$$\frac{dy}{dx} = \sum_{i=0}^{\infty}(c + i)a_ix^{c+i-1}$$

$$\frac{d^2y}{dx^2} = \sum_{i=0}^{\infty}(c + i)(c + i - 1)a_ix^{c+i-2} \, .$$

Now substitute into the given differential equation and equate the coefficients of the successive powers of x to zero. In this case, the lowest power of x is x^{c-1} and its coefficient equated to zero gives

$$4a_0c(c-1) + 2a_0c = 0 ,$$

that is, $$2c(2c-1) = 0 \quad \text{since } a_0 \neq 0 .$$

This is the indicial equation, and in this case it does have roots which are different and differ by a quantity not an integer.

The coefficient of x^c equated to zero gives

$$4a_1(c+1)c + 2a_1(c+1) + a_0 = 0$$

that is, $$2(2c+1)(c+1)a_1 = -a_0 .$$

The coefficient of x^{c+1} equated to zero gives

$$4a_2(c+2)(c+1) + 2a_2(c+2) + a_1 = 0$$

that is, $$2(2c+3)(c+2)a_2 = -a_1 = \frac{a_0}{2(2c+1)(c+1)}$$

and so on.

In general, $$a_n = \frac{(-1)^n a_0}{2^n \prod_{i=1}^{n} (c+i) \prod_{j=1}^{n} (2c+2j-1)} .$$

From the indicial equation, $c = 0$ or $c = \frac{1}{2}$. If $c = 0$,

$$y = a\left(1 - \frac{x}{2!} + \frac{x^2}{4!} \cdots \right) = au, \text{ say,}$$

replacing a_0, which is arbitrary, by a.

If $c = \frac{1}{2}$,

$$y = b\left(1 - \frac{x}{3!} + \frac{x^2}{5!} \cdots \right) = bv , \text{ say,}$$

replacing a_0, which is arbitrary, by b.

Hence, $y = au + bv$ is a solution which contains two arbitrary constants and so may be considered the complete solution.

Thus, if the indicial equation has two unequal roots differing by a quantity not an integer, two independent solutions are found by substituting these values for c in the series for y.

Case 2 Roots of the indicial equation equal.

Consider $$x\frac{d^2y}{dx^2} + \frac{dy}{dx} + xy = 0$$

which is Bessel's equation of order zero.

Again put $y = \sum_{i=0}^{\infty} a_i x^{c+i}$ and, after substituting in the differential equation, equate the coefficients of successive powers of x to zero. The lowest power of x is x^{c-1} and its coefficient equated to zero gives

$$a_0 c(c - 1) + a_0 c = 0$$

that is, $c^2 = 0$ since $a_0 \neq 0$.

Also, $a_1(c + 1)c + a_1(c + 1) = 0$

that is, $a_1 = 0$

and $a_2(c + 2)(c + 1) + a_2(c + 2) = -a_0$

that is, $a_2 = - a_0/(c + 2)^2$.

Similarly,
$$a_3 = 0 \, , \, a_4 = - \frac{a_2}{(c + 4)^2} = \frac{a_0}{(c + 4)^2 (c + 2)^2}$$

and so on.

In general,
$$a_{2n} = \frac{(-1)^n a_0}{\prod\limits_{i=1}^{n} (c + 2i)^2}$$

and all odd-numbered coefficients are zero.

Thus,
$$y = a_0 x^c \left\{ 1 - \frac{x^2}{(c + 2)^2} + \frac{x^4}{(c + 4)^2(c + 2)^2} \cdots \right\}$$

is a solution if $c = 0$.

However, this gives one series instead of two and contains only one arbitrary constant. Hence, it cannot be the complete solution. If the above series is substituted into the given differential equation *without* putting $c = 0$, the single term $a_0 c^2 x^{c-1}$ remains. Since this term contains c^2, its partial derivative with respect to c, that is $2a_0 c x^{c-1} + a_0 c^2 x^{c-1} \log x$, will vanish also when $x = c$. That is

$$\frac{\partial}{\partial c} \left\{ x \frac{d^2}{dx^2} + \frac{d}{dx} + x \right\} y = 2a_0 c x^{c-1} + a_0 c^2 x^{c-1} \log x$$

vanishes when $c = 0$.

Since differential operators commute, this may be written

$$\left\{ x \frac{d^2}{dx^2} + \frac{d}{dx} + x \right\} \frac{\partial y}{\partial c} = 2a_0 c x^{c-1} + a_0 c^2 x^{c-1} \log x \, .$$

Therefore, $\partial y/\partial c$ is a second solution of the differential equation if c is put equal to zero after differentiation.

Now
$$\frac{\partial y}{\partial c} = y\log x + a_0 x^c \left\{ \frac{2x^2}{(c+2)^3} - \frac{2x^4(2c+6)}{(c+4)^3(c+2)^3} \cdots \right\}.$$

Putting $c = 0$ and, since a_0 is arbitrary, putting a_0 equal to a and b respectively in the two series yields

$$y = a\left(1 - \frac{x^2}{2^2} + \frac{x^4}{2^2 \cdot 4^2} \cdots\right) = au$$

and
$$\frac{\partial y}{\partial c} = bu\log x + b\left\{\frac{x^2}{2^2} - \frac{1}{2^2 \cdot 4^2}\left(1 + \frac{1}{2}\right)x^4 \cdots\right\} = bv.$$

Then the complete solution is $au + bv$.

Thus, if the indicial equation has two equal roots $c = \alpha$, two independent solutions are obtained by substituting this value of c in y and $\partial y/\partial c$.

Case 3 Roots of the indicial equation differing by an integer, making a coefficient of y infinite.

Consider
$$x^2 \frac{d^2y}{dx^2} + x \frac{dy}{dx} + (x^2 - 4)y = 0$$

which is Bessel's equation of order two.

Proceeding as before leads to

$$a_0 c(c - 1) + a_0 c - 4a_0 = 0$$

that is,
$$c^2 - 4 = 0 \quad \text{since } a_0 \neq 0.$$

Also,
$$a_1[(c + 1)^2 - 4] = 0 \Rightarrow a_1 = 0$$

$$a_2[(c + 2)^2 - 4] = -a_0$$

and
$$a_n[(c + n)^2 - 4] = -a_{n-2}$$

giving finally

$$y = a_0 x^c \left\{1 - \frac{x^2}{c(c+4)} + \frac{x^4}{c(c+2)(c+4)(c+6)} \cdots\right\}.$$

The roots of the indicial equation are $c = 2$ and $c = -2$. However, owing to the factor $(c + 2)$ in the denominator of some terms, putting $c = -2$ in this series results in some coefficients becoming infinite. To counteract this, replace a_0 by $(c + 2)k$ (this means that the condition $a_0 \neq 0$ is violated but assume instead that $k \neq 0$) to give

$$y = kx^c \left\{(c + 2) - \frac{(c+2)x^2}{c(c+4)} + \frac{x^4}{c(c+4)(c+6)} \cdots\right\}.$$

When this is substituted into the left-hand side of the original differential equation, the result is $kx^c(c + 2)^2(c - 2)$. The occurrence of the squared factor, $(c + 2)^2$, shows that $\partial y/\partial c$ satisfies the differential equation when $c = -2$ as well as y (the same situation as in Case 2). Another solution is given by putting $c = 2$ in y. Hence, three solutions appear to have been found for a second-order differential equation. Evaluating these solutions gives

$$kx^{-2}\left\{-\frac{1}{2^2 \cdot 4}x^4 + \frac{1}{2^3 \cdot 4 \cdot 6}x^6 \cdots\right\} = ku \text{ say,}$$

$$ku\log x + kx^{-2}\left\{1 + \frac{x^2}{2^2} + \frac{1}{2^2 \cdot 4^2}x^4 \cdots\right\} = kv \text{ say,}$$

and
$$kx^2\left\{4 - \frac{x^2}{3} + \frac{x^4}{2 \cdot 6 \cdot 8} \cdots\right\} = kw \text{ say.}$$

Obviously, $w = -2^2 \cdot 4^2 u$, and so only two linearly independent solutions have been found. The complete solution is then $au + bv$.

Thus, if the indicial equation has two roots α and $\beta(\alpha > \beta)$ differing by an integer and if some of the coefficients of y become infinite when $c = \beta$, modify the form of y by replacing a_0 by $k(c - \beta)$. Then two independent solutions are obtained by putting $c = \beta$ in the modified form of y and $\partial y/\partial c$. Putting $c = \alpha$ merely leads to a numerical multiple of the result obtained by putting $c = \beta$.
Case 4 Roots of the indicial equation differing by an integer making a coefficient of y indeterminate.

Consider
$$(1 - x^2)\frac{d^2y}{dx^2} - 2x\frac{dy}{dx} + 2y = 0$$

which is Legendre's equation of order unity.
Proceeding as before leads to

$$c(c - 1) = 0$$

$$a_1(c + 1)c = 0 \qquad\qquad (\alpha)$$

$$a_2(c + 2)(c + 1) - a_0(c + 2)(c - 1) = 0$$

and
$$a_n(c + n)(c + n - 1) - a_{n-2}(c + n)(c + n - 3) = 0.$$

From the indicial equation $c = 0$ or $c = 1$. If $c = 0$, it is seen from (α) that the coefficient of a_1 vanishes. Since there are no other terms in the equation, this makes a_1 indeterminate instead of infinite. Also, if $c = 1$, $a_1 = 0$.
Now, if $c = 0$, the relations between the coefficients become

$$a_2 = -a_0 \,,\, a_3 = 0 \,,\, a_4 = -\tfrac{1}{3}a_0 \,,\, \text{etc.}$$

which leads to

$$[y]_{c=0} = a_0 \left(1 - x^2 - \frac{x^4}{3} \cdots \right) + a_1 x .$$

This contains two arbitrary constants, and so may be taken as the complete solution. If $c = 1$, the resulting expression is

$$[y]_{c=1} = a_0 x$$

that is, a constant multiple of the second series in the first solution.

Thus, if the indicial equation has two roots α and $\beta (\alpha > \beta)$ differing by an integer and if one of the coefficients of y becomes indeterminate when $c = \beta$, the complete solution is given by putting $c = \beta$ in y, which then contains two arbitrary constants. Putting $c = \alpha$ merely leads to a numerical multiple of one of the series obtained by putting $c = \beta$.

As mentioned at the beginning of this section, there are differential equations for which this method fails; that is, those which have solutions that cannot be expanded in ascending powers of x. For example, consider

$$\frac{d^2 y}{dz^2} - y = 0$$

which has e^z and e^{-z} as solutions, and transform it by putting $z = 1/x$, then

$$\frac{dy}{dz} = \frac{dx}{dz}\frac{dy}{dx} = -\frac{1}{z^2}\frac{dy}{dx} = -x^2\frac{dy}{dx}$$

$$\frac{d^2 y}{dz^2} = \frac{dx}{dz}\frac{d}{dx}\left(\frac{dy}{dz}\right) = -x^2\frac{d}{dx}\left(-x^2\frac{dy}{dx}\right) = x^4\frac{d^2 y}{dx^2} + 2x^3\frac{dy}{dx}$$

Hence the equation becomes

$$x^4\frac{d^2 y}{dx^2} + 2x^3\frac{dy}{dx} - y = 0 .$$

If an attempt is made to use the above method of solution, the resulting indicial equation is $-a_0 = 0$ which has no roots since $a_0 \neq 0$ by hypothesis. Such a differential equation is said to have no regular integrals in ascending powers of x.

8.7 LAPLACE TRANSFORMS

Earlier in this section, a method was discussed for solving constant coefficient equations of the general type

$$\frac{d^n y}{dx^n} + a_1\frac{d^{n-1} y}{dx^{n-1}} + \cdots + a_{n-1}\frac{dy}{dx} + a_n y = g(x)$$

where $a_1, a_2, \ldots, a_{n-1}, a_n$ are constants. The general solution of such an equation involves n arbitrary constants and, if the required solution has to be the one satisfying given boundary conditions, the particular values of these constants are found by solving n linear equations. This procedure can prove extremely tedious and is somewhat inelegant. Another method of solving equations of the above type and which overcomes the objections mentioned, involves the use of Laplace transforms.

The **Laplace transform** $\mathscr{F}(p)$ of a function $f(x)$, where $x > 0$, is defined by

$$\mathscr{F}(p) = \int_0^\infty e^{-px} f(x) dx . \tag{8.12}$$

Often this relation is written

$$\mathscr{F}(p) = \mathscr{L}[f(x)]$$

where $\mathscr{L}[\ ]$ represents symbolically the operation of taking the Laplace transform of the function appearing inside the bracket. The function $\mathscr{F}(p)$ is defined for values of p for which the integral (8.12) converges.

An elementary, but extremely useful, property of Laplace transforms is that of linearity. From (8.12), it is seen that

$$\mathscr{L}[kf(x)] = k\mathscr{L}[f(x)]$$

where k is any constant, and, if α and β are constants and $g(x)$ an arbitrary function defined for $x > 0$,

$$\mathscr{L}[\alpha f(x) + \beta g(x)] = \int_0^\infty e^{-px} \{\alpha f(x) + \beta g(x)\} dx$$

$$= \alpha \int_0^\infty e^{-px} f(x) dx + \beta \int_0^\infty e^{-px} g(x) dx$$

$$= \alpha \mathscr{L}[f(x)] + \beta \mathscr{L}[g(x)] .$$

Using equation (8.12), the Laplace transforms of elementary functions are found easily. In the following table, a few useful Laplace transforms are given together with the range of convergence of the relevant integral of type (8.12). Also, a is a real constant and n a non-negative integer in this table.

Table 8.1 Some elementary functions and their Laplace transforms.

$f(x)$	$\mathscr{F}(p)$	Range of p
e^{ax}	$(p-a)^{-1}$	$p > a$
$\cosh ax$	$p(p^2 - a^2)^{-1}$	$p > |a|$
$\sinh ax$	$a(p^2 - a^2)^{-1}$	$p > |a|$

Table 8.1   (continued)

$\cos ax$	$p(p^2 + a^2)^{-1}$	$p > 0$
$\sin ax$	$a(p^2 + a^2)^{-1}$	$p > 0$
x^n	$n!\, p^{-n-1}$	$p > 0$
$\dfrac{x}{2a}\sin ax$	$p(p^2 + a^2)^{-2}$	$p > \lvert a\rvert$
$\dfrac{(\sin ax - ax\cos ax)}{2a^3}$	$(p^2 + a^2)^{-2}$	$p > \lvert a\rvert$

Proving these results is relatively easy. Using (8.12), evaluating $\mathcal{L}[e^{ax}]$ is trivial. Then, since $\cosh ax = \frac{1}{2}(e^{ax} + e^{-ax})$, $\mathcal{L}[\cosh ax]$ follows immediately using the property of linearity of the Laplace transform. Similarly for $\mathcal{L}[\sinh ax]$. Also, provided $p > 0$,

$$\mathcal{L}[e^{jax}] = (p - ja)^{-1}.$$

Taking real and imaginary parts of this result yields $\mathcal{L}[\cos ax]$ and $\mathcal{L}[\sin ax]$ respectively. Hence,

$$\int_0^\infty e^{-px}\cos ax\, dx = p(p^2 + a^2)^{-1}$$

for all a. Differentiating both sides partially with respect to a yields $\mathcal{L}[(x/2a)\sin ax]$. Similarly, differentiating

$$\int_0^\infty e^{-px}\sin ax\, dx = a(p^2 + a^2)^{-1}$$

partially with respect to a yields the final result in the table.

Finally, the formula for $\mathcal{L}[x^n]$ is seen to be true for $n = 0$. Therefore, assume that

$$\int_0^\infty e^{-px} x^{n-1}\, dx = (n - 1)!\, p^{-n}$$

for $n \geq 1$. Integrating by parts yields

$$\frac{1}{n}\left[e^{-px}x^n\right]_0^\infty + \frac{p}{n}\int_0^\infty e^{-px}x^n dx = (n - 1)!\, p^{-n}.$$

Since $n \geq 1$, the first term on the left-hand side is zero, and so

$$\int_0^\infty e^{-px} x^n dx = n!\, p^{-n-1}\,.$$

Thus, by induction the formula for $\mathscr{L}[x^n]$ is seen to be true.

Before proceeding to use Laplace transforms to help in the solution of constant coefficient equations, several further properties of the said transforms will be established. The most important property is

If $\mathscr{F}(p)$ exists for $p > \alpha$, then there is only one function $f(x)$ which satisfies equation (8.12) for all $p > \alpha$.   (8.13)

This implies that $f(x)$ is determined uniquely by $\mathscr{F}(p)$ in (8.12). Then, $f(x)$ is said to be the **inverse Laplace transform** of $\mathscr{F}(p)$ and is written

$$f(x) = \mathscr{L}^{-1}[\mathscr{F}(p)]\,.$$

From (8.12) and this equation, it follows that

$$\mathscr{L}\,\mathscr{L}^{-1} = \mathscr{L}^{-1}\,\mathscr{L} = 1$$

and since $\mathscr{L}[\ ]$ is a linear operator, $\mathscr{L}^{-1}[\ ]$ is seen to be a linear operator also.

Obviously, this property means that, if it is required to find some function $f(x)$, its transform $\mathscr{F}(p)$ may be found instead knowing that that fixes $f(x)$ uniquely. Although this property is so important, the moderately long proof will be omitted.

As a further preliminary to the solution of constant coefficient equations by use of Laplace transforms, it is necessary to evaluate the transforms of the derivatives of a function $f(x)$. It will be shown now that

The Laplace transform of the mth derivative $d^m f(x)/dx^m$ is given by

$$\mathscr{L}[d^m f(x)/dx^m] = p^m \mathscr{F}(p) - \sum_{r=0}^{m-1} p^{m-r-1} f^{(r)}(0)   \qquad (8.14)$$

where $f^{(r)}(0)$, $r = 0,1,\ldots,m-1$, denotes the value of $d^r f(x)/dx^r$ at $x = 0$, and these quantities are constants.

Proof of (8.14)

When $m = 1$, (8.14) becomes

$$\mathscr{L}[d f(x)/dx] = p\mathscr{F}(p) - f(0)\,.$$

Using (8.12)

$$\mathscr{L}[d f(x)/dx] = \int_0^\infty e^{-px}\,\frac{d f(x)}{dx}\,dx$$

$$[e^{-px} f(x)]_0^\infty + p \int_0^\infty e^{-px} f(x) dx$$

$$= -f(0) + p\mathscr{F}(p)$$

which establishes (8.14) for $m = 1$.

Now suppose (8.14) to be true for some particular value of m, $m \geq 1$, then

$$\int_0^\infty e^{-px}\{d^m f(x)/dx^m\}dx = p^m \mathscr{F}(p) - \sum_{r=0}^{m-1} p^{m-r-1} f^{(r)}(0) .$$

Integrating the left-hand side of this equation by parts yields

$$[-p^{-1}e^{-px}\{d^m f(x)/dx^m\}]_0^\infty + p^{-1}\int_0^\infty e^{-px}\{d^{m+1}f(x)/dx^{m+1}\}dx$$

$$= p^{-1}\{f^{(m)}(0) + \mathscr{L}[d^{m+1}f(x)/dx^{m+1}]\}$$

$$= p^m \mathscr{F}(p) - \sum_{r=0}^{m-1} p^{m-r-1} f^{(r)}(0) .$$

Hence $$\mathscr{L}[d^{m+1}f(x)/dx^{m+1}] = p\{p^m \mathscr{F}(p) - \sum_{r=0}^{m-1} p^{m-r-1} f^{(r)}(0)\} - f^{(m)}(0)$$

which establishes (8.14) with m replaced by $m + 1$ and completes the proof by induction of (8.14).

Another result which often proves useful is

$$\mathscr{L}[\int_0^x f(t)dt] = p^{-1}\mathscr{F}(p) . \qquad (8.15)$$

This follows easily from

$$\int_0^\infty e^{-px} f(x)dx = \mathscr{F}(p)$$

since integrating this definition by parts yields

$$[e^{-px}\int_0^x f(t)dt]_0^\infty + p\int_0^\infty e^{-px}\{\int_0^x f(t)dt\}dx = \mathscr{F}(p) .$$

Now e^{-px} vanishes for $x = \infty$ and $\int_0^x f(t)dt$ vanishes for $x = 0$. Thus (8.15) is proved.

This result is useful when it is required to find a function whose Laplace transform is given and contains a factor p^{-1}. In these circumstances, it is written

$$\mathscr{L}^{-1}[p^{-1}\mathscr{F}(p)] = \int_0^x f(t)dt .$$

For example, suppose it is required to find $\mathscr{L}^{-1}[p^{-1}(p^2 - 4)^{-1}]$. From the table, it is seen that

$$\mathscr{L}^{-1}[(p^2 - 4)^{-1}] = \tfrac{1}{2}\sinh 2x .$$

Therefore, using (8.15)

$$\mathcal{L}^{-1}[p^{-1}(p^2 - 4)^{-1}] = \tfrac{1}{2} \int_0^x \sinh 2t \, dt = \tfrac{1}{4}(\cosh 2x - 1) \, .$$

8.7.1 Solution of constant coefficient equations

Now to consider the problem of showing that a solution $y = f(x)$ of the nth-order constant coefficient equation

$$\frac{d^n y}{dx^n} + a_1 \frac{d^{n-1}y}{dx^{n-1}} + \cdots + a_{n-1}\frac{dy}{dx} + a_n y = g(x) \qquad (8.16)$$

is determined uniquely if the values of y and its first $(n - 1)$ derivatives are given for some value x_0 of x.

Assume that (i) $x_0 = 0$, since, if it is not zero, the zero of x may be redefined to be at x_0, and (ii) it is required to solve (8.16) for $x > 0$. (A solution for $x < 0$ may be found using identical methods.)

Suppose $y_0, y_1, y_2, \ldots, y_{n-1}$ are the values taken by y, dy/dx, $d^2y/dx^2, \ldots,$ $d^{n-1}y/dx^{n-1}$ respectively when $x = 0$. Then, the solution $y = f(x)$ must satisfy (8.16) for $x \geqslant 0$ and

$$f(0) = y_0 \, , \, f'(0) = y_1 \, , \, \ldots \, , f^{(n-1)}(0) = y_{n-1} \, .$$

Now take the Laplace transform of (8.16). This gives

$$\mathcal{L}\left[\frac{d^n f(x)}{dx^n}\right] + a_1 \mathcal{L}\left[\frac{d^{n-1}f(x)}{dx^{n-1}}\right] + \cdots + a_n \mathcal{L}[f(x)] = \mathcal{L}[g(x)]$$

where the linearity property has been used.

If the transforms of $f(x)$ and $g(x)$ are $\mathcal{F}(p)$ and $\mathcal{G}(p)$ respectively, using (8.14) yields

$$[p^n\mathcal{F}(p) - \sum_{r=0}^{n-1} p^{n-r-1}f^{(r)}(0)] + a_1[p^{n-1}\mathcal{F}(p) - \sum_{r=0}^{n-2} p^{n-r-2}f^{(r)}(0)] + \cdots$$

$$+ a_n\mathcal{F}(p) = \mathcal{G}(p) \, .$$

Substituting the given values of $f(0)$, $f'(0)$, $\ldots$, $f^{(n-1)}(0)$ leads to

$$(p^n + a_1 p^{n-1} + \cdots a_{n-1}p + a_n)\mathcal{F}(p)$$

$$= \mathcal{G}(p) + \sum_{r=0}^{n-1} p^{n-r-1}y_r + a_1 \sum_{r=0}^{n-2} p^{n-r-2}y_r + \cdots + a_{n-1}y_0 \, .$$

Since $\mathcal{G}(p)$ and y_r $(r = 0,1,2, \ldots, n - 1)$ are given, this equation (called the **subsidiary equation** of (8.16)) determines $\mathcal{F}(p)$ uniquely. However $\mathcal{F}(p)$ is the Laplace transform of $f(x)$ and by (8.13) determines it completely. Thus, the solution $y = f(x)$ is determined uniquely by (8.16) and the initial conditions.

Examples

(1) Find the solution for $x > 0$ of

$$\frac{d^2y}{dx^2} + 4y = 3\sin x ,$$

if $y_0 = 1$ and $y_1 = -2$.

Take Laplace transforms, then use the table and (8.14) to give

$$(p^2 + 4)\mathcal{F}(p) - py_0 - y_1 = 3(p^2 + 1)^{-1} .$$

Thus

$$\mathcal{F}(p) = \frac{3}{(p^2 + 1)(p^2 + 4)} + \frac{p - 2}{p^2 + 4}$$

$$= \frac{1}{p^2 + 1} - \frac{1}{p^2 + 4} + \frac{p - 2}{p^2 + 4}$$

using partial fractions; and so

$$\mathcal{F}(p) = \frac{1}{p^2 + 1} - \frac{3}{p^2 + 4} + \frac{p}{p^2 + 4} .$$

Finally, using the table to give the inverse transform of $\mathcal{F}(p)$ yields

$$f(x) = \sin x - \tfrac{3}{2}\sin 2x + \cos 2x .$$

(2) Find the solution for $x > 0$ of

$$\frac{d^2y}{dx^2} - 2\frac{dy}{dx} = x^2$$

if $y_0 = 3$ and $y_1 = 2$.

Take Laplace transforms, then use the table and (8.14) to

give $\qquad (p^2 - 2p)\mathcal{F}(p) - (py_0 + y_1) + 2y_0 = 2p^{-3}$

or

$$\mathcal{F}(p) = \frac{2}{p^4(p - 2)} + \frac{y_0}{(p - 2)} + \frac{y_1 - 2y_0}{p(p - 2)} .$$

From the table, it is seen that

$$\mathcal{L}^{-1}[(p - 2)^{-1}] = e^{2x} .$$

Using (8.15) gives

$$\mathcal{L}^{-1}[p^{-1}(p - 2)^{-1}] = \int_0^x e^{2t}dt = \tfrac{1}{2}(e^{2x} - 1) .$$

Three further integrations lead to

$$\mathcal{L}^{-1}[p^{-4}(p - 2)^{-1}] = \tfrac{1}{16}(e^{2x} - 1) - \tfrac{1}{12}x^3 - \tfrac{1}{8}x^2 - \tfrac{1}{8}x .$$

Hence, noting that $y_0 = 3$ and $y_1 = 2$, the final solution is

$$f(x) = \frac{9}{8}e^{2x} - \frac{1}{6}x^3 - \frac{1}{4}x^2 - \frac{1}{4}x + \frac{15}{8}.$$

8.7.2 More properties of Laplace transforms

So far, three properties of the Laplace transform which prove useful when solving constant coefficient equations have been established. However, the equations considered in the above two examples are relatively simple. Before proceeding to consider the solution of some more complicated equations, further properties of the Laplace transform will be established.

Using (8.12) it is easy to see that, if b is a constant

$$\mathcal{L}[e^{bx}f(x)] = \mathcal{F}(p - b) . \tag{8.17}$$

Although the proof of this result is trivial, it is, nevertheless, an important result which can be extremely useful. For example, using (8.17) together with results from the table, it is seen that

$$\mathcal{L}[e^{bx} \cos ax] = (p - b)/[(p - b)^2 + a^2]$$

and $\qquad \mathcal{L}[e^{bx} \sin ax] = a/[(p - b)^2 + a^2] .$

Again, it is worth noting these latter two results since they are useful for dealing with Laplace transforms which have quadratic denominators with no real factors. For example,

$$\mathcal{L}^{-1}\left[\frac{p + 5}{p^2 + 2p + 5}\right] = \mathcal{L}^{-1}\left[\frac{p + 1 + 4}{(p + 1)^2 + 2^2}\right].$$

Using the above results with $a = 2$ and $b = -1$ gives as the final result

$$e^{-x}(\cos 2x + 2 \sin 2x) .$$

If λ is a positive constant then it may be shown that

$$\mathcal{L}^{-1}[e^{-\lambda p} \mathcal{F}(p)] = h(x) \tag{8.18}$$

where $\qquad h(x) = \begin{cases} f(x - \lambda) & \text{for } x \geqslant \lambda \\ 0 & \text{for } x < \lambda . \end{cases}$

In the definition of $\mathcal{F}(p)$, $f(x)$ has to be defined for $x > 0$ only. Hence, without contradiction, take $f(x) = 0$ for $x < 0$. Then $h(x)$ may be viewed as the function formed by shifting the graph of $f(x)$ a distance λ along the x axis. By the definition of $h(x)$

$$\mathcal{L}[h(x)] = \int_{\lambda}^{\infty} e^{-px}f(x - \lambda)dx .$$

Changing the variable of integration to $z = x - \lambda$ gives $e^{-\lambda p}\mathcal{F}(p)$ on the right-hand side, thus establishing (8.18).

Finally, it remains to prove the **convolution theorem** which states that

$$\mathcal{L}\left[\int_0^x f_1(t)f_2(x - t)dt\right] = \mathcal{F}_1(p)\mathcal{F}_2(p) \tag{8.19}$$

where $\mathcal{L}[f_1(x)] = \mathcal{F}_1(p)$ and $\mathcal{L}[f_2(x)] = \mathcal{F}_2(p)$.

This result proves useful when it is required to find the function whose transform is the product of two known transforms $\mathcal{F}_1(p)$ and $\mathcal{F}_2(p)$. The above Laplace transform is

$$\int_0^\infty e^{-px}\{\int_0^x f_1(t)f_2(x - t)dt\}dx$$

which is a double integral over t and x. By examining the figure, it is seen that the region of integration in the xt-plane is over the octant between $t = 0$ and $t = x$, the integral over t being along strips MN (see Fig.8.1).

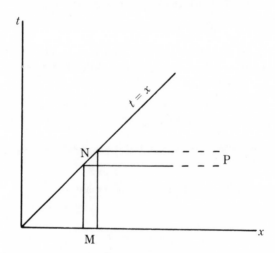

Fig. 8.1

Changing the order of integration so that first x is integrated along strips NP the integral becomes

$$\int_0^\infty f_1(t)\{\int_t^\infty e^{-px}f_2(x - t)dx\}dt$$

t appears as a constant parameter in the x-integral, and so the variable of integration may be changed from x to $z = x - t$. This yields

$$\int_0^\infty f_1(t)\{\int_0^\infty e^{-p(z+t)} f_2(z) dz\} dt$$

$$= \int_0^\infty f_1(t) e^{-pt} dt \int_0^\infty e^{-pz} f_2(z) dz$$

$$= \mathcal{F}_1(p) \mathcal{F}_2(p) .$$

Hence (8.19), which is often expressed in the form

$$\mathcal{L}^{-1}[\mathcal{F}_1(p)\mathcal{F}_2(p)] = \int_0^x f_1(t) f_2(x - t) dt . \tag{8.20}$$

8.7.3 Solution of more constant coefficient equations

It is possible now to solve most constant coefficient equations by finding $\mathcal{F}(p)$ from the subsidiary equation and then evaluating its inverse transform. It should be noted that the method extends to simultaneous constant coefficient equations for two variables y and z, as functions of x. A few harder examples will be solved now to illustrate the techniques involved.

Examples

(1) Find the solution of

$$\frac{d^2 y}{dx^2} + (m + n) \frac{dy}{dx} + mny = Ae^{-mx}$$

if $y_0 = A/m^2$ and $y_1 = 0$.

Taking Laplace transforms and using both the table and (8.14) gives

$$[p^2 + (m + n)p + mn]\mathcal{F}(p) = \frac{A}{p + m} + \frac{A}{m^2}(p + m + n) ,$$

that is,

$$\mathcal{F}(p) = \frac{A}{(p + m)^2(p + n)} + \frac{A(p + m + n)}{m^2(p + m)(p + n)}$$

$$= \frac{A}{(p + m)^2(p + n)} + \frac{A}{m^2}\left[\frac{1}{(p + n)} + \frac{n}{(p + m)(p + n)}\right]$$

The inverse transform for the second term is $Am^{-2}e^{-nx}$, and for the third term, using (8.20), the inverse transform is

$$Anm^{-2}\int_0^x e^{-mt} e^{-n(x-t)} dt = Anm^{-2}e^{-nx}\left[-\frac{e^{-(m-n)t}}{(m-n)}\right]_0^x .$$

Also, for the first term, using (8.20) once again,

$$\mathcal{L}^{-1}[(p + m)^{-2}] = \int_0^x e^{-mt} e^{-m(x-t)} dt = xe^{-mx}$$

and so

$$\mathcal{L}^{-1}[(p+m)^2(p+n)^{-1}] = \int_0^x te^{-mt}e^{-n(x-t)}dt$$

$$= -\frac{xe^{-mx}}{(m-n)} - e^{-nx}\left[\frac{e^{-(m-n)t}}{(m-n)^2}\right]_0^x.$$

Collecting the three results together gives

$$f(x) = \frac{A}{m^2}\left\{\frac{me^{-nx} - ne^{-mx}}{m-n}\right\} - \frac{Axe^{-mx}}{m-n}$$

$$+ \frac{A(e^{-nx} - e^{-mx})}{(m-n)^2}.$$

It should be noted that the inverse transforms for the first and third terms could have been found by using partial fractions rather than result (8.20).

(2) Solve the simultaneous equations

$$\frac{d^2y}{dx^2} - \frac{d^2z}{dx^2} + \frac{dz}{dx} - y = e^x - 2$$

$$2\frac{d^2y}{dx^2} - \frac{d^2z}{dx^2} - 2\frac{dy}{dx} + z = -x$$

for y and z as functions of x, if $y_0 = y_1 = 0$ and $z_0 = z_1 = 0$.

Suppose the solution is $y = f(x)$, $z = g(x)$ and the Laplace transforms of $f(x)$ and $g(x)$ are $\mathcal{F}(p)$ and $\mathcal{G}(p)$ respectively. Then, taking Laplace transforms leads, after some rearranging, to the two subsidiary equations

$$(p+1)\mathcal{F}(p) - p\mathcal{G}(p) = -\frac{p-2}{p(p-1)^2}$$

$$2p\mathcal{F}(p) - (p+1)\mathcal{G}(p) = -\frac{1}{p^2(p-1)}.$$

Eliminating $\mathcal{G}(p)$ gives

$$(p^2 - 2p - 1)\mathcal{F}(p) = \frac{p^2 - 2p - 1}{p(p-1)^2}$$

that is,

$$\mathcal{F}(p) = \frac{1}{p(p-1)^2} = \frac{1}{p} - \frac{1}{p-1} + \frac{1}{(p-1)^2}$$

using partial fractions.

Taking inverse transforms yields

$$f(x) = 1 - e^x + xe^x.$$

Similarly, it is found that

$$\mathcal{G}(p) = \frac{2p-1}{p^2(p-1)^2} = -\frac{1}{p^2} + \frac{1}{(p-1)^2} \,.$$

Taking inverse transforms gives

$$g(x) = -x + xe^x \,.$$

The Laplace transform method for solving constant coefficient equations appears to fail when the term $g(x)$ on the right-hand side of (8.16) is such that

$$\mathcal{G}(p) = \int\limits_0^\infty e^{-px} g(x) dx$$

diverges for all values of p; for example if $g(x)$ is of the form $e^{\alpha x^2}$ with $\alpha > 0$. However, in actual physical situations, terms such as $e^{\alpha x^2}$ are not acting as $x \to \infty$, and so, when such a term occurs, it may be assumed zero for x greater than some large value X say. Then the contribution to $\mathcal{G}(p)$ from $e^{\alpha x^2}$ would be

$$\int\limits_0^X e^{-px} e^{\alpha x^2} dx$$

which is convergent since the integral is over a finite range.

EXERCISES 8
(1) Solve the following equations of the first order and first degree:

   (i) $(3e^{3x}y - 2x)dx + e^{3x}dy = 0$.

   (ii) $\tan x \dfrac{dy}{dx} = \cot y$.

   (iii) $x(y-3)dy = 4ydx$.

   (iv) $(x-2)\dfrac{dy}{dx} = y + 2(x-2)^3$.

   (v) $\dfrac{dy}{dx} + \dfrac{1}{3}y = \dfrac{1}{3}(1-2x)y^4$.

   (vi) $2\dfrac{dy}{dx} = \dfrac{y}{x} + \dfrac{y^2}{x^2}$.

(2) Find the general solutions of the following equations:

   (i) $\dfrac{d^3y}{dx^3} + 2\dfrac{d^2y}{dx^2} - \dfrac{dy}{dx} - 2y = 0$.

(ii) $\dfrac{d^2y}{dx^2} + 4\dfrac{dy}{dx} + 13y = 0$.

(iii) $\dfrac{d^4y}{dx^4} + 6\dfrac{d^3y}{dx^3} + 5\dfrac{d^2y}{dx^2} - 24\dfrac{dy}{dx} - 36y = 0$.

(3) Find the general solutions of the following equations:

(i) $\dfrac{d^2y}{dx^2} - 2\dfrac{dy}{dx} + 5y = 25x^2 + 12$.

(ii) $\dfrac{d^2y}{dx^2} + 10\dfrac{dy}{dx} + 25y = 14e^{-5x}$.

(iii) $\dfrac{d^2y}{dx^2} + 4y = \tan 2x$.

(iv) $\dfrac{d^2y}{dx^2} + 2\dfrac{dy}{dx} + y = e^{-x}\log x$.

(4) Find the complete solutions for each of the following equations:

(i) $(2x + x^3)\dfrac{d^2y}{dx^2} - \dfrac{dy}{dx} - 6xy = 0$.

(ii) $(x - x^2)\dfrac{d^2y}{dx^2} + (1 - 5x)\dfrac{dy}{dx} - 4y = 0$.

(iii) $(x - x^2)\dfrac{d^2y}{dx^2} - 3x\dfrac{dy}{dx} - y = 0$.

(iv) $(2 + x^2)\dfrac{d^2y}{dx^2} + x\dfrac{dy}{dx} + (1 + x)y = 0$.

(5) (a) Write down the Laplace transforms of

$$e^{3x} , x^3 + 4x + 2 , \dfrac{d^2f}{dx^2} + a_1\dfrac{df}{dx} + a_2f .$$

(b) Find the inverse Laplace transforms of

$$p^{-1}(p^2 + 9)^{-1} , p^{-2}(p^2 + 9)^{-1} , (p^2 + a^2)^{-1}(p^2 + b^2)^{-1} .$$

(6) Solve $\dfrac{dy}{dx} - 3y = 2e^x$, if $y = y_0$ when $x = 0$.

(7) Find the solution for $x > 0$ of

$$\dfrac{d^2y}{dx^2} - 3\dfrac{dy}{dx} + 2y = 6x^3$$

which satisfies $y_0 = 0$ and $y_1 = 4$.

(8) Find the inverse Laplace transform of $a(p - c)^{-1}[(p - b)^2 + a^2]^{-1}$.

(9) Find the solution of $\dfrac{d^2y}{dx^2} - 2\dfrac{dy}{dx} + 5y = e^{-2x}$, if $y_0 = 4$ and $y_1 = 0$.

(10) Find the solution of $\dfrac{d^4y}{dx^4} + 2\dfrac{d^2y}{dx^2} + y = A\sin x$, if $y_0 = y_1 = y_2 = 0$

and $y_3 = 2A$.

Chapter 9
Line, Surface and Volume Integrals

9.1 SCALAR AND VECTOR FIELDS

A physical quantity which is defined at each point of a given region of space and which has the properties of a scalar at each point of the region is defined to be a **scalar field**.

The magnitude of a scalar field is a function of position, and so scalar fields are usually denoted by

$$\phi \equiv \phi(\mathbf{r})$$

where $\mathbf{r}$ is the position vector of a general point in the given region, relative to a given origin.

Typical examples of scalar fields are the density and pressure within a fluid, altitude, the speed of a moving particle, and so on.

Now consider those points P for which the magnitude of a given scalar field $\phi(\mathbf{r})$ equals a given constant c. The coordinates x_i of the point P must satisfy

$$\phi(x_1, x_2, x_3) = c \ .$$

In general, this equation may be solved to give one coordinate as a function of the other two. The position vector $\mathbf{r}$ of the point P may then be considered as a function of these two coordinates. Therefore, the locus of the point P is a surface.

The **level surfaces** of the scalar field $\phi(\mathbf{r})$ are defined by

$$\phi(\mathbf{r}) = c \ ,$$

a level surface existing for each choice of the constant c.

A physical quantity which is defined at each point of a given region of space and which has the properties of a vector at each point of the region is called a **vector field**.

In general the three components of a vector field will be functions of position, that is

$$v_i = v_i(\mathbf{r}) \ .$$

Typical examples of vector fields are the velocity of a particle, the flow velocity of the water in a river; the magnetic field of a bar magnet, and so on. A family of curves may be associated with each of these vector fields; for example, a piece of driftwood in a river will move along a curve and, since the driftwood floats with the stream, the tangents to the curve at each point will be in the direction of flow of the water. Such curves may be defined for a general vector field.

A curve C is called a **streamline** of the given vector field $\mathbf{v(r)}$ if and only if
(i) $\mathbf{v(r)}$ is defined at each point of C,
(ii) the tangent to C at the point $\mathbf{r}_0$ is in the direction of $\mathbf{v(r}_0)$.

A vector field which is defined uniquely at each point of a region of space is called **single-valued**; the components of such a field will be single-valued functions of position. If two streamlines of a single-valued vector field $\mathbf{v(r)}$ intersect at a point P then, at P, the vector field will have two distinct directions. This contradicts the hypothesis that $\mathbf{v(r)}$ is single-valued and so, for such vector fields, one and only one streamline passes through a given point. If $\mathbf{v(r)}$ is zero at some point, the direction of $\mathbf{v(r)}$ is unspecified and so no streamline will pass through that point. Such a point is called a **neutral** point of the field.

The equation of the streamlines of a given vector field $\mathbf{v(r)}$ is obtained easily. Suppose $\mathbf{r} = \mathbf{r}(\lambda)$ is a streamline described in terms of the scalar parameter λ. Since $d\mathbf{r}/d\lambda$ is a vector tangent to the curve, the following equation is obtained

$$d\mathbf{r}/d\lambda = k\mathbf{v} \qquad (9.1)$$

where k is a constant. In terms of a Cartesian basis and Cartesian coordinates (x, y, z)

$$\frac{d\mathbf{r}}{d\lambda} = \left(\frac{dx}{d\lambda}, \frac{dy}{d\lambda}, \frac{dz}{d\lambda}\right); \mathbf{v} = (v_x, v_y, v_z) .$$

Then, the three components of (9.1) are

$$\frac{dx}{d\lambda} = kv_x, \frac{dy}{d\lambda} = kv_y, \frac{dz}{d\lambda} = kv_z .$$

Eliminating the scalar k gives the equation of the streamlines in standard form:

$$dx/v_x = dy/v_y = dz/v_z .$$

The solution of differential equations of this form plays an important role in several branches of applied mathematics.

9.2 ORTHOGONAL CURVILINEAR COORDINATES

Suppose (u_1, u_2, u_3) is a given set of coordinates in three-dimensional Euclidean space. Then, the position vector $\mathbf{r}$ of some point P relative to a given origin

O will be a function of the three independent variables u_1, u_2, u_3;

$$\mathbf{r} \equiv \mathbf{r}(u_1, u_2, u_3) \ .$$

If u_2 and u_3 are kept fixed, $\mathbf{r}$ will be a function of the single parameter u_1 and, as u_1 varies, the locus of P will be a curve. Different constant values of u_2 and u_3 will yield a whole family of curves F_1. The tangents to these curves are in the direction $\partial \mathbf{r}/\partial u_1$. Similarly, if u_3 and u_1 are fixed, a second family of curves F_2 is obtained with tangents in the direction $\partial \mathbf{r}/\partial u_2$. Finally, with u_1 and u_2 fixed, the family F_3 is obtained with tangents in the direction $\partial \mathbf{r}/\partial u_3$. These three families define a 'coordinate mesh' in space which is a generalisation of the mesh printed on a piece of graph paper. A member of each family passes through each point P of space.

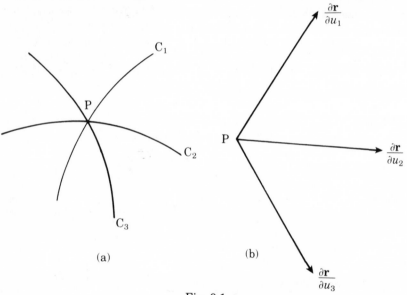

Fig. 9.1

In Fig. (9.1a) the curves C_1, C_2, C_3 belong to the families F_1, F_2, F_3 respectively. The tangents to these curves may be depicted pictorially as shown in Fig. (9.1b). If these tangents are mutually orthogonal at each point P, the coordinate system is called an **orthogonal curvilinear coordinate system**. Two examples of such systems are provided by spherical polar coordinates and cylindrical polar coordinates.

The coordinate system (u_1, u_2, u_3) is an orthogonal curvilinear coordinate system if and only if

$$\frac{\partial \mathbf{r}}{\partial u_i} \cdot \frac{\partial \mathbf{r}}{\partial u_j} = 0 \quad \text{for } i \neq j \ .$$

The three vectors $\partial\mathbf{r}/\partial u_i$ form a basis at each point P, called the **natural basis**. In the case of orthogonal coordinate systems it is usual to introduce an orthonormal basis $\hat{\mathbf{u}}_i$ defined by

$$\hat{\mathbf{u}}_i = \frac{1}{h_i} \frac{\partial\mathbf{r}}{\partial u_i} \qquad (i = 1,2,3)$$

where h_i is the magnitude of $\partial\mathbf{r}/\partial u_i$, that is

$$h_i = + \sqrt{\left(\frac{\partial\mathbf{r}}{\partial u_i} \cdot \frac{\partial\mathbf{r}}{\partial u_i}\right)}. \qquad (i = 1,2,3)$$

It should be noted that the summation and range conventions have been abandoned here. The three functions h_i are called the **fundamental quantities** of the orthogonal curvilinear coordinate system and they play an important role in the expression for the Euclidean distance ds between neighbouring points having coordinates u_i and $u_i + du_i$. In terms of Cartesian coordinates,

$$ds^2 = dx^2 + dy^2 + dz^2 = d\mathbf{r}\cdot d\mathbf{r} .$$

In terms of the coordinates u_i,

$$d\mathbf{r} = \sum_{i=1}^{3} \frac{\partial\mathbf{r}}{\partial u_i} du_i$$

and so,

$$ds^2 = \sum_{i=1}^{3} \frac{\partial\mathbf{r}}{\partial u_i} du_i \cdot \sum_{j=1}^{3} \frac{\partial\mathbf{r}}{\partial u_j} du_j = \sum_{i=1}^{3} \sum_{j=1}^{3} g_{ij} du_i du_j$$

where

$$g_{ij} = \frac{\partial\mathbf{r}}{\partial u_i} \cdot \frac{\partial\mathbf{r}}{\partial u_j} \qquad (i,j = 1,2,3) .$$

For an orthogonal coordinate system

$$g_{ij} = 0 \quad \text{if } i \neq j$$

$$g_{ii} = \frac{\partial\mathbf{r}}{\partial u_i} \cdot \frac{\partial\mathbf{r}}{\partial u_i} = h_i^2 \qquad (i = 1,2,3) .$$

Therefore,

$$ds^2 = \sum_{i=1}^{3} h_i^2 du_i^2$$

$$= h_1^2 du_1^2 + h_2^2 du_2^2 + h_3^2 du_3^2 .$$

Examples

(a) Consider Cartesian coordinates with $(u_1, u_2, u_3) \equiv (x, y, z)$.

$$ds^2 = dx^2 + dy^2 + dz^2$$

and so,

$$h_1 = h_2 = h_3 = 1 .$$

(b) Consider cylindrical polar coordinates with

$$(u_1, u_2, u_3) \equiv (q, \theta, z) \, .$$

Then

$$x = q \cos\theta \, , \quad y = q \sin\theta \, , \quad z = z \, .$$
$$ds^2 = dx^2 + dy^2 + dz^2$$
$$= (dq \cos\theta - q \sin\theta \, d\theta)^2 + (dq \sin\theta + q \cos\theta \, d\theta)^2 + dz^2$$
$$= dq^2 + q^2 d\theta^2 + dz^2 \, ,$$

and so, $h_1 = h_3 = 1 \, , \quad h_2 = q \, .$

(c) Consider spherical polar coordinates with

$$(u_1, u_2, u_3) \equiv (r, \theta, \phi) \, .$$

Then

$$x = r\sin\theta\cos\phi \, , \quad y = r\sin\theta\sin\phi \, , \quad z = r\cos\theta \, .$$
$$ds^2 = dx^2 + dy^2 + dz^2 = dr^2 + r^2 d\theta^2 + r^2\sin^2\theta d\phi^2$$

and so, $h_1 = 1 \, , \quad h_2 = r \, , \quad h_3 = r\sin\theta \, .$

9.3 LINE INTEGRALS

An elementary result of the integral calculus is that every bounded continuous function is integrable. Only such functions will be considered here, although it is possible to weaken this condition for integrability. Now consider a curve C joining the two points A and B (Fig. 9.2).

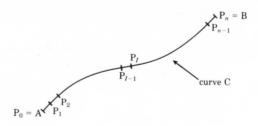

Fig. 9.2

Suppose a scalar field $\phi(\mathbf{r})$ is defined at all points of C. Subdivide the curve into n segments by the set of points

$$A = P_0, P_1, P_2, \ldots , P_{n-1}, P_n = B \, .$$

and denote by δs_I the arc length between the points P_I and P_{I-1}. Let $\phi|_I$ be the magnitude of the scalar field at some point lying between P_I and P_{I-1}. Then, by analogy with the definition of an integral as given in Chapter 3, the following definition may be given:

The limit $\qquad\qquad \lim_{max\ \delta s_I \to 0} \sum_{I=1}^{n} \phi|_I \delta s_I ,$ $\qquad$ if it exists and is

unique, is defined to be the line integral from A to B along C of the scalar field $\phi(\mathbf{r})$ and is denoted by

$$\int_A^B \phi ds .$$

along C.

When the points A and B coincide, that is when the integration is over a **closed** curve C, the line integral is denoted by $\oint_c \phi ds$.

The line integral of a vector field may be defined in a similar manner:

The limit $\qquad\qquad \lim_{max\ \delta s_I \to 0} \sum_{i=1}^{n} \mathbf{v}|_I \delta s_I ,$ $\qquad$ if it exists and is

unique, is defined to be the line integral from A to B along C of the vector field $\mathbf{v}(\mathbf{r})$ and is denoted by

$$\int_A^B \mathbf{v} ds .$$

along C

Line integrals of vector fields are met in practice only rarely and, in any case, may be reduced to line integrals of scalar fields by the following theorem:

Theorem

The line integral of a vector field $\mathbf{v}(\mathbf{r})$ is a vector whose Cartesian components are the line integrals of the Cartesian components of $\mathbf{v}$.

Proof

Let $\hat{\mathbf{c}}_i$ be a Cartesian basis (the vectors are fixed, therefore). Then,

$$\int_A^B \mathbf{v} ds = \lim_{max\ \delta s_I \to 0} \sum_{I=1}^{n} (v_i\,\hat{\mathbf{c}}_i)_I \,\delta s_I$$

along C

$$= \hat{\mathbf{c}}_i \left\{ \lim_{max\ \delta s_I \to 0} \sum_{I=1}^{n} v_i|_I \,\delta s_I \right\} = \hat{\mathbf{c}}_i \int_A^B v_i ds .$$

along C

Now, if $\hat{\varepsilon}$ is the unit tangent vector to the curve C, the line integral of the scalar field $\mathbf{v} \cdot \hat{\varepsilon}$,

$$\int_A^B \mathbf{v}\cdot\hat{\mathbf{\epsilon}}\ ds\ ,$$

along C

is called the **tangential line integral** of $\mathbf{v}$ from A to B along C. Since $\hat{\mathbf{\epsilon}} = d\mathbf{r}/ds$, this integral is usually written

$$\int_A^B \mathbf{v}\cdot d\mathbf{r}\ .$$

along C

Such integrals are of great importance in physics. For example, if $\mathbf{v}(\mathbf{r})$ is a force field, $\mathbf{v}\cdot d\mathbf{r}$ is the work done in the small displacement $d\mathbf{r}$. Therefore, the tangential line integral represents the total work done in moving from A to B along C.

The curve C is given in terms of a parameter λ by an equation of the form

$$\mathbf{r} = \mathbf{r}(\lambda)$$

and so

$$d\mathbf{r} = \frac{d\mathbf{r}}{d\lambda}\, d\lambda$$

and

$$ds = (d\mathbf{r}\cdot d\mathbf{r})^{1/2} = |d\mathbf{r}| = \left|\frac{d\mathbf{r}}{d\lambda}\right|\, d\lambda\ .$$

Using these relations, line integrals may be written as ordinary integrals:

$$\int_A^B \phi\ ds = \int_{\lambda_a}^{\lambda_b} \phi\ \left|\frac{d\mathbf{r}}{d\lambda}\right|\, d\lambda$$

along C

and

$$\int_A^B \mathbf{v}\cdot d\mathbf{r} = \int_{\lambda_a}^{\lambda_b} \mathbf{v}\cdot\frac{d\mathbf{r}}{d\lambda}\, d\lambda$$

along C

where λ_a, λ_b are the values of the parameter λ corresponding to the end-points A and B. Here

$$\phi\left|\frac{d\mathbf{r}}{d\lambda}\right| \quad \text{and} \quad \mathbf{v}\cdot\frac{d\mathbf{r}}{d\lambda}$$

are considered as functions of λ.

Example

Evaluate the tangential line integral of

$$\mathbf{v} = (3x^2 - 6yz,\ 2y + 3xz,\ 1 - 4xyz^2)$$

from (0,0,0) to (1,1,1) along the curve C defined by $x = t$, $y = t^2$, $z = t^3$.

On the curve C,

$$\mathbf{v} = (3t^2 - 6t^5, 2t^2 + 3t^4, 1 - 4t^9)$$

and

$$\mathbf{dr} = (1, 2t, 3t^2)dt \ .$$

Hence

$$\int_A^B \mathbf{v} \cdot \mathbf{dr} = \int_0^1 (3t^2 - 6t^5 + 4t^3 + 6t^5 + 3t^2 - 12t^{11})dt$$

along C

$$= \int_0^1 (6t^2 + 4t^3 - 12t^{11})dt$$

$$= [2t^3 + t^4 - t^{12}]_0^1 = 2 \ .$$

9.3.1 Change of variable

Suppose the tangential line integral

$$\int_A^B \mathbf{v} \cdot \mathbf{dr}$$

along C

has been represented by

$$\int_{\lambda_a}^{\lambda_b} f(\lambda) d\lambda \tag{i}$$

where

$$f(\lambda) = \mathbf{v} \cdot \frac{\mathbf{dr}}{d\lambda} \ .$$

It may happen that the choice of λ as parameter along the curve C leads to an integral (i) which is difficult to solve. The substitution of some new parameter $\mu = \mu(\lambda)$ may simplify things. The new tangential line integral will be of the form

$$\int_{\mu_a}^{\mu_b} F(\mu) d\mu \tag{ii}$$

where

$$F(\mu) = \mathbf{v} \cdot \frac{\mathbf{dr}}{d\mu} \ .$$

Integral (ii) may be obtained from (i) directly as follows:
By the chain rule

$$\frac{\mathbf{dr}}{d\mu} = \frac{\mathbf{dr}}{d\lambda} \frac{d\lambda}{d\mu} \ .$$

Then, in (i) if $f(\lambda)$ is written as a function of μ and if $d\lambda$ is replaced by $(d\lambda/d\mu)d\mu$,

$$\int\limits_{\lambda_a}^{\lambda_b} f(\lambda)d\lambda \rightarrow \int\limits_{\lambda_a}^{\lambda_b} \mathbf{v} \cdot \frac{d\mathbf{r}}{d\lambda} \frac{d\lambda}{d\mu} d\mu$$

$$= \int\limits_{\mu_a}^{\mu_b} \mathbf{v} \cdot \frac{d\mathbf{r}}{d\mu} d\mu = \int\limits_{\mu_a}^{\mu_b} F(\mu)d\mu$$

where $\mu_a = \mu(\lambda_a)$, $u_b = u(\lambda_b)$. This is not new but has been included to help understand corresponding results for surface and volume integrals.

9.4 SURFACE INTEGRALS

Consider a scalar field $\phi(\mathbf{r})$ defined at all points of a given surface S. Subdivide the surface into n segments of area δS_I and suppose the maximum linear dimension of these areas is δ. Consider the sum

$$\sum_{I=1}^{n} \phi|_I \, \delta S_I$$

where $\phi|_I$ is the value of ϕ at some point in the Ith segment. The limit, as $n\rightarrow\infty$ and $\delta\rightarrow 0$, of this sum is defined if it exists and is unique, to be the surface integral of $\phi(\mathbf{r})$ over the surface S and is written

$$\int_s \phi dS \, .$$

Here unique means that the limit is to be independent of the segmentation and of the choice of point in the Ith segment at which ϕ is evaluated. A similar definition holds if ϕ is replaced by a vector field $\mathbf{v}(\mathbf{r})$.

Consider the vector field $\mathbf{v}(\mathbf{r})$ defined at all points of a surface S. If the unit vector normal to S is $\hat{\mathbf{n}}$, the component of $\mathbf{v}$ normal to S is $\mathbf{v}\cdot\hat{\mathbf{n}}$ and the surface integral

$$\int_s \mathbf{v}\cdot\hat{\mathbf{n}}dS = \int_s \mathbf{v}\cdot d\mathbf{S}$$

is defined to be the normal surface integral of $\mathbf{v}$ over S. Here $d\mathbf{S}$ is an element of **directed** area.

Attention will be focused now on the systematic evaluation of surface integrals.

Suppose the surface S is described by two independent parameters λ and μ so that, on the surface

$$\mathbf{r} \equiv \mathbf{r}(\lambda,\mu) \, .$$

If λ is kept fixed, $\mathbf{r}$ will be a function of μ alone and so will describe a curve lying in S. Such a curve is called a **parametric curve** and a whole family of such curves exists, each curve corresponding to a different fixed value of λ. A second family exists also corresponding to different fixed values of μ. If the parametric curves are smooth, that is, if $\partial\mathbf{r}/\partial\lambda$ and $\partial\mathbf{r}/\partial\mu$ exist and are continuous, the surface is said to be **smooth**. Suppose the surface is smooth and that λ has values $\lambda_0, \lambda_1, \ldots, \lambda_n$ and μ has values $\mu_0, \mu_1, \ldots, \mu_n$. The two sets of parametric curves corresponding to these fixed values of λ and μ form a mesh on the surface S.

This mesh divides the surface into segments, the directed area of the I, Jth segment being (Fig. 9.3).

$$\delta \mathbf{S}_{IJ} = \mathbf{a} \times \mathbf{b} \, .$$

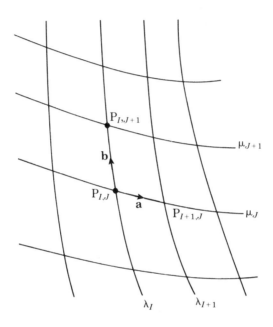

Fig. 9.3

Now,
$$\mathbf{a} = \overrightarrow{P_{I,J} P_{I+1,J}} = \mathbf{r}(\lambda_{I+1}, \mu_J) - \mathbf{r}(\lambda_I, \mu_J)$$

$$= \mathbf{r}(\lambda_I + \delta\lambda_I, \mu_J) - \mathbf{r}(\lambda_I, \mu_J)$$

$$= \left. \frac{\partial \mathbf{r}}{\partial \lambda} \right|_{I,J} \delta\lambda_I \, .$$

Similarly,

$$\mathbf{b} = \overrightarrow{P_{I,J} P_{I,J+1}} = \left. \frac{\partial \mathbf{r}}{\partial \mu} \right|_{I,J} \delta\mu_J \, .$$

Here $|_{I,J}$ denotes evaluation at $\lambda = \lambda_I$, $\mu = \mu_J$ and $\delta\lambda_I$ is the difference between λ_{I+1} and λ_I, $\delta\mu_J$ the difference between μ_{J+1} and μ_J. Then, the magnitude of the area of the I, Jth segment is

$$\delta S_{I,J} = \left| \frac{\partial \mathbf{r}}{\partial \lambda} \times \frac{\partial \mathbf{r}}{\partial \mu} \right|_{I,J} \delta \lambda_I \, \delta \mu_J \, .$$

Now suppose that ϕ is a scalar field defined at all points of the surface S and also that $\int_s \phi dS$ exists, then

$$\int_s \phi dS = \lim_{\substack{max \, (\delta\lambda_I) \to 0 \\ max \, (\delta\mu_J) \to 0}} \sum_{I=1}^{n} \sum_{J=1}^{n} \phi|_{I,J} \delta S_{I,J}$$

$$= \lim_{\substack{max \, (\delta\lambda_I) \to 0 \\ max \, (\delta\mu_J) \to 0}} \sum_{I=1}^{n} \sum_{J=1}^{n} \phi|_{I,J} \left| \frac{\partial \mathbf{r}}{\partial \lambda} \times \frac{\partial \mathbf{r}}{\partial \mu} \right|_{I,J} \delta \lambda_I \, \delta \mu_J$$

$$= \lim_{max \, (\delta\lambda_I) \to 0} \sum_{I=1}^{n} \left\{ \lim_{max \, (\delta\mu_J) \to 0} \sum_{J=1}^{n} \phi|_{I,J} \left| \frac{\partial \mathbf{r}}{\partial \lambda} \times \frac{\partial \mathbf{r}}{\partial \mu} \right|_{I,J} \delta \mu_J \right\} \delta \lambda_I$$

$$= \lim_{max \, (\delta\lambda_I) \to 0} \sum_{I=1}^{n} \left\{ \int \phi \left| \frac{\partial \mathbf{r}}{\partial \lambda} \times \frac{\partial \mathbf{r}}{\partial \mu} \right| d\mu \right\}_I \delta \lambda_I \, .$$

The integral in the brackets is evaluated at λ equal to the fixed value λ_I. In general, the limits on the integral will depend on λ_I and are chosen so that the upper limit is greater than or equal to the lower limit. Again, in general, the value of the integral will be different for each of the λ_I, and so, completing the calculation,

$$\int_s \phi dS = \int \left\{ \int \phi \left| \frac{\partial \mathbf{r}}{\partial \lambda} \times \frac{\partial \mathbf{r}}{\partial \mu} \right| d\mu \right\} d\lambda \, .$$

The integral on the right-hand side is called a **double integral** and usually is written

$$\iint \phi \left| \frac{\partial \mathbf{r}}{\partial \lambda} \times \frac{\partial \mathbf{r}}{\partial \mu} \right| d\lambda \, d\mu \, .$$

The double integral is evaluated by first integrating, keeping λ fixed so that the limits of integration are functions of λ, and then integrating the result from λ_0 to λ_n. For well-behaved fields the order of integration may be interchanged.

The normal surface integral $\int_s \mathbf{v} \cdot \mathbf{dS}$ may be written as a double integral also:

$$\iint \mathbf{v} \cdot \left(\frac{\partial \mathbf{r}}{\partial \lambda} \times \frac{\partial \mathbf{r}}{\partial \mu} \right) d\lambda \, d\mu \, .$$

Example

Evaluate $\int_s \mathbf{v} \cdot \mathbf{dS}$ where $\mathbf{v}(\mathbf{r}) = \mathbf{r}$, and S

is the surface of the paraboloid $z = 2 - x^2 - y^2$ above the xy plane.

x and y may be chosen as independent parameters, then, on S,

$$\mathbf{v} = (x, y, 2 - x^2 - y^2) = \mathbf{r}$$

$$\partial \mathbf{r}/\partial x = (1, 0, -2x), \quad \partial \mathbf{r}/\partial y = (0, 1, -2y).$$

Hence,

$$\mathbf{v} \cdot \left(\frac{\partial \mathbf{r}}{\partial x} \times \frac{\partial \mathbf{r}}{\partial y} \right) = \mathbf{v} \cdot (2x, 2y, 1) = 2 + x^2 + y^2.$$

Therefore, the normal surface integral becomes the double integral

$$\iint (x^2 + y^2 + 2)dx\,dy.$$

It now remains to find the domain of integration.

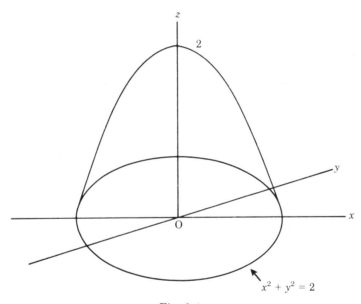

Fig. 9.4

Consider Fig. 9.4. It is seen that, within the region of space under considera-tion, if x is kept fixed, y may vary between the values $\pm(2 - x^2)^{1/2}$. Integrating the double integral with respect to y keeping x fixed, gives

$$\int [x^2 y + \tfrac{1}{3}y^3 + 2y]_{-(2-x^2)^{1/2}}^{(2-x^2)^{1/2}}\,dx$$

$$= 2\int (2 - x^2)^{1/2}\{2 + x^2 + \tfrac{1}{3}(2 - x^2)\}dx$$

$$= 4\int (2 - x)^2)^{1/2}(\tfrac{1}{3}x^2 + \tfrac{4}{3})\,dx.$$

The limits on x are $\pm\sqrt{2}$ and, with these limits, the value of the above in-tegral is 6π.

9.4.1 Change of variable

Suppose the surface integral $\int_s \phi dS$ is written in the form

$$\iint f(\lambda,\mu)d\lambda\, d\mu \qquad \text{(i)}$$

where

$$f(\lambda,\mu) = \phi \left|\frac{\partial \mathbf{r}}{\partial \lambda} \times \frac{\partial \mathbf{r}}{\partial \mu}\right|.$$

If ξ and ζ are two other independent parameters, the surface integral may be written

$$\iint g(\xi,\zeta)d\xi d\zeta \qquad \text{(ii)}$$

where

$$g(\xi,\zeta) = \phi \left|\frac{\partial \mathbf{r}}{\partial \xi} \times \frac{\partial \mathbf{r}}{\partial \zeta}\right|.$$

The question of how (ii) may be obtained directly from (i) now arises.

$$\left|\frac{\partial \mathbf{r}}{\partial \xi} \times \frac{\partial \mathbf{r}}{\partial \zeta}\right| = \left|\left(\frac{\partial \mathbf{r}}{\partial \lambda}\frac{\partial \lambda}{\partial \xi} + \frac{\partial \mathbf{r}}{\partial \mu}\frac{\partial \mu}{\partial \xi}\right) \times \left(\frac{\partial \mathbf{r}}{\partial \lambda}\frac{\partial \lambda}{\partial \zeta} + \frac{\partial \mathbf{r}}{\partial \mu}\frac{\partial \mu}{\partial \zeta}\right)\right|$$

$$= \left|\left(\frac{\partial \mathbf{r}}{\partial \lambda} \times \frac{\partial \mathbf{r}}{\partial \mu}\right)\frac{\partial \lambda}{\partial \xi}\frac{\partial \mu}{\partial \zeta} + \left(\frac{\partial \mathbf{r}}{\partial \mu} \times \frac{\partial \mathbf{r}}{\partial \lambda}\right)\frac{\partial \mu}{\partial \xi}\frac{\partial \lambda}{\partial \zeta}\right|$$

$$= \left|\left(\frac{\partial \mathbf{r}}{\partial \lambda} \times \frac{\partial \mathbf{r}}{\partial \mu}\right)\left(\frac{\partial \lambda}{\partial \xi}\frac{\partial \mu}{\partial \zeta} - \frac{\partial \mu}{\partial \xi}\frac{\partial \lambda}{\partial \zeta}\right)\right|.$$

The term in brackets is simply the determinant

$$J = \begin{vmatrix} \dfrac{\partial \lambda}{\partial \xi} & \dfrac{\partial \mu}{\partial \xi} \\[2ex] \dfrac{\partial \lambda}{\partial \zeta} & \dfrac{\partial \mu}{\partial \zeta} \end{vmatrix}.$$

This determinant is called the **Jacobian** of the transformation from the parameters λ,μ to the parameters ξ,ζ. Now

$$\left|\frac{\partial \mathbf{r}}{\partial \xi} \times \frac{\partial \mathbf{r}}{\partial \zeta}\right| = |J|\left|\frac{\partial \mathbf{r}}{\partial \lambda} \times \frac{\partial \mathbf{r}}{\partial \mu}\right|.$$

Thus, (ii) is obtained from (i) directly by writing $f(\lambda,\mu)$ as a function of ξ and ζ and replacing $d\lambda d\mu$ by $|J|d\xi d\zeta$.

Example

Consider the double integral already evaluated, namely

$$\iint (x^2 + y^2 + 2)dxdy.$$

Also, consider the substitution

$$x = r\cos\theta, \quad y = r\sin\theta.$$

The Jacobian is

$$\begin{vmatrix} \partial x/\partial r & \partial x/\partial \theta \\ \partial y/\partial r & \partial y/\partial \theta \end{vmatrix} = \begin{vmatrix} \cos\theta & -r\sin\theta \\ \sin\theta & r\cos\theta \end{vmatrix} = r \ .$$

Hence, the double integral becomes

$$\iint (r^2 + 2)r \, dr d\theta \ .$$

From the earlier discussion of limits, it follows that the limits on r and θ are 0 to $\sqrt{2}$ and 0 to 2π respectively (these are independent). Then, the integral becomes

$$2\pi \int_0^{\sqrt{2}} (r^3 + 2r) dr = 2\pi [\tfrac{1}{4} r^4 + r^2]_0^{\sqrt{2}} = 6\pi \ .$$

Now consider the normal surface integral of $\mathbf{v}$ over S:

$$\int_s \mathbf{v} \cdot \hat{\mathbf{n}} dS = \int_s \mathbf{v} \cdot d\mathbf{S}$$

where $\hat{\mathbf{n}}$ is the unit vector normal to S and $d\mathbf{S}$ is an element of directed area.

The orientation of $\hat{\mathbf{n}}$ at any point of the given surface S is *not* defined uniquely, since $\hat{\mathbf{n}}$ may be in one of two opposite directions. In the case of a closed surface, the outward normals are taken to be the positively orientated normals usually.

Suppose the surface S is described by the two parameters λ and μ. The vectors $\partial\mathbf{r}/\partial\lambda$ and $\partial\mathbf{r}/\partial\mu$ are tangent to the two families of parametric curves, and so at each point of the surface, $\partial\mathbf{r}/\partial\lambda \times \partial\mathbf{r}/\partial\mu$ will be a vector normal to the surface. When evaluating normal surface integrals, it is usual to assume that $\hat{\mathbf{n}}$ is in the direction of this vector product. However, if the orientation of the surface is specified, $\hat{\mathbf{n}}$ is taken in the direction of the positively orientated normal, so defining a directed normal surface integral. Here it is important to choose the ordering of the parameters so that, at each point of S, $\partial\mathbf{r}/\partial\lambda \times \partial\mathbf{r}/\partial\mu$ is in the direction of the positively orientated normal. Hence,

$$\int_s \mathbf{v} \cdot \hat{\mathbf{n}} \, dS = \iint \mathbf{v} \cdot \hat{\mathbf{n}} \left| \frac{\partial\mathbf{r}}{\partial\lambda} \times \frac{\partial\mathbf{r}}{\partial\mu} \right| d\lambda \, d\mu$$

$$= \iint \mathbf{v} \cdot \left(\frac{\partial\mathbf{r}}{\partial\lambda} \times \frac{\partial\mathbf{r}}{\partial\mu} \right) d\lambda \, d\mu = \int_s \mathbf{v} \cdot d\mathbf{S} \ .$$

Again, if a change of variable is necessary to evaluate a surface integral, the Jacobian is introduced, for example in transforming from parameters λ, μ to ξ, ζ, $d\lambda \, d\mu$ is replaced by $Jd\xi d\zeta$. Hence, to retain the original orientation of the normal to the surface, J must be positive. Hence, it is important for directed normal surface integrals (that is, when the orientation of the surface S is prescribed) that transformations are restricted to those having a positive Jacobian.

9.5 VOLUME INTEGRALS

Consider a scalar field $\phi(\mathbf{r})$ defined at all points of a given bounded, closed, three-dimensional region of space V. Divide the region into n segments of volume δV_I and suppose the maximum linear dimension of these segments is δ. Consider the sum

$$\sum_{I=1}^{n} \phi|_I \, \delta V_I$$

where ϕ_I is the value of ϕ at some point in the Ith segment.

Now the limit as $n \to \infty$ and $\delta \to 0$ of this sum is defined, if it exists and is unique, to be the volume integral of $\phi(\mathbf{r})$ throughout the volume V, and it is denoted by $\int_V \phi dV$.

Also, as might be expected, the volume integral of a given vector field $\mathbf{v}(\mathbf{r})$ is the vector whose components are the volume integrals of the Cartesian components of $\mathbf{v}(\mathbf{r})$.

Suppose u_1, u_2, u_3 are coordinates in space (Fig. 9.5). These coordinates will form a mesh. Construct a parallelepiped, each side of which corresponds to a small change in one coordinate only. The sides of this parallelepiped will be represented by the vectors $(\partial \mathbf{r}/\partial u_1)du_1$, $(\partial \mathbf{r}/u_2)du_2$, $(\partial \mathbf{r}/\partial u_3)du_3$.

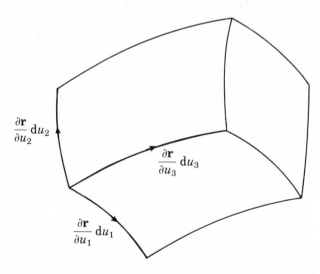

Fig. 9.5

The volume of the parallelepiped is

$$\left[\frac{\partial \mathbf{r}}{\partial u_1} \cdot \left(\frac{\partial \mathbf{r}}{\partial u_2} \times \frac{\partial \mathbf{r}}{\partial u_3}\right)\right] du_1 du_2 du_3 .$$

By a calculation completely analogous to that in the previous section on surface integrals, it may be shown that the volume integral $\int_V \phi dV$ may be written as a triple integral:

$$\iiint \phi \frac{\partial \mathbf{r}}{\partial u_1} \cdot \left(\frac{\partial \mathbf{r}}{\partial u_2} \times \frac{\partial \mathbf{r}}{\partial u_3}\right) du_1 du_2 du_3 .$$

In the case of Cartesian coordinates, this triple integral is simply $\iiint \phi dx\, dy\, dz$. The evaluation of these triple integrals is carried out in the same manner as is the evaluation of double integrals.

It might be noticed that, in the above discussion, if $\phi = 1$, the value of the volume integral will be the total volume of the region under consideration. If V is a solid body of density ϕ, then the value of the volume integral will be the total mass of the body.

Example

Find the volume of the region bounded by $z = 2 - x^2 - y^2$ and the xy plane (Fig. 9.6).

The required volume is given by

$$V = \iiint dx\, dy\, dz .$$

First keep x and y fixed and integrate with

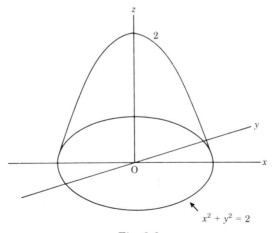

Fig. 9.6

respect to z. The limits on z will be 0 and $2 - x^2 - y^2$. Hence,

$$V = \iint (2 - x^2 - y^2)\, dx\, dy .$$

Now keep x fixed and integrate with respect to y. The limits on y will be $\pm(2-x^2)^{1/2}$. Hence,

$$V = \int [2y - x^2y - \tfrac{1}{3}y^3]_{-(2-x^2)^{1/2}}^{(2-x^2)^{1/2}} \; dx$$

$$= \tfrac{4}{3}\int(2-x^2)^{3/2}dx \; .$$

The limits on x are $\pm\sqrt{2}$ and so $V = 2\pi$.

9.5.1 Change of variable

Suppose the volume integral $\int_V \phi \, dV$ is written in the form

$$\iiint f(u_1, u_2, u_3) \, du_1 \, du_2 \, du_3 \qquad\qquad \text{(i)}$$

where

$$f(u_1, u_2, u_3) = \phi\,\frac{\partial \mathbf{r}}{\partial u_1}\cdot\left(\frac{\partial \mathbf{r}}{\partial u_2}\times\frac{\partial \mathbf{r}}{\partial u_3}\right).$$

If v_1, v_2, v_3 is another set of coordinates such that the volume integral may be written

$$\iiint g(v_1, v_2, v_3) \, dv_1 \, dv_2 \, dv_3 \qquad\qquad \text{(ii)}$$

where

$$g(v_1, v_2, v_3) = \phi\,\frac{\partial \mathbf{r}}{\partial v_1}\cdot\left(\frac{\partial \mathbf{r}}{\partial v_2}\times\frac{\partial \mathbf{r}}{\partial v_3}\right),$$

proceeding in the same manner as for surface integrals, it is found that

$$\frac{\partial \mathbf{r}}{\partial v_1}\cdot\left(\frac{\partial \mathbf{r}}{\partial v_2}\times\frac{\partial \mathbf{r}}{\partial v_3}\right) = J\,\frac{\partial \mathbf{r}}{\partial u_1}\cdot\left(\frac{\partial \mathbf{r}}{\partial u_2}\times\frac{\partial \mathbf{r}}{\partial u_3}\right)$$

where J is the Jacobian of the transformation from u_1, u_2, u_3 to v_1, v_2, v_3; that is,

$$J = \begin{vmatrix} \partial u_1/\partial v_1 & \partial u_2/\partial v_1 & \partial u_3/\partial v_1 \\ \partial u_1/\partial v_2 & \partial u_2/\partial v_2 & \partial u_3/\partial v_2 \\ \partial u_1/\partial v_3 & \partial u_2/\partial v_3 & \partial u_3/\partial v_3 \end{vmatrix} = \left|\frac{\partial u_i}{\partial v_j}\right| \; .$$

Using this result, (ii) may be obtained from (i) by writing $f(u_1, u_2, u_3)$ as a function of v_1, v_2, v_3 and replacing $du_1 \, du_2 \, du_3$ by $J dv_1 \, dv_2 \, dv_3$.

Example

Consider the example already dealt with in this section on volume integrals and make the substitution

$$x = r\cos\theta, \quad y = r\sin\theta, \quad z = z$$

so that

$$J = \begin{vmatrix} \cos\theta & -r\sin\theta & 0 \\ \sin\theta & r\cos\theta & 0 \\ 0 & 0 & 1 \end{vmatrix} = r \; .$$

Then, $V = \iiint r\, dr\, d\theta\, dz$.

The equation of the paraboloid is $z = 2 - r^2$. First integrate with respect to θ. The limits are 0 and 2π so that

$$V = \iint 2\pi\, r\, dr\, dz \ .$$

Now integrate with respect to z. The limits are 0 and $2 - r^2$.

$$V = 2\pi \int\limits_{0}^{\sqrt{2}} (2 - r^2) r\, dr = 2\pi \ .$$

EXERCISES 9

(1) If $\mathbf{A} = (3x^2 + 6y, - 14yz, 20xz^2)$, evaluate $\int_c \mathbf{A} \cdot d\mathbf{r}$ from $(0,0,0)$ to $(1,1,1)$ along the following paths C:

    (a) $x = t$, $y = t^2$, $z = t^3$,

    (b) the straight lines from $(0,0,0)$ to $(1,0,0)$ then to $(1,1,0)$ and then to $(1,1,1)$,

    (c) the straight line joining $(0,0,0)$ and $(1,1,1)$.

(2) Find the total work done in moving a particle in a force field given by $\mathbf{F} = (3xy, - 5z, 10x)$ along the curve $x = t^2 + 1$, $y = 2t^2$, $z = t^3$ from $t = 1$ to $t = 2$.

(3) If $\mathbf{F} = (2y, - z, x)$ evaluate $\int_c \mathbf{F} \times d\mathbf{r}$ along the curve $x = \cos t$, $y = \sin t$, $z = 2 \cos t$ from $t = 0$ to $t = \pi/2$.

(4) Evaluate $\int_s \mathbf{A} \cdot d\mathbf{S}$ over the entire surface S of the region bounded by the cylinder $x^2 + z^2 = 9$ and the planes $x = 0$, $y = 0$, $z = 0$ and $y = 8$ if $\mathbf{A} = (6z, 2x + y, -x)$.

(5) Evaluate $\int_s \mathbf{A} \cdot d\mathbf{S}$ over the entire region above the xy plane bounded by the cone $z^2 = x^2 + y^2$ and the plane $z = 4$ if $\mathbf{A} = (4xz, xyz^2, 3z)$.

(6) Evaluate $\int_v (2x + y)dV$ where V is the closed region bounded by the cylinder $z = 4 - x^2$ and the planes $x = 0$, $y = 0$, $z = 0$ and $y = 2$.

Chapter 10
Vector Analysis

10.1 GRADIENT OF A SCALAR FIELD

The concept of 'rate of change' of a function is fundamental in differential calculus. To discuss the change of a scalar field $\phi(\mathbf{r})$, in a region of three-dimensional space, a vector field—known as the **gradient of** $\phi(\mathbf{r})$—may be defined throughout the region. Actually, since the magnitude of a scalar field is a function of position, it is quite natural to seek geometrical interpretations of the derivatives of the magnitude.

Suppose u_1, u_2, u_3 are three coordinates in space. Then, the position vector $\mathbf{r}$ will be a function of u_1, u_2, u_3. It follows that ϕ will be a function of u_1, u_2, u_3, also:

$$\phi \equiv \phi(u_1, u_2, u_3) .$$

If ϕ is differentiable,

$$\phi(\mathbf{r} + \delta\mathbf{r}) = \phi(\mathbf{r}) + \frac{\partial\phi}{\partial u_i}\, \delta u_i + \text{higher-order terms.}$$

Here $\delta\mathbf{r}$ is the displacement arising from changes δu_i in the three coordinates u_i. In general, δu_i will not be the components of $\delta\mathbf{r}$. However, Cartesian coordinates x_i are defined to be the Cartesian components of $\mathbf{r}$ and so δx_i are the Cartesian components of $\delta\mathbf{r}$. Thus, Cartesian coordinates simplify the work considerably. Hence

$$d\phi = \phi(\mathbf{r} + \delta\mathbf{r}) - \phi(\mathbf{r}) = \nabla\phi\cdot\delta\mathbf{r} = \text{higher-order terms}$$

where
$$[\nabla\phi]_i = \partial\phi/\partial x_i .$$

Thus, the gradient of the scalar field $\phi(\mathbf{r})$, denoted by grad ϕ or $\nabla\phi$ (del ϕ), is defined to be the vector whose Cartesian components are $\partial\phi/\partial x_i$.

The gradient of ϕ may be written also in the form

$$\nabla\phi = \frac{\partial\phi}{\partial x}\,\mathbf{i} + \frac{\partial\phi}{\partial y}\,\mathbf{j} + \frac{\partial\phi}{\partial z}\,\mathbf{k}$$

where $\mathbf{i}$, $\mathbf{j}$, $\mathbf{k}$ are the usual basis vectors, which have been encountered frequently already.

However, in terms of the orthogonal curvilinear coordinates u_1, u_2, u_3,

$$d\phi = \frac{\partial \phi}{\partial u_1} \, du_1 + \frac{\partial \phi}{\partial u_2} \, du_2 + \frac{\partial \phi}{\partial u_3} \, du_3$$

$$= \left(\frac{1}{h_1} \frac{\partial \phi}{\partial u_1}, \frac{1}{h_2} \frac{\partial \phi}{\partial u_2}, \frac{1}{h_3} \frac{\partial \phi}{\partial u_3} \right) \cdot (h_1 du_1, h_2 du_2, h_3 du_3) \, .$$

But $\mathbf{dr} = (h_1 du_1, h_2 du_2, h_3 du_3)$, and so, if ϕ is expressed in terms of the orthogonal curvilinear coordinates u_1, u_2, u_3,

$$\nabla \phi = \left(\frac{1}{h_1} \frac{\partial \phi}{\partial u_1}, \frac{1}{h_2} \frac{\partial \phi}{\partial u_2}, \frac{1}{h_3} \frac{\partial \phi}{\partial u_3} \right) .$$

Now consider a small change of the position vector $\mathbf{r}$ in the direction $\hat{\varepsilon}$ from $\mathbf{r}_0$ to $\mathbf{r}_0 + \hat{\varepsilon}\delta\lambda$. If $\phi(\mathbf{r})$ is differentiable, the corresponding change in $\phi(\mathbf{r})$ is

$$\phi(\mathbf{r}_0 + \hat{\varepsilon}\delta\lambda) - \phi(\mathbf{r}_0) = \left. \nabla \phi \right|_{\mathbf{r}_0} \cdot \hat{\varepsilon}\delta\lambda + \text{ higher-order terms.}$$

and so
$$\left. \nabla \phi \right|_{\mathbf{r}_0} \cdot \hat{\varepsilon} = \lim_{\delta\lambda \to 0} \frac{\phi(\mathbf{r}_0 + \hat{\varepsilon}\delta\lambda) - \phi(\mathbf{r}_0)}{\delta\lambda} \, .$$

This limit, if it exists, is defined to be the directional derivative of $\phi(\mathbf{r})$ at $\mathbf{r}_0$ in the direction $\hat{\varepsilon}$. Also, it is seen immediately from the above expression that the directional derivative of $\phi(\mathbf{r})$ in the direciton $\hat{\varepsilon}$ is the component of $\nabla\phi$ in the direction $\hat{\varepsilon}$.

It may be noticed that the directional derivative of ϕ at any point is greatest in the direction of $\nabla\phi$ since the directional derivative is

$$\nabla \phi \cdot \hat{\varepsilon} = |\nabla\phi| \cos\theta$$

where θ is the angle between $\nabla\phi$ and $\hat{\varepsilon}$. This is greatest when $\cos\theta$ is a maximum, that is, when $\theta = 0$. Thus the maximum directional derivative is $|\nabla\phi|$. Again, although the proofs will not be given here, it may be shown that the normal to the level surface $\phi(\mathbf{r}) = c$, at the point $\mathbf{r}_0$, is in the direction of $\left. \nabla\phi \right|_{\mathbf{r}_0}$. Also, the gradient of a scalar field $\phi(\mathbf{r})$ at the point $\mathbf{r}_0$ is given by

$$\nabla \phi = \hat{\mathbf{n}} \frac{d\phi}{dn} \, ,$$

where $\hat{\mathbf{n}}$ is the unit normal to the level surface passing through $\mathbf{r}_0$ and $d\phi/dn$ is the directional derivative of $\phi(\mathbf{r})$ at $\mathbf{r}_0$ in the direction $\hat{\mathbf{n}}$.

Examples

(1) Find $\nabla\phi$ when $\phi(\mathbf{r})$ is a function of r alone.

Since ϕ is a function of r alone

$$[\nabla\phi]_i = \frac{\partial\phi}{\partial x_i} = \frac{d\phi}{dr}\frac{\partial r}{\partial x_i}.$$

Now

$$r^2 = x^2 + y^2 + z^2$$

and so

$$2r\frac{\partial r}{\partial x} = 2x \Rightarrow \frac{\partial r}{\partial x} = \frac{x}{r}.$$

Hence, in general,

$$\frac{\partial r}{\partial x_i} = \frac{x_i}{r}.$$

Alternatively, using index notation

$$r^2 = x_j x_j$$

and so

$$2r\frac{\partial r}{\partial x_i} = 2x_j\frac{\partial x_j}{\partial x_i} = 2x_j\,\delta_{ij} = 2x_i\,.$$

Substituting back yields

$$[\nabla\phi]_i = \frac{d\phi}{dr}\frac{x_i}{r} \equiv \phi'\,\frac{x_i}{r}.$$

Therefore,

$$\nabla\phi = \phi'\,\frac{\mathbf{r}}{r}.$$

(2) Find the directional derivative of

$$u(x, y, z) = xy + yz + zx$$

at the point (1,1,1) in the direction normal to the plane $x + 2y + 3z = 6$.

Now

$$\nabla u = (y + z, z + x, x + y)$$

$$= (2,2,2) \text{ at the point } (1,1,1)\,.$$

The unit normal to the plane is

$$\hat{\mathbf{n}} = (1,2,3)/\sqrt{(1 + 4 + 9)}\,.$$

The required directional derivative is

$$\hat{\mathbf{n}} \cdot \nabla u = (2,2,2)\cdot(1,2,3)/\sqrt{14} = 12/\sqrt{14}\,.$$

Theorem
If $\nabla\phi$ is integrable then

$$\int_A^B \nabla\phi \cdot d\mathbf{r} = \phi\big|_B - \phi\big|_A$$

along C

for all smooth curves C.

Proof

As in the introduction to line integrals, subdivide the curve C into n segments with $P_0 = A$ and $P_n = B$. (Fig. 10.1).

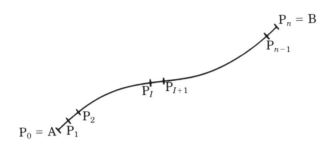

Fig. 10.1

Suppose the position vector of the point P_I is $\mathbf{r}_I = \mathbf{r}(\lambda_I)$, then

$$\phi(\mathbf{r}_{I+1}) - \phi(\mathbf{r}_I) = \phi(\lambda_{I+1}) - \phi(\lambda_I) = \phi(\lambda_I + \delta\lambda_I) - \phi(\lambda_I)$$

$$= \frac{d\phi}{d\lambda}\bigg|_I \delta\lambda_I .$$

Thus,

$$\phi(\mathbf{r}_n) - \phi(\mathbf{r}_0) = \sum_{I=0}^{n-1} \frac{d\phi}{d\lambda}\bigg|_I \delta\lambda_I .$$

Referring to the idea of line integrals once more, it is seen that

$$\phi\big|_B - \phi\big|_A = \lim_{max\ \delta\lambda_I \to 0} \sum_{I=0}^{n-1} \frac{d\phi}{d\lambda}\bigg|_I \delta\lambda_I = \int_{\lambda_A}^{\lambda_B} \frac{d\phi}{d\lambda}\, d\lambda .$$

Using the chain rule,

$$\frac{d\phi}{d\lambda} = \frac{\partial\phi}{\partial x_i}\frac{dx_i}{d\lambda} = \nabla\phi \cdot \frac{d\mathbf{r}}{d\lambda} .$$

Hence,

$$\phi\big|_B - \phi\big|_A = \int_{\lambda_A}^{\lambda_B} \nabla\phi \cdot \frac{d\mathbf{r}}{d\lambda}\, d\lambda = \int_A^B \nabla\phi \cdot d\mathbf{r} .$$

$$\text{along C}$$

The theorem expresses the directed tangential line integral of $\nabla\phi$ along a curve in terms of the value of $\phi(\mathbf{r})$ on the boundary of the curve (i.e. at the end-point A and B).

10.2 CONSERVATIVE FIELDS

An important class of vector fields, called **conservative vector fields**, will be defined now, and several theorems concerning them will be proved.

A vector field $\mathbf{v}(\mathbf{r})$ is said to be conservative if and only if, for any two points A and B, the directed tangential line integral

$$\int_A^B \mathbf{v}\cdot\mathbf{dr}$$

along C

is independent of the curve C joining A and B.

Again, if $\mathbf{v}(\mathbf{r})$ is a conservative field, the potential $\phi(\mathbf{r})$ at the point P having position vector $\mathbf{r}$ relative to a fixed origin O is defined by

$$\phi(\mathbf{r}) = -\int_O^P \mathbf{v}\cdot\mathbf{dr}\,.$$

By definition, a force field is conservative if and only if, the work done in moving between any two points is independent of the path taken between the points. The potential at a point P (called the potential energy of the force field at P) is the work done *against* the field in moving from the fixed origin O to the point P. The potential $\phi(\mathbf{r})$ of a conservative field $\mathbf{v}(\mathbf{r})$ is defined relative to a fixed origin, but choosing another origin merely adds a constant to the potential.

Theorem

A vector field $\mathbf{v}(\mathbf{r})$ is conservative if and only if the tangential line integral of $\mathbf{v}(\mathbf{r})$ around any closed curve is zero.

Proof

Let A and B be any two points and suppose C_1 and C_2 are any two curves joining A and B. Also, suppose the closed curve $C_1 + C_2$ is described in a clockwise sense (Fig. 10.2).

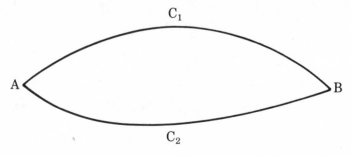

Fig. 10.2

Then,
$$\oint_{C_1+C_2} \mathbf{v}\cdot d\mathbf{r} = \int_A^B \mathbf{v}\cdot d\mathbf{r} + \int_B^A \mathbf{v}\cdot d\mathbf{r}$$
$$\text{along } C_1 \quad \text{along } C_2$$

$$= \int_A^B \mathbf{v}\cdot d\mathbf{r} - \int_A^B \mathbf{v}\cdot d\mathbf{r}$$
$$\text{along } C_1 \text{ along } C_2$$

If the field is conservative, the two integrals on the right-hand side are equal and so the integral around the closed curve is zero.

Conversely, if the integral around the closed curve is zero, the two integrals on the right-hand side are equal. Since the curves C_1 and C_2 are arbitrary, this proves that the integral $\int_A^B \mathbf{v}\cdot d\mathbf{r}$ is independent of the curve joining A and B. Hence, the field is conservative.

Theorem

A vector field $\mathbf{v}(\mathbf{r})$ is conservative if and only if there exists a scalar field $\phi(\mathbf{r})$ such that $\mathbf{v} = -\nabla\phi$.

Proof

Suppose such a scalar field exists, then using the result of an earlier theorem

$$\int_A^B \mathbf{v}\cdot d\mathbf{r} = - \int_A^B \nabla\phi\cdot d\mathbf{r} = -\phi\big|_B + \phi\big|_A .$$

Since the right-hand side of this equation is independent of the curve C, the field is conservative.

Conversely, suppose $\mathbf{v}(\mathbf{r})$ is conservative. The potential $\phi(\mathbf{r})$ is defined by

$$\phi(\mathbf{r}) = - \int_0^P \mathbf{v}\cdot d\mathbf{r} .$$

However,
$$\int_0^P \nabla\phi \cdot d\mathbf{r} = \phi(\mathbf{r}) - \phi(0) = \phi(\mathbf{r}) .$$

Hence,
$$\int_0^P (\nabla\phi + \mathbf{v}) \cdot d\mathbf{r} = 0 .$$

This integral vanishes for all points P and for all curves joining O and P and, therefore, the integrand must be zero.

Therefore,
$$\mathbf{v} = -\nabla\phi .$$

Examples

(1) Show that the electrostatic field $\mathbf{E}(\mathbf{r}) = q\mathbf{r}/4\pi\varepsilon_0 r^3$ is a conservative field

$$\nabla(r^{-1}) = - \mathbf{r}/r^3$$

and so,
$$\mathbf{E}(\mathbf{r}) = - \nabla(q/4\pi\varepsilon_0 r) .$$

Therefore, $\mathbf{E}(\mathbf{r})$ is a conservative field.

(2) Prove that the force field

$$\mathbf{F}(\mathbf{r}) = (3x^2z + y^2,\, 2yx + z,\, x^3 + y)$$

is conservative and find the work done by this field in moving a particle from the origin to the point (1,1,1).

To show that $\mathbf{F}(\mathbf{r})$ is conservative, it is necessary to find $\phi(\mathbf{r})$ such that $\mathbf{F} = -\nabla\phi$. Such a scalar field must satisfy

$$-\frac{\partial\phi}{\partial x} = 3x^2z + y^2 \,,\quad -\frac{\partial\phi}{\partial y} = 2yx + z \,,\quad -\frac{\partial\phi}{\partial z} = x^3 + y \,.$$

The first equation gives

$$\phi = -x^3z - y^2x + f(y,z) \,.$$

Substituting into the second equation leads to

$$-\partial f/\partial y = z$$

and so,
$$f(y,z) = -zy + g(z) \,.$$

Using the third equation shows that

$$dg/dz = 0$$

and so, g is a constant. Hence, the function

$$\phi(x,y,z) = -x^3z - xy^2 - yz + \text{constant}$$

satisfies $\mathbf{F} = -\nabla\phi$ and so, $\mathbf{F}$ is a conservative force field.

The required work done is

$$\int_{(0,0,0)}^{(1,1,1)} \mathbf{F}\cdot\mathbf{dr} = -\int_{(0,0,0)}^{(1,1,1)} \nabla\phi\cdot\mathbf{dr}$$

$$= -\phi(1,1,1) + \phi(0,0,0) = 3 \,.$$

10.3 THE CURL OF A VECTOR FIELD

For a general vector field $\mathbf{v}(\mathbf{r})$, the integral $\oint\mathbf{v}\cdot\mathbf{dr}$ round a closed path measures the 'tendency to circulate' round the path. This may be pictured most easily by considering the velocity field $\mathbf{v}$ in a fluid. If the fluid is swirling around some axis near a whirlpool, the integral $\oint\mathbf{v}\cdot\mathbf{dr}$ along a path around this axis will measure the **circulation** of the fluid, as it is called. It proves useful to have a function which represents the circulation of a vector field $\mathbf{v}$ at a point and such a function may be obtained by letting the closed path of integration in the above integral become very small. Circulation is a vector of the same type as angular velocity, which is known as an **axial vector**, and first it is necessary to define an axis about which the circulation is being measured.

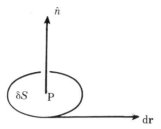

Fig. 10.3

Specify an axis at some point P (Fig. 10.3), by choosing a unit vector $\hat{\mathbf{n}}$ along it. Let δS be a small surface element, which becomes plane as $\delta S \to 0$ with its normal lying along $\hat{\mathbf{n}}$. The boundary of δS is a simple closed curve, and an element of this is $d\mathbf{r}$. Then, the **circulation vector** at P, denoted by curl $\mathbf{v}$ is defined to have its component in direction $\hat{\mathbf{n}}$ given by

$$\hat{\mathbf{n}} \cdot \text{curl } \mathbf{v} = \lim_{\delta S \to 0} \frac{1}{\delta S} \oint \mathbf{v} \cdot d\mathbf{r} \qquad (10.1)$$

the integral being around the bounding curve of δS.

Thus, (10.1) defines the 'circulation per unit area' about the axis $\hat{\mathbf{n}}$, and for well-behaved vector fields this limit does exist. The direction of integration is, however, undefined, but it is customary to choose $\hat{\mathbf{n}}$ and $d\mathbf{r}$ to obey the right-hand rule as shown in the diagram. Also, since the right-hand side of (10.1) is a scalar, $\hat{\mathbf{n}} \cdot \text{curl } \mathbf{v}$ is a scalar product.

The easiest way of showing that the limit (10.1) exists for well-behaved fields $\mathbf{v}$ is to evaluate the components of curl $\mathbf{v}$ in particular coordinate systems. First, consider Cartesian coordinates x, y, z. Here the z component $(\text{curl } \mathbf{v})_z$, is given by taking $\hat{\mathbf{n}}$ along the z axis. Choose the surface δS to be a small rectangle $P_1 P_2 P_3 P_4$ perpendicular to $\hat{\mathbf{n}}$ as shown in Fig. 10.4, the integration round the boundary being in the sense indicated by the arrows.

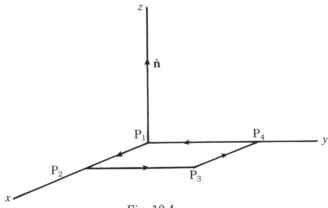

Fig. 10.4

Suppose $\mathbf{v}$ has components v_x, v_y, v_z, then the contribution to $\oint \mathbf{v} \cdot d\mathbf{r}$ from $P_1 P_2$ and $P_3 P_4$ is

$$\int_{P_1}^{P_2} v_x \, dx - \int_{P_4}^{P_3} v_x \, dx . \tag{10.2}$$

Now points on $P_1 P_2$ and $P_3 P_4$ with the same x-coordinate differ by a displacement $P_1 P_4$ (equal to δy) in the y-direction. Hence, if v_x is written as $v_x(x,y)$ on $P_1 P_2$, it must be written as $v_x(x,y + \delta y)$ on $P_3 P_4$—remembering that z is constant throughout. Using Taylor's theorem, it is seen that to first order

$$v_x(x, y + \delta y) \sim v_x(x,y) + \frac{\partial v_x(x,y)}{\partial y} \, \delta y .$$

Hence, to first order in δy, (10.2) becomes

$$- \int_{P_1}^{P_2} \left[\frac{\partial v_x(x,y)}{\partial y} \, \delta y \right] dx$$

since y is the coordinate value on $P_1 P_2$. If $P_1 P_2 = \delta x$, then to first order in δx this integral is

$$- \frac{\partial v_x}{\partial y} \, \delta x \, \delta y = - \, \delta S \, \frac{\partial v_x}{\partial y}$$

where $\delta S = \delta x \delta y$ is the area of the surface element and $\partial v_x / \partial y$ is evaluated at P_1. Similarly, the contribution to $\oint \mathbf{v} \cdot d\mathbf{r}$ from $P_2 P_3$ and $P_4 P_1$ is $+ \delta S \, (\partial v_y / \partial x)$. Hence,

$$(\text{curl } \mathbf{v})_z = \frac{\partial v_y}{\partial x} - \frac{\partial v_x}{\partial y} .$$

In this derivation all higher-order terms in δx and δy have been omitted. However, if included, they would lead to terms of higher order then $\delta S = \delta x \delta y$, and so would not contribute in the limit $\delta S \to 0$.

The x and y components of curl $\mathbf{v}$ may be evaluated in a similar manner, and it is seen that

$$\text{curl } \mathbf{v} = \left(\frac{\partial v_z}{\partial y} - \frac{\partial v_y}{\partial z} , \, \frac{\partial v_x}{\partial z} - \frac{\partial v_z}{\partial x} , \, \frac{\partial v_y}{\partial x} - \frac{\partial v_x}{\partial y} \right) .$$

When the gradient of a scalar field was discussed, the symbol del, ∇, was introduced. ∇ itself is *not* a vector but is rather an operator and does not exist unless it is acting on some scalar field or, indeed, some vector field. However, if the symbol ∇ is formally manipulated as a vector having components $\partial/\partial x_i$ or $(\partial/\partial x, \partial/\partial y, \partial/\partial z)$ then it is seen that

$$\text{curl } \mathbf{v} = \left(\frac{\partial}{\partial x}, \frac{\partial}{\partial y}, \frac{\partial}{\partial z} \right) \times (v_x, v_y, v_z) = \nabla \times \mathbf{v} = \varepsilon_{ijk} \frac{\partial v_k}{\partial x_j}.$$

The value of the curl may be put in determinantal form also:

$$\nabla \times \mathbf{v} = \begin{vmatrix} \mathbf{i} & \mathbf{j} & \mathbf{k} \\ \partial/\partial x & \partial/\partial y & \partial/\partial z \\ v_x & v_y & v_z \end{vmatrix}.$$

The components of $\nabla \times \mathbf{v}$ in terms of orthogonal coordinates may be found in a manner similar to that used above. The result is

$$\nabla \times \mathbf{v} = \frac{1}{h_2 h_3} \left[\frac{\partial}{\partial u_2} (h_3 v_3) - \frac{\partial}{\partial u_3} (h_2 v_2) \right] \hat{\mathbf{u}}_1 .$$

+ cyclic permutations.

10.3.1 Stokes' Theorem

Suppose S is a smooth orientable surface bounded by a smooth closed curve C. If the vector field $\mathbf{v(r)}$ is continuous and has continuous first derivatives on S then

$$\int_s \nabla \times \mathbf{v} \cdot d\mathbf{S} = \oint_c \mathbf{v} \cdot d\mathbf{r}$$

where the unit normal (and therefore the element of area $d\mathbf{S}$) is orientated by applying the right-handed corkscrew rule to the sense in which C is described.
Proof
Since the surface S and its bounding curve C are both smooth, the surface integral and the line integral may be written as a double integral and a single integral respectively. The hypothesis concerning the continuity of both the vector field $\mathbf{v(r)}$ and its first partial derivatives then ensures that the integrands are continuous and that both integrals exist. Now suppose that S is described by the two parameters λ and μ so that, on S, $\mathbf{r} = \mathbf{r}(\lambda, \mu)$. Then,

$$\int_s \nabla \times \mathbf{v} \cdot d\mathbf{S} = \int\int \nabla \times \mathbf{v} \cdot \left(\frac{\partial \mathbf{r}}{\partial \lambda} \times \frac{\partial \mathbf{r}}{\partial \mu} \right) d\lambda d\mu$$

$$= \int\int \varepsilon_{ijk} \frac{\partial v_k}{\partial x_j} \varepsilon_{ilm} \frac{\partial x_l}{\partial \lambda} \frac{\partial x_m}{\partial \mu} d\lambda d\mu$$

$$= \int\int (\delta_{jl} \delta_{km} - \delta_{jm} \delta_{kl}) \frac{\partial v_k}{\partial x_j} \frac{\partial x_l}{\partial \lambda} \frac{\partial x_m}{\partial \mu} d\lambda d\mu$$

$$= \int\int \left(\frac{\partial v_m}{\partial x_j} \frac{\partial x_j}{\partial \lambda} \frac{\partial x_m}{\partial \mu} - \frac{\partial v_k}{\partial x_j} \frac{\partial x_k}{\partial \lambda} \frac{\partial x_j}{\partial \mu} \right) d\lambda d\mu$$

$$= \int\int \left(\frac{\partial v_m}{\partial \lambda} \frac{\partial x_m}{\partial \mu} - \frac{\partial v_k}{\partial \mu} \frac{\partial x_k}{\partial \lambda} \right) d\lambda d\mu$$

$$= \iint \left[\frac{\partial}{\partial \lambda} \left(v_m \frac{\partial x_m}{\partial \mu} \right) - \frac{\partial}{\partial \mu} \left(v_m \frac{\partial x_m}{\partial \lambda} \right) \right] d\lambda d\mu \ .$$

This last expression is obtained by changing the summation index from k to m and using the identity

$$\partial^2 x_m / (\partial \lambda \ \partial \mu) = \partial^2 x_m / (\partial \mu \ \partial \lambda) \ .$$

Both the double integrals above may be integrated once. In order to simplify the proof, it is assumed that each parametric curve on S meets the boundary at two points only. The limits of integration may be found from Fig. 10.5.

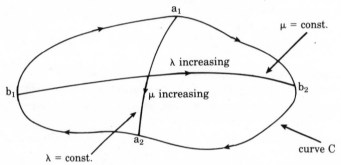

Fig. 10.5

The parameters λ and μ are assumed to be increasing in the sense indicated in the figure, and so $(\partial \mathbf{r}/\partial \lambda \times \partial \mathbf{r}/\partial \mu)$ is directed into the page. The curve C must, therefore, by hypothesis, be described as indicated by the arrow heads on the curve. Now

$$\int_S \nabla \times \mathbf{v} \cdot d\mathbf{S} = \iint \left\{ \mathbf{v} \cdot \frac{\partial \mathbf{r}}{\partial \mu} \Big|_{b_2} - \mathbf{v} \cdot \frac{\partial \mathbf{r}}{\partial \mu} \Big|_{b_1} \right\} d\mu$$

$$- \iint \left\{ \mathbf{v} \cdot \frac{\partial \mathbf{r}}{\partial \lambda} \Big|_{a_2} - \mathbf{v} \cdot \frac{\partial \mathbf{r}}{\partial \lambda} \Big|_{a_1} \right\} d\lambda \ .$$

The integration with respect to μ includes every point of C as does the integration with respect to λ. However, the increases in λ and μ at the points a_2 and b_1 respectively are in the opposite sense to that in which the curve C is described. Therefore, the last equation may be written

$$\int_S \nabla \times \mathbf{v} \cdot d\mathbf{S} = \oint_C \mathbf{v} \cdot \frac{\partial \mathbf{r}}{\partial \mu} d\mu + \oint_C \mathbf{v} \cdot \frac{\partial \mathbf{r}}{\partial \lambda} d\lambda$$

$$= \oint_C \mathbf{v} \cdot \left(\frac{\partial \mathbf{r}}{\partial \lambda} d\lambda + \frac{\partial \mathbf{r}}{\partial \mu} d\mu \right) = \oint_C \mathbf{v} \cdot d\mathbf{r}$$

This completes the proof of the theorem relative to a Cartesian basis. However, both integrals are sums of scalars, and so are scalars themselves. The result of the theorem will hold, therefore, relative to any basis.

Although not included here, the proof of Stokes' Theorem may be extended to cover the case when S is a piecewise smooth orientable surface bounded by a piecewise smooth curve C.

Theorem

If the normal surface integral of $\mathbf{A}(\mathbf{r})$ over *all* open surfaces is equal to the tangential line integral of $\mathbf{v}(\mathbf{r})$ around their bounding curves, then

$$\mathbf{A} = \nabla \times \mathbf{v}$$

(This is a converse to Stokes' Theorem)

Proof

By hypothesis: $\oint \mathbf{v} \cdot d\mathbf{r} = \int_s \mathbf{A} \cdot d\mathbf{S}$

By Stokes' theorem: $\oint \mathbf{v} \cdot d\mathbf{r} = \int_s \nabla \times \mathbf{v} \cdot d\mathbf{S}$.

Hence, $\int_s (\mathbf{A} - \nabla \times \mathbf{v}) \cdot d\mathbf{S}$ is zero for all surfaces and so the integrand must vanish. Therefore, $\mathbf{A} = \nabla \times \mathbf{v}$.

It has been shown already that a field $\mathbf{v}(\mathbf{r})$ is conservative if and only if $\oint \mathbf{v} \cdot d\mathbf{r} = 0$ round all closed circuits. This condition may be expressed as

$$\nabla \times \mathbf{v} = \mathbf{0} \qquad (10.3)$$

throughout space.

The proof is immediate for, if $\oint \mathbf{v} \cdot d\mathbf{r} = 0$ round all circuits, then $\nabla \times \mathbf{v} = \mathbf{0}$ by definition (10.1). Also, if $\nabla \times \mathbf{v} = \mathbf{0}$ everywhere, then Stokes' theorem shows that $\oint \mathbf{v} \cdot d\mathbf{r} = 0$ round any closed circuit.

A field $\mathbf{v}$ for which (10.3) holds is called an **irrotational field**, there being no tendency to circulate in any region of space.

10.4 THE DIVERGENCE OF A VECTOR FIELD

The concept of the flow or flux of a vector field is fundamental in many branches of physics, most notably fluid dynamics and current electricity. Consider the velocity $\mathbf{v}$ of a fluid, then the rate of flow of fluid through a surface element dS is $v\cos\theta dS$, where θ is the angle between $\mathbf{v}$ and the normal $\hat{\mathbf{n}}$ to dS. Only the component of $\mathbf{v}$ along $\hat{\mathbf{n}}$ contributes to the flow since any component normal to $\hat{\mathbf{n}}$ does not flow *through* dS (Fig. 10.6).

The rate of flow may be written $(\mathbf{v} \cdot \hat{\mathbf{n}})dS$. This is negative if the normal component of $\mathbf{v}$ is in the opposite direction to $\hat{\mathbf{n}}$. More generally, the flux of any vector field, through an element dS, is defined as $(\mathbf{v} \cdot \hat{\mathbf{n}})dS$, which is clearly a scalar but depends on both the magnitude of dS and the direction of its normal $\hat{\mathbf{n}}$.

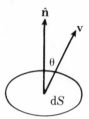

Fig. 10.6

Now consider a finite region V of 3-space bounded by a simple closed surface S. Then, the flux of **v** out of the region V is given by summing the above expression over all small elements δS of the surface S. In the limit with every $\delta S \to 0$, the outward flux becomes the surface integral $\iint_s (\mathbf{v} \cdot \hat{\mathbf{n}}) dS$, the normal $\hat{\mathbf{n}}$ pointing out of V at every point of S. Earlier, it was found convenient to define curl **v** to measure the 'circulation of **v** at a point'. It is convenient also to define a scalar field to measure the 'outflow at a point'. This scalar field is called the **divergence** of **v**, is denoted by div **v**, and is defined by

$$\text{div } \mathbf{v} = \lim_{\delta V \to 0} \frac{1}{\delta V} \iint_s (\mathbf{v} \cdot \hat{\mathbf{n}}) dS \, , \qquad (10.4)$$

δV being the small volume enclosed by the small closed surface δS. It is seen that div **v** measures the 'outflow per unit volume.'

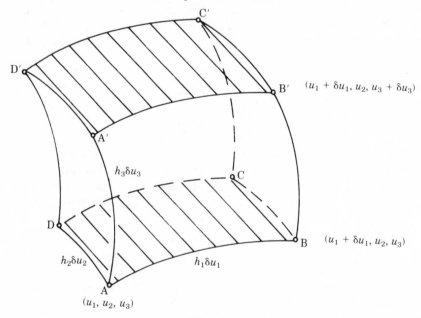

Fig. 10.7

An expression for div $\mathbf{v}$ may be found, fairly easily, in terms of arbitrary orthogonal coordinates u_1, u_2, u_3. The volume δV in (10.4) may be chosen to be a nearly rectangular solid with opposite corners at points $A(u_1, u_2, u_3)$ and $C'(u_1 + \delta u_1, u_2 + \delta u_2, u_3 + \delta u_3)$ as shown in Fig. 10.7. The edges AB, AD, AA' are along the orthogonal coordinate axes and so are of lengths $h_1 \delta u_1$, $h_2 \delta u_2$, $h_3 \delta u_3$ respectively. Now to calculate the contribution to $\iint (\mathbf{v} \cdot \hat{\mathbf{n}}) dS$ from the shaded faces ABCD and A'B'C'D'. Suppose $\mathbf{v}$ has components v_1, v_2, v_3 along the coordinate axes, then

$$\mathbf{v} \cdot \hat{\mathbf{n}} = \begin{cases} - v_3 \text{ on ABCD} \\ + v_3 \text{ on A'B'C'D'} . \end{cases}$$

Thus, the contribution is

$$\iint_{A'B'C'D'} v_3 h_1 h_2 du_1 du_2 - \iint_{ABCD} v_3 h_1 h_2 du_1 du_2$$

$$= \iint_{ABCD} \delta u_3 \frac{\partial}{\partial u_3} (v_3 h_1 h_2) du_1 du_2 ,$$

since corresponding points on ABCD and A'B'C'D' differ only by a change δu_3 in the coordinate u_3. To the lowest order in δu_1, δu_2, δu_3 the contribution becomes

$$\delta u_1 \delta u_2 \delta u_3 \frac{\partial}{\partial u_3} (v_3 h_1 h_2) ,$$

the derivative being evaluated at the point A. Since the volume $\delta V = h_1 \delta u_1 h_2 \delta u_2 h_3 \delta u_3$, this may be written

$$\frac{\delta V}{h_1 h_2 h_3} \frac{\partial}{\partial u_3} (v_3 h_1 h_2) .$$

Therefore, the contribution of the two faces to the limit (10.4) is

$$\frac{1}{h_1 h_2 h_3} \frac{\partial}{\partial u_3} (v_3 h_1 h_2) .$$

Similar contributions arise from the other two pairs of faces, and so

$$\text{div } \mathbf{v} = \frac{1}{h_1 h_2 h_3} \left[\frac{\partial}{\partial u_1} (v_1 h_2 h_3) + \frac{\partial}{\partial u_2} (v_2 h_3 h_1) + \frac{\partial}{\partial u_3} (v_3 h_1 h_2) \right] .$$

For rectangular Cartesian coordinates x, y, z,

$$h_1 = h_2 = h_3 = 1 ,$$

and so, $\text{div } \mathbf{v} = \partial v_x / \partial x + \partial v_y / \partial y + \partial v_z / \partial z$

$$= (\partial/\partial x , \partial/\partial y , \partial/\partial z) \cdot (v_x , v_y , v_z) = \nabla \cdot \mathbf{v} .$$

Thus, $$\text{div } \mathbf{v} = \partial v_i/\partial x_i = \nabla\cdot\mathbf{v}\ .$$

10.4.1 The Divergence Theorem

Suppose V is a closed bounded region whose boundary is a smooth orientable closed surface S. If the vector field $\mathbf{v}(\mathbf{r})$ is continuous and has continuous first derivatives on V then $\int_V \nabla\cdot\mathbf{v}\ dV = \int_s \mathbf{v}\cdot d\mathbf{S}$ where the unit normal (and therefore the element of area $d\mathbf{S}$) points out of the region V.

Proof

The volume and surface integrals may be written as triple and double integrals respectively. The hypotheses that the vector field $\mathbf{v}(\mathbf{r})$ and its first partial derivatives are continuous and that S is a smooth surface then ensure that the integrands are continuous and that both integrals exist. Now, in terms of a right-handed rectangular Cartesian coordinate system

$$\int_V \nabla\cdot\mathbf{v}\ dV = \iiint\left(\frac{\partial v_x}{\partial x} + \frac{\partial v_y}{\partial y} + \frac{\partial v_z}{\partial z}\right) dxdydz\ .$$

Consider the first integral

$$\iiint\frac{\partial v_x}{\partial x}\ dxdydz\ .$$

This triple integral may be integrated once. In order to simplify the proof it is assumed now that any line drawn parallel to a coordinate axis will intersect the boundary S in at most two points. Therefore, the limits of integration may be found from Fig. 10.8.

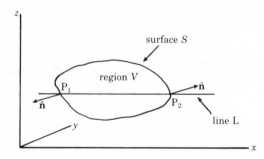

Fig. 10.8

If the line L drawn parallel to the x-axis meets the boundary S in the points P_1 and P_2, then

$$\iiint\frac{\partial v_x}{\partial x}\ dxdydz = \iint (v_x|_{P_2} - v_x|_{P_1})dydz\ .$$

Now dydz is the projection of the element of area onto the yz plane, and since $\hat{n}$, and so d$\mathbf{S}$, are assumed to point out of the region V,

$$dydz = \begin{cases} \mathbf{i} \cdot d\mathbf{S} \text{ at } P_2 \\ -\mathbf{i} \cdot d\mathbf{S} \text{ at } P_1 \end{cases}.$$

Thus,

$$\iiint \frac{\partial v_x}{\partial x} dxdydz = \iint (v_x \mathbf{i} \cdot d\mathbf{S}|_{P_2} - v_x \mathbf{i} \cdot d\mathbf{S}|_{P_1}) .$$

As the line L varies, the points P_1 and P_2 will cover the whole of the surface S and so

$$\iiint \frac{\partial v_x}{\partial x} dxdydz = \int_s v_x \mathbf{i} \cdot d\mathbf{S} .$$

Similarly for the remaining two terms in the triple integral and so, finally,

$$\int_V \nabla \cdot \mathbf{v} dV = \int_s (v_x \mathbf{i} + v_y \mathbf{j} + v_z \mathbf{k}) \cdot d\mathbf{S} = \int_s \mathbf{v} \cdot d\mathbf{S} .$$

as required.

It might be noted that, although not included here, the proof of the Divergence Theorem may be extended to cover the case w   :e boundary of V is a piecewise smooth orientable closed surface S.

The normal surface integral $\int_s \mathbf{v} \cdot d\mathbf{S}$ is often called the **flux** of the field $\mathbf{v}(\mathbf{r})$ across the surface S.

For the vector field $\mathbf{v} = \mathbf{r}$

$$\nabla \cdot \mathbf{v} = \nabla \cdot \mathbf{r} = \partial x/\partial x + \partial y/\partial y + \partial z/\partial z = 3 .$$

Substituting in the divergence theorem gives

$$\int_V 3dV = \int_s \mathbf{r} \cdot d\mathbf{S} .$$

Thus, the volume enclosed by a surface S is $\frac{1}{3}\int_s \mathbf{r} \cdot d\mathbf{S}$.

Stokes' Theorem and the Divergence Theorem are easily the most important of the various integral theorems, but there are others which prove to be of great use on occasions.

10.5 GREEN'S THEOREM IN THE PLANE

If R is a closed region of the xy plane bounded by a simple closed curve B, and if P and Q are continuous functions of x and y having continuous derivatives on R, then

$$\oint_B Pdx + Qdy = \iint_R \left(\frac{\partial Q}{\partial x} - \frac{\partial P}{\partial y}\right) dxdy .$$

As has been seen, when written in vector notation

$$Pdx + Qdy = (P\mathbf{i} + Q\mathbf{j}) \cdot (dx\mathbf{i} + dy\mathbf{j}) = \mathbf{A} \cdot d\mathbf{r} \text{ say.}$$

With $\mathbf{A}$ so defined

$$\nabla \times \mathbf{A} = \begin{vmatrix} \mathbf{i} & \mathbf{j} & \mathbf{k} \\ \partial/\partial x & \partial/\partial y & \partial/\partial z \\ P & Q & 0 \end{vmatrix}$$

$$= -\frac{\partial Q}{\partial z}\mathbf{i} + \frac{\partial P}{\partial z}\mathbf{j} + \left(\frac{\partial Q}{\partial x} - \frac{\partial P}{\partial y}\right)\mathbf{k}.$$

Therefore, $(\nabla \times \mathbf{A})\cdot\mathbf{k} = \partial Q/\partial x - \partial P/\partial y$.

Then, Green's theorem in the plane may be written

$$\oint_B \mathbf{A}\cdot\mathbf{dr} = \int_R (\nabla \times \mathbf{A})\cdot\mathbf{k}dR.$$

A generalisation of this result to surfaces S in space having a curve C as boundary leads to Stokes' theorem. Also, it may be noticed in passing that the divergence theorem is another generalisation of this result where the (plane) region R and its closed boundary (curve) B are replaced by a (space) region V and its closed boundary (surface) S. It is for this reason that the divergence theorem is sometimes called **Green's theorem in space**. This follows because of a slightly modified form of the theorem in vector notation:

Again,

$$Pdx + Qdy = \mathbf{A}\cdot\mathbf{dr} = \mathbf{A}\cdot\frac{\mathbf{dr}}{ds}ds = \mathbf{A}\cdot\mathbf{T}ds$$

where $\mathbf{dr}/ds = \mathbf{T} =$ unit tangent vector to B, as in Fig. 10.9.

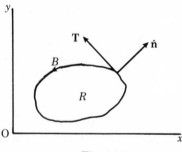

Fig. 10.9

If $\hat{\mathbf{n}}$ is the outward drawn unit normal to B, then $\mathbf{T} = \mathbf{k} \times \hat{\mathbf{n}}$ so that

$$\mathbf{A}\cdot\mathbf{T}ds = \mathbf{A}\cdot(\mathbf{k} \times \hat{\mathbf{n}})ds = (\mathbf{A} \times \mathbf{k})\cdot\hat{\mathbf{n}}ds.$$

Since $\mathbf{A} = P\mathbf{i} + Q\mathbf{j}$, $\mathbf{B} = \mathbf{A} \times \mathbf{k} = Q\mathbf{i} - P\mathbf{j}$

and $\partial Q/\partial x - \partial P/\partial y = \nabla\cdot\mathbf{B}$.

Then Green's theorem in the plane may be written

$$\oint_B \mathbf{B} \cdot \hat{\mathbf{n}} ds = \int_R \nabla \cdot \mathbf{B} dR \ .$$

It is straightforward now to see that the divergence theorem is another generalisation of Green's theorem in the plane.

Other related integral theorems which may prove of use are:

(1) For two scalar fields $\phi(\mathbf{r})$ and $\psi(\mathbf{r})$

$$\int_V [\phi \nabla^2 \psi + (\nabla \phi) \cdot (\nabla \psi)] dV = \int_s (\phi \nabla \psi) \cdot d\mathbf{S} \ .$$

This is known as **Green's first identity** or theorem.

(2) For two scalar fields $\phi(\mathbf{r})$ and $\psi(\mathbf{r})$,

$$\int_V (\phi \nabla^2 \psi - \psi \nabla^2 \phi) dV = \int_s (\phi \nabla \psi - \psi \nabla \phi) \cdot d\mathbf{S} \ .$$

This is **Green's second identity** or theorem.

(3) For the vector field $\mathbf{u}(\mathbf{r})$,

$$\int_V (\nabla \times \mathbf{u}) dV = \int_s (\hat{\mathbf{n}} \times \mathbf{u}) dS = \int_s d\mathbf{S} \times \mathbf{u} \ .$$

(4) For the scalar $\phi(\mathbf{r})$,

$$\oint_c \phi d\mathbf{r} = \int_s (\hat{\mathbf{n}} \times \nabla \phi) dS = \int_s d\mathbf{S} \times \nabla \phi \ .$$

The proofs of these results follow quite easily. Firstly, in the divergence theorem, let

$$\mathbf{v} = \phi \nabla \psi$$

then $$\int_V \nabla \cdot (\phi \nabla \psi) dV = \int_s (\phi \nabla \psi) \cdot d\mathbf{S} \ .$$

But $$\nabla \cdot (\phi \nabla \psi) = \phi \nabla^2 \psi + (\nabla \phi) \cdot (\nabla \psi) \ .$$

Substituting back gives

$$\int_V [\phi \nabla^2 \psi + (\nabla \phi) \cdot (\nabla \psi)] dV = \int_s (\phi \nabla \psi) \cdot d\mathbf{S} \ . \tag{i}$$

Interchanging ϕ nd ψ in this result gives

$$\int_V [\psi \nabla^2 \phi + (\nabla \psi) \cdot (\nabla \phi)] dV = \int_s (\psi \nabla \phi) \cdot d\mathbf{S} \ . \tag{ii}$$

Subtracting (ii) from (i) leads to Green's second identity.

Hence results (1) and (2).

Now let $\mathbf{v} = \mathbf{u} \times \mathbf{c}$ in the divergence theorem, where $\mathbf{c}$ is a constant vector, then

$$\int_V \nabla\cdot(\mathbf{u} \times \mathbf{c})dV = \int_s (\mathbf{u} \times \mathbf{c})\cdot d\mathbf{S} = \int_s (\mathbf{u} \times \mathbf{c})\cdot\hat{\mathbf{n}}dS \ .$$

Since $$\nabla\cdot(\mathbf{u} \times \mathbf{c}) = \mathbf{c}\cdot(\nabla \times \mathbf{u})$$

and $$(\mathbf{u} \times \mathbf{c})\cdot\hat{\mathbf{n}} = \mathbf{c}\cdot(\hat{\mathbf{n}} \times \mathbf{u})$$

$$\int_V \mathbf{c}\cdot(\nabla \times \mathbf{u})dV = \int_s \mathbf{c}\cdot(\hat{\mathbf{n}} \times \mathbf{u})dS \ .$$

Taking **c** outside the integrals,

$$\mathbf{c}\cdot \int_V (\nabla \times \mathbf{u})dV = \mathbf{c}\cdot \int_s (\hat{\mathbf{n}} \times \mathbf{u})dS \ ,$$

and since **c** is an arbitrary constant vector

$$\int_V (\nabla \times \mathbf{u})dV = \int_s (\hat{\mathbf{n}} \times \mathbf{u})dS \ .$$

Hence result 3.

Result 4 follows in a similar manner by putting $\mathbf{v} = \phi\mathbf{c}$, where **c** is again a constant vector, in Stokes' theorem.

To illustrate one of the more important uses of the integral theorems, attention will now be turned to the derivation of an equation of great importance in many areas of physics—the **equation of continuity**.

Consider some volume of space V_0. The mass of fluid in this volume is $\int\rho dV$, where ρ is the fluid density and the integration is taken over the volume V_0. The mass of fluid flowing in unit time through an element d**S** of the surface bounding this volume is $\rho\mathbf{v}\cdot d\mathbf{S}$, where **v** is the velocity of the fluid. Also, the magnitude of the vector d**S** equals the area of the surface element and its direction is along the normal; by convention, along the outward normal. Hence, $\rho\mathbf{v}\cdot d\mathbf{S}$ is positive if the fluid is flowing out of the volume, and negative if the flow is into the volume. The total mass of fluid flowing out of the volume V_0 in unit time is $\int\rho\mathbf{v}\cdot d\mathbf{S}$ where the integration is taken over the entire closed surface surrounding the volume in question.

Again, the decrease per unit time in the mass of fluid in the volume V_0 may be written

$$-\frac{\partial}{\partial t}\int\rho dV \ .$$

Equating the two expressions gives

$$\frac{\partial}{\partial t}\int_V \rho dV = -\int_s \rho\mathbf{v}\cdot d\mathbf{S} \ .$$

However, the surface integral may be transformed to a volume integral by using the divergence theorem

$$\int_s \rho\mathbf{v}\cdot d\mathbf{S} = \int_V \nabla\cdot(\rho\mathbf{v})dV \ .$$

Thus,

$$\int_V \left[\frac{\partial \rho}{\partial t} + \nabla \cdot (\rho \mathbf{v}) \right] dV = 0 \ .$$

However, since this equation must hold for any volume, the integrand must vanish; that is

$$\partial \rho / \partial t + \nabla \cdot (\rho \mathbf{v}) = 0 \ .$$

This is the equation of continuity.

10.6 FURTHER PROPERTIES OF CURL AND DIV

Mention has been made already of the fact that ∇ is not a vector but is, rather, an operator. Hence, great care must be taken when manipulating ∇ as a vector. Bearing this in mind, several further properties of curl and divergence will be examined.

If $\mathbf{u}(\mathbf{r})$ and $\mathbf{v}(\mathbf{r})$ are both differentiable vector fields then

$$\nabla \cdot (\mathbf{u} + \mathbf{v}) = \nabla \cdot \mathbf{u} + \nabla \cdot \mathbf{v}$$

and
$$\nabla \times (\mathbf{u} + \mathbf{v}) = \nabla \times \mathbf{u} + \nabla \times \mathbf{v} \ .$$

The proofs of these identities are left as exercises.

Also, there are several 'product' rules obeyed by the gradient, divergence, and curl. The results are as follows and hold for all scalar fields $\phi(\mathbf{r})$ and all vector fields $\mathbf{u}(\mathbf{r})$ and $\mathbf{v}(\mathbf{r})$:

$$\nabla \cdot (\phi \mathbf{v}) = \nabla \phi \cdot \mathbf{v} + \phi \nabla \cdot \mathbf{v} \tag{10.5}$$

$$\nabla \times (\phi \mathbf{v}) = \nabla \phi \times \mathbf{v} + \phi \nabla \times \mathbf{v} \tag{10.6}$$

$$\nabla \cdot (\mathbf{u} \times \mathbf{v}) = \mathbf{v} \cdot (\nabla \times \mathbf{u}) - \mathbf{u} \cdot (\nabla \times \mathbf{v}) \tag{10.7}$$

$$\nabla (\mathbf{u} \cdot \mathbf{v}) = \mathbf{v} \times (\nabla \times \mathbf{u}) + \mathbf{u} \times (\nabla \times \mathbf{v}) + (\mathbf{v} \cdot \nabla) \mathbf{u} + (\mathbf{u} \cdot \nabla) \mathbf{v} \tag{10.8}$$

$$\nabla \times (\mathbf{u} \times \mathbf{v}) = (\mathbf{v} \cdot \nabla) \mathbf{u} - (\mathbf{u} \cdot \nabla) \mathbf{v} - \mathbf{v} \nabla \cdot \mathbf{u} + \mathbf{u} \nabla \cdot \mathbf{v} \ . \tag{10.9}$$

These identities occur quite frequently, and two of them will be proved now. *Proof of (10.9)*

$$[\nabla \times (\mathbf{u} \times \mathbf{v})]_i = \varepsilon_{ijk} \frac{\partial}{\partial x_j} (\varepsilon_{klm} u_l v_m) = \varepsilon_{kij} \varepsilon_{klm} \frac{\partial}{\partial x_j} (u_l v_m)$$

$$= (\delta_{il} \delta_{jm} - \delta_{im} \delta_{jl}) \frac{\partial}{\partial x_j} (u_l v_m)$$

$$= \frac{\partial}{\partial x_j} (u_i v_j) - \frac{\partial}{\partial x_j} (u_j v_i)$$

$$= u_i \frac{\partial v_j}{\partial x_j} + v_j \frac{\partial u_i}{\partial x_j} - v_i \frac{\partial u_j}{\partial x_j} - u_j \frac{\partial v_i}{\partial x_j} \ .$$

$$= u_i \frac{\partial v_j}{\partial x_j} + v_j \frac{\partial u_i}{\partial x_j} - v_i \frac{\partial u_j}{\partial x_j} - u_j \frac{\partial v_i}{\partial x_j}.$$

That is, $\qquad \nabla \times (\mathbf{u} \times \mathbf{v}) = \mathbf{u}\nabla\cdot\mathbf{v} + (\mathbf{v}\cdot\nabla)\mathbf{u} - \mathbf{v}\nabla\cdot\mathbf{u} - (\mathbf{u}\cdot\nabla)\mathbf{v}$

where $\mathbf{v}\cdot\nabla \equiv v_i\, \partial/\partial x_i$.

Proof of (10.8)

This proof is the most difficult in this group. It proves convenient to start by considering

$$[\mathbf{v} \times (\nabla \times \mathbf{u})]_i = \varepsilon_{ijk}\, v_j\, \varepsilon_{klm} \frac{\partial u_m}{\partial x_l} = \varepsilon_{kij}\, \varepsilon_{klm}\, v_j \frac{\partial u_m}{\partial x_l}$$

$$= (\delta_{il}\delta_{jm} - \delta_{im}\delta_{jl})v_j \frac{\partial u_m}{\partial x_l}$$

$$= v_j \frac{\partial u_j}{\partial x_i} - v_j \frac{\partial u_i}{\partial x_j}.$$

Now

$$[\nabla(\mathbf{v}\cdot\mathbf{u})]_i = \frac{\partial}{\partial x_i}(v_j u_j) = v_j \frac{\partial u_j}{\partial x_i} + u_j \frac{\partial v_j}{\partial x_i}$$

$$= [\mathbf{v} \times (\nabla \times \mathbf{u})]_i + v_j\frac{\partial u_i}{\partial x_j}$$

$$+ [\mathbf{u} \times (\nabla \times \mathbf{v})]_i + u_j\frac{\partial v_i}{\partial x_j}.$$

Hence, $\qquad \nabla(\mathbf{v}\cdot\mathbf{u}) = \mathbf{v} \times (\nabla \times \mathbf{u}) + (\mathbf{v}\cdot\nabla)\mathbf{u} + \mathbf{u} \times (\nabla \times \mathbf{v}) + (\mathbf{u}\cdot\nabla)\mathbf{v}.$

Now assuming that the scalar field $\phi(\mathbf{r})$ and the vector field $\mathbf{v}(\mathbf{r})$ are both twice differentiable, then the following second derivatives exist

$$\nabla\cdot(\nabla\phi)\,,\ \nabla \times (\nabla\phi)\,,\ \nabla(\nabla\cdot\mathbf{v})\,,\ \nabla\cdot(\nabla \times \mathbf{v})\,,\ \nabla \times (\nabla \times \mathbf{v})\,.$$

The first expression occurs frequently in physics and is denoted usually by $\nabla^2\phi$. In terms of rectangular Cartesian coordinates

$$\nabla^2\phi = \nabla\cdot(\nabla\phi) = \frac{\partial}{\partial x_i}(\nabla\phi)_i = \frac{\partial}{\partial x_i}\left(\frac{\partial\phi}{\partial x_i}\right)$$

$$= \frac{\partial^2\phi}{\partial x^2} + \frac{\partial^2\phi}{\partial y^2} + \frac{\partial^2\phi}{\partial z^2}.$$

The operator $\qquad \nabla^2 \equiv \partial^2/\partial x^2 + \partial^2/\partial y^2 + \partial^2/\partial z^2$

is called the **Laplacian**.

It might be noted that, in terms of orthogonal curvilinear coordinates,

$$\nabla^2\phi = \frac{1}{h_1 h_2 h_3}\left[\frac{\partial}{\partial u_1}\left(\frac{h_2 h_3}{h_1}\frac{\partial\phi}{\partial u_1}\right) + \text{cyclic permutations}\right].$$

The second and fourth expressions vanish identically. For example,

$$[\nabla \times (\nabla\phi)]_i = \varepsilon_{ijk} \frac{\partial}{\partial x_j} (\nabla\phi)_k = \varepsilon_{ijk} \frac{\partial^2\phi}{\partial x_j \, \partial x_k} .$$

Now ε_{ijk} is antisymmetric in j and k while $\partial^2/\partial x_j \partial x_k$ is symmetric in j and k for the functions under discussion here. Hence it follows that

$$\nabla \times (\nabla\phi) = 0 .$$

For rectangular Cartesian coordinates

$$\nabla \times (\nabla\phi) = \text{curl}\left(\frac{\partial\phi}{\partial x}\mathbf{i} + \frac{\partial\phi}{\partial y}\mathbf{j} + \frac{\partial\phi}{\partial z}\mathbf{k}\right)$$

$$= \left(\frac{\partial^2\phi}{\partial y\partial z} - \frac{\partial^2\phi}{\partial z\partial y}\right)\mathbf{i} + \cdots + \cdots = 0.$$

Similarly, $$\nabla\cdot(\nabla \times \mathbf{v}) = 0 .$$

The remaining two expressions are related by the identity

$$\nabla \times (\nabla \times \mathbf{v}) = \nabla(\nabla\cdot\mathbf{v}) - \nabla^2\mathbf{v} .$$

This may be shown as follows

$$[\nabla \times (\nabla \times \mathbf{v})]_i = \varepsilon_{ijk} \frac{\partial}{\partial x_j}\left(\varepsilon_{klm} \frac{\partial v_m}{\partial x_l}\right)$$

$$= \varepsilon_{kij}\varepsilon_{klm} \frac{\partial}{\partial x_j}\left(\frac{\partial v_m}{\partial x_l}\right)$$

$$= (\delta_{il}\delta_{jm} - \delta_{im}\delta_{jl}) \frac{\partial}{\partial x_j}\left(\frac{\partial v_m}{\partial x_l}\right)$$

$$= \frac{\partial}{\partial x_j}\left(\frac{\partial v_j}{\partial x_i}\right) - \frac{\partial}{\partial x_j}\left(\frac{\partial v_i}{\partial x_j}\right)$$

$$= \frac{\partial}{\partial x_i}\left(\frac{\partial v_j}{\partial x_j}\right) - \frac{\partial^2 v_i}{\partial x_j\partial x_j}$$

Hence the required result.

EXERCISES 10

(1) If $\phi(x,y,z) = x^3 + 6xz^2 + 3y^4$, find $\nabla\phi$ at the point $(1,1,1)$. Obtain the directional derivative of $\phi(x,y,x)$ at the point $(1,1,1)$ in the direction of the vector $(1,2,3)$. Also, in what direction is the directional derivative of $\phi(x,y,z)$ greatest at the point $(1,1,1)$?

(2) Find the unit normal to the surface

$$x^2/a^2 + y^2/b^2 + z^2/c^2 = 3$$

at the point (a, b, c).

(3) If $\mathbf{a}$ is a constant vector, show that $\nabla(\mathbf{r} \cdot \mathbf{a}) = \mathbf{a}$.

(4) Prove that (i) $\nabla(\phi + \psi) = \nabla\phi + \nabla\psi$

        (ii) $\nabla(\phi\psi) = \phi\nabla\psi + (\nabla\phi)\psi$.

for a scalar fields $\phi(\mathbf{r})$ and $\psi(\mathbf{r})$.

(5) Given that $\mathbf{v} = (2x^2z, 3xyz, y^2)$, find $\nabla \cdot \mathbf{v}$ and $\nabla \times \mathbf{v}$.

(6) Evaluate the following:

      (i) ∇r^3 ,   (ii) $\nabla^2(\log r)$,   (iii) $\nabla^2 r^n$,   (iv) $\nabla \cdot (r^3 \mathbf{r})$.

(7) If $\mathbf{m}$ is a constant vector, show that

      (i) $\nabla \times (\mathbf{m} \times \mathbf{r}) = 2\mathbf{m}$,   (ii) $\nabla \cdot (\mathbf{m} \times \mathbf{r}) = 0$.

(8) Prove that   (i) $\nabla \cdot (\phi\mathbf{v}) = \nabla\phi \cdot \mathbf{v} + \phi\nabla \cdot \mathbf{v}$

        (ii) $\nabla \times (\phi\mathbf{v}) = \nabla\phi \times \mathbf{v} + \phi\nabla \times \mathbf{v}$

        (iii) $\nabla \cdot (\mathbf{u} \times \mathbf{v}) = \mathbf{v} \cdot (\nabla \times \mathbf{u}) - \mathbf{u} \cdot (\nabla \times \mathbf{v})$

for the scalar field $\phi(\mathbf{r})$ and vector fields $\mathbf{v}(\mathbf{r})$ and $\mathbf{u}(\mathbf{r})$.

(9) Evaluate $$\nabla^2 \left(\nabla \cdot \frac{\mathbf{r}}{r^2} \right).$$

(10) Prove that $\mathbf{F} = (y^2\cos x + z^3, \ 2y\sin x - 4, \ 3xz^2 + 2)$ is a conservative field. Find the scalar potential and also the work done in moving an object in this field from $(0,1,-1)$ to $(\pi/2,-1,2)$

(11) If C is a circle of radius 2 with centre at the origin traversed in the anticlockwise direction, evaluate

(i) $\oint_c (3x + 4y)dx + (2x - 3y)dy$,

(ii) $\oint_c (x^2 + y^2)dx + 3xy^2 dy$

(12) Evaluate $\int_{(0,0)}^{(\pi,2)} (6xy - y^2)dx + (3x^2 - 2xy)dy$ along the cycloid $x = \theta - \sin\theta$, $y = 1 - \cos\theta$.

(13) Evaluate $\oint (3x^2 + 2y)dx - (x + 3\cos y)dy$ around   the   parallelogram having vertices at $(0,0)$, $(2,0)$, $(3,1)$ and $(1,1)$.

(14) Verify Stokes' Theorem for $\mathbf{F} = (xz, -y, x^2 y)$ where S is the surface of the region bounded by $x = 0$, $y = 0$, $z = 0$ and $2x + y + 2z = 8$, which is not included in the xz plane.

(15) Verify Stokes' Theorem for $\mathbf{F} = (y, x - 2xz, -xy)$, where S is the surface of the sphere $x^2 + y^2 + z^2 = a^2$ above the xy plane.

Chapter 11
Fourier Series

11.1 FOURIER SERIES

A function $f(x)$ is said to be 'expanded as a Fourier series' when it is expressed as a series of sine and cosine terms:

$$f(x) = \frac{1}{2}a_0 + \sum_{n=1}^{\infty} (a_n\cos nx + b_n\sin nx) \qquad (11.1)$$

where a_n $(n = 0,1,2,\ldots)$ and b_n $(n = 1,2,\ldots)$ are constants referred to as the **Fourier coefficients** of $f(x)$.

In order to calculate a_n and b_n, note that if m and n are positive integers,

$$\int_{\alpha}^{\alpha+2\pi} \cos(m - n)x \, dx = 2\pi\delta_{mn}$$

$$\int_{\alpha}^{\alpha+2\pi} \cos(m + n)x \, dx = 0$$

where the Kronecker delta, δ_{mn}, is defined by

$$\delta_{mn} = \begin{cases} 1 & \text{when } m = n \\ 0 & \text{when } m \neq n . \end{cases}$$

Adding and subtracting the above equations gives

$$\int_{\alpha}^{\alpha+2\pi} \cos mx \cos nx \, dx = \pi\delta_{mn}$$

$$\int_{\alpha}^{\alpha+2\pi} \sin mx \sin nx \, dx = \pi\delta_{mn} .$$

Similarly, it may be shown that

$$\int_{\alpha}^{\alpha+2\pi} \cos mx \sin nx \, dx = 0 .$$

and also

$$\int\limits_{\alpha}^{\alpha+2\pi} \cos nx \; dx = \int\limits_{\alpha}^{\alpha+2\pi} \sin nx \; dx = 0 \; .$$

The most obvious property of the series in (11.1) is that each term is periodic with period 2π, so that the series itself has this period. Suppose that a function $f(x)$ is given and that (11.1) is satisfied for values of x in the range $(\alpha, \alpha + 2\pi)$, where α is some constant. The equation cannot be satisfied outside this range unless $f(x)$ is also periodic of period 2π.

Now assume (11.1) to hold in the range $(\alpha, \alpha + 2\pi)$, multiply throughout by $\cos mx \; (m > 0)$, and integrate over the range to give

$$\int\limits_{\alpha}^{\alpha+2\pi} f(x) \cos mx \; dx = \sum_{n=1}^{\infty} a_n \int\limits_{\alpha}^{\alpha+2\pi} \cos nx \cos mx \; dx$$

$$= \pi \sum_{n=1}^{\infty} a_n \delta_{mn} = \pi a_m \; .$$

Therefore,

$$a_n = \frac{1}{\pi} \int\limits_{\alpha}^{\alpha+2\pi} f(x) \cos nx \; dx \; . \tag{11.2}$$

Similarly, by multiplying throughout by $\sin mx$ and integrating over the same range, it is found that

$$b_n = \frac{1}{\pi} \int\limits_{\alpha}^{\alpha+2\pi} f(x) \sin nx \; dx \; . \tag{11.3}$$

The coefficient a_0 is given by integrating (11.1) over the range $(\alpha, \alpha + 2\pi)$. This leads to

$$a_0 = \frac{1}{\pi} \int\limits_{\alpha}^{\alpha+2\pi} f(x) dx$$

so that the equation for a_0 is the same as for a_n. This is why the constant term in (11.1) is written as $\frac{1}{2}a_0$ instead of a_0.

Example

Expand the function $f(x) = x$ as a Fourier series
(i) in the range $(0, 2\pi)$, (ii) in the range $(-\pi, \pi)$.

To evaluate the coefficients by using (11.2) and (11.3) the following integrals are needed:

$$\int x \cos nx \, dx = \begin{cases} \dfrac{1}{n} x \sin nx + \dfrac{1}{n^2} \cos nx \, , n \neq 0 \\[2ex] \dfrac{1}{2} x^2 \qquad\qquad\qquad , n = 0 \end{cases}$$

$$\int x \sin nx \, dx = -\frac{1}{n} x \cos nx + \frac{1}{n^2} \sin nx \, , n \neq 0 \, .$$

(i) Putting in the limits 0 and 2π,

$$a_n = \frac{1}{\pi} \int_0^{2\pi} x \cos nx \, dx = \begin{cases} 0 \, , n \neq 0 \\ 2\pi \, , n = 0 \end{cases}$$

$$b_n = \frac{1}{\pi} \int_0^{2\pi} x \sin nx \, dx = -\frac{2}{n} \, , n \neq 0 \, .$$

Hence, the Fourier expansion of x in the range $(0,2\pi)$ is

$$x = \pi - 2 \sum_{n=1}^{\infty} \frac{1}{n} \sin nx \, .$$

(ii) Putting in the limits $-\pi$ and π, it is found that in the range $(-\pi,\pi)$ x is represented by the series

$$x = 2 \sum_{n=1}^{\infty} \frac{(-1)^{n-1}}{n} \sin nx \, .$$

So far it has been shown that, if equation (11.1) holds, that is, if the trigonometrical series on the right-hand side of (11.1) converges to the value $f(x)$ for all x in the given range, then the Fourier coefficients will be given by equations (11.2) and (11.3). Also, although it has not been mentioned, in the discussion it has been assumed that $f(x)$ is continuous in the range $(\alpha, \alpha + 2\pi)$. However, Fourier series may represent functions with a finite number of discontinuities if (11.1) is modified slightly. Suppose $f(x)$ is discontinuous at some point x in the range and that $f(x+)$ and $f(x-)$ are the limiting values as x is approached from above and below respectively. Then (11.1) is replaced by

$$\frac{1}{2} [f(x+) + f(x-)] = \frac{1}{2} a_0 + \sum_{n=1}^{\infty} (a_n \cos nx + b_n \sin nx) \, . \qquad (11.4)$$

At points where $f(x)$ is continuous, this equation is identical with (11.1). At points where $f(x)$ is discontinuous, the Fourier series gives the mean of the values to the right and left of the discontinuity. Similarly, it gives the mean value of $f(x)$ at the end points of the range.

Now consider the converse question to that which has been discussed: if a_n and b_n are given by equations (11.2) and (11.3) for some function $f(x)$ which is defined in the range $(\alpha, \alpha + 2\pi)$, is equation (11.1) satisfied in this range? Once the a_n and b_n are calculated as indicated, then it is not unreasonable to write

$$f(x) \sim \frac{1}{2} a_0 + \sum_{n=1}^{\infty} (a_n \cos nx + b_n \sin nx)$$

where the symbol $\sim$ has been used to indicate that $f(x)$ is not necessarily equal to the series on the right-hand side. In fact, it is possible that the series on the right-hand side will be divergent or, if convergent, will converge to some function other than $f(x)$. All the above relation really implies is that the function $f(x)$ and the coefficients a_0, a_n, b_n are connected via equations (11.2) and (11.3). Actually the theory of Fourier series is concerned with studying series of the above type and determining, in particular, the conditions under which the Fourier series equals the function.

The first rigorous proof that, for a general class of functions, the Fourier series, defined as above, does converge to $f(x)$ was given by Dirichlet in 1829. Although the proof will not be included here, formula (11.4) may be shown to be valid provided the so-called **Dirichlet conditions** are satisfied. These conditions are:
(i) $f(x)$ is infinite at only a finite number of points in the range $(\alpha, \alpha + 2\pi)$;
(ii) the integral

$$\int_{\alpha}^{\alpha + 2\pi} |f(x)| \, dx$$

is convergent; that is, the integral of $f(x)$ is absolutely convergent. This ensures that all the integrals (11.2) and (11.3) converge;
(iii) the interval $\alpha < x < \alpha + 2\pi$ may be divided into a finite number of subintervals, in each of which $f(x)$ is monotonic; that is, $f(x)$ oscillates only a finite number of times in the range.

11.1.1 Odd and even functions
In the worked example considered earlier, it is seen that, in the range $(-\pi, \pi)$, the Fourier series for $f(x) = x$ contains sine terms only. Since x is an odd function in the stated range, this observation is not surprising.

A function $f(x)$ defined in the range $(-\pi, \pi)$ is said to be an **odd** function of x if for all values of x in the range $f(-x) = -f(x)$. Obviously, if this definition is to be consistent $f(0) = 0$. For such a function, it is seen that the coefficients a_n are given by

$$a_n = \frac{1}{\pi} \int_{-\pi}^{\pi} f(x) \cos nx \, dx$$

where (11.2) has been used with $\alpha = -\pi$.

Now

$$\pi a_n = \int\limits_{-\pi}^{0} f(x) \cos nx \, dx + \int\limits_{0}^{\pi} f(x) \cos nx \, dx$$

$$= \int\limits_{0}^{\pi} f(-y) \cos ny \, dy + \int\limits_{0}^{\pi} f(x) \cos nx \, dx$$

where x has been put equal to $-y$ in the first integral. Using the above definition of an odd function, it is seen that $a_n = 0$.

Quite generally, odd functions of x are represented in the range $(-\pi,\pi)$ by
Fourier series consisting of sine terms only. For such series, the coefficients b_n
are given by

$$\pi b_n = \int\limits_{-\pi}^{0} f(x) \sin nx \, dx + \int\limits_{0}^{\pi} f(x) \sin nx \, dx$$

$$= -\int\limits_{-\pi}^{0} f(-x) \sin nx \, dx + \int\limits_{0}^{\pi} f(x) \sin nx \, dx$$

since $f(x)$ is an odd function of x.

Therefore,
$$\pi b_n = \int\limits_{0}^{\pi} f(u) \sin nu \, du + \int\limits_{0}^{\pi} f(x) \sin nx \, dx$$

putting $u = -x$.

Hence,
$$b_n = \frac{2}{\pi} \int\limits_{0}^{\pi} f(x) \sin nx \, dx \ .$$

Similarly, a function $f(x)$ defined in the range $(-\pi,\pi)$ is said to be an **even**
function of x if, for every value of x in the range $f(-x) = f(x)$.
Such functions of x are found to have Fourier series in the range $(-\pi,\pi)$ of the
form

$$\frac{1}{2} a_0 + \sum\limits_{n=1}^{\infty} a_n \cos nx \ ,$$

where
$$a_n = \frac{2}{\pi} \int\limits_{0}^{\pi} f(x) \cos nx \, dx$$

and, quite obviously, $b_n = 0$.

11.1.2 Sine and cosine series

Occasionally it is required to expand a function $f(x)$ in a Fourier series in the range $(0,\pi)$. This may be done by extending the range of definition of $f(x)$ to $(-\pi,\pi)$ and then constructing the Fourier series for the 'extended' function. For example, the odd function $F(x)$ defined by

$$F(x) = \begin{cases} f(x) & , 0 < x < \pi \\ -f(-x) & , -\pi < x < 0 \end{cases}$$

might be constructed from the original $f(x)$.

From the above results for odd functions, it may be deduced that, in the range $(0,\pi)$, the function $f(x)$ may be represented by the sine series

$$f(x) = \sum_{n=1}^{\infty} b_n \sin nx$$

where
$$b_n = \frac{2}{\pi} \int_0^{\pi} f(x) \sin nx \, dx .$$

Alternatively, instead of extending the function $f(x)$ beyond its range of definition by constructing an odd function, an even function $F(x)$ defined by

$$F(x) = \begin{cases} f(x) & , 0 < x < \pi \\ f(-x) & , -\pi < x < 0 \end{cases}$$

might be constructed.

In this case, from the above results for even functions, it may be deduced that, in the range $(0,\pi)$, the function $f(x)$ may be represented by the cosine series

$$f(x) = \frac{1}{2} a_0 + \sum_{n=1}^{\infty} a_n \cos nx$$

where
$$a_n = \frac{2}{\pi} \int_0^{\pi} f(x) \cos nx \, dx .$$

Example

Find a Fourier sine series to represent the function $f(x) = x^2$ in the range $(0,\pi)$.

To achieve this, the odd function $F(x)$ is defined by

$$F(x) = \begin{cases} f(x) = x^2 & , (0,\pi) \\ -f(-x) = -x^2 & , (-\pi,0) . \end{cases}$$

Then, using the above results, the required series is

$$x^2 = \sum_{n=1}^{\infty} b_n \sin nx$$

where
$$b_n = \frac{2}{\pi}\int_0^\pi x^2 \sin nx \, dx$$

$$= \frac{2\pi(-1)^{n+1}}{n} + \frac{4}{\pi n^3}\{(-1)^n - 1\}.$$

11.2 FOURIER SERIES EXPANSIONS IN THE RANGE $(-l,l)$

The discussion so far has been concerned solely with Fourier series representing functions in a range of length 2π. It is proposed now to find the formula for the Fourier series representing a function in a range of length $2l$. Consider the function $g(y)$ defined in the range $(-l,l)$. Now put $y = lx/\pi$ and define $f(x) = g(lx/\pi)$; then $f(x)$ is given in the range $(-\pi,\pi)$ of x. With $f(x)$ so defined, its Fourier series in the range $(-\pi,\pi)$ is given by (11.1) as

$$\frac{1}{2}a_0 + \sum_{n=1}^\infty (a_n \cos nx + b_n \sin nx)$$

with the coefficients a_n and b_n given by (11.2) and (11.3) with $\alpha = -\pi$.

Therefore, $g(y) = g(lx/\pi)$ is represented in the range $(-l,l)$ by the Fourier series

$$g(y) = \frac{1}{2}a_0 + \sum_{n=1}^\infty \left(a_n \cos \frac{n\pi y}{l} + b_n \sin \frac{n\pi y}{l}\right) \tag{11.5}$$

with
$$a_n = \frac{1}{l}\int_{-l}^l g(y) \cos \frac{n\pi y}{l} \, dy$$

$$b_n = \frac{1}{l}\int_{-l}^l g(y) \sin \frac{n\pi y}{l} \, dy.$$

At discontinuities, $g(y)$ in equation (11.5) must be replaced by $\frac{1}{2}[g(y+) + g(y-)]$.

11.3 DIFFERENTIATION OF FOURIER SERIES

Consider a differentiable function $f(x)$ which has a continuous first derivative $f'(x)$ in the range $(\alpha,\alpha + 2\pi)$. The Fourier series for $f'(x)$ in the range $(\alpha,\alpha + 2\pi)$ will be of the form

$$f'(x) = \frac{1}{2}a_0' + \sum_{n=1}^\infty (a_n' \cos nx + b_n' \sin nx)$$

where

$$a'_n = \frac{1}{\pi} \int\limits_{\alpha}^{\alpha+2\pi} f'(x) \cos nx \, dx$$

$$= \frac{1}{\pi} [f(x) \cos nx]_{\alpha}^{\alpha+2\pi} + \frac{n}{\pi} \int\limits_{\alpha}^{\alpha+2\pi} f(x) \sin nx \, dx$$

$$= \frac{1}{\pi} [f(\alpha + 2\pi) - f(\alpha)] \cos n\alpha + nb_n . \tag{11.6}$$

Similarly,

$$b'_n = \frac{1}{\pi} [f(\alpha + 2\pi) - f(\alpha)] \sin n\alpha - na_n \tag{11.7}$$

where a_n and b_n are the Fourier coefficients of $f(x)$ in the given range.

In general, the Fourier series for $f'(x)$ is *not* given by differentiating equation (11.1) term by term; that process would give

$$a'_n = nb_n , \quad b'_n = -na_n \tag{11.8}$$

However, there are two important cases when term by term differentiation of a Fourier series is correct:
(i) If a function is fully periodic. In this case, $f(\alpha) = f(\alpha + 2\pi)$ and (11.6), (11.7) reduce to (11.8).
(ii) If $f(x)$ is an even function in the range $(-\pi,\pi)$, $f(\pi) = f(-\pi)$ and equations (11.6) and (11.7) with $\alpha = -\pi$ reduce to (11.8) once again.

11.4 THE FOURIER INTEGRAL THEOREM

As has been seen already, subject to certain conditions a function $f(x)$ may be expanded in the finite interval $-l < x < l$ as

$$f(x) = \frac{1}{2} a_0 + \sum_{n=1}^{\infty} \left(a_n \cos \frac{n\pi x}{l} + b_n \sin \frac{n\pi x}{l} \right) \tag{11.9}$$

with

$$a_n = \frac{1}{l} \int\limits_{-l}^{l} f(\xi) \cos \frac{n\pi\xi}{l} \, d\xi , \, n = 0,1,2, \ldots$$

$$b_n = \frac{1}{l} \int\limits_{-l}^{l} f(\xi) \sin \frac{n\pi\xi}{l} \, d\xi , \, n = 1,2, \ldots$$

where ξ is the variable of integration.

This representation is valid for $-l < x < l$, but since the right-hand side is a function of period $2l$, it cannot represent $f(x)$ outside the range unless $f(x)$ itself is also periodic and of period $2l$. It would seem desirable to let $l \to \infty$ in

(11.9) since then it would no longer be necessary to require that $f(x)$ be
continued periodically. Thus it would be hoped to obtain a representation for a
non-periodic function defined for all real x.

As well as the conditions necessary to ensure the validity of (11.9) assume
further that $f(x)$ is such that $\int_{-\infty}^{\infty} f(x)\,dx$ exists (that is, is finite). If this is so,
the first term in (11.9) is zero in the limit and the remaining terms may be
written in the form

$$f(x) = \frac{1}{\pi} \sum_{n=1}^{\infty} \Delta\lambda \int_{-l}^{l} f(\xi) \cos [n\Delta\lambda(\xi - x)]d\xi \tag{11.10}$$

where $\Delta\lambda = \pi/l$.

Now, as $l\to\infty$, $\Delta\lambda\to 0$ and, under suitable conditions, the sum in (11.10)
may be replaced by an integral; that is

$$f(x) = \frac{1}{\pi}\int_{0}^{\infty} d\lambda \int_{-\infty}^{\infty} f(\xi) \cos\lambda(\xi - x)d\xi$$

for $-\infty < x < \infty$.

This is the **Fourier integral formula**, which may be written

$$f(x) = \int_{0}^{\infty}[A(\lambda) \cos \lambda x + B(\lambda) \sin \lambda x]d\lambda \tag{11.11}$$

where

$$A(\lambda) = \frac{1}{\pi}\int_{-\infty}^{\infty} f(\xi) \cos \lambda\xi \, d\xi$$

$$B(\lambda) = \frac{1}{\pi}\int_{-\infty}^{\infty} f(\xi) \sin \lambda\xi \, d\xi.$$

It might be noted that, if $f(x)$ is an even function in $-\infty < x < \infty$, $f(\xi) = f(-\xi)$ and

$$A(\lambda) = \frac{2}{\pi}\int_{0}^{\infty} f(\xi) \cos \lambda\xi \, d\xi, B(\lambda) = 0.$$

Inserting these in (11.11) leads to the Fourier cosine integral

$$f(x) = \frac{2}{\pi}\int_{0}^{\infty} \cos \lambda x \left\{\int_{0}^{\infty} f(\xi) \cos\lambda\xi \, d\xi\right\} d\lambda.$$

Also, if $f(x)$ is an odd function in $-\infty < x < \infty$, $f(\xi) = -f(-\xi)$ and

$$A(\lambda) = 0, B(\lambda) = \frac{2}{\pi} \int_0^\infty f(\xi) \sin \lambda \xi \, d\xi .$$

Inserting these in (11.11) gives the Fourier sine integral

$$f(x) \quad \frac{2}{\pi} \int_0^\infty \sin \lambda x \left\{ \int_0^\infty f(\xi) \sin \lambda \xi \, d\xi \right\} d\lambda .$$

It may be proved that, for functions for which a Fourier integral representation is possible, the integral representation converges to $f(x)$ at all points where $f(x)$ is continuous. At a point of finite discontinuity, x_0 say, the Fourier integral converges to the mean of the right- and left-hand limits of $f(x)$ as $x \to x_0$.

EXERCISES 11

(1) Find the Fourier series (i) in the range $(0,2\pi)$ and (ii) in the range $(-\pi,\pi)$ of the following:

$$\text{(a) } x^2 \quad , \quad \text{(b) } \sin ax ,$$

where a is a constant but not necessarily integral.

(2) Expand as a Fourier series in the range $(0,2\pi)$ the function $f(x)$ defined by

$$f(x) = \begin{cases} 0 \text{ in } (0,\pi) \\ \pi \text{ in } (\pi,2\pi) . \end{cases}$$

(3) Find the Fourier series which represents $f(x)$ for $0 < x < 2\pi$ where

$$f(x) = \begin{cases} (x - \pi)^2 \text{ for } 0 < <x < \pi \\ \pi^2 \quad \text{ for } \pi < x < 2\pi . \end{cases}$$

Deduce that (i) $\Sigma_{n=1}^\infty n^{-2} = \pi^2/6$, (ii) $\Sigma_{n=1}^\infty (-1)^{n+1}/n^2 = \pi^2/12$.

(4) Show that the Fourier expansion of

$$f(x) = \begin{cases} 1 + (x/\pi) \text{ for } -\pi < x < 0 \\ 1 - (x/\pi) \text{ for } 0 < x < \pi \end{cases}$$

in the range $(-\pi,\pi)$ is

$$f(x) = \frac{1}{2} + \frac{4}{\pi^2} \left(\cos x + \frac{1}{3^2} \cos 3x + \frac{1}{5^2} \cos 5x + \cdots \right) .$$

Deduce that

$$\frac{\pi^2}{8} = 1 + \frac{1}{3^2} + \frac{1}{5^2} + \cdots .$$

(5) Show that, for the range $(0,\pi)$,

$$\sin x = \frac{4}{\pi}\left\{\frac{1}{2} - \frac{1}{1.3}\cos 2x - \frac{1}{3.5}\cos 4x - \cdots\right\}.$$

Deduce that

$$\frac{1}{1.3} - \frac{1}{3.5} + \cdots = \frac{\pi}{4} - \frac{1}{2}.$$

.(6) A function $f(x)$ has the Fourier expansion

$$f(x) = \frac{1}{2}a_0 + \sum_{n=1}^{\infty}(a_n \cos nx + b_n \sin nx)$$

valid for $-\pi < x < \pi$ and where

$$a_n = \frac{1}{\pi}\int_{-\pi}^{\pi} f(x) \cos nx\, dx\ ,\ b_n = \frac{1}{\pi}\int_{-\pi}^{\pi} f(x) \sin nx\, dx\ .$$

Show that, if the series converges uniformly to the function $f(x)$, then

$$\frac{1}{2}a_0^2 + \sum_{n=1}^{\infty}(a_n^2 + b_n^2) = \frac{1}{\pi}\int_{-\pi}^{\pi}\{f(x)\}^2 dx\ .$$

If $f(x) = \pi^2 x - x^3$, show that $a_n = 0$, $b_n = 12(-1)^{n+1}/n^3$, and deduce that

$$\sum_{n=1}^{\infty} n^{-6} = \pi^6/945\ .$$

Chapter 12
Partial Differential Equations

12.1 INTRODUCTION

Any differential equation which contains partial derivatives is called a **partial differential equation**. The order of such an equation is determined by the order of the highest partial derivative appearing. Obviously, in any partial differential equation, the dependent variable must be a function of at least two independent variables since, if this was not the case, partial derivatives would not arise. Examples of typical partial differential equations of the first and second orders are provided by

$$\frac{\partial u}{\partial x} + \frac{\partial u}{\partial y} = u \quad \text{and} \quad \sin y \, \frac{\partial^2 u}{\partial x^2} + \cos x \, \frac{\partial^2 u}{\partial y^2} = 0$$

respectively. Here x and y are the independent variables and $u \equiv u(x,y)$ is the dependent variable whose specific form is found by solving the appropriate equation. It might be noted also that both these equations are linear in the sense that the independent variable and its derivatives occur to the first degree only and products between them are absent. However, here, attention will be focussed on linear partial differential equations; non-linear equations will not be discussed.

The solution of partial differential equations usually presents a much more difficult problem than the solution of ordinary differential equations and, except for certain special types of linear partial differential equations, no general method of solution is available. Hence, attention will be concentrated on the solution of particular types of linear equations. At the outset, it is worth realising that partial differential equations occur as frequently as they do because most physical processes or events are described by functions of two or more (usually four) independent variables—for example, one, two, or three space variables x, y and z, and a time variable t. Consequently any relation between such a function, $u(x,y,z,t)$ say, and its derivatives with respect to any of the independent variables will lead to a partial differential equation. As might be expected, the complexity of the solution of a linear equation, besides depending on the order of the equation, is strongly dependent on the number of independent variables involved, and so in many cases a particular method of solution is best illustrated by first taking as examples partial differential equations in two independent variables.

A linear equation is said to be **homogeneous** if each term contains either the dependent variable or one of its derivatives. Hence, Laplace's equation in two dimensions

$$\nabla^2 u = 0$$

where ∇^2 is the two-dimensional Laplace operator defined in rectangular Cartesian coordinates (x,y) by

$$\nabla^2 \equiv \partial^2/\partial x^2 + \partial^2/\partial y^2$$

is homogeneous. However, the two-dimensional Poisson equation

$$\nabla^2 u = f(x,y) \, ,$$

where $f(x,y)$ is any given (non-zero) function, is termed **inhomogeneous**.

For linear homogeneous ordinary differential equations it is known that a linear combination of two or more solutions is also a solution. A similar result applies to partial differential equations, and if $u_1, u_2, \ldots, u_n$ are n different solutions of a linear homogeneous partial differential equation in some given domain then

$$u = c_1 u_1 + c_2 u_2 + \cdots + c_n u_n$$

is also a solution in the same domain, where the coefficients $c_1, c_2, \ldots, c_n$ are arbitrary constants.

One of the most important differences between the solutions of partial differential equations and those of ordinary differential equations is that, whereas the general solution of a linear ordinary differential equation contains arbitrary constants of integration, the general solution of a linear partial differential equation contains arbitrary functions. To illustrate this consider the problem of the formation of partial differential equations from given functions. As was seen in Chapter 7, the function

$$u = f(x + y) + g(x - y) \, ,$$

where $f(x + y)$ and $g(x - y)$ are arbitrary functions of $x + y$ and $x - y$ respectively, satisfies the equation

$$\partial^2 u/\partial x^2 = \partial^2 u/\partial y^2$$

irrespective of the functional forms of $f(x + y)$ and $g(x - y)$ provided f and g are at least twice-differentiable functions.

In most cases the general solution of a partial differential equation is of little use since it has to be made to satisfy other conditions—boundary and/or initial conditions—which arise from the physics of the problem. This is much more difficult to accomplish for partial differential equations than for ordinary differential equations owing to the great variety of choice available for the arbitrary functions.

The term 'boundary condition' is clearly appropriate when an equation has to be solved within a given region of space, with prescribed values of the dependent variable given on the boundary. The boundary need not enclose a finite volume—in which case part of the boundary will be at infinity. In the case of partial differential equations in which one of the independent variables is the time t, the values of the dependent variable and often its time derivative at some instant of time, often $t = 0$, may be given. Such conditions are called **initial conditions**.

Some of the more important linear partial differential equations are:

(1) $$\nabla^2 u = \frac{1}{c^2} \frac{\partial^2 u}{\partial t^2} ,$$ the wave equation.

(2) $$\nabla^2 u = \frac{1}{k} \frac{\partial u}{\partial t} ,$$ the heat conduction or diffusion equation.

(3) $$\nabla^2 u = 0 ,$$ Laplace's equation.

(4) $$\nabla^2 u = f(x,y,z) ,$$ Poisson's equation.

In these equations ∇^2 is the Laplacian operator in the appropriate number of space dimensions, t is the time variable, and c, k are constants whose physical interpretation—like that of the dependent variable u—is dictated by the particular problem under discussion. The function f is usually assumed to be known.

As has been mentioned already, in common with ordinary differential equations the solutions of partial differential equations are normally required to satisfy certain constraints or boundary conditions. These conditions depend, of course, on the specific problem being considered.

Before concluding this brief introduction to what is a vast, expanding subject, it should be pointed out that very few actual partial differential equations have been mentioned and all have been linear equations. It is important to realise that a great number of physical phenomena—for example, viscous fluid flow—is described by various non-linear equations. However, the simpler linear equations form a basis for the understanding of many physical processes, and also they are soluble by a variety of important mathematical techniques.

12.2 CLASSIFICATION OF EQUATIONS

When only two independent variable are present, many of the physically important linear equations are special cases of the general linear homogeneous equation of the second order:

$$a\frac{\partial^2 u}{\partial x^2} + 2h\frac{\partial^2 u}{\partial x\, \partial y} + b\frac{\partial^2 u}{\partial y^2} + 2f\frac{\partial u}{\partial x} + 2g\frac{\partial u}{\partial y} + eu = 0 \qquad (12.1)$$

where a,h,b,f,g,e may be constants or functions of x and y. For example, the one-dimensional wave equation

$$\frac{\partial^2 u}{\partial x^2} = \frac{1}{c^2}\frac{\partial^2 u}{\partial t^2}$$

may be obtained from (12.1) by letting $y = t$ and choosing $a = 1$, $h = 0$, $b = -1/c^2$, $f = g = e = 0$.

The form of (12.1) is seen to resemble that of a general conic section

$$ax^2 + 2hxy + by^2 + 2fx + 2gy + e = 0 .$$

This equation represents an ellipse, parabola, or hyperbola according as $ab - h^2 > 0$, $= 0$, < 0 respectively. A similar classification for the partial differential equation (12.1) may be used, and it is said to be of

$$\left.\begin{matrix} \text{elliptic} \\ \text{parabolic} \\ \text{hyperbolic} \end{matrix}\right\} \text{ type when } \begin{cases} ab - h^2 > 0, \\ ab - h^2 = 0, \\ ab - h^2 < 0. \end{cases}$$

Consequently, the wave equation (1) is of hyperbolic type since

$$ab - h^2 = -c^{-2} < 0 .$$

Laplace's equation in two variables

$$\partial^2 u/\partial x^2 + \partial^2 u/\partial y^2 = 0$$

is obtained from (12.1) by putting $a = 1$, $h = 0$, $b = 1$, $f = g = e = 0$ and, since $ab - h^2 = 1 > 0$, is of elliptic type. However, the equation

$$\frac{\partial^2 u}{\partial x^2} = \frac{1}{k}\frac{\partial u}{\partial y}$$

is of parabolic type since, comparing with (12.1), $a = 1$, $h = b = f = 0$, $g = -1/2k$, $e = 0$ and $ab - h^2 = 0$.

It might be noted that equations in which a, b and h are functions of x and y may change their type on passing from one region of the xy plane to another.

A similar but more complicated classification may be performed for linear equations in three or more independent variables. However, it is customary to continue to use the two-dimensional terms, and equations such as the wave equation

$$\nabla^2 u = \frac{1}{c^2}\frac{\partial^2 u}{\partial t^2},$$

whether in two, three, or four independent variables, are called hyperbolic. Likewise Laplace's equation

$$\nabla^2 u = 0$$

is elliptic in type and the heat conduction equation

$$\nabla^2 u = \frac{1}{k}\frac{\partial u}{\partial t}$$

is of parabolic type.

It will be seen that the forms of the general solutions of linear partial differential equations depend on the type of equation considered. Similarly, the forms of the boundary conditions which may be imposed on the three types of equations to yield unique solutions also depend on the type of equation.

Now consider the equation

$$a\frac{\partial^2 u}{\partial x^2} + 2h\frac{\partial^2 u}{\partial x\,\partial y} + b\frac{\partial^2 u}{\partial y^2} = 0 \tag{12.2}$$

where a,h,b are constants, This is a special case of (12.1) known as **Euler's equation**.

To obtain the general solution of this equation, define two new independent variables ξ and η by

$$\xi = px + qy \, , \, \eta = rx + sy \, ,$$

where p,q,r,s are arbitrary constants. Then

$$\frac{\partial u}{\partial x} = \frac{\partial u}{\partial \xi}\frac{\partial \xi}{\partial x} + \frac{\partial u}{\partial \eta}\frac{\partial \eta}{\partial x} = p\frac{\partial u}{\partial \xi} + r\frac{\partial u}{\partial \eta}$$

and

$$\frac{\partial u}{\partial y} = q\frac{\partial u}{\partial \xi} + s\frac{\partial u}{\partial \eta} \, .$$

Also,

$$\frac{\partial^2 u}{\partial x^2} = \frac{\partial}{\partial x}\left(\frac{\partial u}{\partial x}\right) = \left(p\frac{\partial}{\partial \xi} + r\frac{\partial}{\partial \eta}\right)\left(p\frac{\partial u}{\partial \xi} + r\frac{\partial u}{\partial \eta}\right)$$

$$= p^2\frac{\partial^2 u}{\partial \xi^2} + 2pr\frac{\partial^2 u}{\partial \xi\,\partial \eta} + r^2\frac{\partial^2 u}{\partial \eta^2} \, .$$

Similarly,

$$\frac{\partial^2 u}{\partial y^2} = q^2\frac{\partial^2 u}{\partial \xi^2} + 2qs\frac{\partial^2 u}{\partial \xi\,\partial \eta} + s^2\frac{\partial^2 u}{\partial \eta^2}$$

and

$$\frac{\partial^2 u}{\partial x\,\partial y} = pq\frac{\partial^2 u}{\partial \xi^2} + (rq + sp)\frac{\partial^2 u}{\partial \xi\,\partial \eta} + rs\frac{\partial^2 u}{\partial \eta^2} \, .$$

Substituting into (12.2) leads to

$$(ap^2 + 2hpq + bq^2)\frac{\partial^2 u}{\partial \xi^2} + 2[apr + bsq + h(rq + sp)]\frac{\partial^2 u}{\partial \xi\, \partial \eta} \qquad (12.3)$$

$$+ (ar^2 + 2hrs + bs^2)\frac{\partial^2 u}{\partial \eta^2} = 0 .$$

Now choose the arbitrary constants p,q,r,s, so that $p = r = 1$ and q,s are the two roots λ_1, λ_2 of the equation

$$a + 2h\lambda + b\lambda^2 = 0 \qquad (12.4)$$

and so, $\qquad \lambda_1 + \lambda_2 = -2h/b, \ \lambda_1\lambda_2 = a/b .$

Then (12.3) reduces to

$$[a + h(\lambda_1 + \lambda_2) + b\lambda_1\lambda_2]\frac{\partial^2 u}{\partial \xi \partial \eta} = 0$$

or

$$\frac{2}{b}(ab - h^2)\frac{\partial^2 u}{\partial \xi \partial \eta} = 0 . \qquad (12.5)$$

Provided (12.2) is not parabolic (that is, $ab - h^2 \neq 0$) and $b \neq 0$, this equation may be integrated to give

$$u = F(\xi) + G(\eta)$$

where F and G are arbitrary functions. Consequently, since $\xi = x + \lambda_1 y$, $\eta = x + \lambda_2 y$, the general solution of (12.2), when it is not of parabolic type, is

$$u = F(x + \lambda_1 y) + G(x + \lambda_2 y) \qquad (12.6)$$

where λ_1, λ_2 are the roots of (12.4).

Now consider two cases.

Case 1 $ab - h^2 < 0$ (hyperbolic equations)

The roots of (12.4) will be real and distinct, and so the general solution will be the sum of two arbitrary functions of real arguments.

For example, consider the wave equation

$$\frac{\partial^2 u}{\partial x^2} - \frac{1}{c^2}\frac{\partial^2 u}{\partial t^2} = 0$$

which is a special case of (12.2) obtained by putting $a = 1$, $h = 0$, $b = -c^{-2}$ and replacing the y coordinate by t. Since $ab - h^2 < 0$, this equation is hyperbolic, and from (12.4)

$$1 - \lambda^2/c^2 = 0$$

whence $\qquad \lambda_1 = c , \ \lambda_2 = -c .$

Thus, the required general solution is

$$u = F(x + ct) + G(x - ct) .$$

Case 2 $ab - h^2 > 0$ (elliptic equations)
The roots of (12.4) will be complex with $\lambda_1 = p + j\sigma$(say) $= \overline{\lambda_2}$, the bar denoting the complex conjugate.

Hence, $\xi = x + py + j\sigma y$, $\eta = x + py - j\sigma y = \overline{\xi}$.

Now (12.5) becomes $\partial^2 u / \partial \xi \, \partial \overline{\xi} = 0$

with general solution $u = F(\xi) + G(\overline{\xi})$.

The appearance of complex arguments is a general property of the solution of elliptic equations.

For example, consider Laplace's equation in two dimensions.

$$\partial^2 u / \partial x^2 + \partial^2 u / \partial y^2 = 0$$

which is a special case of (12.2) obtained by putting $a = b = 1$ and $h = 0$. Since $ab - h^2 > 0$, this equation is elliptic, and from (12.4)

$$1 + \lambda^2 = 0$$

whence $\lambda_1 = j$, $\lambda_2 = -j$.

Thus, the general solution is

$$u = F(x + jy) + G(x - jy) .$$

In deriving (12.6) it was assumed that equation (12.2) was not parabolic, for in that case $ab - h^2 = 0$ and (12.5) is then satisfied identically. Under these circumstances, make the transformation as before but choose $p = 1$ and leave q,r,s arbitrary for the moment. Then

$$(a + 2hq + bq^2) \frac{\partial^2 u}{\partial \xi^2} + 2[ar + bsq + h(rq + s)] \frac{\partial^2 u}{\partial \xi \, \partial \eta}$$

$$+ (ar^2 + bs^2 + 2hrs) \frac{\partial^2 u}{\partial \eta^2} = 0 . \qquad (12.7)$$

If q is now chosen to be a root of

$$a + 2hq + bq^2 = 0$$

then, since $ab - h^2 = 0$ by assumption,

$$q = -h/b \quad \text{(twice)},$$

and because of this choice, the first term of (12.7) is zero. Also, the second term is zero since

$$ar + bsq + h(rq + s) = ar - hs - \frac{h^2 r}{b} + hs$$

$$= (ab - h^2)\frac{r}{b} = 0 \, .$$

Consequently, provided r and s are not both zero, (12.7) becomes

$$\partial^2 u/\partial \eta^2 = 0 \, .$$

By direct integration

$$u = F(\xi) + \eta G(\xi)$$

where F and G are arbitrary functions. Also, since $p = 1$ and $q = -h/b = \lambda$, say,

$$\xi = x + \lambda y \, , \eta = rx + sy$$

where r and s are arbitrary but not both zero. Choosing $r = 0, s = 1$ for simplicity, the general solution of (12.2) in the parabolic case is

$$u = F(x + \lambda y) + yG(x + \lambda y)$$

where λ is the double root of equation (12.4).

For example, consider the equation

$$\frac{\partial^2 u}{\partial x^2} + 4\frac{\partial^2 u}{\partial x \, \partial y} + 4\frac{\partial^2 u}{\partial y^2} = 0$$

which is parabolic since $a = 1$, $h = 2$, $b = 4$ and $ab - h^2 = 0$. Equation (12.4) becomes

$$1 + 4\lambda + 4\lambda^2 = 0$$

that is, $\qquad\qquad \lambda = -\tfrac{1}{2}$ (twice).

Thus, the required general solution is

$$u = F(x - \tfrac{1}{2}y) + yG(x - \tfrac{1}{2}y) \, .$$

It should be realised that usually these general solutions cannot be fitted to the boundary conditions of a particular problem easily.

12.3 BOUNDARY CONDITIONS

As has been mentioned already, the general solutions of partial differential equations derived earlier are often of little value in boundary-value problems owing to the extreme difficulty of determining the unknown functions. However, the mathematical representation of a physical phenomenon by a partial differential equation and a set of boundary conditions is said to be well-formulated if two criteria are satisfied:

(1) the solution should be unique—experience of nature indicates that a given set of circumstances results in one outcome,

(2) the solution should be stable—that is, a small change in the given boundary conditions should produce only a small change in the solution (This second
criterion is vital since, if boundary conditions are determined by experiment,
small observational errors in their values will exist always, and these errors
should not lead to large changes in the solution).

A great deal of work has been carried out to determine what types of
boundary conditions lead to unique, stable solutions when imposed on linear
partial differential equations. There are, in fact, three main types of boundary
conditions which arise frequently in the description of physical phenomena:
(a) **Dirichlet conditions**, where u is specified at each point of a boundary of a
region; for example, the bounding curve of a plane region or the surface of a
three-dimensional domain. (The problem of solving Laplace's equation, $\nabla^2 u =
0$, inside a region with prescribed values of u on the boundary is called the
Dirichlet problem.)
(b) **Neumann conditions**, where values of the normal derivative du/dn of the
function are prescribed on the boundary.
(c) **Cauchy conditions**, if one of the independent variables is time t, say, and
the values of both u and $\partial u/\partial t$ on a boundary $t = 0$ (that is, the initial values of
u and $\partial u/\partial t$) are given, the boundary conditions are of Cauchy type with respect
to the variable t.

Although uniqueness theorems for systems of partial differential equations and boundary conditions will not be considered, it is worth realising that
some do exist but are usually very difficult to prove. However, as a rule, unique
stable solutions of both elliptic and parabolic equations may be obtained by
imposing either Dirichlet or Neumann boundary conditions whereas unique
stable solutions of hyperbolic equations arise by imposing Cauchy type conditions.

12.4 d'ALEMBERT'S SOLUTION OF THE WAVE EQUATION
Consider the one-dimensional wave equation

$$\frac{\partial^2 u}{\partial x^2} = \frac{1}{c^2}\frac{\partial^2 u}{\partial t^2}$$

where $u = u(x,t)$, subject to the Cauchy initial conditions

$$u(x,0) = f(x) , \ (\partial u/\partial t)_{t=o} = g(x) .$$

As has been shown already, the general solution of this equation is

$$u(x,t) = F(x + ct) + G(x - ct) ,$$

where F and G are arbitrary twice-differentiable functions of their arguments.
Using the initial conditions leads to

$$F(x) \ + \ G(x) \ = f(x)$$

$$cF'(x) - cG'(x) = g(x)$$

where the primes refer to derivatives.

Integrating this last equation gives

$$F(x) - G(x) = \frac{1}{c}\int_a^x g(\xi)d\xi$$

where the constant of integration has been incorporated in the lower limit via the arbitrary constant a. Now, the two equations for $F(x)$ and $G(x)$ give

$$F(x) = \frac{1}{2}f(x) + \frac{1}{2c}\int_a^x g(\xi)d\xi$$

and

$$G(x) = \frac{1}{2}f(x) - \frac{1}{2c}\int_a^x g(\xi)d\xi .$$

Hence

$$F(x + ct) = \frac{1}{2}f(x + ct) + \frac{1}{2c}\int_a^{x+ct} g(\xi)d\xi$$

and

$$G(x - ct) = \frac{1}{2}f(x - ct) - \frac{1}{2c}\int_a^{x-ct} g(\xi)d\xi .$$

Thus, the solution of the one-dimensional wave equation subject to the given initial conditions is

$$u(x,t) = \frac{1}{2}[f(x + ct) + f(x - ct)] + \frac{1}{2c}\int_{x-ct}^{x+ct} g(\xi)d\xi .$$

This is d'Alembert's solution.

Note that the value of $u(x,t)$ depends only on the initial values at points between $x - ct$ and $x + ct$ and not at all on initial values outside this range. This range, or interval, is called the **domain of dependence** of the variables (x,t). Clearly the solution is unique and is stable also since it depends continuously on the values of the initial conditions.

12.5 SEPARATION OF VARIABLES

As has been mentioned already, the general solutions of partial differential equations are of little use owing to the difficulty of choosing the arbitrary functions so as to satisfy the boundary conditions. For some linear partial differential equations, this difficulty may be avoided in various ways. One such method is based on the principle of superposition which was encountered in Chapter 8. A set of solutions of a given linear homogeneous partial differential equation may be found by using the method of separation of variables. Here the dependent variable is assumed to be a product of functions, each depending on just one of the independent variables. It may be possible, at this stage, to find a solution to the original equation, which satisfies all the given boundary conditions, by choosing an appropriate linear combination of the solutions found by the separation of variables technique. This complete method, a combination of separation of variables and the superposition of solutions, is far less complicated than it sounds and is probably introduced most easily by means of an example:

Obtain a solution of the one-dimensional wave equation

$$\frac{\partial^2 u}{\partial x^2} = \frac{1}{c^2} \frac{\partial^2 u}{\partial t^2} \tag{i}$$

which satisfies the Cauchy boundary conditions

$$u(0,t) \;=\; u(l,t) = 0 \quad \text{for } t \geq 0 \tag{ii}$$

$$u(x,0) \;=\; f(x) \qquad \text{for } 0 \leq x \leq l \tag{iii}$$

$$(\partial u / \partial t)_{t=0} = \; g(x) \qquad \text{for } 0 \leq x \leq l \tag{iv}$$

where f and g are given functions and l is a given constant.

Assume a separable solution of the form

$$u(x,t) = X(x)T(t)$$

where X is a function of x only, and T is a function of t only. Then (i) becomes

$$\frac{1}{X} \frac{d^2 X}{dx^2} = \frac{1}{c^2 T} \frac{d^2 T}{dt^2}.$$

The left-hand side of this equation is a function of x only, and the right-hand side is independent of x. Hence, the equation may hold only if both sides have the same constant value, say k. In this way the pair of ordinary differential equations

$$d^2 X / dx^2 = kX \qquad \text{(v)}, \qquad\qquad d^2 T / dt^2 = kc^2 T \qquad \text{(vi)}$$

is obtained. The functions X and T may now be found by solving these equations. However, the resulting solution $u(x,t)$ must satisfy the boundary values also. Now from (ii)

$$u(0,t) = X(0)T(t) = 0, \quad \text{for all } t.$$

$$u(l,t) = X(l)T(t) = 0, \quad \text{for all } t.$$

Taking $T(t) \neq 0$, so excluding the trivial solution $u(x,t) = 0$, gives

$$X(0) = X(l) = 0 . \tag{vii}$$

There are now three possible cases to consider: k zero, positive, and negative.
$k = 0$
In this case, (v) gives

$$X(x) = Ax + B .$$

Then using (vii), shows $A = B = 0$ and consequently $X(x) = 0$, and so $u(x,t) = 0$.
k positive $(=w^2)$
In this case, (v) gives

$$X(x) = Ae^{wx} + Be^{-wx}$$

which together with (vii) leads to $A = B = 0$. Again this leads to the trivial solution $u(x,t) = 0$.
k negative $(= - w^2)$.
In this case (v) gives

$$X(x) = A \cos wx + B \sin wx .$$

This time, use of (vii) leads to the non-trivial solution

$$X(x) = B \sin wx$$

where B is arbitrary but $\sin wl = 0$, which shows that the parameter w has the form

$$w = r\pi/l , r = 1,2,3, \ldots \tag{viii}$$

the case $r = 0$ being excluded since it would lead to the trivial solution once more.

Now solving (vi) with $k = -w^2$ gives

$$T(t) = C \cos wct + D \sin wct$$

where C and D are constants of integration. Then the solution takes the form

$$u(x,t) = X(x)T(t) = \sin wx \, (C \cos wct + D \sin wct) ,$$

the arbitrary constant B having been put equal to unity for simplicity.

However, (viii) shows that an infinite set of discrete values of w (the eigenvalues) exists, and to each of these values will correspond a particular solution (eigenfunction) having the above form. These are

$$w_r = r\pi/l , u_r(x,t) = \sin \frac{r\pi x}{l} \left(C_r \cos \frac{r\pi ct}{l} + D_r \sin \frac{r\pi ct}{l} \right)$$

for $r = 1,2,3, \ldots$; the C_r and D_r being arbitrary constants. Each of these solutions is in fact a solution of the original wave equation which satisfies the boundary conditions (ii). Also the original equation is a linear equation, and so any linear combination of these solutions is also a solution. Hence, take

$$u(x,t) = \sum_{r=1}^{\infty} \left(C_r \cos \frac{r\pi ct}{l} + D_r \sin \frac{r\pi ct}{l} \right) \sin \frac{r\pi x}{l} \qquad \text{(ix)}$$

as the general solution which satisfies the boundary conditions (ii). Now it is necessary to choose the arbitrary constants C_r and D_r so that the boundary conditions (iii) and (iv) are satisfied.

First consider (iii). Putting $t = 0$ in (ix) gives

$$\sum_{r=1}^{\infty} C_r \sin \frac{r\pi x}{l} = u(x,0) = f(x) . \qquad \text{(x)}$$

Again, (iv) is satisfied by differentiating (ix) with respect to t and then putting $t = 0$. This gives

$$\frac{\pi c}{l} \sum_{r=1}^{\infty} r D_r \sin \frac{r\pi x}{l} = \left(\frac{\partial u}{\partial t} \right)_{t=0} = g(x) . \qquad \text{(xi)}$$

The sets of coefficients C_r and D_r may be found from these latter two equations by a Fourier series technique; that is,

$$C_r = \frac{2}{l} \int_0^l f(x) \sin \frac{r\pi x}{l} \, dx \; ; D_r = \frac{2}{r\pi c} \int_0^l g(x) \sin \frac{r\pi x}{l} \, dx \; ;$$

where $r = 1,2,3, \ldots$.

Substituting back into (ix) gives

$$u(x,t) = \sum_{r=1}^{\infty} \left\{ \left[\frac{2}{l} \int_0^l f(y) \sin \frac{r\pi y}{l} \, dy \right] \cos \frac{r\pi ct}{l} \sin \frac{r\pi x}{l} \right.$$

$$\left. + \left[\frac{2}{r\pi c} \int_0^l g(y) \sin \frac{r\pi y}{l} \, dy \right] \sin \frac{r\pi ct}{l} \sin \frac{r\pi x}{l} \right\}$$

as the final solution. Here y has been written as the variable of integration to distinguish it from the independent variable x. This function is a solution of the one-dimensional wave equation which satisfies the given boundary conditions.

In this solution, the final expressions for the sets of coefficients C_r and D_r are relatively easy to obtain owing to the form of equations (x) and (xi), which means that, if r and s are positive integers,

$$\int_0^l \sin\frac{r\pi x}{l} \sin\frac{s\pi x}{l}\, dx = \begin{cases} 0 & \text{for } r \neq s \\ l/2 & \text{for } r = s, \end{cases}$$

as was seen in Chapter 11. Hence, to obtain the expressions for C_r and D_r, it was necessary simply to multiply equations (x) and (xi) throughout by sin $(s\pi x/l)$ and integrate from 0 to l. As indicated above, this is the method of Fourier series, and it should be remembered that it is assumed that functions expanded in this way satisfy certain conditions which ensure that, except at points of discontinuity, the series converge to the given functions at each point of the specified range.

If the functions $\psi_r(x)$ are defined by

$$\psi_r(x) = (2/l)^{1/2} \sin\frac{r\pi x}{l}, r = 1,2,3, \ldots$$

then using the above relation,

$$\int_0^l \psi_r(x)\, \psi_s(x)\, dx = \begin{cases} 0 & \text{for } r \neq s \\ 1 & \text{for } r = s. \end{cases}$$

Such functions are said to be **orthonormal on the interval** $[0,l]$. In general, a set of functions $\psi_r(x)$ is said to be orthonormal on the interval $[a,b]$ with respect to a weight function $\rho(x)$ if

$$\int_a^b \rho(x)\, \psi_r(x)\, \psi_s(x)\, dx = \delta_{rs} ; r,s = 1,2,3, \ldots \qquad (12.8)$$

where the weight function, $\rho(x)$, is not necessarily a constant. It might be noted that the concept of orthonormal functions was encountered in the discussion of vector algebra in Chapter 6. Also in Chapter 6, it was shown possible to represent every vector **a** in a three-dimensional space by a linear combination of three orthogonal unit vectors $\mathbf{e}_1$, $\mathbf{e}_2$, $\mathbf{e}_3$ by

$$\mathbf{a} = \alpha_1\mathbf{e}_1 + \alpha_2\mathbf{e}_2 + \alpha_3\mathbf{e}_3$$

where $\alpha_1,\alpha_2,\alpha_3$ are constants. Similarly, it may be possible to represent an arbitrary function, $f(x)$, on an interval $[a,b]$ as a linear combination of an infinite number of orthonormal functions $\psi_r(x)$ such that

$$f(x) = \sum_{r=1}^{\infty} \beta_r\psi_r(x) \qquad (12.9)$$

where β_r are constants. Such an expansion is termed a **generalised Fourier series**. Now, if the $\psi_r(x)$ are orthonormal on the interval $[a,b]$ with respect to a weight function $\rho(x)$ then, multiplying both sides of (12.9) by $\rho(x)\psi_s(x)$ and integrating between the limits a and b gives

$$\int_a^b \rho(x)\, f(x)\, \psi_s(x)\mathrm{d}x = \int_a^b \sum_{r=1}^\infty \beta_r \rho(x)\, \psi_r(x)\, \psi_s(x)\mathrm{d}x = \beta_s$$

where (12.8) has been used also. In this evaluation of the coefficients β_s, the expansion of $f(x)$ in the form (12.9) has been assumed to be valid although, strictly speaking, the equality sign in (12.9) should not appear since it is not known yet if the series will converge and, even if it does, if it will converge to $f(x)$. In fact, such an expansion is found to be valid if the set of orthonormal functions satisfies the condition of completeness. Although it is not intended to examine in detail the conditions to be satisfied for the above procedure to be valid, it might be noted that a set of orthonormal functions $\psi_r(x)$ is said to be complete if it is impossible to add to it another non-zero function which is orthogonal to each of the $\psi_r(x)$.

In the example quoted to illustrate the method of separation of variables, the technique was seen to lead to two ordinary differential equations which had to be solved, subject to the given boundary conditions, for $X(x)$ and $T(t)$. In solving for $X(x)$, a set of orthonormal functions arose. It is found that the method often leads to an ordinary differential equation of the general form

$$\frac{\mathrm{d}}{\mathrm{d}x}\left(p\, \frac{\mathrm{d}\psi(x)}{\mathrm{d}x}\right) + (q + \lambda r)\psi(x) = 0$$

when applied to second-order linear partial differential equations. In this general equation, p,q,r are given functions of the independent variable x on a given interval, $[a,b]$ say, λ is a parameter, and $\psi(x)$ the dependent variable. This equation is the well-known **Sturm-Liouville equation** and, if certain types of boundary condition are applied, various sets of orthogonal functions are generated by it. When subject to boundary conditions of a particular type, the Sturm-Liouville equation has non-trivial solutions for specific values of the parameter λ only. Such solutions are called the eigenfunctions of the equation, and the corresponding values of λ are termed the eigenvalues.

If $\psi_t(x)$ and $\psi_s(x)$ are two different eigenfunctions of the Sturm-Liouville equation corresponding to the two different eigenvalues λ_t and λ_s respectively, then

$$\frac{\mathrm{d}}{\mathrm{d}x}\left(p\, \frac{\mathrm{d}\psi_t}{\mathrm{d}x}\right) + (\lambda_t r + q)\psi_t = 0$$

and

$$\frac{\mathrm{d}}{\mathrm{d}x}\left(p\, \frac{\mathrm{d}\psi_s}{\mathrm{d}x}\right) + (\lambda_s r + q)\psi_s = 0 .$$

If the first of these equations is multiplied by ψ_s, the second by ψ_t, and one of the resultant equations subtracted from the other, it follows that

$$\frac{\mathrm{d}}{\mathrm{d}x}\left(p\psi_t\, \frac{\mathrm{d}\psi_s}{\mathrm{d}x} - p\psi_s\, \frac{\mathrm{d}\psi_t}{\mathrm{d}x}\right) = (\lambda_t - \lambda_s)r\psi_t\psi_s .$$

Then, integrating between arbitrary limits, say a and b, gives,

$$\left[p\psi_t \frac{d\psi_s}{dx} - p\psi_s \frac{d\psi_t}{dx} \right]_a^b = (\lambda_t - \lambda_s)\int_a^b r\psi_t\psi_s dx \ . \tag{12.10}$$

Hence, if the boundary conditions are such that the left-hand side of this equation is zero, then

$$(\lambda_t - \lambda_s)\int_a^b r\psi_t\psi_s dx = 0 \ ,$$

and since $\lambda_t \neq \lambda_s$ this shows that ψ_t and ψ_s are orthogonal on the interval $[a,b]$ with respect to the weight function r.

It is seen immediately that the left-hand side of (12.10) is zero if the boundary conditions are such that

(i) $\psi_t(a) = \psi_t(b) = 0$, $\psi_s(a) = \psi_s(b) = 0$,

or (ii) $\psi_t'(a) = \psi_t'(b) = 0$, $\psi_s'(a) = \psi_s'(b) = 0$,

or (iii) $\psi_t(a)\psi_s'(a) - \psi_t'(a)\psi_s(a) = \psi_t(b)\psi_s'(b) - \psi_t'(b)\psi_s(b) = 0$

where $\psi_t'(a)$ represents $d\psi_t/dx$ evaluated at $x = a$, etc. In each case mentioned, the boundary conditions are homogeneous so that if ψ is replaced by $c\psi$, where c is a constant, the boundary conditions are unaltered. This would not be so for non-homogeneous boundary conditions and, in such cases, the eigenfunctions of the Sturm-Liouville equation will not form an orthogonal set necessarily. Finally, it should be noted that the above are only examples of boundary conditions for which the left-hand side of (12.10) is zero. It is not, nor is it meant to be, an exhaustive list.

Thus, the method used to solve the example discussed earlier (sometimes called Fourier's method) is seen to be applicable if, after separating the variables, the ordinary differential equations which result are of the Sturm-Liouville type and the boundary conditions are such that the eigenfunctions form an orthogonal set. However, it should be realised that the question of separability of a partial differential equation into ordinary differential equations is not trivial, and obviously, if a particular partial differential equation proves to be inseparable, the method is of no use. It is found that separability is linked closely with the choice of coordinate system and, in fact, if an equation is separable in one coordinate system, it is not separable in another necessarily. The most useful coordinate systems for many practical problems are Cartesian, cylindrical polar, and spherical polar coordinates; —the latter two being particularly useful in examining problems involving cylindrical and spherical symmetry.

To illustrate the general method further, a few more examples will be considered.

(1) Consider the one-dimensional heat equation

$$\frac{\partial^2 u}{\partial x^2} = \frac{1}{k} \frac{\partial u}{\partial t}$$

where k is a constant. It is required to find a solution of this equation satisfying the boundary conditions

$$u(0,t) = u(l,t) = 0 \quad \text{for } t \geqslant 0 , \qquad \text{(i)}$$

$$u(x,0) = f(x) \qquad \text{for } 0 \leqslant x \leqslant l , \qquad \text{(ii)}$$

where l is a constant and f a given function.
    Assume a solution of the form

$$u(x,t) = X(x)T(t)$$

then, substituting in the given equation gives

$$\frac{1}{X} \frac{d^2 X}{dx^2} = \frac{1}{kT} \frac{dT}{dt} .$$

Here the left-hand side is a function of x only, while the right-hand side depends on t alone. Hence, each side must equal a constant, λ say. For $\lambda \geqslant 0$ it may be shown easily that the only solution of the above type consistent with the boundary conditions (i) is $u(x,t) = 0$. However, for negative λ, $(\lambda = -w^2,$ say)

$$X(x) = A \cos wx + B \sin wx , \; T(t) = Ce^{-w^2 kt} ,$$

where A, B, C are arbitrary constants.
    Then the solution is

$$u(x,t) = (A \cos wx + B \sin wx)e^{-w^2 kt}$$

where, without any loss of generality, the constant C has been absorbed into A and B.
    Now putting $x = 0$ in this solution and using (i) gives

$$0 = Ae^{-w^2 kt}$$

for all t and so, $A = 0$.

Similarly, putting $x = l$ in the solution and using (i) gives

$$0 = (B \sin wl)e^{-w^2 kt} .$$

This leads to a non-trivial solution provided

$$\sin wl = 0$$

or $$w_r = r\pi/l , r = 1,2,3, \ldots$$

Thus, an infinity of eigenfunctions and eigenvalues is obtained

$$u_r(x,t) = B_r \exp(-w_r^2 kt) \sin w_r x \quad \text{for } w_r = r\pi/l \,,$$

where $r = 1,2,3 \ldots$ and $B_1, B_2, B_3, \ldots$ are arbitrary constants.

The general solution of the one-dimensional heat equation which satisfies the boundary conditions (i) is then

$$u(x,t) = \sum_{r=1}^{\infty} B_r e^{-r^2\pi^2 kt/l^2} \sin(r\pi x/l) \,. \tag{iii}$$

The constants B_r must be chosen now to satisfy the boundary condition (ii). From (iii)

$$u(x,0) = \sum_{r=1}^{\infty} B_r \sin(r\pi x/l) = f(x) \,.$$

Using the orthonormality of the sine function, it follows that

$$B_r = \frac{2}{l} \int_0^l f(x) \sin(r\pi x/l)dx \qquad r = 1,2,3, \ldots$$

Thus, the solution of the one-dimensional heat equation subject to the given boundary conditions is

$$u(x,t) = \sum_{r=1}^{\infty} \left\{ \left[\frac{2}{l} \int_0^l f(y)\sin(r\pi y/l)dy \right] \exp(-r^2\pi^2 kt/l^2)\sin(r\pi x/l) \right\}$$

where y has been written as the variable of integration to distinguish it from the independent variable x.

This example is really quite general, almost in fact a piece of theory, since in the boundary condition (ii) a quite general function of x, $f(x)$, is introduced. This means that the expression for the constants B_r has to be left as an unevaluated integral. Hence, now consider an example in which the function $f(x)$ is specified:

(2) Consider the same problem as tackled in the above example but suppose the function $f(x)$ given by

$$f(x) = \begin{cases} x & \text{for } 0 < x < l/2 \\ l - x & \text{for } l/2 < x < l \,. \end{cases}$$

The solution follows the same pattern as example (1) but, in this case, the constants B_r are given by

$$B_r = \frac{2}{l} \left\{ \int_0^{1/2} x \sin(r\pi x/l)dx + \int_{1/2}^l (l - x) \sin(r\pi x/l)dx \right\} \,.$$

Evaluation shows that $B_r = 0$ if r is even and

$$B_r = 4l/r^2\pi^2 \quad \text{for } r = 1,5,9,\ldots$$

$$B_r = -4l/r^2\pi^2 \quad \text{for } r = 3,7,11,\ldots.$$

Hence, the final solution is

$$u(x,t) = \frac{4l}{\pi^2}\left\{ \sin(\pi x/l)\exp(-\pi^2 kt/l^2) - \frac{1}{9}\sin(3\pi x/l)\exp(-9\pi^2 kt/l^2) + \cdots \right\}.$$

In the examples discussed so far, the boundary conditions at fixed values of x have been homogeneous, and so it has proved possible to obtain a solution of the boundary value problem immediately in terms of sets of orthogonal functions. As may be seen from the exercises at the end of the chapter, a slight modification of the method allows problems in which the boundary conditions on the space variable x are non-homogeneous to be solved.

12.6 TRANSFORM METHODS

In Chapter 8, the Laplace transform and its properties were examined in some detail, and it was found to be an extremely useful tool for solving constant coefficient ordinary differential equations. However, it can be of use also for some boundary value problems, as can the Fourier transform which will be introduced now. In the discussion of Fourier series given in Chapter 11, it was noted that, under certain conditions, a function $f(x)$ may be represented in the interval $0 < x < \infty$ by

$$f(x) = \int_0^\infty A(\lambda)\cos \lambda x \, d\lambda$$

where

$$A(\lambda) = \frac{2}{\pi}\int_0^\infty f(x)\cos \lambda x \, dx \,.$$

A minor modification of the notation in these two equations allows the **Fourier cosine transform** $\bar{f}_c(p)$ of a function $f(x)$, and the inverse Fourier cosine transform, $f(x)$, of $\bar{f}_c(p)$ to be defined by

$$\bar{f}_c(p) = \int_0^\infty f(x)\cos px \, dx$$

and

$$f(x) = \frac{2}{\pi}\int_0^\infty \bar{f}_c(p)\cos px \, dp$$

respectively.

Similarly, the **Fourier sine transform** $\bar{f}_s(p)$ of a function $f(x)$ and its inverse are defined by

$$\bar{f}_s(p) = \int_0^\infty f(x)\sin px \, dx$$

and

$$f(x) = \frac{2}{\pi}\int_0^\infty \bar{f}_s(p)\sin px \, dp \, .$$

respectively.

It might be noted that the inverses of both the Fourier cosine and sine transforms are given by real integrals, whereas the inverse of the Laplace transform involves an integration in the complex plane (although this latter point has not been stressed). Hence, the Fourier transforms are more convenient to use, although whether or not they may be used to solve a particular partial differential equation, for example, will depend on the precise nature of both the equation and the boundary conditions. Generally speaking, the Laplace transform is better suited to problems in which Cauchy-type boundary conditions are given. Such problems arise in the solution of the wave equation and heat conduction equation. However, somewhat surprisingly, the Laplace transform does not prove suitable when solutions to Laplace's equation, subject of course to Dirichlet type boundary conditions, are required. In such cases, the Fourier transforms often prove more appropriate. Also, for both Laplace and Fourier transforms, the only independent variables suitable as transformation variables are those for which the dependent variable in the partial differential equation is defined over an infinite range. This is due to the range of integration in both types of transform being infinite itself. Obviously, the problem of using transform methods in the solution of partial differential equations is a vast one and will only be touched on here. However, the results and worked examples which follow should provide an introduction to the topic.

Suppose $f(x,t)$ is a function defined for $0 < x < \infty$ and $t > 0$, then the Fourier cosine transform with respect to x is

$$\bar{f}_c(p,t) = \int_0^\infty f(x,t)\cos px \, dx$$

with inverse

$$f(x,t) = \frac{2}{\pi}\int_0^\infty \bar{f}_c(p,t)\cos px \, dp \, .$$

Similarly, the Fourier sine transform with respect to x and its inverse are

$$\bar{f}_s(p,t) = \int_0^\infty f(x,t)\sin px \, dx$$

and
$$f(x,t) = \frac{2}{\pi}\int_0^\infty \overline{f}_s(p,t)\sin px \; dp \; .$$

Using these equations, it is seen that the cosine transform of $\partial f/\partial x$ with respect to x is

$$\int_0^\infty \frac{\partial f}{\partial x}\cos px \; dx = [f \cos px]_0^\infty + p\int_0^\infty f(x,t)\sin px \; dx$$

$$= p\,\overline{f}_s(p,t) - f(0,t)$$

if $f(x,t)\to 0$ as $x\to\infty$.

Similarly, the sine transform of $\partial f/\partial x$ with respect to x is

$$\int_0^\infty \frac{\partial f}{\partial x}\sin px \; dx = -p\overline{f}_c(p,t)$$

again if $f(x,t)\to 0$ as $x\to\infty$.

If it is assumed also that $\partial f/\partial x\to 0$ as $x\to\infty$ the cosine and sine transforms of $\partial^2 f/\partial x^2$ are

$$\int_0^\infty \frac{\partial^2 f}{\partial x^2}\cos px \; dx = -p^2\overline{f}_c(p,t) - (\partial f/\partial x)_{x=0}$$

and
$$\int_0^\infty \frac{\partial^2 f}{\partial x^2}\sin px \; dx = -p^2\overline{f}_s(p,t) + pf(0,t)$$

respectively.

It is obvious immediately from these equations that, as far as the solution of second-order partial differential equations is concerned, the choice of cosine or sine transform depends on the boundary conditions given. This is because the cosine transform of $\partial^2 f/\partial x^2$ requires knowledge of $\partial f/\partial x$ at $x = 0$, while the corresponding sine transform requires $f(0,t)$.

As far as applications based on the Laplace transform are concerned, using equation (8.12), it is seen fairly easily that, if $f(x,t)$ is a function defined for $a \leqslant x \leqslant b$ and $t > 0$ where a and b are arbitrary constants,

$$\mathscr{L}[\partial f/\partial t] = p\mathscr{L}[f(x,p)] - f(x,0)$$

and
$$\mathscr{L}[\partial^2 f/\partial t^2] = p^2\mathscr{L}[f(x,p)] - pf(x,0) - (\partial f/\partial t)_{t=0} \; .$$

These results are obvious extensions of equation (8.14) to the case of a function of two variables. Using (8.12) once more, also leads to

$$\mathcal{L}[\partial f/\partial x] = \frac{d}{dx}\{\mathcal{L}[f(x,p)]\}$$

and

$$\mathcal{L}[\partial^2 f/\partial x^2] = \frac{d^2}{dx^2}\{\mathcal{L}[f(x,p)]\}.$$

The use of these results in the solution of linear partial differential equations will be illustrated by the following examples:

(1) Obtain a solution of the one-dimensional heat conduction equation

$$\frac{\partial^2 u}{\partial x^2} = \frac{1}{k}\frac{\partial u}{\partial t}$$

if it is given that $u(0,t) = u_0$, a constant, and $u(x,0) = 0$.

This problem is suitable for solution using Fourier transforms and, since $u(0,t)$ is given, the sine transform is appropriate. Hence, taking the sine transform of the equation gives

$$-p^2\bar{u}_s(p,t) + pu(0,t) = \frac{1}{k}\frac{d}{dt}\bar{u}_s(p,t)$$

or

$$\frac{d}{dt}\bar{u}_s(p,t) + kp^2\bar{u}_s(p,t) = kpu_0$$

which is an ordinary differential equation having the solution

$$\bar{u}_s(p,t) = A\exp(-kp^2 t) + u_0/p$$

where A is a constant of integration.

Also, the solution must satisfy the condition $u(x,0) = 0$ and so

$$\bar{u}_s(p,0) = \int_0^\infty u(x,0)\sin px\, dx = 0$$

from which it follows that $A = -u_0/p$. Therefore,

$$u_s(p,t) = (1 - e^{-kp^2 t})(u_0/p)$$

Thus, finally

$$u(x,t) = \frac{2u_0}{\pi}\int_0^\infty (1 - e^{-kp^2 t})\frac{\sin px}{p}dx$$

$$= u_0\left[1 - \frac{2}{\pi}\int_0^\infty e^{-kp^2 t}\frac{\sin px}{p}dx\right\}$$

(2) Obtain a solution of

$$\frac{\partial^2 u}{\partial x\, \partial t} + \sin t = 0$$

for $t > 0$ if it is given that $u(x,0) = x$ and $u(0,t) = 0$.

This problem is amenable to solution using Laplace transforms so, taking the Laplace transform of the given equation

$$\frac{d}{dx} \{p\mathscr{L}[u(x,p)] - u(x,0)\} + (1 + p^2)^{-1} = 0.$$

Using the first of the two boundary conditions leads to this equation becoming

$$\frac{d}{dx} \mathscr{L}[u(x,p)] = \frac{p}{1 + p^2}$$

that is,

$$\mathscr{L}[u(x,p)] = \frac{xp}{1 + p^2} + A$$

where A is a constant of integration which may be determined by using the second boundary condition. This particular boundary condition means that $\mathscr{L}[u(0,p)] = 0$ and so, it follows that $A = 0$. Therefore,

$$\mathscr{L}[u(x,p)] = \frac{xp}{1 + p^2}$$

and so, $$u(x,t) = x \cos t$$

where reference has been made to the table of the Laplace transforms of some elementary functions given in Chapter 8.

EXERCISES 12

(1) Obtain the solution of the two-dimensional Laplace equation

$$\partial^2 u/\partial x^2 + \partial^2 u/\partial y^2 = 0$$

within the rectangle defined by $0 \leqslant x \leqslant a$, $0 \leqslant y \leqslant b$, where a and b are constants, which satisfies the Dirichlet conditions

$$u(x,y) = \begin{cases} 0 & \text{when} \quad x = 0, 0 \leqslant y \leqslant b \\ 0 & \text{when} \quad x = a, 0 \leqslant y \leqslant b \\ f(x) & \text{when} \quad y = 0, 0 \leqslant x \leqslant a \\ 0 & \text{when} \quad y = b, 0 \leqslant x \leqslant a. \end{cases}$$

(2) Find the solution of the two-dimensional Laplace equation which satisfies the boundary conditions.

(i) $u \to 0$ as $y \to \infty$,

    (ii) $u = 0$ for $x = 0$ and $x = l$,

    (iii) $u(x,0) = \begin{cases} x & \text{for } 0 \leqslant x \leqslant l/2 \\ l - x & \text{for } l/2 \leqslant x \leqslant l. \end{cases}$

(3) Find the solution of the diffusion equation

$$\frac{\partial u}{\partial t} = k \frac{\partial^2 u}{\partial x^2}$$

which satisfies the conditions

    (i) u remains finite as $t \to \infty$,
    (ii) $(\partial u / \partial x) = 0$ for $x = 0$ and $x = c$, for all values of t,
    (iii) $u = u_0(1 - x^2/c^2)$ for $0 < x < c$ when $t = 0$.

(4) The temperature θ at a distance r from the centre of a sphere of radius a has radial symmetry and satisfies

$$\frac{\partial(r\theta)}{\partial t} = k \frac{\partial^2(r\theta)}{\partial r^2}$$

where k is a positive constant. The surface of the sphere is kept at zero temperature and θ is finite everywhere. If θ is a given function $f(r)$ when $t = 0$, show that

$$\theta = r^{-1} \sum_{n=1}^{\infty} A_n \exp(-n^2\pi^2 kt/a^2)\sin(n\pi r/a)$$

where

$$A_n = \frac{2}{a} \int_0^a rf(r)\sin(n\pi r/a)dr.$$

(5) Using the substitution $u(x,t) = v(x) + w(x,t)$, where $v(x)$ is a time-independent function, show that the solution of the equation

$$\frac{\partial^2 u}{\partial x^2} = \frac{1}{k} \frac{\partial u}{\partial t}$$

subject to the boundary conditions

$$u(0,t) = u_0 \quad \text{for } t \geqslant 0$$

$$u(l,t) = u_1 \quad \text{for } t \geqslant 0$$

and

$$u(x,0) = f(x) \quad \text{for } 0 \leqslant x \leqslant a$$

is

$$u(x,t) = u_0 + \frac{x}{a}(u_1 - u_0) + \sum_{r=1}^{\infty} B_r \exp(-r^2\pi^2 kt/a^2)\sin(r\pi x/a)$$

where
$$B_r = \frac{2}{a} \int_0^a f(x)\sin(r\pi x/a)dx + \frac{2}{r\pi}[(-1)^r u_1 - u_0].$$

(6) Consider the equation

$$\frac{\partial^2 u}{\partial x^2} = \frac{1}{k}\frac{\partial u}{\partial t} + \frac{\beta}{k}(u - u_0)$$

where k, β and u_0 are constants, together with the boundary conditions.

$$u(x,0) = f(x) , u(0,t) = u_1 , u(a,t) = u_2$$

where u_1 and u_2 are constants. Show by means of the substitution

$$u(x,t) = u_0 + v(x,t)e^{-\beta t}$$

that the equation reduces to

$$\frac{\partial^2 v}{\partial x^2} = \frac{1}{k}\frac{\partial v}{\partial t}$$

and the boundary conditions to

$$v(x,0) = f(x) - u_0, \ v(0,t) = (u_1 - u_0)e^{\beta t}, \ v(a,t) = (u_2 - u_0)e^{\beta t}.$$

Hence show that, in the case $u_1 = u_2 = u_0$,

$$u(x,t) = u_0 + \sum_{n=1}^{\infty} B_n \sin\left(\frac{n\pi x}{a}\right)\exp[-(\beta a^2 + n^2\pi^2 k)t/a^2]$$

where
$$Bn = \frac{2}{a}\int_0^a f(x)\sin\left(\frac{n\pi x}{a}\right)dx - \frac{2u_0}{n\pi}(1 - \cos n\pi).$$

(7) Using the method of separation of variables, show that the solution of the equation

$$\frac{\partial^2 u}{\partial x \, \partial t} = -\sin t$$

for $t > 0$, which satisfies $u(x,0) = x$ and $u(0,t) = 0$ is

$$u(x,t) = x \cos t .$$

(8) Using the appropriate Fourier transform show that the solution of the one-dimensional heat equation

$$\frac{\partial^2 u}{\partial x^2} = \frac{1}{k}\frac{\partial u}{\partial t}$$

which satisfies $(\partial u/\partial x)_{x=0} = -w$, a constant, and $u(x,0) = 0$ is

$$u(x,t) = \frac{2w}{\pi} \int\limits_0^\infty (1 - \exp(-kp^2t)) \, \frac{\cos px}{p^2} \, dp \ .$$

(9) By taking the Laplace transform with respect to t, show that the solution of the equation

$$\frac{\partial u}{\partial t} + x \, \frac{\partial u}{\partial x} = x \ ,$$

subject to boundary conditions $u(x,0) = 0$ for $x > 0$ and $u(0,t) = 0$ for $t > 0$, is

$$u(x,t) = x(1 - e^{-t}) \ .$$

(10) By taking the Laplace transform with respect to t, show that the solution of the equation

$$\frac{\partial^2 u}{\partial x^2} + k \sin \pi x = \frac{1}{c^2} \, \frac{\partial^2 u}{\partial t^2} \ ,$$

for $0 < x < 1$ and $t > 0$, which satisfies the conditions

$$u(x,0) = 0 \ , \left(\frac{\partial u}{\partial t}\right)_{t=0} = 0 \quad \text{and} \quad u(0,t) = 0 \ , u(1,t) = 0$$

is

$$u(x,t) = \frac{k}{\pi^2} \, (1 - \cos \pi ct) \sin \pi x \ .$$

Chapter 13
Some Special Functions

___

13.1 THE GAMMA FUNCTION

The idea of the factorial of some number n

$$n! = n(n-1)(n-2)\ldots 2.1$$

is familiar. By considering the Laplace transform of x^n, the factorial may be expressed as an integral. As has been seen already

$$\int_0^\infty x^n \, e^{-px} \, dx = n!/p^{n+1}$$

and so, putting $p = 1$ yields

$$n! = \int_0^\infty x^n \, e^{-x} \, dx \ .$$

The idea of the factorial may be extended to defining what has been termed the **factorial function**

$$u! = \int_0^\infty x^u \, e^{-x} \, dx$$

for all real values of x for which this integral converges. The factor e^{-x} ensures convergence at the upper end of the range of integration for all values of u. In the vicinity of $x = 0$ the integral behaves like $\int_0 x^u dx$, which converges for $u > -1$. Hence, provided $u > -1$, the factorial function is defined by the above equation. This equation also defines the factorial function for complex values of u provided $\mathrm{Re}(u) > -1$.

Usually this factorial function is called the **gamma function** and is written

$$z! = \Gamma(z + 1) = \int_0^\infty e^{-t} \, t^z \, dt \ . \tag{13.1}$$

This notation will be used from now on. It should be noted that, historically, the gamma function was defined first by Euler as the limit of a product from which the integral (13.1) may be derived. The notation $\Gamma(z + 1)$ was introduced by Legendre.

On integration, the integral in (13.1) yields

$$\left[\frac{e^{-t}\,t^{z+1}}{z + 1}\right]_0^x + \int_0^\infty \frac{e^{-t}\,t^{z+1}}{z + 1}\,dt\,.$$

Provided $z > -1$, the first term is zero and the second term is seen to be $\Gamma(z + 2)/(z + 1)$ and so, the gamma function is seen to satisfy the relation

$$\Gamma(z + 2) = (z + 1)\Gamma(z + 1)\,. \tag{13.2}$$

It should be noted that the derivation of this result does not depend on z being an integer, and so the result holds for integral and non-integral values of z.

It follows from (13.2) that for $z > -1$ and for any positive integer m,

$$(z + m)! = (z + m)(z + m - 1) \cdots (z + 1)z! \tag{13.3}$$

The range of definition of $z!$ may be extended to $z < -1$ by assuming this equation valid in this range also. If $z > -(m + 1)$, where m is a positive integer, then $(z + m) > -1$ and so $(z + m)!$ is defined by (13.1) with $(z + m)$ replacing z. Then equation (13.3) is taken to be the definition of $z!$—obviously $z!$ is finite everywhere except when $z = -1, -2, -3, \ldots$, where it is infinite.

Now to consider the case when z is a half odd integer. Factorials such as $(l - \frac{1}{2})!$, where l is integral, will be met later. Using (13.3), these may be expressed in terms of $(-\frac{1}{2})!$ and by (13.1)

$$(-\tfrac{1}{2})! = \Gamma(\tfrac{1}{2}) = \int_0^\infty e^{-t}\,t^{-\frac{1}{2}}\,dt = 2\int_0^\infty \exp(-x^2)\,dx$$

where the substitution $t = x^2$ has been used.

Put $$I = \int_0^\infty \exp(-x^2)\,dx\,.$$

This integral is evaluated by writing its square as a double integral and then changing variables. Hence,

$$I^2 = \int_0^\infty dx\int_0^\infty dy\, \exp(-x^2 - y^2)\,.$$

Changing to polar coordinates (r,θ) gives

$$I^2 = \int_0^\infty r\,dr\int_0^{\pi/2} d\theta\, \exp(-r^2)$$

$$= \tfrac{1}{2}\pi\int_0^\infty \exp(-r^2)\, r\, dr = \tfrac{1}{4}\pi .$$

Therefore,
$$I = \int_0^\infty \exp(-x^2)\, dx = \tfrac{1}{2}\pi^{1/2} .$$

Thus, finally,
$$\Gamma(\tfrac{1}{2}) = \pi^{1/2} .$$

Hence, for $l \geqslant 1$,
$$\Gamma(l + \tfrac{1}{2}) = (l - \tfrac{1}{2})! = (l - \tfrac{1}{2})(l - \tfrac{3}{2}) \ldots \tfrac{3}{2}\cdot\tfrac{1}{2}\,\pi^{1/2}$$

and for $l \leqslant -1$, equation (13.3) gives

$$(l - \tfrac{1}{2})! = \frac{\pi^{1/2}}{(l + \tfrac{1}{2})(l + \tfrac{3}{2}) \ldots (-\tfrac{3}{2})(-\tfrac{1}{2})} .$$

Now consider

$$\Gamma(u)\Gamma(v) = \int_0^\infty dx \int_0^\infty dy\; e^{-(x+y)}\, x^{u-1}\, y^{v-1} .$$

This integral is over the entire positive quadrant. However, to see from where the significant contributions come, consider the form

$$\Gamma(u)\Gamma(v) = \lim_{R\to\infty} \int_0^R dx \int_0^R dy\; e^{-(x+y)}\, x^{u-1}\, y^{v-1} .$$

The region of integration is now the square in the positive quadrant $0 \leqslant x \leqslant R$, $0 \leqslant y \leqslant R$. This may be divided into two equal triangles Δ_1 and Δ_2 by the line $x + y = R$. Then, in Δ_2, $x + y \geqslant R$, $x \leqslant R$ and $y \leqslant R$ and so

$$\int_{\Delta_2} dx\, dy\; e^{-(x+y)}\, x^{u-1}\, y^{v-1} \leqslant \tfrac{1}{2} e^{-R}\, R^{u+v}$$

which tends to zero as $R \to \infty$. Hence,

$$\Gamma(u)\Gamma(v) = \lim_{R\to\infty} \int_{\Delta_1} dx\, dy\; e^{-(x+y)}\, x^{u-1}\, y^{v-1} .$$

Change variables from x and y to z and t where

$$x = zt , \quad y = z(1 - t) .$$

If z and t vary independently over the ranges $0 < t < 1$, $0 < z < R$, the point (x,y) ranges over triangle Δ_1. Also, the transformation has Jacobian

$$\frac{\partial(x,y)}{\partial(t,z)} = \begin{vmatrix} z & t \\ -z & 1-t \end{vmatrix} = z$$

and so

$$\Gamma(u)\Gamma(v) = \lim_{R \to \infty} \int_0^1 dt \int_0^R dz \, z e^{-z} z^{u+v-2} t^{u-1} (1-t)^{v-1}$$

$$= \lim_{R \to \infty} \int_0^R dz \, e^{-z} z^{u+v-1} \int_0^1 dt \, t^{u-1}(1-t)^{v-1}$$

$$= \Gamma(u+v) \int_0^1 dt \, t^{u-1}(1-t)^{v-1} \, ,$$

that is,

$$\frac{\Gamma(u)\Gamma(v)}{\Gamma(u+v)} = \int_0^1 t^{u-1} (1-t)^{v-1} \, dt \, .$$

The integral on the right-hand side is symmetrical between u and v; it is known as the **Beta Function** and is denoted by $B(u,v)$. Thus

$$B(u,v) = \Gamma(u)\Gamma(v)/\Gamma(u+v) \, .$$

13.2 LAPLACE'S EQUATION

13.2.1 Simple solutions of Laplace's equation

(a) Cylindrical symmetry

Using the form of the Laplacian in cylindrical polar coordinates, Laplace's equation is

$$\nabla^2 u = \frac{1}{r} \frac{\partial}{\partial r}\left(r \frac{\partial u}{\partial r}\right) + \frac{1}{r^2} \frac{\partial^2 u}{\partial \phi^2} + \frac{\partial^2 u}{\partial z^2} = 0 \, .$$

If consideration is restricted to the case of two dimensions, there is no z dependence and, if circular symmetry is assumed, there is no dependence on the angular coordinate ϕ. Then

$$\nabla^2 u = \frac{1}{r} \frac{d}{dr}\left(r \frac{du}{dr}\right) = 0$$

where $u = u(r)$.

Solving leads to

$$u(r) = A \log r + B \qquad\qquad \text{(i)}$$

where A and B are arbitrary constants.

It should be noted that $v(r) = u(1/r)$ is an harmonic function also since

$$u(1/r) = A \log (1/r) + B$$

$$= A \log 1 - A \log r + B = A' \log r + B$$

which has the same form as (i).

Note that any function which satisfies Laplace's equation, $\nabla^2 u = 0$, is called an **harmonic function**.

(b) Spherical symmetry

In spherical polar coordinates (r, ϕ, θ) Laplace's equation is

$$\nabla^2 u = \frac{1}{r^2}\left\{\frac{\partial}{\partial r}\left(r^2 \frac{\partial u}{\partial r}\right) + \frac{1}{\sin^2\theta}\left(\frac{\partial^2 u}{\partial \phi^2}\right) + \frac{1}{\sin\theta}\frac{\partial}{\partial\theta}\left(\sin\theta \frac{\partial u}{\partial\theta}\right)\right\} = 0 \ .$$

This specialisation to spherical symmetry is obtained by taking u as a function of r only. Then, the equation becomes

$$\frac{d}{dr}\left(r^2 \frac{du}{dr}\right) = 0$$

which has the solution

$$u(r) = \frac{A}{r} + B$$

where A and B are arbitrary constants. Provided $A \neq 0$, this solution is singular at $r = 0$.

13.3 LAPLACE'S EQUATION IN SPHERICAL POLAR COORDINATES

From above, Laplace's equation in spherical polar coordinates is

$$\frac{1}{r^2}\left\{\frac{\partial}{\partial r}\left(r^2 \frac{\partial u}{\partial r}\right) + \frac{1}{\sin^2\theta}\frac{\partial^2 u}{\partial \phi^2} + \frac{1}{\sin\theta}\frac{\partial}{\partial\theta}\left(\sin\theta \frac{\partial u}{\partial\theta}\right)\right\} = 0 \ .$$

Look for a solution of the form

$$u = R(r)S(\theta, \phi)$$

where R is a function of r only and S is a function of θ and ϕ. Substituting into the equation gives

$$S \frac{\partial}{\partial r}\left(r^2 \frac{\partial R}{\partial r}\right) + \frac{R}{\sin^2\theta}\frac{\partial^2 S}{\partial \phi^2} + \frac{R}{\sin\theta}\frac{\partial}{\partial\theta}\left(\sin\theta \frac{\partial S}{\partial\theta}\right) = 0 \ ,$$

that is,

$$\frac{1}{R}\frac{\partial}{\partial r}\left(r^2 \frac{\partial R}{\partial r}\right) = -\frac{1}{S\sin^2\theta}\frac{\partial^2 S}{\partial \phi^2} - \frac{1}{S\sin\theta}\frac{\partial}{\partial\theta}\left(\sin\theta \frac{\partial S}{\partial\theta}\right) \ .$$

Here the left-hand side is a function of r only, while the right-hand side depends on θ and ϕ. Hence, each side must equal a constant which will be written $n(n + 1)$ for convenience. There are now two equations to solve:

$$\frac{d}{dr}\left(r^2 \frac{dR}{dr}\right) = n(n + 1)R$$

and
$$\frac{1}{\sin^2\theta} \frac{\partial^2 S}{\partial\phi^2} + \frac{1}{\sin\theta} \frac{\partial}{\partial\theta}\left(\sin\theta \frac{\partial S}{\partial\theta}\right) + n(n+1)S = 0 .$$

The solution of the first is
$$R = Ar^n + B/r^{n+1} .$$

For the second equation, look once more for a separable solution of the form
$$S(\theta,\phi) = \Theta(\theta)\Phi(\phi) .$$

Substituting this solution into the equation gives
$$\frac{\Theta(\theta)}{\sin^2\theta} \frac{\partial^2 \Phi}{\partial\phi^2} + \frac{\Phi(\phi)}{\sin\theta} \frac{\partial}{\partial\theta}\left(\sin\theta \frac{\partial\Theta}{\partial\theta}\right) + n(n+1)\Theta(\theta)\Phi(\phi) = 0 ,$$

that is,
$$-\frac{1}{\Phi} \frac{d^2\Phi}{d\phi^2} = \frac{\sin^2\theta}{\Theta}\left\{\frac{1}{\sin\theta} \frac{d}{d\theta}\left(\sin\theta \frac{d\Theta}{d\theta}\right) + n(n+1)\Theta\right\} .$$

Here the left-hand side is a function of ϕ only and the right-hand side is dependent only on θ, so both sides must equal a constant which will be denoted by m^2. Thus
$$d^2\Phi/d\phi^2 = -m^2\Phi$$

that is
$$\Phi = C \cos(m\phi + \varepsilon) .$$

In actual problems ϕ is the azimuthal angle and it is usual in physical problems to seek solutions which are unaltered if ϕ is increased by 2π. Hence, m is taken to be a real integer.

Now Θ satisfies
$$\frac{1}{\sin\theta} \frac{d}{d\theta}\left(\sin\theta \frac{d\Theta}{d\theta}\right) + \{n(n+1) - m^2\sin^{-2}\theta\}\Theta = 0 .$$

This equation may be simplified by putting
$$\cos\theta = \mu$$

so that
$$\sin^2\theta = 1 - \mu^2 \quad \text{and} \quad \frac{1}{\sin\theta} \frac{d}{d\theta} = -\frac{d}{d\mu} .$$

Substituting leads to
$$\frac{d}{d\mu}\left\{(1 - \mu^2) \frac{d\Theta}{d\mu}\right\} + \{n(n+1) - m^2(1 - \mu^2)^{-1}\}\Theta = 0 .$$

For given values of n and the integer m, two independent solutions of this second-order equation will exist. However, attention will be focussed exclusively now on the equation with $m = 0$; that is,

$$\frac{d}{d\mu}\left\{(1 - \mu^2)\frac{d\Theta}{d\mu}\right\} + n(n + 1)\Theta = 0 \ . \tag{13.4}$$

13.3.1 Legendre's equation

Obviously, the corresponding solutions of Laplace's equation are independent of ϕ, and so have azimuthal symmetry. This equation (13.4) is **Legendre's equation** which, for a given value of n, has two independent solutions known as **Legendre functions**.

To see if Legendre's equation possesses a solution represented by a power series, substitute

$$\Theta = \sum_{l=0}^{\infty} c_l\mu^l \tag{13.5}$$

in equation (13.4). This substitution leads to

$$(1 - \mu^2) \sum_{l=2}^{\infty} l(l - 1)c_l\mu^{l-2} - 2\mu \sum_{l=1}^{\infty} lc_l\mu^{l-1} + n(n + 1) \sum_{l=0}^{\infty} c_l\mu^l = 0$$

which may be written

$$\sum_{l=2}^{\infty} l(l - 1)c_l\mu^{l-2} + \sum_{l=0}^{\infty} \{n(n + 1) - l(l + 1)\}c_l\mu^l = 0 \ .$$

In the first term write $l \rightarrow l + 2$ to give

$$\sum_{l=0}^{\infty} [(l + 2)(l + 1)c_{l+2} + \{n(n + 1) - l(l + 1)\}c_l]\mu^l = 0 \ .$$

This equation is an identity in μ if the coefficients c_l satisfy the recurrence relation

$$c_{l+2} = -\frac{n(n + 1) - l(l + 1)}{(l + 2)(l + 1)} c_l \ , \ (l = 0,1,2,\ldots) \ .$$

The power series (13.5) then represents a solution of Legendre's equation within its interval of convergence provided its coefficients satisfy this relation. Of course, this leaves a_0 and a_1 as arbitrary constants. It may be noted that if $a_0 = 0$, $a_{2l} = 0$; while if $a_1 = 0$, $a_{2l-1} = 0$, when $l = 1,2,\ldots$.

Also, if n is an integer, $(n = 0,1,2,\ldots)$, then $a_{n+2} = 0$ and consequently $a_{n+4} = a_{n+6} = \ldots = 0$. If the integer n is odd and a_0 is taken to be zero so that $a_{2l} = 0$, and if $a_1 \neq 0$, the only non-vanishing coefficients are a_1, a_3,

$a_5, \ldots, a_n$. In this case, the series reduces to a polynomial of degree n containing only odd powers of x. If n is even and $a_1 = 0$ while $a_0 \neq 0$, the series reduces to a polynomial of degree n containing only even powers of x.

Thus, if n is an integer, a polynomial solution of equation (13.4) always exists and no questions of convergence or continuity arise.

If $n = 0$, the polynomial is a constant a_0; if $n = 1$, it is $a_1 x$. When $n = 2, 3, \ldots$ the above recurrence relation may be written

$$c_{l+2} = -\frac{(n - l)(n + l + 1)}{(l + 1)(l + 2)} c_l , \, l = 0, 1, \ldots, n - 2 .$$

Now write $k = l + 2$, then

$$c_{k-2} = -\frac{k(k - 1)}{(n - k + 2)(n + k - 1)} c_k , \, k = 2, 3, \ldots, n .$$

Whether n is even or odd, this formula gives the coefficients of the polynomial in terms of c_n:

$$c_{n-2} = -\frac{n(n - 1)}{2(2n - 1)} c_n$$

$$c_{n-4} = -\frac{(n - 2)(n - 3)}{4(2n - 3)} c_{n-2} = \frac{(-1)^2 \, n(n - 1)(n - 2)(n - 3)}{2^2 \, 2! \, (2n - 1)(2n - 3)} c_n$$

etc. In general, therefore,

$$c_{n-2l} = \frac{(-1)^l}{2^l l!} \frac{n(n - 1) \cdots (n - 2l + 1)}{(2n - 1)(2n - 3) \cdots (2n - 2l + 1)} c_n .$$

Here c_n is left arbitrary so let it take the value

$$c_n = \frac{(2n)!}{2^n (n!)^2} ,$$

Then

$$c_{n-2l} = \frac{(-1)^l}{2^l l!} \frac{n!}{(n - 2l)!} \frac{(2n - 2l)! \, [(2n - 2)(2n - 4) \cdots (2n - 2l + 2)](2n)!}{(2n - 1)! \, 2^n (n!)^2}$$

$$= \frac{(-1)^l}{2^l l!} \frac{(2n - 2l)!}{(n - 2l)!} \frac{2^{l-1} \, (n - 1)(n - 2) \cdots (n - l + 1) \, 2n}{2^n n!}$$

$$= \frac{1}{2^n} \frac{(-1)^l}{l!} \frac{(2n - 2l)!}{(n - 2l)! \, (n - l)!} .$$

If n is even, the polynomial begins with a constant term a_0 given by this formula with $l = n/2$. If n is odd, the first term is $a_1 x$ where a_1 is again given by this formula but with $l = (n - 1)/2$.

Hence, a polynomial solution of Legendre's equation for all μ is

$$y = P_n(\mu)$$

where $P_n(\mu)$, the Legendre polynomial of degree n, is given by

$$P_n(\mu) = \frac{1}{2^n} \sum_{l=0}^{m} \frac{(-1)^l}{l!} \frac{(2n - 2l)!}{(n - 2l)!(n - l)!} \mu^{n-2l} \qquad (13.6)$$

where $m = n/2$ if n is even or zero and $m = (n - 1)/2$ if n is odd.

The first six Legendre polynomials are

$$P_0(\mu) = 1 \qquad\qquad , P_1(\mu) = \mu$$

$$P_2(\mu) = \tfrac{1}{2}(3\mu^2 - 1) \qquad , P_3(\mu) = \tfrac{1}{2}(5\mu^3 - 3\mu)$$

$$P_4(\mu) = \tfrac{1}{8}(35\mu^4 - 30\mu^2 + 3) , P_5(\mu) = \tfrac{1}{8}(63\mu^5 - 70\mu^3 + 15\mu) .$$

It follows, from earlier considerations, that $r^n P_n(\mu)$ $(n = 0,1,2, \ldots)$ are solutions of Laplace's equation. It may be remembered that, if $r^n S(\theta,\phi)$ is a solution of Laplace's equation, then so is $r^{-(n+1)}S(\theta,\phi)$ and so, $r^{-(n+1)}P_n(\mu)$ are solutions also.

The result of integrating the polynomial $P_n(\mu)$, given by equation (13.6), n times with respect to μ from $\mu = 0$ to $\mu = t$ is

$$\frac{1}{2^n} \sum_{l=0}^{m} \frac{(-1)^l}{l!} \frac{(2n - 2l)!}{(n - 2l)! \, (n - l)!} \frac{t^{2n-2l}}{(n - 2l + 1)(n - 2l + 2) \cdots (2n - 2l)}$$

$$= \frac{1}{2^n n!} \sum_{l=0}^{m} (-1)^l \frac{n!}{l! \, (n - l)!} (t^2)^{n-l} .$$

The lowest power of t in this expression is t^{2n-2m}; that is, t^n if n is even, t^{n+1} if n is odd. If the sum is extended to the range $l = 0$ to $l = n$, it represents the binomial expansion of $(t^2 - 1)^n$. The additional polynomial introduced is one of degree less than n, and so is one whose nth derivative is zero. Since the nth derivative of the above sum is $P_n(t)$, it follows that $P_n(t)$ must be the nth derivative of $(2^n n!)^{-1}(t^2 - 1)^n$ also; that is

$$P_n(\mu) = \frac{1}{2^n n!} \frac{d^n}{d\mu^n} (\mu^2 - 1)^n \; ; n = 0,1,2, \ldots$$

This is **Rodrigues' formula** for the Legendre polynomials

By Leibniz' rule for the nth derivative of a product

$$P_n(\mu) = \frac{1}{2^n n!} \sum_{k=0}^{n} \frac{n!}{k! \, (n - k)!} \frac{d^k}{d\mu^k} [(\mu + 1)^n] \frac{d^{n-k}}{d\mu^{n-k}} [(\mu - 1)^n]$$

where $d^0 w/d\mu^0 = w$. Now, only the term with $k = 0$, that is the first term, in this sum is independent of the factor $(\mu - 1)$. Consequently,

$$P_n(1) = \frac{1}{2^n n!} \{2^n n!\} = 1$$

for $n = 0,1,2, \ldots$.

13.3.2 Generating function for Legendre polynomials

It will be shown now that if the function

$$(1 - 2\mu h + h^2)^{-\frac{1}{2}}$$

is expanded in a Maclaurin series in powers of h, the coefficient of h^n is (for all n) the Legendre polynomial $P_n(\mu)$. The above-mentioned function is a generating function for the Legendre polynomials.

Now

$$(1 - 2\mu h + h^2)^{-\frac{1}{2}} = \{1 + h(h - 2\mu)\}^{-\frac{1}{2}}$$

$$= \sum_{m=0}^{\infty} \frac{(-\frac{1}{2})(-\frac{3}{2}) \cdots (\frac{1}{2} - m)}{m!} h^m (h - 2\mu)^m .$$

Also,

$$(h - 2\mu)^m = \sum_{k=0}^{m} \binom{m}{k} h^k (- 2\mu)^{m-k} \qquad \text{and so, the}$$

coefficient of h^n in the above expansion of $(1 - 2\mu h + h^2)^{-\frac{1}{2}}$ is

$$\sum_{\substack{m+k=n \\ 0 \leqslant k \leqslant m}} \frac{(-\frac{1}{2})(-\frac{3}{2}) \cdots (\frac{1}{2} - m)}{m!} \frac{m!}{k!\,(m-k)!} (-2\mu)^{m-k} .$$

Putting $m = n - k$ leads to

$$\sum_{k=0}^{P} \left[(-\frac{1}{2})^{n-k} \frac{1.3 \cdots (2n - 2k - 1)}{k!\,(n - 2k)!} (-2)^{n-2k} \right] \mu^{n-2k}$$

where $p = n/2$ if n is even or zero and $p = (n - 1)/2$ if n is odd.

Some simplification shows that the required coefficient of h^n may be written

$$\sum_{k=0}^{P} \frac{(-1)^k (2n - 2k)!}{2^n k!\,(n - k)!\,(n - 2k)!} \mu^{n-2k} .$$

Note that $\quad 1.3 \ldots (2n - 2k - 1) = (2n - 2k)!/2^{n-k}(n - k)!$

The above expression is precisely $P_n(\mu)$. Hence, the coefficient of h^n in the expansion is $P_n(\mu)$, and so

$$(1 - 2\mu h + h^2)^{-\frac{1}{2}} = \sum_{n=0}^{\infty} h^n P_n(\mu) .$$

13.3.3 Orthogonality of Legendre polynomials

This important property of the Legendre polynomials may be expressed as

$$\int_{-1}^{1} P_m(\mu) P_n(\mu) d\mu = \frac{2\delta_{mn}}{2n + 1} .$$

This property is important since it allows functions of μ to be expanded in terms of $P_n(\mu)$.

Now, using Rodrigues' formula

$$\int_{-1}^{1} P_m(\mu) P_n(\mu) d\mu = \frac{1}{2^{m+n} m! n!} \int_{-1}^{1} \left\{ \frac{d^m}{d\mu^m} (\mu^2 - 1)^m \right\} \left\{ \frac{d^n}{d\mu^n} (\mu^2 - 1)^n \right\} d\mu .$$

By Leibniz' theorem

$$\frac{d^t}{d\mu^t} (\mu^2 - 1)^m = \frac{d^t}{d\mu^t} \{ (\mu - 1)^m (\mu + 1)^m \}$$

$$= \sum_{s=0}^{t} \binom{t}{s} \left\{ \frac{d^s}{d\mu^s} (\mu - 1)^m \right\} \left\{ \frac{d^{t-s}}{d\mu^{t-s}} (\mu + 1)^m \right\} .$$

If $t < m$, each term in this summation contains at least one factor $\mu - 1$ and one factor $\mu + 1$. Hence for $t < m$

$$\frac{d^t}{d\mu^t} (\mu^2 - 1)^m = 0 \quad \text{when} \quad \mu = \pm 1 .$$

Now integrating the original integral by parts gives

$$\left[\left\{ \frac{d^{m-1}}{d\mu^{m-1}} (\mu^2 - 1)^m \right\} \left\{ \frac{d^n}{d\mu^n} (\mu^2 - 1)^n \right\} \right]_{-1}^{1}$$

$$- \int_{-1}^{1} \left\{ \frac{d^{m-1}}{d\mu^{m-1}} (\mu^2 - 1)^m \right\} \left\{ \frac{d^{n+1}}{d\mu^{n+1}} (\mu^2 - 1)^n \right\} d\mu .$$

Here the first term vanishes since $m - 1 < m$, and so the result of the integration is an integral similar to the original one. This process may be repeated a further $m - 1$ times—in each case the integrated term vanishes for $\mu = \pm 1$—and the end result is

$$\frac{(-1)^m}{2^{m+n} m! n!} \int_{-1}^{1} (\mu^2 - 1)^m \left\{ \frac{d^{n+m}}{d\mu^{n+m}} (\mu^2 - 1)^n \right\} d\mu .$$

If $m > n$, $d^{n+m}(\mu^2 - 1)^n/d\mu^{n+m}$ is zero and so

$$\int_{-1}^{1} P_m(\mu)\, P_n(\mu)\, d\mu = 0 \quad \text{if } m \neq n .$$

If $m = n$,

$$\int_{-1}^{1} [P_n(\mu)]^2 d\mu = \frac{1}{2^{2n}\,(n!)^2} \int_{-1}^{1} (1 - \mu^2)^n \left\{ \frac{d^{2n}}{d\mu^{2n}}\,(\mu^2 - 1)^n \right\}\, d\mu .$$

The only non-zero term in $d^{2n}(\mu^2 - 1)^n/d\mu^{2n}$ is $d^{2n}(\mu^{2n})/d\mu^{2n}$ which equals $(2n)!$ and so

$$\int_{-1}^{1} [P_n(\mu)]^2 d\mu = \frac{(2n)!}{2^{2n}\,(n!)^2} \int_{-1}^{1} (1 - \mu^2)^n d\mu$$

$$= \frac{(2n)!}{2^{2n}\,(n!)^2}\, \frac{2^{2n+1}\,(n!)^2}{(2n + 1)!}$$

$$= \frac{2}{2n + 1} .$$

The results for $m \neq n$ and $m = n$ may be combined, using the Kronecker delta, to give

$$\int_{-1}^{1} P_m(\mu)\, P_n(\mu) d\mu = \frac{2\delta_{mn}}{2n + 1}$$

as required.

13.3.4 Expansion of polynomials in terms of Legendre polynomials
Any nth-order polynomial in μ, $f_n(\mu)$, may be expressed in terms of the first n Legendre polynomials:

$$f_n(\mu) = \sum_{l=0}^{n} a_l\, P_l(\mu) . \tag{13.7}$$

This is possible because, in principle, the constants $a_n, a_{n-1}, \ldots, a_1, a_0$ may be found by equating the coefficients of $\mu^n, \mu^{n-1}, \ldots, \mu, 1$ in turn. However, a formula may be found for a_l.

Multiply (13.7) by $P_m(\mu)$ and integrate with respect to μ from $\mu = -1$ to $\mu = 1$, then

$$\int_{-1}^{1} f_n(\mu)\, P_m(\mu) d\mu = \sum_{l=0}^{n} a_l \int_{-1}^{1} P_l(\mu) P_m(\mu) d\mu$$

$$= \sum_{l=0}^{n} a_l \frac{2\delta_{lm}}{2m + 1} = \frac{2a_m}{2m + 1} .$$

Hence

$$a_m = (m + \tfrac{1}{2}) \int_{-1}^{1} f_n(\mu) P_m(\mu) d\mu . \tag{13.8}$$

Since $f_n(\mu)$ is a polynomial in μ, all the terms in this integral are of the form

$$\int_{-1}^{1} \mu^k P_m(\mu) d\mu \quad \text{with } k \leq n . \tag{13.9}$$

Using Rodrigues' formula and integrating by parts m times gives

$$\frac{1}{2^m m!} \int_{-1}^{1} \left\{ \frac{d^m}{d\mu^m} (\mu^2 - 1)^m \right\} \mu^k d\mu = \frac{(-1)^m}{2^m m!} \int_{-1}^{1} (\mu^2 - 1)^m \frac{d^m}{d\mu^m} (\mu^k) d\mu .$$

If $m > k$, this integral is clearly zero.
If $m < k$,

$$\frac{d^m}{d\mu^m} (\mu^k) = \frac{k!}{(k - m)!} \mu^{k-m}$$

and so the integral becomes

$$\frac{k!}{2^m (k - m)! \, m!} \int_{-1}^{1} (1 - \mu^2)^m \mu^{k-m} d\mu .$$

This integral may be evaluated by using the substitution $\mu = \cos\theta$, and it is found that, if $k - m$ is odd, the integral is zero. Therefore, an odd power μ^k is expanded in terms of odd polynomials $P_m(\mu)$ only, and similarly for even powers. If $k - m$ is even, the value of the integral is

$$\frac{2^m k! \, (\tfrac{1}{2}m + \tfrac{1}{2}k)!}{(\tfrac{1}{2}k - \tfrac{1}{2}m)! \, (m + k + 1)!}$$

for $m < k$, and zero otherwise.

Hence, it is fairly easy to find the coefficients a_l in the expansion (13.7).

Provided suitable convergence conditions are satisfied, n may be allowed to tend to ∞ in (13.7), and an expansion of a function $f(\mu)$ may be obtained as an infinite series in $P_n(\mu)$:

$$f(\mu) = \sum_{l=0}^{\infty} a_l P_l(\mu) ,$$

the coefficients being given by (13.8) once more. However, in this case the integral does not reduce to the form (13.9) in general.

Now referring once more to the equation

$$(1 - 2\mu h + h^2)^{-\frac{1}{2}} = \sum_{n=0}^{\infty} h^n P_n(\mu) \,.$$

Putting $\mu = \pm 1$ gives

$$(1 \mp h)^{-1} = \sum_{n=0}^{\infty} h^n P_n(\pm 1) \,.$$

Expanding $(1 \mp h)^{-1}$ in powers of h and equating coefficients of h^n gives

$$P_n(1) = 1 \,, \quad P_n(-1) = (-1)^n$$

for all n.

Putting $\mu = \cos\theta$ gives

$$(1 - 2\mu h + h^2)^{-\frac{1}{2}} = (1 - he^{j\theta})^{-\frac{1}{2}}(1 - he^{-j\theta})^{-\frac{1}{2}}$$

$$= \left\{ \sum_{r=0}^{\infty} \alpha_r (he^{j\theta})^r \right\} \left\{ \sum_{s=0}^{\infty} \alpha_s (he^{-j\theta})^s \right\}$$

where the coefficients $\alpha_r = 1.3 \ldots (2r + 1)/2^{r+1}r!$ are positive. Comparing coefficients of h^n gives

$$P_n(\cos\theta) = \sum_{\substack{r+s=n \\ r,s \geq 0}} \alpha_r \alpha_s e^{j\theta(r-s)} = \sum_{\substack{r+s=n \\ r,s \geq 0}} \alpha_r \alpha_s \cos(r - s)\theta \,.$$

Since all terms in this summation have positive coefficients, $P_n(\cos\theta)$ has its maxima for θ in $(0,\pi)$ when $\theta = 0$ or π, since the terms all have the same sign under these conditions and each takes its maximum value.

Therefore, for all μ in $(-1,1)$

$$|P_n(\mu)| \leq |P_n(\pm 1)| = 1 \,.$$

A consequence of this result is that the series $\sum_{n=0}^{\infty} h^n P_n(\mu)$ is convergent for $h < 1$ by comparison with the geometric progression $\sum_{n=0}^{\infty} h^n$.

13.3.5 Recurrence relations for Legendre polynomials
Again consider

$$(1 - 2\mu h + h^2)^{-\frac{1}{2}} = \sum_{n=0}^{\infty} h^n P_n(\mu) \,. \tag{13.10}$$

Differentiating partially with respect to h,

$$\frac{\mu - h}{(1 - 2\mu h + h^2)^{-\frac{3}{2}}} = \sum_{n=1}^{\infty} nh^{n-1} P_n(\mu) \,,$$

that is,

$$(\mu - h) \sum_{n=0}^{\infty} h^n P_n(\mu) = (1 - 2\mu h + h^2) \sum_{n=1}^{\infty} n h^{n-1} P_n(\mu) .$$

Equating coefficients of h^n leads to the first recurrence relation

$$(n + 1)P_{n+1}(\mu) - (2n + 1)\mu P_n(\mu) + n P_{n-1}(\mu) = 0 .$$

Differentiating (13.10) partially with respect to μ gives

$$h \sum_{n=0}^{\infty} h^n P_n(\mu) = (1 - 2\mu h + h^2) \sum_{n=0}^{\infty} h^n P_n'(\mu)$$

or

$$h \sum_{n=1}^{\infty} n h^{n-1} P_n(\mu) = (\mu - h) \sum_{n=0}^{\infty} h^n P_n'(\mu)$$

where $P_n'(\mu) = \mathrm{d}P_n(\mu)/\mathrm{d}\mu$.

Equating coefficients of h^n leads to the second recurrence relation

$$n P_n(\mu) = \mu P_n'(\mu) - P_{n-1}'(\mu) .$$

Differentiating the first recurrence relation and using the second gives

$$P_{n+1}'(\mu) - P_{n-1}'(\mu) = (2n + 1)P_n(\mu) .$$

Subtracting the second recurrence relation from this equation gives

$$P_{n+1}'(\mu) - \mu P_n'(\mu) = (n + 1)P_n(\mu) .$$

Finally, multiplying the second relation by μ and subtracting the fourth relation with $n - 1$ replacing n yields.

$$(\mu^2 - 1)P_n'(\mu) = n\mu P_n(\mu) - n P_{n-1}(\mu) .$$

13.3.6 Application of Legendre polynomials

To illustrate the use of the Legendre polynomials, consider the following example:

It is required to solve Laplace's equation, $\nabla^2 u = 0$, in a spherical domain of radius a subject to the Dirichlet boundary conditions

$$u(a,\theta) = u_1 = \text{const.} , \ 0 \leq \theta < \pi/2 ,$$

$$u(a,\theta) = u_2 = \text{const.} , \ \pi/2 < \theta \leq \pi ,$$

where the line $\theta = 0$ is taken as the axis of symmetry.

This is the problem of solving Laplace's equation within a sphere, the surface of the upper hemisphere having $u = u_1$ and the surface of the lower hemisphere having $u = u_2$. Since, by assumption, there is no dependence on ϕ, Laplace's equation in spherical polar coordinates becomes

$$\frac{\partial}{\partial r}\left(r^2 \frac{\partial u}{\partial r}\right) + \frac{1}{\sin\theta} \frac{\partial}{\partial \theta}\left(\sin\theta \frac{\partial u}{\partial \theta}\right) = 0 . \tag{i}$$

Now look for a solution of the form

$$u(r,\theta) = R(r)H(\theta) .$$

Substituting into the equation gives

$$\frac{1}{R} \frac{d}{dr}\left(r^2 \frac{dR}{dr}\right) = -\frac{1}{H\sin\theta} \frac{d}{d\theta}\left(\sin\theta \frac{dH}{d\theta}\right) .$$

Here the left-hand side is a function of r only, while the right-hand side is a function of θ only. Hence, each side must equal a constant which will be written $n(n + 1)$, then

$$\frac{1}{R} \frac{d}{dr}\left(r^2 \frac{dR}{dr}\right) = n(n + 1)$$

which may be integrated to give

$$R(r) = Ar^n + Br^{-(n+1)}$$

where A and B are arbitrary constants.

Also, $H(\theta)$ is given by

$$\frac{1}{\sin\theta} \frac{d}{d\theta}\left(\sin\theta \frac{dH}{d\theta}\right) + n(n + 1)H = 0 .$$

This is Legendre's equation once more and, as is known from earlier considerations, provided n is an integer, a polynomial solution always exists. These finite solutions are the usual Legendre polynomials

$$P_n(\mu) = \frac{1}{2^n n!} \frac{d^n}{d\mu^n} \{(\mu^2 - 1)^n\} , n = 0,1,2,\dots . \tag{ii}$$

where $\mu = \cos\theta$.

Thus, the solution of (i) which is finite inside the sphere $r = a$ is

$$u(r,\mu) = Ar^n P_n(\mu) ,$$

the constant B having been put equal to zero to exclude the singularity at the origin.

Taking linear combinations of these solutions gives the general solution

$$u(r,\mu) = \sum_{n=0}^{\infty} A_n r^n P_n(\mu) . \tag{iii}$$

It remains to choose the coefficients A_n so that the given boundary conditions are satisfied.

First put $r = a$ in the above equation, multiply throughout by $P_m(\mu)$ and integrate from $\mu = -1$ to $\mu = 1$ using the orthogonality property of the Legendre polynomials. Assuming that the integral and summation signs may be interchanged, this yields

$$\int_{-1}^{1} u(a,\mu)P_m(\mu)d\mu = A_m a^m \int_{-1}^{1} P_m^2(\mu)d\mu \, , \, m = 0,1,2, \ldots \, .$$

But $\qquad\qquad \int_{-1}^{1} P_m^2(\mu)d\mu = 2/(2m + 1) \, , \, m = 0,1,2, \ldots$

and so, $\qquad\qquad A_m = \dfrac{2m + 1}{2a^m} \int_{-1}^{1} u(a,\mu)P_m(\mu)d\mu \, .$

Since $\mu = \cos\theta$, the range $-1 \leqslant \mu < 0$ corresponds to $\pi \geqslant \theta > \pi/2$ and $0 < \mu \leqslant 1$ to $\pi/2 > \theta \geqslant 0$, and so,

$$A_m = \frac{2m + 1}{2a^m}\left\{\int_{-1}^{0} u(a,\mu)P_m(\mu)d\mu + \int_{0}^{1} u(a,\mu)P_m(\mu)d\mu\right\}$$

$$= \frac{2m + 1}{2a^m}\left\{u_2 \int_{-1}^{0} P_m(\mu)d\mu + u_1 \int_{0}^{1} P_m(\mu)d\mu\right\} \, .$$

From (ii) the first four Legendre polynomials are

$$P_0(\mu) = 1 \qquad\qquad , P_1(\mu) = \mu$$
$$P_2(\mu) = \tfrac{1}{2}(3\mu^2 - 1) \quad , P_3(\mu) = \tfrac{1}{2}(5\mu^3 - 3\mu) \, .$$

Inserting these into the above formula allows the corresponding A_m to be evaluated. These are inserted into (iii) to give the required solution, the first few terms of which are

$$u(r,\theta) = \tfrac{1}{2}(u_1 + u_2) + \tfrac{3}{4}(u_2 - u_1)(r/a)P_1(\cos\theta)$$

$$+ \tfrac{7}{16}(u_2 - u_1)(r/a)^3 P_3(\cos\theta) + \cdots$$

13.4 LAPLACE'S EQUATION IN CYLINDRICAL POLAR COORDINATES

As has been seen already, Laplace's equation in cylindrical polar coordinates is

$$\frac{1}{r}\frac{\partial}{\partial r}\left(r\frac{\partial u}{\partial r}\right) + \frac{1}{r^2}\frac{\partial^2 u}{\partial \phi^2} + \frac{\partial^2 u}{\partial z^2} = 0 \, .$$

As when dealing with this equation in spherical polar coordinates, look for separable solutions of the form

$$u = R(r)\Phi(\phi)Z(z) \ .$$

Substituting into the equation gives

$$\frac{1}{rR}\frac{d}{dr}\left(r\frac{dR}{dr}\right) + \frac{1}{r^2\Phi}\frac{d^2\Phi}{d\phi^2} = -\frac{1}{Z}\frac{d^2Z}{dz^2} \ .$$

Here the left-hand side is independent of z, while the right-hand side depends on z only. Hence, each side must equal a constant which will be written as $-k^2$, then

$$Z(z) = Ae^{kz} + Be^{-kz} \ .$$

The value of k may be real or complex, depending on the physical problem to be solved. Again, putting the left-hand side equal to $-k^2$ yields

$$\frac{r}{R}\frac{d}{dr}\left(r\frac{dR}{dr}\right) + k^2r^2 = -\frac{1}{\Phi}\frac{d^2\Phi}{d\phi^2} \ .$$

In this equation, the left-hand side depends on r only, while the right-hand side is a function of ϕ alone. Again each side must equal a constant, ν^2 say. Then,

$$\Phi(\phi) = \cos(\nu\phi + \alpha) \ .$$

Often it is required that $\Phi(\phi)$ be periodic of period 2π, so that ν must equal some integer n. However, solutions with ν equalling half an odd integer are of importance also. If ν is real, then for definiteness take $\nu > 0$.

13.4.1 Bessel's equation

Now put $x = kr$ and $R(r) = R(x/k) = g(x)$, then the solution has the form

$$u = g(x)\{Ae^{kz} + Be^{-kz}\}\cos(\nu\phi + \alpha)$$

where $g(x)$ satisfies

$$x\frac{d}{dx}\left(x\frac{dg(x)}{dx}\right) + (x^2 - \nu^2)\,g(x) = 0 \ . \tag{13.11}$$

This linear homogeneous differential equation is **Bessel's equation**, and its solutions are called **Bessel functions** or, sometimes **cylindrical functions**.

Now it is required to seek a solution of Bessel's equation of the form of a power series multiplied by x^p, where p is some constant. Thus, it is necessary to determine p and the coefficients c_l, so that

$$g(x) = x^p \sum_{l=0}^{\infty} c_l x^l = \sum_{l=0}^{\infty} c_l x^{p+l} \tag{13.12}$$

satisfies equation (13.11).

Substituting (13.12) into (13.11) leads to

$$\sum_{l=0}^{\infty} \{(p + l)(p + l - 1) + (p + l) + (x^2 - v^2)\}c_l x^{p+l} = 0$$

that is

$$\sum_{l=0}^{\infty} \{(p + l)^2 - v^2\}c_l x^{p+l} + x^2 \sum_{l=0}^{\infty} c_l x^{p+l} = 0$$

or

$$\sum_{l=0}^{\infty} \{(p + l)^2 - v^2\}c_l x^{p+l} + \sum_{l=2}^{\infty} c_{l-2} x^{p+l} = 0 .$$

This equation is satisfied provided the coefficient of each power of x is zero. Then, for $l \geqslant 2$,

$$c_l = -\frac{c_{l-2}}{(p + l)^2 - v^2} = -\frac{c_{l-2}}{(l + p + v)(l + p - v)} \qquad (13.12a)$$

and for $l = 1$ and $l = 0$,

$$(p^2 - v^2)c_0 = 0 = \{(p + 1)^2 - v^2\}c_1 .$$

This latter equation shows that p may be chosen so that either c_0 or c_1 is non-zero. If c_1 is taken equal to zero, then $c_0 \neq 0$ provided $p = \pm v$. Also, under these conditions, (13.12a) shows that all the odd coefficients $c_3, c_5, \ldots$ are zero while the even coefficients $c_2, c_4, \ldots$ are evaluated successively in terms of c_0.

Consider the solution obtained by taking $p = + v$. If $r = l/2$ is used as the summation suffix instead of l,

$$c_{2r} = \frac{(-1)^r c_0}{2^{2r} [(r + v)(r + v - 1) \cdots (v + 1)][r(r - 1) \ldots 2.1]}$$

$$= \frac{(-1)^r v! \, c_0}{2^{2r}(r + v)! r!} .$$

Then, choosing $v! c_0 = (\frac{1}{2})^v$ gives

$$c_{2r} = \frac{(-1)^r (\frac{1}{2})^{v+2r}}{(r + v)! \, r!}$$

and the solution (13.12) takes the form

$$g(x) = \sum_{r=0}^{\infty} \frac{(-1)^r (\frac{1}{2}x)^{v+2r}}{(r + v)! \, r!}$$

which is known as the **Bessel function of the first kind,** of order ν and usually denoted by $J_\nu(x)$. When ν is an integer n, $(r + n)!$ is an ordinary factorial. When $\nu = n + \frac{1}{2}$, n bring an integer, $(r + n + \frac{1}{2})!$ is given by

$$(r + n + \tfrac{1}{2})! = (r + n + \tfrac{1}{2})(r + n - \tfrac{1}{2}) \cdots (\tfrac{3}{2})(\tfrac{1}{2})\pi^{\frac{1}{2}} .$$

If ν is not an integer, the solution obtained by taking

$$p = -\nu , c_1 = 0 \text{ is } g(x) = J_{-\nu}(x) , \text{ where } J_{-\nu}(x) = \sum_{r=0}^{\infty} \frac{(-1)^r (x/2)^{-\nu+2r}}{(r - \nu)! \, r!} .$$

However, if ν is an integer n and p is taken equal to $-\nu$, then, with $l = 2r$, (13.13) yields

$$c_{2r} = - \frac{c_{2r-2}}{4r(r - n)}$$

and obviously c_{2n} will be infinite unless $c_{2n-2} = 0$. Therefore, the coefficients $c_{2n-2}, c_{2n-4}, \ldots, c_2, c_0$ must each be chosen equal to zero so that the first non-zero coefficient in (13.12) will be c_{2n}. In this case, the solution becomes

$$J_{-n}(x) = \sum_{r=n}^{\infty} \frac{(-1)^r (\frac{1}{2}x)^{-n+2r}}{(r - n)! \, r!} .$$

Now, if r is altered to $r + n$, this expression becomes

$$J_{-n}(x) = \sum_{r=0}^{\infty} \frac{(-1)^{r+n} (\frac{1}{2}x)^{n+2r}}{r! \, (r + n)!} = (-1)^n J_n(x) .$$

Thus, for non-integral ν, the general solution of Bessel's equation is

$$AJ_\nu(x) + BJ_{-\nu}(x) ,$$

since $J_\nu(x)$ and $J_{-\nu}(x)$ are two independent solutions. However, if ν is an integer n, $J_n(x)$ and $J_{-n}(x)$ are related as shown, and so only *one* independent solution has been found, and a further solution of Bessel's equation is required.

The situation arising when ν is an integer n is precisely that encountered when discussing the Förbenius method for solving an ordinary differential equation and the indicial equation is such that its roots differ by an integer and one makes a coefficient in the series expansion solution infinite. The required series solution has been derived already for the specific case $\nu = 1$ in the section dealing with the method of Fröbenius. Clearly this method could be extended easily to deal with other values of ν. This power series procedure gives a solution $Y_n(x)$, where Y_n is a **Bessel function of the second kind** and is represented by the sum of $J_n(x)\log x$ and a power series that converges for all x (as may be seen by referring back to the section on the method of Fröbenius). In particular, when $x > 0$, $Y_0(x)$ is

$$J_0(x) \log x + \frac{x^2}{2^2} - \frac{x^4}{2^2 4^2} (1 + \tfrac{1}{2}) + \cdots .$$

Since Y_n is unbounded and J_n is bounded as $x \to 0$, Y_n is not a constant multiplied by J_n; that is Y_n and J_n are linearly independent solutions of Bessel's equation.

Thus for integral ν, the general solution of Bessel's equation is

$$AJ_n(x) + BY_n(x)$$

for $\nu = n = 0,1,2, \ldots ; x > 0$.

13.4.2 Differentiation and recurrence formulae for Bessel functions
From above

$$x^{-n} J_n(x) = \frac{1}{2^n} \sum_{r=0}^{\infty} \frac{(-1)^r (\frac{1}{2}x)^{2r}}{(r+n)! \, r!}, \quad n = 0,1,2, \ldots$$

and so

$$\frac{d}{dx} [x^{-n} J_n(x)] = \frac{1}{2^n} \sum_{r=1}^{\infty} \frac{(-1)^r (\frac{1}{2}x)^{2r-1}}{(r+n)! \, (r-1)!}$$

$$= x^{-n} \left(\frac{x}{2}\right)^n \sum_{k=0}^{\infty} \frac{(-1)^{k+1} (\frac{1}{2}x)^{2k+1}}{(n+k+1)! \, k!}$$

$$= -x^{-n} \sum_{k=0}^{\infty} \frac{(-1)^k (\frac{1}{2}x)^{n+2k+1}}{(n+k+1)! \, k!}$$

$$= -x^{-n} J_{n+1}(x) . \tag{13.13}$$

As a special case, $\qquad J_0'(x) = -J_1(x) .$

Similarly, from the power series representation of $x^n J_n(x)$, it follows that

$$\frac{d}{dx} [x^n J_n(x)] = x^n J_{n-1}(x) ; n = 1,2, \ldots . \tag{13.14}$$

Now formulae (13.13) and (13.14) may be written

$$x J_n'(x) - n J_n(x) = -x J_{n+1}(x)$$

and

$$x J_n'(x) + n J_n(x) = x J_{n-1}(x)$$

respectively.

Eliminating $J_n'(x)$ between these two equations gives

$$x J_{n+1}(x) = 2n J_n(x) - x J_{n-1}(x) \tag{13.15}$$

for $n = 1,2, \ldots .$

Again, from (13.14) comes the integration formula

$$\int_0^x t^n J_{n-1}(t) dt = x^n J_n(x) ; n = 1,2, \ldots$$

of which an important special case is

$$\int_0^x t\, J_0(t)\mathrm{d}t = x\, J_1(x)\,.$$

It should be noted that formulae (13.13), (13.14) and (13.15) are all valid when n is replaced by the unrestricted parameter v; that is, they are valid for non-integer v.

Also, formula (13.13) may be written

$$x^{-n-1}\, J_{n+1}(x) = -\frac{1}{x}\frac{\mathrm{d}}{\mathrm{d}x}\,[x^{-n}\, J_n(x)]\,.$$

Putting $n \to n+1$ in this formula gives

$$x^{-n-2}\, J_{n+2}(x) = -\frac{1}{x}\frac{\mathrm{d}}{\mathrm{d}x}\,[x^{-n-1}\, J_{n+1}(x)]\,,$$

that is,

$$x^{-n-2}\, J_{n+2}(x) = \frac{(-1)^2}{x^2}\frac{\mathrm{d}^2}{\mathrm{d}x^2}\,[x^{-n}\, J_n(x)]\,.$$

Hence, by induction, it follows that

$$x^{-n-r}\, J_{n+r}(x) = \frac{(-1)^r}{x^r}\frac{\mathrm{d}^r}{\mathrm{d}x^r}\,[x^{-n}\, J_n(x)] \tag{13.16}$$

where n is unrestricted and r is any positive integer. Alternatively it may be written

$$x^{-n-r}\, J_{n+r}(x) = (-2)^r\frac{\mathrm{d}^r}{\mathrm{d}(x^2)^r}\,[x^{-n}\, J_n(x)]\,.$$

Formula (13.14) proves extremely useful in evaluating integrals involving Bessel functions. This will be illustrated by the following examples:

(i) Consider $$I = \int_0^b x^3\, J_0(ax)\mathrm{d}x\,.$$

Put $ax = t$, then $$I = a^{-4}\int_0^{ab} t^3\, J_0(t)\mathrm{d}t\,.$$

Note that, by the above relation

$$t\, J_0(t) = \frac{\mathrm{d}}{\mathrm{d}t}\,[t\, J_1(t)]\,.$$

Using this and integrating by parts leads to

$$a^4 I = [t^3 J_1(t)]_0^{ab} - 2 \int_0^{ab} t^2 J_1(t) dt$$

$$= a^3 b^3 J_1(ab) - 2 \int_0^{ab} t^2 J_1(t) dt .$$

Again by the above relation

$$t^2 J_1(t) = \frac{d}{dt} [t^2 J_2(t)]$$

and so, finally

$$a^4 I = a^3 b^3 J_1(ab) - 2a^2 b^2 J_2(ab) .$$

(ii) Now consider

$$I = \int_0^b x^2 J_0(ax) dx .$$

Put $ax = t$, then

$$a^3 I = \int_0^{ab} t^2 J_0(t) dt .$$

Again noting that

$$t J_0(t) = \frac{d}{dt} [t J_1(t)]$$

integrating by parts gives

$$a^3 I = a^2 b^2 J_1(ab) - \int_0^{ab} t J_1(t) dt .$$

Now using the relation (13.13), it is seen that

$$\frac{d}{dt} [J_0(t)] = - J_1(t)$$

and so

$$a^3 I = a^2 b^2 J_1(ab) + ab J_0(ab) - \int_0^{ab} J_0(t) dt .$$

The integral of $J_0(t)$ may be evaluated approximately with any degree of accuracy by termwise integration of the series for $J_0(t)$.
Note. It is found that integrals of the form $\int_0^b x^n J_0(ax) dx$ may be evaluated in closed form if n is an odd positive integer but, if n is an even positive integer, this is not so—the last term is always of the form $C \int_0^b J_0(ax) dx$, where C is a constant.

Relation (13.16) proves particularly useful for evaluating Bessel functions of positive half-odd-integral order. From the earlier definition

$$J_{1/2}(x) = \sum_{r=0}^{\infty} \frac{(-1)^r \left(\frac{1}{2}x\right)^{2r+1/2}}{(r+\frac{1}{2})! \, r!} \, .$$

As was seen earlier

$$\left(r + \tfrac{1}{2}\right)! = \left(r + \tfrac{1}{2}\right)\left(r - \tfrac{1}{2}\right) \cdots \tfrac{3}{2} \cdot \tfrac{1}{2} \pi^{1/2}$$

and so

$$J_{1/2}(x) = \left(\frac{2}{\pi x}\right)^{1/2} \sum_{r=0}^{\infty} \frac{(-1)^r \, x^{2r+1}}{(2r+1)!} \, .$$

The series indicated by the summation is the well-known Maclaurin's series for sin x, and so

$$J_{1/2}(x) = \left(\frac{2}{\pi x}\right)^{1/2} \sin x \, .$$

Similarly, it may be shown that

$$J_{-1/2}(x) = \left(\frac{2}{\pi x}\right)^{1/2} \cos x \, .$$

Now, if l is an integer, using (13.16) in conjunction with the expression for $J_{1/2}(x)$ gives

$$x^{-l-1/2} J_{l+1/2}(x) = (-1)^l \left(\frac{d}{x dx}\right)^l [x^{-1/2} J_{1/2}(x)] = (-1)^l \left(\frac{d}{x dx}\right)^l \left[x^{-1/2} \left(\frac{2}{\pi x}\right)^{1/2} \sin x\right],$$

that is,

$$J_{l+1/2}(x) = (-1)^l \left(\frac{2}{\pi}\right)^{1/2} x^{l+1/2} \left(\frac{d}{x dx}\right)^l \left[\frac{\sin x}{x}\right] . \tag{13.17}$$

Thus, Bessel functions of positive half-odd-integral order may be expressed in terms of x, sin x and cos x; for example

$$J_{3/2}(x) = -\left(\frac{2}{\pi}\right)^{1/2} x^{-3/2} \left(x\cos x - \sin x\right) .$$

In the original derivation of Bessel's equation given here, it was noted that the constant k, and hence $x = kr$, might be complex. Hence, if $x = jy$, Bessel's equation becomes

$$y \frac{d}{dy}\left(y \frac{dg}{dy}\right) - (y^2 + v^2)g = 0 \, ,$$

and this has solutions

$$I_{\pm v}(y) = \sum_{r=0}^{\infty} \frac{\left(\frac{1}{2}y\right)^{2r \pm v}}{r! \, (r \pm v)!}$$

which are constant multiples of $J_{\pm\nu}(x)$ with $x = jy$. The functions $I_{\pm\nu}(y)$ are the **Bessel functions of imaginary argument**. For such functions $I_{l+\frac{1}{2}}(x)$ may be obtained (apart from a constant factor) by replacing x by jx in (13.17). The function is given by

$$I_{l+\frac{1}{2}}(x) = \left(\frac{2}{\pi}\right)^{\frac{1}{2}} x^{l+\frac{1}{2}} \left(\frac{d}{xdx}\right)^{l} \left[\frac{\sinh x}{x}\right].$$

Again, it is quite common to eliminate a factor $x^{\frac{1}{2}}$ from $J_{l+\frac{1}{2}}(x)$ when $l \geqslant 0$, by defining the spherical Bessel function:

$$j_l(x) = \left(\frac{\pi}{2x}\right)^{\frac{1}{2}} J_{l+\frac{1}{2}}(x) = (-x)^{l} \left(\frac{d}{xdx}\right)^{l} \left[\frac{\sin x}{x}\right].$$

Spherical Bessel functions are well behaved near $x = 0$. In fact

$$j_l(x) = (-x)^{l} 2^{l} \frac{d^{l}}{d(x^{2})^{l}} \sum_{r=0}^{x} \frac{(-x^{2})^{r}}{(2r+1)!}.$$

Near $x = 0$, this gives the approximate behaviour

$$j_l(x) \sim (-x)^{l} 2^{l} \frac{d^{l}}{d(x^{2})^{l}} \left[\frac{(-x^{2})^{l}}{(2l+1)!}\right].$$

$$= x^{l}2^{l}l!/(2l+1)! = x^{l}/[1.3.5. \cdots . (2l+1)] .$$

By reference to the known properties of $J_{l+\frac{1}{2}}(x)$, the following properties of $j_l(x)$ may be established easily:

$$(2l+1)j_l(x) = xj_{l+1}(x) + xj_{l-1}(x) , l > 0 .$$

$$(2l+)j_l'(x) = lj_{l-1}(x) - (l+1)j_{l+1}(x)$$

$$\frac{d}{dx} [x^{l+1}j_l(x)] = x^{l+1}j_{l-1}(x)$$

$$\frac{d}{dx} [x^{-l}j_l(x)] = -x^{-l}j_{l+1}(x) .$$

A formula, similar to (13.17), may be derived for the Bessel functions of negative half-odd-integral order:

$$J_{-l-\frac{1}{2}}(x) = \left(\frac{2}{\pi}\right)^{\frac{1}{2}} x^{l+\frac{1}{2}} \left(\frac{d}{xdx}\right)^{l} \left[\frac{\cos x}{x}\right]$$

and from these are derived the spherical Neumann functions:

$$n_l(x) = (-1)^{l+1} \left(\frac{\pi}{2x}\right)^{\frac{1}{2}} J_{-l-\frac{1}{2}}(x) .$$

These functions are infinite at $x = 0$ and, in fact, for small x

$$n_l(x) \sim 1.3.5. \ \cdots \ .(2l + 1)x^{-l-1} .$$

Again, the $n_l(x)$ satisfy the same recurrence relations as the spherical Bessel functions.

13.4.3 An integral form for $J_n(x)$

If n is zero or a positive integer, consider

$$y = g(x) = \int_0^\pi \cos (x \sin\phi - n\phi)d\phi .$$

Now Bessel's equation (13.11) may be written

$$x^2y'' + xy' + (x^2 - n^2)y = 0$$

and for the given y,

$$y' = - \int_0^\pi \sin (x \sin\phi - n\phi) \sin\phi \ d\phi$$

$$y'' = - \int_0^\pi \cos (x \sin\phi - n\phi) \sin^2\phi \ d\phi$$

where $'$ denotes d/dx.

Again,

$$y' = -\int_0^\pi \cos\phi \ \cos(x\sin\phi - n\phi) \cdot (x\cos\phi - n)d\phi$$

on integrating by parts.

Substituting into the above form of Bessel's equation leads to the right-hand side being given by

$$n \int_0^\pi (x\cos\phi - n)\cos(x\sin\phi - n\phi)d\phi .$$

Noting that, if $u = x \sin\phi - n\phi$, this integral may be written $n\int\cos u \ du$, it follows that the above integral may be evaluated as

$$n \ [\sin(x\sin\phi - n\phi)]_{\phi=0}^{\phi=\pi}$$

which equals zero.

Hence, the given function y satisfies Bessel's equation of order n when n is zero or a positive integer. This function y is a continuous function of x for all x and so is finite at $x = 0$. Hence, it must equal $J_n(x)$ multiplied by some constant. This constant may be shown to have the value π, and so

$$J_n(x) = \frac{1}{\pi}\int_0^\pi \cos(x\,\sin\phi - n\phi)d\phi \; ; \; n = 0,1,2, \ldots$$

In particular,

$$J_0(x) = \frac{1}{\pi}\int_0^\pi \cos(x\sin\phi)d\phi \; .$$

13.4.4 Approximations for small and large arguments
Consider

$$J_\nu(x) = \sum_{r=0}^\infty \frac{(-1)^r \left(\frac{1}{2}x\right)^{\nu+2r}}{r!\,\Gamma(r + \nu + 1)}$$

where $\nu \neq -1,-2,-3, \ldots$.
   Now $\Gamma(\nu + r + 1) = (\nu + r)(\nu + r - 1) \cdots (\nu + 1)\Gamma(\nu + 1)$.

Therefore, for each value of r in the summation, the denominator contains the factor $\Gamma(\nu + 1)$ and so

$$\lim_{x\to 0}\left[\frac{J_\nu(x)}{x^\nu}\right] = \frac{1}{2^\nu \Gamma(\nu + 1)}\lim_{x\to 0}\sum_{r=0}^\infty \frac{(-1)^r \left(\frac{1}{2}x\right)^{2r}}{r!\,(\nu + r)(\nu + r - 1) \cdots (\nu + 1)} \; .$$

The series indicated by this summation is not only convergent for all x; it is uniformly convergent on any chosen finite interval of values of x. Hence, the function $f(x)$ denoted by the series is continuous at every x, in particular at $x = 0$. Therefore, $\lim_{x\to 0} f(x) = f(0) = 1$, the first term of the series. Thus, for small values of x, $J_\nu(x)$ is given by $x^\nu/2^\nu\Gamma(\nu + 1)$ approximately.
   By considering the integral form for $J_n(x)$,

$$J_n(x) = \frac{1}{\pi}\int_0^\pi \cos(x\sin\phi - n\phi)d\phi$$

it may be shown that as $x\to\infty$,

$$J_n(x) = \left(\frac{2}{\pi x}\right)^{1/2}\cos\left(x - \frac{\pi}{4} - \frac{n\pi}{2}\right) + \text{terms of order } x^{-3/5} \; .$$

As $x\to\infty$,

$$J_n(x) \sim \left(\frac{2}{\pi x}\right)^{1/2}\cos\left(x - \frac{\pi}{4} - \frac{n\pi}{2}\right) \; .$$

13.4.5 Zeros of Bessel functions

Although it will not be proved here, the function $J_\nu(x)$ does have infinitely many real zeros; that is, there are infinitely many values of x for which

$$J_\nu(x) = 0 \,.$$

Actually this result may be inferred from the large argument approximation just given.

Now consider the recurrence relation

$$x\,J_\nu'(x) = \nu\,J_\nu(x) - x\,J_{\nu+1}(x) \,.$$

Suppose $J_\nu(x_0)$ and $J_{\nu+1}(x_0)$ both vanish for some $x_0 > 0$. Then, this equation shows that $J_\nu'(x_0) = 0$ also.

However, this would imply that $J_\nu(x)$ is identically zero. This is not true, and so it follows that the zeros of $J_\nu(x)$ and $J_{\nu+1}(x)$ are distinct.

Now let x_1 and x_2 be consecutive positive zeros of $J_\nu(x)$. By the above equation

$$J_\nu'(x_1) = -\,J_{\nu+1}(x_1) \,;\, J_\nu'(x_2) = -\,J_{\nu+1}(x_2) \,.$$

However, $J_\nu'(x_1)$ and $J_\nu'(x_2)$ must have opposite signs, and these equalities imply, therefore, that $J_{\nu+1}(x)$ vanishes at least once between x_1 and x_2.

A similar argument using the recurrence relation

$$x\,J_\nu'(x) + \nu J_\nu(x) = x\,J_{\nu-1}(x)$$

shows that $J_\nu(x)$ must vanish between consecutive zeros of $J_{\nu+1}(x)$.

Thus, finally, it is seen that the zeros of $J_\nu(x)$ and $J_{\nu+1}(x)$ are distinct and alternate on the positive x-axis.

The fact that $J_\nu(x)$ has infinitely many real zeros is not a surprising result since the series formula for $J_\nu(x)$ bears a marked resemblance to the Maclaurin series for $\sin x$ or $\cos x$. Also, the presence of the two additional factors $2^{\nu+2r}$ and $\Gamma(\nu + r + 1)$ is what accounts apparently for the decrease in the absolute value of $J_\nu(x)$ as $x \to \infty$.

To give some idea of the behaviour of Bessel functions of the first kind, the graphs of $J_0(x)$, $J_1(x)$ and $J_2(x)$ are as shown in Fig. 13.1.

13.4.6 Orthogonality property

First it will be shown that

$$x^{1/2}\,J_n(\alpha_i x) \,;\, i = 1,2,3,\ldots$$

are orthogonal on the interval $0 \leqslant x \leqslant 1$, where $\alpha_1,\alpha_2,\alpha_3,\ldots$ are the positive zeros of the Bessel function $J_n(x)$; that is, it is to be shown that

$$\int_0^1 x\,J_n(\alpha_i x)\,J_n(\alpha_j x)\mathrm{d}x = 0 \quad \text{for } i \neq j \,.$$

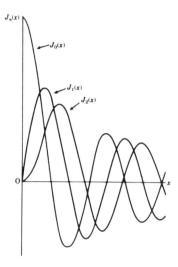

Fig. 13.1

Using Bessel's equation gives

$$x \frac{d}{dx}\left[x \frac{d}{dx} J_n(\alpha_i x) \right] + (\alpha_i^2 x^2 - n^2)J_n(\alpha_i x) = 0 \qquad (13.18)$$

$$x \frac{d}{dx}\left[x \frac{d}{dx} J_n(\alpha_j x) \right] + (\alpha_j^2 x^2 - n^2)J_n(\alpha_j x) = 0 . \qquad (13.19)$$

Multiplying (13.18) by $J_n(\alpha_j x)$ and (13.19) by $J_n(\alpha_i x)$ and then subtracting leads to

$$J_n(\alpha_j x) \frac{d}{dx}\left[x \frac{d}{dx} J_n(\alpha_i x) \right] - J_n(\alpha_i x) \frac{d}{dx}\left[x \frac{d}{dx} J_n(\alpha_j x) \right] = (\alpha_j^2 - \alpha_i^2)x J_n(\alpha_i x)J_n(\alpha_j x) .$$

The left-hand side of this equation is seen to be the derivative of a difference, and so the equation may be written

$$\frac{d}{dx}\left[x J_n(\alpha_j x) \frac{d}{dx} J_n(\alpha_i x) - x J_n(\alpha_i x) \frac{d}{dx} J_n(\alpha_j x) \right]$$
$$= (\alpha_j^2 - \alpha_i^2)x J_n(\alpha_i x)J_n(\alpha_j x) .$$

Now
$$\frac{d}{dx} J_n(\alpha_i x) = \frac{dJ_n(\alpha_i x)}{d(\alpha_i x)} \frac{d(\alpha_i x)}{dx} = \alpha_i J_n'(\alpha_i x) \qquad (13.20)$$

where $'$ denotes differentiation with respect to the argument of the function. Then, using

$$J_n'(x) = -J_{n+1}(x) + \frac{n}{x} J_n(x)$$

leads to

$$\frac{d}{dx} [- \alpha_i x \, J_n(\alpha_j x) J_{n+1}(\alpha_i x) + \alpha_j x J_n(\alpha_i x) J_{n+1}(\alpha_j x)]$$

$$= (\alpha_j^2 - \alpha_i^2) x \, J_n(\alpha_i x) J_n(\alpha_j x) .$$

Now, $J_n(\alpha_i) = 0 = J_n(\alpha_j)$ by definition, and $J_n(0) = 0$ for $n > 0$, and so integrating the above equation over the interval $0 \leq x \leq 1$ gives

$$0 = (\alpha_j^2 - \alpha_i^2) \int_0^1 x J_n(\alpha_i x) J_n(\alpha_j x) dx .$$

Since $\alpha_i \neq \alpha_j$ when $i \neq j$, it follows that

$$\int_0^1 x \, J_n(\alpha_i x) \, J_n(\alpha_j x) dx = 0 \quad \text{for } i \neq j .$$

This orthogonality property is described by saying that the family $\{J_n(\alpha_i x)\}$ is orthogonal on the interval $0 \leq x \leq 1$ with respect to the weight function $w(x) = x$.

It now remains to examine the case $i = j$. It will be shown that

$$2 \int_0^1 x [J_n(\alpha_i x)]^2 dx = [J_n'(\alpha_i)]^2 .$$

The differential equation satisfied by $J_n(\alpha_i x)$ is

$$\frac{d}{dx} \left[x \frac{d}{dx} J_n(\alpha_i x) \right] + \left(\alpha_i^2 x - \frac{n^2}{x} \right) J_n(\alpha_i x) = 0 .$$

Multiply throughout by $x(d/dx)J_n(\alpha_i x)$ and integrate from 0 to r. Integrating by parts leads to

$$\left[r \left\{ \frac{d}{dx} J_n(\alpha_i x) \right\} \right]_{x=r}^2 - n^2 J_n^2(\alpha_i r) + 2\alpha_i^2 \int_0^r x^2 J_n(\alpha_i x) \frac{d}{dx} J_n(\alpha_i x) dx = 0 ,$$

that is,

$$\left[r \left\{ \frac{d}{dx} J_n(\alpha_i x) \right\} \right]_{x=r}^2 - n^2 J_n^2(\alpha_i r) + \alpha_i^2 r^2 J_n^2(\alpha_i r)$$

$$- 2\alpha_i^2 \int_0^r x\, J_n^2(\alpha_i x)dx = 0 .$$

Putting $r = 1$ leads to

$$\left[\left\{\frac{d}{dx}\, J_n(\alpha_i x)\right\}_{x=1}\right]^2 = 2\alpha_i^2 \int_0^1 x\, J_n^2(\alpha_i x)dx$$

or

$$[J_n'(\alpha_i)]^2 = 2 \int_0^1 x\, J_n^2(\alpha_i x)dx$$

as required. (Here (13.20) has been used.)
    Note that, when $n = 0$, this becomes

$$J_1^2(\alpha_i) = 2 \int_0^1 x\, J_0^2(\alpha_i x)dx .$$

Also, using the recurrence relation

$$x\, J_n'(x) - n\, J_n(x) = - x\, J_{n+1}(x)$$

it is seen that, if α_i is a zero of $J_n(x)$

$$J_n'(\alpha_i) = - J_{n+1}(\alpha_i)$$

and so,

$$2 \int_0^1 x\, J_n^2(\alpha_i x)dx = [J_{n+1}(\alpha_i)]^2 \quad .$$

    As with other orthogonality properties, the main use of this property of Bessel functions is that it allows the expansion of some given function in Bessel functions. For example, suppose the function $f(x)$ may be expanded in the form

$$f(x) = \sum_{i=1}^{\infty} A_i\, J_n(\alpha_i x)$$

where $\alpha_1, \alpha_2, \alpha_3, \ldots$ are the positive zeros of the Bessel function $J_n(x)$. The coefficients A_i may be found as follows:
    Multiply both sides of the above equation by $x\, J_n(\alpha_j x)$ and integrate with respect to x from 0 to 1; then

$$\int_0^1 xf(x) J_n(\alpha_j x)dx = \sum_{i=1}^{\infty} A_i \int_0^1 J_n(\alpha_i x)J_n(\alpha_j x)x\, dx .$$

Using the above orthogonality property, it follows that

$$A_j = \frac{2}{[J_{n+1}(\alpha_j)]^2} \int_0^1 xf(x)\, J_n(\alpha_j x)dx .$$

To illustrate the real use of this technique consider the following example:

In the two-dimensional case in which there is no z dependence, the heat conduction equation in cylindrical polar coordinates takes the form

$$\frac{1}{r}\frac{\partial}{\partial r}\left(r\frac{\partial u}{\partial r}\right) = \frac{1}{k}\frac{\partial u}{\partial t}$$

if it is assumed that the dependent variable u is independent of the angular coordinate ϕ. (This corresponds to an assumption of circular symmetry about the z-axis.)

The problem is to solve this equation subject to the boundary conditions

$$u(1,t) = 0 \quad \text{for } t \geq 0 ,$$

$$u(r,0) = f(r) \quad \text{for } 0 \leq r < 1 ,$$

where $f(r)$ is assumed to be a known function.

Assuming a solution of the form $u(r,t) = R(r)T(t)$ leads to

$$\frac{1}{rR}\frac{d}{dr}\left(r\frac{dR}{dr}\right) = -\lambda^2$$

and
$$\frac{1}{kT}\frac{dT}{dt} = -\lambda^2$$

where λ is an arbitrary constant. These equations give

$$r^2\frac{d^2R}{dr^2} + r\frac{dR}{dr} + r^2\lambda^2 R = 0$$

and
$$T(t) = C \exp(-k\lambda^2 t)$$

where C is an arbitrary constant.

The equation for $R(r)$ is a particular case of Bessel's equation. Referring back, it is seen to be the case $\nu = 0$, and so has the solution

$$R(r) = AJ_0(\lambda r) + BY_0(\lambda r) .$$

However, like all the Y_n, Y_0 is singular at the origin $r = 0$, and so for a non-singular solution it is necessary to choose $B = 0$, and so

$$u(r,t) = AJ_0(\lambda r)\exp(-k\lambda^2 t) .$$

Imposing the first boundary condition gives

$$0 = AJ_0(\lambda)\exp(-k\lambda^2 t) \quad \text{for } t \geq 0$$

and so, in order to obtain a non-trivial solution

$$J_0(\lambda) = 0 ,$$

which determines the eigenvalues λ_i of the boundary value problem. (There will be an infinity of solutions.)

To each eigenvalue, there corresponds an eigenfunction

$$u_i(r,t) = A_i\, J_0(\lambda_i r)\exp(-k\lambda_i^2 t) \, ,$$

and so a general solution is

$$u(r,t) = \sum_{}^{\infty} A_i\, J_0(\lambda_i r)\exp(-k\lambda_i^2 t)$$

where the coefficients A_i must be chosen to satisfy the second boundary condition:

$$u(r,0) = f(r) = \sum_{i=1}^{\infty} A_i J_0(\lambda_i r) \quad \text{for } 0 \leqslant r < 1 \, .$$

Using the above technique for finding the coefficients A_i gives

$$A_j = \frac{2}{J_j^{\,2}(\lambda_j)} \int_0^1 rf(r) J_0(\lambda_j r)\mathrm{d}r \, , \quad j = 1,2,3, \dots \, .$$

Hence, the solution of the given boundary value problem is

$$u(r,t) = 2 \sum_{i=1}^{\infty} \frac{J_0(\lambda_i r)\exp(-k\lambda_i^2 t)}{J_i^{\,2}(\lambda_i)} \int_0^1 xf(x)J_0(\lambda_i x)\mathrm{d}x \, ,$$

where x has been written as the variable of integration to avoid confusion with the independent variable r, and the λ_i are the positive roots of $J_0(\lambda) = 0$.

13.5 SOME OTHER SPECIAL FUNCTIONS
The Legendre polynomials and Bessel functions have been discussed in some detail because of their frequent appearance in a wide variety of problems in mathematics, physical science, and engineering. However, there are other special functions which deserve to be mentioned.
(i) **Laguerre's differential equation**

$$x\frac{\mathrm{d}^2 y}{\mathrm{d}x^2} + (1 - x)\frac{\mathrm{d}y}{\mathrm{d}x} + vy = 0$$

admits as a solution the Laguerre polynomial, $L_n(x)$, in the case when v is a positive integer n. It may be shown that $L_n(x)$ is given by

$$L_n(x) = \sum_{m=0}^{n} \frac{(-1)^m\, n!}{(m!)^2\,(n - m)!} x^m \, .$$

(ii) **Hermite's differential equation**

$$\frac{d^2y}{dx^2} - 2x\frac{dy}{dx} + 2vy = 0$$

is found to admit as a solution the Hermite polynomial, $H_n(x)$, in the case when v is an integer n. It may be shown that

$$H_n(x) = (2x)^n - \frac{n(n-1)}{1!}(2x)^{n-2} + \frac{n(n-1)(n-2)(n-3)}{2!}(2x)^{n-4} \cdots .$$

(iii) **Chebyshev's differential equation**

$$(1-x^2)\frac{d^2y}{dx^2} - x\frac{dy}{dx} + v^2y = 0$$

has as solution the Chebyshev polynomials of the first kind, $T_n(x)$, if v is an integer n. In this case, it may be shown that

$$T_n(x) = \cos(n\cos^{-1}x)$$

$$= x^n - \frac{n!}{2!(n-2)!}x^{n-2}(1-x^2) + \frac{n!}{4!(n-4)!}x^{n-4}(1-x^2)^2 \cdots .$$

The Laguerre, Hermite, and Chebyshev polynomials may be examined in the same way as the Legendre polynomials and Bessel functions. Recurrence relations may be deduced, generating functions may be found, and orthogonality properties may be established. Some of these useful properties are included in the exercises which follow.

EXERCISES 13

(1) Show that the following functions may be represented in the form:

$$f(x) = c_0P_0 + c_1P_1(x) + \cdots + c_nP_n(x) :$$

(a) $f(x) = 3x^2 - 4x + 5$,

(b) $f(x) = 10x^3 - 3x^2 - 5x - 1$.

(2) Evaluate the first few terms of the generalised Fourier series involving Legendre polynomials which represents

(a) $$f(x) = \begin{cases} 0 & \text{if } -1 < x < 0 \\ 1 & \text{if } 0 < x < 1, \end{cases}$$

(b) $$f(x) = |x| \text{ if } -1 < x < 1.$$

(3) If λ_r are the positive roots of $J_0(\lambda a) = 0$, find the Fourier-Bessel expansions of the following functions:

(a) $$f(x) = 1 \ , 0 < x < a \ ,$$

(b) $$f(x) = x^2 , 0 < x < a .$$

(4) Show that the solution of the equation

$$\frac{1}{x} \frac{\partial}{\partial x}\left(x \frac{\partial u}{\partial x}\right) = \frac{\partial u}{\partial t}$$

for $0 \leqslant x \leqslant a$ and $t \geqslant 0$, subject to the boundary conditions $u(x,0) = \text{const.} = u_0$, and $u(a,t) = 0$ for all t, is

$$u(x,t) = \frac{2u_0}{a} \sum_{r=1}^{\infty} \frac{J_0(\lambda_r x)}{\lambda_r J_1(\lambda_r a)} \exp(-\lambda_r^2 t) ,$$

where λ_r are the positive roots of $J_0(\lambda a) = 0$.

(5) The Laguerre polynomials may be defined by

$$L_0 = 1 , L_n(x) = \frac{e^x}{n!} \frac{d^n}{dx^n} (x^n e^{-x}) , n = 1,2, \dots .$$

Show that $L_1(x) = 1 - x$, $L_2(x) = 1 - 2x + \frac{1}{2}x^2$, $L_3(x) = 1 - 3x + \frac{3}{2}x^2 - \frac{1}{6}x^3$. Also show that

$$L_n(x) = \sum_{m=0}^{n} \frac{(-1)^m n!}{(m!)^2(n-m)!} x^m = 1 - nx + \frac{n(n-1)}{4} x^2 - \dots + \frac{(-1)^n}{n!} x^n .$$

(6) Show that

$$\frac{e^{-xt/(1-t)}}{(1-t)} = \sum_{n=0}^{\infty} \frac{L_n(x)}{n!} t^n .$$

(7) Deduce the following recurrence formulae for the Laguerre polynomials:

(a) $$L_{n+1}(x) + (x - 2n - 1)L_n(x) + n^2 L_{n-1}(x) = 0 .$$

(b) $$L_n'(x) - nL_{n-1}'(x) + nL_{n-1}(x) = 0 .$$

(8) Show that the Laguerre polynomials are orthogonal for $0 \leqslant x < \infty$ with respect to the weight function e^{-x}.

(9) The Hermite polynomials are given by

$$H_0 = 1, H_n(x) = (-1)^n \exp(x^2) \frac{d^n}{dx^n} [\exp(-x^2)] , n = 1,2, \dots .$$

Show that

$$H_1(x) = 2x , H_2(x) = 4x^2 - 2 , H_3(x) = 8x^3 - 12x ,$$

$$H_4(x) = 16x^4 - 48x^2 + 12 , H_5(x) = 32x^5 - 160x^3 + 120x .$$

(10) Show that

$$\exp(2tx - t^2) = \sum_{n=0}^{\infty} \frac{H_n(x)}{n!} t^n .$$

(11) Deduce the following recurrence formulae for the Hermite polynomials:

(a) $\qquad\qquad\qquad H_n'(x) = 2n H_{n-1}(x) .$

(b) $\qquad\qquad 2x H_n(x) = H_{n+1}(x) + 2n H_{n-1}(x) .$

(12) Show that the Hermite polynomials are orthogonal for $-\infty < x < \infty$ with respect to the weight function e^{-x^2}.

(13) From the definition of the Chebyshev polynomials, show that

$$T_0(x) = 1 , T_1(x) = x , T_2(x) = 2x^2 - 1 ,$$
$$T_3(x) = 4x^3 - 3x , T_4(x) = 8x^4 - 8x^2 + 1 .$$

(14) Show that

$$\frac{1 - tx}{1 - 2tx + t^2} = \sum_{n=0}^{\infty} T_n(x)t^n .$$

(15) Deduce the following recurrence formula for the Chebyshev polynomials, $T_n(x)$:

$$T_{n+1}(x) + T_{n-1}(x) = 2x T_n(x) .$$

(16) Show that the Chebyshev polynomials, $T_n(x)$, are orthogonal for $-1 \leq x \leq 1$ with respect to the weight function $(1 - x^2)^{-1/2}$.

Chapter 14
Functions of a Complex Variable

14.1 INTRODUCTION

Complex numbers were introduced in Chapter 2 and their properties discussed. However, in the discussion of functions of one variable given in Chapters 1, 3, and 4, as well as in the consideration of functions of several variables contained in Chapter 7, attention was restricted to the case when the variables concerned are real. In the present chapter, it is intended to present a brief introduction to various aspects of the theory of functions of a complex variable.

If $z = x + jy$ and $w = u + jv$ are any two complex numbers, a possible definition of a complex function $w = f(z)$ of the complex variable z is that, if with every point $z = x + jy$ in a given domain, $\mathcal{D}$, a complex number $w = u + jv$ is associated by means of a relation $w = f(z)$, then w is said to be a complex function of z in that domain. It follows that the complex variable z is the same as a complex function $[u(x,y) + jv(x,y)]$ of the two real variables x and y. Although quite legitimate, this concept of function is much too wide, and so it must have certain limits placed upon it. Firstly, it is required that $u(x,y)$ and $v(x,y)$ be continuous functions with continuous first derivatives in the given domain. Also, for practical purposes, the functions of z which are of use are those which are differentiable in the given domain. Hence, it is required also that the function $f(z)$ be differentiable in the domain $\mathcal{D}$ with respect to the complex independent variable z; that is, the limit

$$\lim_{\delta z \to 0} \frac{f(z + \delta z) - f(z)}{\delta z} = f'(z)$$

exists for all z in $\mathcal{D}$. This limit is called the **derivative** of $f(z)$.

It should be noted that u and v possessing continuous derivatives with respect to x and y is not sufficient to ensure the differentiability of the function $f(z)$. The above idea of differentiability implies a great deal since $\delta z (= \alpha + j\beta$ say) may tend to zero through real values (if $\beta = 0$) or imaginary values (if $\alpha = 0$), or in any other way; but, if the function is to be differentiable, the same limit $f'(z)$ must result in all cases. Hence, to ensure that the function $f(z)$ is differentiable, a further condition must be imposed:

If $w = u(x,y) + jv(x,y) = f(z) = f(x + jy)$, where $u(x,y)$ and $v(x,y)$ are continuously differentiable, the necessary and sufficient conditions that the function $f(z)$ be differentiable in the domain $\mathcal{D}$ are

$$\partial u/\partial x = \partial v/\partial y \, , \, \partial u/\partial y = - \, \partial v/\partial x \, , \tag{14.1}$$

the **Cauchy-Riemann equations**.

In every region where u and v satisfy these conditions, $f(z)$ is said to be an **analytic** or **regular**, function of the complex variable z, and its derivative is given by

$$f'(z) = \frac{\partial u}{\partial x} + j \frac{\partial v}{\partial x} = \frac{\partial v}{\partial y} - j \frac{\partial u}{\partial y} .$$

To show that the Cauchy-Riemann equations provide a necessary condition, assume that $f'(z)$ exists. To obtain the limit $f'(z)$ by taking δz equal to a real quantity α,

$$f'(z) = \lim_{\alpha \to 0} \left\{ \frac{u(x + \alpha,y) - u(x,y)}{\alpha} + j \frac{v(x + \alpha,y) - v(x,y)}{\alpha} \right\}$$

$$= \frac{\partial u}{\partial x} + j \frac{\partial v}{\partial x} .$$

Alternatively, if the limit $f'(z)$ is found by taking δz equal to an imaginary quantity $j\beta$,

$$f'(z) = \lim_{\beta \to 0} \left\{ \frac{u(x,y + \beta) - u(x,y)}{j\beta} + j \frac{v(x,y + \beta) - v(x,y)}{j\beta} \right\}$$

$$= - j \frac{\partial u}{\partial y} + \frac{\partial v}{\partial y} .$$

If these two expressions for $f'(z)$ are to be equivalent, it is seen, by equating real and imaginary parts, that the Cauchy-Riemann equations must be satisfied.

To show that these equations provide a sufficient condition also, note that

$$\frac{f(z + \delta z) - f(z)}{\delta z}$$

$$= \frac{u(x + \alpha,y + \beta) - u(x,y) + j\,[v(x + \alpha,y + \beta) - v(x,y)]}{\alpha + j\beta}$$

$$= \left\{ \alpha \frac{\partial u}{\partial x} + \beta \frac{\partial u}{\partial y} + j\alpha \frac{\partial v}{\partial x} + j\beta \frac{\partial v}{\partial y} + (\varepsilon_1 + \varepsilon_2) |\delta z| \right\} /(\alpha + j\beta)$$

where ε_1, ε_2 are two real quantities which tend to zero with $|\delta z|$. If the Cauchy-Riemann equations hold, this final expression becomes

$$\frac{\partial u}{\partial x} + j\frac{\partial v}{\partial x} + \frac{(\varepsilon_1 + \varepsilon_2)|\delta z|}{(\alpha + j\beta)} .$$

As $\delta z \to 0$, this expression tends to the limit

$$\left(\frac{\partial u}{\partial x} + j\frac{\partial v}{\partial x}\right)$$

and this is achieved independently of the path to the limit. Hence the required result.

Now, if the partial derivatives of u and v satisfy the Cauchy-Riemann equations,

$$\frac{\partial^2 v}{\partial x \partial y} = \frac{\partial^2 u}{\partial x^2} = -\frac{\partial^2 u}{\partial y^2} \quad \text{and} \quad \frac{\partial^2 u}{\partial x \partial y} = -\frac{\partial^2 v}{\partial x^2} = \frac{\partial^2 v}{\partial y^2} ,$$

where it has been assumed that the derivatives concerned exist and satisfy

$$\frac{\partial^2 \phi}{\partial x \partial y} = \frac{\partial^2 \phi}{\partial y \partial x}$$

This result means that u and v, the real and imaginary parts of an analytic function of z, both satisfy Laplace's equation in two dimensions. This is an equation of great importance in mathematical physics, being satisfied, for example, by the velocity potential and stream function of two-dimensional irrotational flow of an incompressible non-viscous fluid. Hence, functions of complex variables have an important part to play in the solution of two-dimensional problems in mathematical physics.

In the theory of functions of a complex variable, the Argand diagram (introduced in Chapter 2) is termed the z-plane. Then, just as $z = x + jy$ may be represented as a point in the z-plane, so the relation

$$w = f(z) = u(x,y) + jv(x,y)$$

allows the complex function w to be represented by the point (u,v) in the w-plane. Here the coordinates $u(x,y)$ and $v(x,y)$ would be determined by the values of x and y, and so each point in the z-plane determines a point in the w-plane via the above equation. Hence, the above equation defines a transformation from the z-plane into the w-plane and, if $f(z)$ is analytic, the transformation is said to be **conformal**. Usually, a transformation is defined to be conformal if, when any two curves are transformed by it into two other curves, the angle between the curves is preserved. However, it may be shown that a necessary and sufficient condition for a transformation to be conformal is that the Cauchy-Riemann equations hold. Hence, the above definition and the more usual one are compatible.

14.2 COMPLEX INTEGRATION

Before proceeding further, it is necessary to consider the definition of the integral of a function of a complex variable along a plane curve. In this section, since τ will denote the variable of integration, it proves convenient to let $\tau = \alpha + j\beta$. Now suppose the function $f(\tau)$ to be analytic in a domain $\mathcal{D}$, and $\tau = \tau_0$ and $\tau = \tau_n$ be two points in this domain joined by a piecewise smooth curve C which lies wholly within $\mathcal{D}$. Subdivide the curve C into n parts by the points $\tau_0, \tau_1 \tau_2, \ldots, \tau_n$ and form the sum

$$S_n = \sum_{r=1}^{n} f(\tau_r')(\tau_r - \tau_{r-1})$$

where τ_r' denotes any point lying on the curve C between τ_r and τ_{r-1}. If the subdivision is made increasingly fine by allowing the number of points to increase without limit but so that the largest of the intervals $|\tau_r - \tau_{r-1}|$ tends to zero, S_n tends to a limit which is independent of the intermediate point τ_r' and of the points τ_v. This follows since, if

$$f(\tau) = u(\alpha,\beta) + jv(\alpha,\beta)$$

and $\quad \tau_r = \alpha_r + j\beta_r$, $\delta\tau_r = \tau_r - \tau_{r-1} = \delta\alpha_r + j\delta\beta_r$, $\quad$ then

$$S_n = \sum_{r=1}^{n} [u(\alpha_r',\beta_r') + jv(\alpha_r',\beta_r')][\delta\alpha_r + j\delta\beta_r]$$

$$= \sum_{r=1}^{n} \{u(\alpha_r',\beta_r')\delta\alpha_r - v(\alpha_r',\beta_r')\delta\beta_r + j[v(\alpha_r',\beta_r')\delta\alpha_r + u(\alpha_r',\beta_r')\delta\beta_r]\}.$$

As n increases, the right-hand side tends to the sum of the two line integrals $\int_c (udx - vdy)$ and $j\int_c (vdx + udy)$ and so, as stated, S_n does tend to a limit. This limit is called the **definite integral of the function** $f(\tau)$ along the curve C from τ_0 to τ_n and is written $\int_c f(\tau)d\tau$ so that

$$\int_c f(\tau)d\tau = \int_c (udx - vdy) + j \int_c (vdx + udy). \qquad (14.2)$$

It follows immediately from this definition that, if $|f(z)| \leq M$ on the path of integration, where M is a constant, and l is the length of the path of integration, then

$$\left|\int_c f(z)dz\right| \leq Ml. \qquad (14.3)$$

If $x = x(t)$ and $y = y(t)$ along the curve for $a \leq t \leq b$, then using (14.2)

$$\left|\int_c f(z)dz\right| = \left|\int_a^b (u + jv) [x'(t) + jy'(t)]dt\right|$$

$$\leq \int_a^b M[\{x'(t)\}^2 + \{y'(t)\}^2]^{1/2} dt = Ml.$$

Here the dash refers to differentiation with respect to t.

14.3 CAUCHY'S THEOREM

The elementary proof of this important theorem requires that $f'(z)$ be assumed continuous. It was shown first by Goursat that this assumption is not necessary and that the theorem holds if it is assumed that $f'(z)$ exists at all points within and on the path of integration. Here, only the elementary proof will be given, and readers interested in the proof of the theorem under less restrictive conditions are referred to the standard texts on the theory of functions of a complex variable. The form of the result which will be proved here is as follows:

If $f(z)$ is an analytic function and if $f'(z)$ is continuous in a simply connected domain $\mathcal{D}$, then

$$\int_c f(z)\mathrm{d}z = 0 \tag{14.4}$$

on every simple closed contour C in $\mathcal{D}$.

(Here a contour is just a curve drawn in the z-plane and, if it consists of a closed loop which does not cross itself, it is termed a **simple closed contour**. Also, the interior of a simple closed curve is called a **simply connected domain** so the above theorem is to be proved for such a domain. A domain which is not simply connected is said to be multiply connected.)

Proof

Using (14.2), the integral in the theorem may be written

$$\int_c f(z)\mathrm{d}z = \int_c (u\mathrm{d}x - v\mathrm{d}y) + \mathrm{j} \int_c (v\mathrm{d}x + u\mathrm{d}y) .$$

Each integral on the right-hand side may be transformed using Green's theorem in the plane (see Chapter 10). Since

$$f'(z) = \frac{\partial u}{\partial x} + \mathrm{j}\frac{\partial v}{\partial x} = \frac{\partial v}{\partial y} - \mathrm{j}\frac{\partial u}{\partial y}$$

and $f'(z)$ is assumed continuous in $\mathcal{D}$, the conditions of Green's theorem are satisfied and

$$\int_c f(z)\mathrm{d}z = -\iint_{\mathcal{D}} \left(\frac{\partial v}{\partial x} + \frac{\partial u}{\partial y}\right)\mathrm{d}x\mathrm{d}y + \mathrm{j}\iint_{\mathcal{D}} \left(\frac{\partial u}{\partial x} - \frac{\partial v}{\partial y}\right)\mathrm{d}x\mathrm{d}y = 0$$

where the Cauchy-Riemann equations (14.1) have been used.

If the path C in the statement of Cauchy's theorem is divided into two arcs C_1 and C_2 then (14.4) takes the form

$$\int_c f(z)\mathrm{d}z = \int_{C_1} f(z)\mathrm{d}z + \int_{C_2} f(z)\mathrm{d}z = 0$$

and, if the sense of integration along C_2 is reversed, so that the situation is as shown in Fig. 14.1., this equation becomes

$$\int_{C_1} f(z)dz = \int_{C_2} f(z)dz$$

where C_2' is the same path as C_2 but taken in the opposite sense. Hence, if $f(z)$ is analytic in a domain and C_1, C_2' are any paths in that domain joining two points in the domain, this equation holds. The result holds also if C_1 and C_2' have a finite number of points in common as is seen by applying the result to the portions of C_1 and C_2' between each pair of consecutive points of intersection. Actually, although the proof will not be included here, the result holds for any paths completely in the given domain where $f(z)$ is analytic and joining any points z_1 and z_2 in that domain. Hence the integral of $f(z)$ from z_1 to z_2 is independent of the path of integration in the domain, although it will depend on z_1 and z_2.

The path of integration C_2' might be imagined to have been obtained from C_1 by a continuous deformation (see Fig. 14.2). Hence, for a given integral, a continuous deformation may be imposed on the path of integration, keeping the end-points fixed, and provided a point where $f(z)$ is not analytic is not encountered, the value of the integral will not change. This is termed the principle of **deformation of path**.

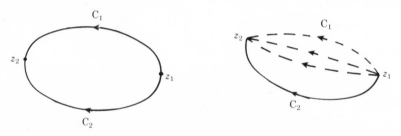

Fig. 14.1.   Fig. 14.2.

The discussion so far has been restricted to simply connected domains but a multiply connected domain may be cut so that the resulting domain is simply connected. Consider the doubly connected domain shown in Fig. 14.3. Here one cut, I, is needed to make the resulting domain simply connected.

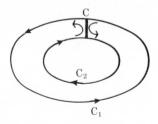

Fig. 14.3.

If the function $f(z)$ is analytic in the given domain and at each point of C_1 and C_2 then, since C_1, I, C_2 bound a simply connected region, Cauchy's theorem shows that the integral of $f(z)$ taken over C_1, I, C_2 in the sense indicated in Fig. 14.3 is zero. Since integration along I is performed in both directions, the corresponding integrals cancel, and the final result is

$$\int_{C_1} f(z)dz + \int_{C_2} f(z)dz = 0$$

where, as shown, the curves C_1 and C_2 are traversed in opposite directions.

For more complicated domains, more than one cut may be needed but the basic idea remains the same.

14.4 CAUCHY'S INTEGRAL

This integral is one of the basic results in the complex integral calculus. Suppose a function $f(z)$ is analytic in a simply connected domain $\mathcal{D}$ and on its boundary C. Also suppose z_0 is a point within C. Then

$$f(z_0) = \frac{1}{2\pi j} \int_c \frac{f(z)dz}{z - z_0}. \tag{14.5}$$

About the point $z = z_0$ describe a small circle γ of radius ε lying entirely inside C. In the region between C and γ, the function $f(z)/(z - z_0)$ is analytic. However, this region is not simply connected but, by making a cut joining any point of γ with any point of C, the region becomes simply connected and so, by Cauchy's theorem

$$\int_C \frac{f(z)dz}{z - z_0} - \int_\gamma \frac{f(z)dz}{z - z_0} = 0.$$

But

$$\int_\gamma \frac{f(z)dz}{z - z_0} = \int_\gamma \frac{f(z_0)dz}{z - z_0} + \int_\gamma \frac{f(z) - f(z_0)}{z - z_0} dz.$$

By (14.3), since $\lim_{z \to z_0} [f(z) - f(z_0)]/(z - z_0) = f'(z_0)$ for z near z_0,

$$\left| \frac{f(z) - f(z_0)}{z - z_0} \right| \leqslant M \quad \text{and so} \quad \left| \int_\gamma \frac{f(z) - f(z_0)}{z - z_0} dz \right| \leqslant M \cdot 2\pi\varepsilon.$$

As $\varepsilon \to 0$, the contribution of this integral tends to zero.

Also, on γ, $z - z_0 = \varepsilon e^{j\theta}$ and so

$$\int_\gamma \frac{f(z_0)dz}{z - z_0} = f(z_0) \int_0^{2\pi} \frac{\varepsilon j e^{j\theta}}{\varepsilon e^{j\theta}} d\theta = 2\pi j f(z_0).$$

Hence,

$$\int_C \frac{f(z)dz}{z - z_0} = 2\pi j f(z_0).$$

One useful consequence of this result is that, if $f(z)$ is analytic in a domain $\mathscr{D}$, its derivative is given by

$$f'(z_0) = \frac{1}{2\pi j}\int_C \frac{f(z)dz}{(z - z_0)^2}$$

where C is any simple closed contour in $\mathscr{D}$ surrounding the point $z = z_0$.

Using (14.5), it is seen that

$$\frac{f(z_0 + \delta z_0) - f(z_0)}{\delta z_0} = \frac{1}{2\pi j}\int_C \frac{f(z)dz}{(z - z_0)(z - z_0 - \delta z_0)}.$$

Now let $\delta z_0 \to 0$. The integrand is finite everywhere on the contour C and so

$$f'(z_0) = \frac{1}{2\pi j}\int_C \frac{f(z)dz}{(z - z_0)^2}.$$

Hence, it has been shown that (14.5) may be differentiated with respect to the parameter z_0 to give $f'(z_0)$. If the process is repeated again and again, the formula

$$f^{(n)}(z_0) = \frac{n!}{2\pi j}\int_C \frac{f(z)dz}{(z - z_0)^{n+1}} \tag{14.6}$$

for the nth derivative of $f(z)$ at an interior point of the domain $\mathscr{D}$ in which $f(z)$ is analytic, is established.

14.5 POWER SERIES

In Chapter 4, it was noted that, owing to their properties, power series appeared as somewhat special types of infinite series. Here it is proposed to extend the discussion of Chapter 4 to cover power series with complex terms. Hence, consider the function $f(z)$ defined as an infinite series in z with complex coefficients:

$$f(z) = \sum_{r=0}^{\infty} a_r z^r.$$

The main result for such power series is the same as the corresponding one for real power series, that is, if the power series has a radius of convergence ρ then it is absolutely convergent for $|z| < \rho$ and, further, it is uniformly convergent within the circle $|z| \leq q\rho$ where q is a positive number less than 1.

As with real power series, one important consequence of this result is that a complex power series may be differentiated (or integrated) term by term and, in each case, the resulting series will be another power series with the same radius of convergence as the original series. Hence, the new power series may be differentiated (or integrated) once again and, indeed, the process may be repeated as often as required. The end result is that a power series may be differentiated (or integrated) as often as required within its circle of convergence.

The proofs of these results follow the same pattern as those given for real power series in Chapter 4.

Cauchy's Integral (14.5) has many applications, and one of the most important is to show that, if the function $f(z)$ is analytic within and on the circle $|z - z_0| \leqslant \rho$ and if ζ is a point such that $|\zeta - z_0| = \rho_1(<\rho)$ then

$$f(\zeta) = \sum_{n=0}^{\infty} a_n(\zeta - z_0)^n$$

where $a_n = f^{(n)}(z_0)/n!$

Consider the identity

$$\frac{1}{z - \zeta} = \frac{1}{z - z_0} + \frac{\zeta - z_0}{(z - z_0)^2} + \cdots + \frac{(\zeta - z_0)^{n-1}}{(z - z_0)^n} + \frac{(\zeta - z_0)^n}{(z - z_0)^n} \frac{1}{(z - \zeta)}.$$

Multiply each term by $f(z)/2\pi j$ and integrate around the contour C, where C is a circle of radius ρ', centre $z = z_0$, where $\rho_1 < \rho' < \rho$. Using (14.5) and (14.6), this yields

$$f(\zeta) = f(z_0) + (\zeta - z_0)f'(z_0) + \cdots + \frac{(\zeta - z_0)^{n-1}}{(n-1)!} f^{(n-1)}(z_0) + R_n$$

where

$$R_n = \frac{(\zeta - z_0)^n}{2\pi j} \int_C \frac{f(z)dz}{(z - z_0)^n(z - \zeta)}.$$

This is actually Taylor's series with remainder for a function of a complex variable.

Also, if $|f(z)| \leqslant M$ on C then it follows that

$$|R_n| \leqslant \frac{\rho_1{}^n}{2\pi} \frac{2\pi\rho'M}{\rho'^n(\rho' - \rho_1)} = K\left(\frac{\rho_1}{\rho'}\right)^n$$

where K is a constant independent of n. Since $\rho_1 < \rho'$, it follows that $|R_n| \to 0$ as $n \to \infty$. Hence the required result that the series $\sum_{n=0}^{\infty} a_n(\zeta - z_0)^n$, where $a_n = f^{(n)}(z_0)/n!$, converges to the sum $f(\zeta)$.

14.6 ZEROS, POLES AND RESIDUES OF AN ANALYTIC FUNCTION

If the analytic function $f(z)$ vanishes at some point $z = z_0$, the constant term in the Taylor series of the function in powers of $(z - z_0)$,

$$f(z) = f(z_0) + (z - z_0)f'(z_0) + \cdots$$

vanishes. It is possible that further terms in this series vanish also in which case a factor $(z - z_0)^n$ may be removed from the power series, and it may be written

$$f(z) = (z - z_0)^n g(z)$$

where $g(z_0) \neq 0$. A point z_0 for which this occurs is called a **zero of order** n of the function $f(z)$.

It is quite straightforward to show that, if $f(z)$ is an analytic function, its reciprocal $1/f(z) = \phi(z)$ is analytic also, except at those points for which $f(z)$ is zero. If z_0 is a zero of order n of $f(z)$ then, in the neighbourhood of z_0, the function $\phi(z)$ may be represented by

$$\phi(z) = \frac{1}{(z - z_0)^n} \frac{1}{g(z)} = \frac{1}{(z - z_0)^n} \psi(z),$$

where $\psi(z)$ is analytic in the neighbourhood of $z = z_0$. However, at the point $z = z_0$, the function $\phi(z)$ ceases to be analytic, and this point is called a **singularity** which, in this case, is a **pole of order** n of the function $\phi(z)$ since $\phi(z)$ is infinite at the point $z = z_0$.

Since the function $\psi(z)$ is analytic in the neighbourhood of $z = z_0$, it may be expanded in powers of $(z - z_0)$. If this is done and the result divided term by term by $(z - z_0)^n$ then, in the neighbourhood of the pole

$$\phi(z) = b_n(z - z_0)^{-n} + \cdots + b_1(z - z_0)^{-1} + a_0 + a_1(z - z_0) + \cdots \quad (14.7)$$

where $b_n, \ldots, b_1, a_0, a_1, \ldots$ denote the coefficients of powers of $(z - z_0)$.

If the pole under consideration is of the first order, the relation

$$b_1 = \lim_{z \to z_0} \{(z - z_0)\phi(z)\}$$

immediately gives the coefficient b_1. Again

$$\frac{1}{(z - z_0)\phi(z)} = \frac{f(z)}{(z - z_0)} = \frac{f(z) - f(z_0)}{(z - z_0)}$$

and so, $$b_1 = 1/f'(z_0).$$

Similarly, if $\phi(z) = p(z)/q(z)$ and $q(z)$ has a first-order zero at $z = z_0$, but $p(z_0) \neq 0$, then

$$b_1 = p(z_0)/q'(z_0).$$

If a function is defined and analytic everywhere in the neighbourhood of a point z_0 but not at the point itself, its integral around a complete circle enclosing the point z_0 will not be zero in general. It is possible to evaluate integrals around contours which encircle poles of arbitrary order by using equation (14.6) since, if $\psi(z)$ is analytic in a simply connected domain $\mathcal{D}$ and on its boundary C,

$$\int_c \frac{\psi(z)dz}{(z - z_0)^n} = 2\pi j\, R(z_0) \qquad (14.8)$$

where $R(z_0) = \psi^{(n-1)}(z_0)/(n - 1)!$ is called the **residue** of $\psi(z)/(z - z_0)^n$ at $z = z_0$. For a first-order pole $n = 1$ and the residue of $\psi(z)/(z - z_0)$ is simply $\psi(z_0)$. In the notation used above

$$\psi(z_0) = \lim_{z \to z_0} \{(z - z_0)\phi(z)\} = b_1$$

and so, if the function to be integrated around the contour C is of the form $\phi(z) = p(z)/q(z)$ where $q(z)$ has a first-order zero at $z = z_0$ but $p(z_0) \neq 0$, the residue of $\phi(z)$ at $z = z_0$ is $p(z_0)/q'(z_0)$.

Consider the following examples of the evaluation of residues at first order poles:

(i) If $\phi(z) = z/(1 - \cos z)$, there is a pole at $z = 0$. Also $\phi(z)$ is of the form $p(z)/q(z)$ but, at $z = 0$, $p(z)$ is zero. Hence, the residue is found by looking at $\lim_{z \to 0} \{z\phi(z)\}$; that is,

$$\lim_{z \to 0} \frac{z^2}{1 - \cos z} = \lim_{z \to 0} \frac{z^2}{2\sin^2(z/2)} = 2 .$$

(ii) If $\phi(z) = (4 - 3z)/(z^2 - z)$, there are first-order poles at $z = 0$ and $z = 1$. Also, $\phi(z)$ is the form $p(z)/q(z)$ with $p(z)$ being non-zero at both poles. Hence, the residue at each pole is found by looking at $p(z)/q'(z)$.

At $z = 0$, the residue is

$$\left[\frac{4 - 3z}{2z - 1}\right]_{z=0} = -4 .$$

At $z = 1$, the residue is

$$\left[\frac{4 - 3z}{2z - 1}\right]_{z=1} = 1 .$$

Note that these two results also follow easily from the expression $\lim_{z \to z_0}\{(z - z_0)\phi(z)\}$ for the residue of $\phi(z)$ at the simple pole at $z = z_0$.

If a function $\phi(z)$ has a pole of higher order than the first at $z = z_0$, the residue is more difficult to evaluate in general. Suppose the pole in question is of order n, then the expansion of $\phi(z)$ in powers of $(z - z_0)$ is given by (14.7), and if this is integrated around a small circle C with centre at $z = z_0$, the integral of the series with positive indices is zero as this power series is still analytic at $z = z_0$. The term $b_1(z - z_0)^{-1}$ gives $2\pi j b_1$ when integrated, but the terms with higher negative indices give zero since, for $v > 1$, $(z - z_0)^{-v} =$ $(d/dz)\{(z - z_0)^{-v+1}/(1 - v\}$ which leads to $\int_c (z - z_0)^{-v} dz = 0$ for $v > 1$. Hence, the required residue is given by b_1, the coefficient of $(z - z_0)^{-1}$ in (14.7) once again.

Also, if z_0 is a pole of order n of the functions $\phi(z)$, the residue of $\phi(z)$ at $z = z_0$ is given by

$$\lim_{z \to z_0} \frac{1}{(n - 1)!} \frac{d^{n-1}}{dz^{n-1}} \{(z - z_0)^n \phi(z)\} .$$

This follows directly since, from (14.7)

$$(z - z_0)^n \phi(z) = b_n + \cdots + b_1(z - z_0)^{n-1} + a_0(z - z_0)^n + a_1(z - z_0)^{n+1} + \cdots$$

and so

$$\frac{d^{n-1}}{dz^{n-1}} \{(z - z_0)^n \phi(z)\} = (n - 1)! b_1 + n! a_0(z - z_0) + \cdots$$

from which the required result follows.

The following examples will illustrate the use of this result:

(i) If $\phi(z) = [(z + 1)/(z - 1)]^2$, there is a second-order pole at $z = 1$. Accordingly the residue of $\phi(z)$ at $z = 1$ is

$$\lim_{z \to 1} \frac{d}{dz} \left\{ (z - 1)^2 \left(\frac{z + 1}{z - 1} \right)^2 \right\} = \lim_{z \to 1} (2z + 2) = 4 .$$

(ii) If $\phi(z) = (z^2 - 1)^{-2}$, there are two second-order poles, one at $z = 1$, the other at $z = -1$. The residue of $\phi(z)$ at $z = 1$ is

$$\lim_{z \to 1} \frac{d}{dz} \{(z - 1)^2 (z^2 - 1)^{-2}\} = \lim_{z \to 1} \{- 2 (z + 1)^{-3}\} = - \frac{1}{4} .$$

The residue of $\phi(z)$ at $z = -1$ is

$$\lim_{z \to -1} \frac{d}{dz} \{(z + 1)^2 (z^2 - 1)^{-2}\} = \lim_{z \to -1} \{- 2(z - 1)^{-3}\} = \frac{1}{4} .$$

There are occasions when the techniques for evaluating residues illustrated in the above examples are either not applicable or the calculations become difficult. In cases such as these, it is necessary to find the relevant part of the expansion (14.7) for the function $\phi(z)$; it should be noted that all that is required is the coefficient of $(z - z_0)^{-1}$, that is b_1, in this expansion. This method will be illustrated by the following examples.

(i) If $\phi(z) = z^{-2} \cot z$, there is a pole at $z = 0$. Now using the Taylor series expansions for $\cos z$ and $\sin z$,

$$\frac{\cot z}{z^2} = \frac{\cos z}{z^2 \sin z} = \frac{(1 - \frac{1}{2}z^2 + \cdots)}{z^3(1 - \frac{1}{6}z^2 + \cdots)} = z^{-3}(1 - \frac{1}{2}z^2 + \cdots)(1 + \frac{1}{6}z^2 \cdots)$$

and the coefficient of z^{-1} in this expansion, and hence the residue of $\phi(z)$ at $z = 0$, is seen to be $-\frac{1}{3}$.

(ii) If $\phi(z) = e^{jkz}(a^2 + z^2)^{-2}$, there is a pole at $z = ja$ and the residue of $\phi(z)$ at this pole may be determined by expanding $\phi(z)$ in powers of $z_1 = z - ja$. This gives

$$\frac{e^{jk(z_1 + ja)}}{z_1^2(z_1 + 2ja)^2} = -\frac{e^{-ka}}{4a^2 z_1^2}(1 + jkz_1 + \cdots)(1 - \frac{z_1}{ja} + \cdots) .$$

The coefficients of z_1^{-1} in this expansion, and hence the residue of $\phi(z)$ at $z = ja$, is seen to be $-je^{-ka}(1 + ka)/4a^3$.

It is possible now to evaluate contour integrals whose integrands have only one pole inside the contour of integration since the residue at the pole may be found by one of the methods discussed above and equation (14.8) may be used to evaluate the contour integral.

Examples

(i) Integrate $\phi(z) = z^{-4}\sin z$ around the unit circle C in the positive (that is, anticlockwise) sense.

The function $\phi(z)$ has a fourth-order pole at $z = 0$, and the required residue is seen to be

$$\lim_{z \to 0} \frac{1}{3!}\frac{d^3}{dz^3}(\sin z) = -\frac{1}{3!} .$$

Using (14.8) it follows that

$$\int_C z^{-4}\sin z\, dz = -\frac{1}{3}\pi j .$$

(ii) Integrate $\phi(z) = (z^2 + 1)/(z^2 - 2z)$ around the unit circle C in the positive sense.

In this case, although $\phi(z)$ has two first-order poles, one at $z = 0$ and the other at $z = 2$, only the one at $z = 0$ lies within the prescribed contour. The residue of $\phi(z)$ at $z = 0$ is seen to be $-\frac{1}{2}$ and so, using (14.8), it follows that

$$\int_C \frac{z^2 + 1}{z^2 - 2z}\, dz = -\pi j .$$

However, this method is restricted to contour integrals where the integrand has one pole only within the contour of integration. Now it is proposed to extend this simple method to the case when the integrand has several poles inside the contour.

14.7 THE RESIDUE THEOREM

If the function $f(z)$ is analytic in the interior of a domain $\mathscr{D}$ and on its boundary C, except at a finite number of poles, then

$$\int_C f(z)\mathrm{d}z = 2\pi\mathrm{j}\Sigma R_i\,,$$

where ΣR_i represents the sum of the residues of $f(z)$ at its pole within C and the integral is taken in the positive sense around C.

Proof

Let $a_1, a_2, \ldots, a_n$ be n poles within C and enclose each of these poles in a circle γ_i, centre a_i, $(i = 1, 2, \ldots, n)$, and with a radius small enough to ensure that they do not intersect and all lie within C. Then $f(z)$ is analytic in the multiply-connected domain bounded by C and $\gamma_1, \gamma_2, \ldots, \gamma_n$ as well as on the complete boundary of that domain. It follows from Cauchy's theorem that

$$\int_C f(z)\mathrm{d}z + \int_{\gamma_1} f(z)\mathrm{d}z + \int_{\gamma_2} f(z)\mathrm{d}z + \cdots + \int_{\gamma_n} f(z)\mathrm{d}z = 0$$

where the integral around C is taken in the positive sense but the other integrals in the negative sense. If the sense of integration along $\gamma_1, \gamma_2, \ldots, \gamma_n$ is reversed, the equation becomes

$$\int_C f(z)\mathrm{d}z = \int_{\gamma_1} f(z)\mathrm{d}z + \int_{\gamma_2} f(z)\mathrm{d}z + \cdots + \int_{\gamma_n} f(z)\mathrm{d}z$$

all the integrals now being taken in the positive sense.

However, using (14.8), it is seen that

$$\int_{\gamma_i} f(z)\mathrm{d}z = 2\pi\mathrm{j}\,R_i\,, i = 1, 2, \ldots, n\,,$$

where R_i is the residue of $f(z)$ at the pole $z = a_i$.

Hence,

$$\int_C f(z)\mathrm{d}z = 2\pi\mathrm{j}\Sigma R_i$$

where ΣR_i represents the sum of the residues of $f(z)$ at its poles $a_1, a_2, \ldots, a_n$.

This theorem has various applications in connection with the evaluation of both complex and real integrals. As far as complex integrals are concerned, consider the following examples:

(i) The function $\phi(z) = (4 - 3z)/(z^2 - z)$ is analytic except at $z = 0$ and $z = 1$ where it has first-order poles. As shown earlier, the residues at these poles are -4 and 1 respectively and so, if C is any simple closed contour enclosing both $z = 0$ and $z = 1$,

$$\int_C \frac{4 - 3z}{z^2 - z}\,\mathrm{d}z = 2\pi\mathrm{j}(-4 + 1) = -6\pi\mathrm{j}\,.$$

(ii) Consider the function $\phi(z) = (z^2 + 2)^3/(2z^2 - z)$ and suppose it is required to integrate $\phi(z)$ around the simple closed contour C, where C is the unit circle, in the positive sense. Now, $\phi(z)$ is analytic within and on C except at $z = 0$ and $z = \frac{1}{2}$ where it has first-order poles.

At $z = 0$, the residue is $[(z^2 + 2)^3/(4z - 1)]_{z=0} = -8$.

At $z = \frac{1}{2}$, the residue is $[(z^2 + 2)^3/(4z - 1)]_{z=\frac{1}{2}} = 729/64$.

Hence the required integral is

$$\int_C \phi(z)dz = 2\pi j \left(\frac{729}{64} - 8\right) = \frac{217}{32}\,\pi j .$$

However, possibly the most useful application of the residue theorem is concerned with the evaluation of certain classes of real integrals. In fact, it provides an elegant and simple method for evaluating these as will be seen and, in many cases, this method of integration can be made routine. At the outset, although it has been mentioned before, it is worth noting that the residue theorem applies when $f(z)$, the function to be integrated, has no singularities inside C other than poles.

Now it will be shown how the residue theorem may be used to evaluate certain classes of integrals.

14.8 INTEGRALS OF THE FORM $\int_0^{2\pi} \phi(\cos\theta, \sin\theta)d\theta$

This type of integral may be evaluated by putting $e^{j\theta} = z$ so that

$$\cos\theta = \tfrac{1}{2}(e^{j\theta} + e^{-j\theta}) = \tfrac{1}{2}(z + z^{-1})$$

$$\sin\theta = \frac{1}{2j}(e^{j\theta} - e^{-j\theta}) = \frac{1}{2j}(z - z^{-1})$$

and the integrand becomes a function of z, $f(z)$ say. Also, as θ ranges from 0 to 2π, z ranges around the unit circle in the positive (anticlockwise) sense. Again $dz/d\theta = je^{j\theta}$ and so the given integral becomes

$$\int_C f(z)\,\frac{dz}{jz}$$

where C is the unit circle.

Example

Evaluate

$$I = \int_0^{2\pi} \frac{d\theta}{5 - 3\cos\theta} .$$

Making the substitution $e^{j\theta} = z$ leads to

$$I = \frac{2}{j}\int_C \frac{dz}{-3z^2 + 10z - 3}$$

$$= -\frac{2}{j}\int_C \frac{dz}{(3z - 1)(z - 3)}$$

The integrand has first-order poles at $z = \frac{1}{3}$ and $z = 3$, but only the first of these lies inside the unit circle C. The residue at $z = \frac{1}{3}$ is seen to be

$$\lim_{z \to \frac{1}{3}} \left\{ (z - \frac{1}{3}) \frac{1}{(3z - 1)(z - 3)} \right\} = -\frac{1}{8}.$$

Then the residue theorem yields

$$\int_0^{2\pi} \frac{d\theta}{5 - 3\cos\theta} = -\frac{2}{j} 2\pi j \left(-\frac{1}{8} \right) = \frac{\pi}{2}.$$

14.9 INTEGRALS OF THE FORM $\int_{-\infty}^{\infty} f(x)dx$

Suppose the function $f(x)$ satisfies the following conditions:
(i) $f(z)$ is analytic at all points on the real axis,
(ii) $f(z)$ is meromorphic in the upper half-plane (that is, the only singularities of $f(z)$ in the upper half-plane are poles),
(iii) $zf(z) \to 0$ uniformly as $|z| \to \infty$, for $0 \le \arg z \le \pi$; and

$$\lim_{R \to \infty} \int_{-R}^{R} f(x)dx = \int_{-\infty}^{\infty} f(x)dx.$$

Now, choose as contour C a semicircle, centre the origin and radius R, in the upper half-plane, together with the range $(-R,R)$ of the real axis. If R is chosen large enough for the semicircle to enclose all the poles of $f(z)$, and if the semicircle is denoted by S, the residue theorem gives

$$\int_C f(z)dz = \int_S f(z)dz + \int_{-R}^{R} f(x)dx = 2\pi j \Sigma R^+$$

where ΣR^+ denotes the sum of residues of $f(z)$ at its poles in the upper half-plane.

From condition (iii) above, if R is large enough, $|zf(z)| < \varepsilon$ for all points on S and so

$$\left| \int_S f(z)dz \right| = \left| \int_0^{\pi} f(Re^{j\theta})jRe^{j\theta}d\theta \right| < \varepsilon \int_0^{\pi} d\theta = \pi\varepsilon.$$

Therefore, as $R \to \infty$, the integral around S tends to zero and, if the remaining part of condition (iii) is satisfied, it is seen that

$$\int_{-\infty}^{\infty} f(x)dx = 2\pi j \Sigma R^+.$$

It might be noted usefully that, if $f(z)$ is the ratio of two polynomials $n(z)/d(z)$, the final part of condition (iii) is satisfied if the degree of $d(z)$ exceeds that of $n(z)$ by at least *two*. This follows since, in this case, $f(x)$ would behave like $x^{-\nu}$, where $\nu \ge 2$, when x is large, and the integrals $\int_{-\infty}^{-a} x^{-\nu}dx, \int_b^{\infty} x^{-\nu}dx$ both exist.

Example

Evaluate

$$\int_{-\infty}^{\infty} \frac{dx}{(x^2 + a^2)(x^2 + b^2)}, \quad \text{where } a > 0 \,, b > 0 \text{ and } a \neq b \,.$$

The function $f(z) = [(z^2 + a^2)(z^2 + b^2)]^{-1}$ is seen to satisfy the conditions laid down above, and the only singularities it possesses in the upper half-plane are poles at $z = ja$ and $z = jb$. The residue at $z = ja$ is

$$\lim_{z \to ja} \left[\frac{z - ja}{(z^2 + a^2)(z^2 + b^2)} \right] = \frac{1}{2ja \, (b^2 - a^2)}$$

and, similarly, the residue at $z = jb$ is $[2jb(a^2 - b^2)]^{-1}$. Then, by the above argument,

$$\int_{-\infty}^{\infty} \frac{dx}{(x^2 + a^2)(x^2 + b^2)} = 2\pi j\{[2ja(b^2 - a^2)]^{-1} + [2jb(a^2 - b^2)]^{-1}\}$$

$$= \frac{\pi}{ab(a + b)} \,.$$

The general result of this section may be extended to cover the case when $f(z)$ has first-order poles on the real axis. This is done by indenting the contour and making small semicircles in the upper half-plane so as to bypass the simple poles on the real axis. If $f(z)$ has only one pole on the real axis at $z = a$, say, the contour may be modfied by making a semicircle in the upper half-plane with centre at the point $x = a$ and with small radius r. Suppose this semicircle is denoted by σ then the path of integration will consist of the semicircle S as before, the portion of the real axis $(-R, a - r)$, the small semi-circle σ and a second portion of the real axis $(a + r, R)$. If this contour is described in a positive sense

$$\int_C f(z)dz = \int_S f(z)dz + \int_{-R}^{a-r} f(z)dz + \int_\sigma f(z)dz + \int_{a+R}^R f(z)dz$$

$$= 2\pi j \Sigma R^+ \,.$$

In this expression, the integral around S tends to zero as R tends to infinity as before. Next consider the integral around σ. On σ, $z = a + re^{j\theta}$ and so

$$\int_\sigma f(z)dz = \int_\pi^0 f(a + re^{j\theta})rje^{j\theta}d\theta \,.$$

But $f(z)$ contains the factor $(z - a)$ and so, $f(z) = (z - a)^{-1} g(z)$, where $g(z)$ is analytic at and near $z = a$. Hence

$$\int_\sigma f(z)\mathrm{d}z = \int_\pi^0 g(a + re^{j\theta})j\ \mathrm{d}\theta$$

$$= j \int_\pi^0 \{g(a) + \text{(terms in } r)\}\ \mathrm{d}\theta$$

where $g(a + re^{j\theta})$ has been expanded by Taylor's theorem. Hence, as $r{\to}0$,

$$\int_\sigma f(z)\mathrm{d}z \to -\pi j\ g(a)\ .$$

But $g(a)$ is the residue of $f(z)$ at $z = a$ and so the result may be written

$$\int_\sigma f(z)\mathrm{d}z \to -\pi j\ R^\circ$$

where R° is the residue of $f(z)$ at its pole on the real axis. If $f(z)$ has several first-order poles on the real axis, the right-hand side of this equation would become $(-\pi j\Sigma R^\circ)$, where ΣR° denotes the sum of the residues of $f(z)$ at its first-order poles on the real axis.

Finally note that if c, $a < c < b$, is a point for which $f(x)$ becomes infinite,

$$P \int_a^b f(x)\mathrm{d}x = \lim_{\varepsilon\to 0} \{\int_a^{c-\varepsilon} f(x)\mathrm{d}x + \int_{c+\varepsilon}^b f(x)\mathrm{d}x\}$$

defines the **principal value** of the improper integral $\int_a^b f(x)\mathrm{d}x$. Hence, in the case under consideration, as R tends to infinity

$$\int_{-R}^{a-r} f(x)\mathrm{d}x + \int_{a+r}^R f(x)\mathrm{d}x{\to}P \int_{-\infty}^\infty f(x)\mathrm{d}x\ .$$

Finally, it is seen that, if a function $f(z)$ satisfies conditions (i), (ii), (iii) except that it has poles on the real axis, then

$$P \int_{-\infty}^\infty f(x)\mathrm{d}x = 2\pi j\Sigma R^+ + \pi j\Sigma R^\circ$$

14.10 INTEGRALS OF THE FORM $\int_{-\infty}^\infty e^{jmx}f(x)\mathrm{d}x$

Integrals of this form are evaluated fairly easily by making use of a result, known as **Jordan's Lemma**, which states that, if S is a semicircle, centre the origin and radius R, and $f(z)$ is such that
(i) $f(z)$ is meromorphic in the upper half-plane,
(ii) $f(z){\to}0$ uniformly as $|z|{\to}\infty$ for $0 \leqslant \arg z \leqslant \pi$, then, if m is positive,

$$\int_S e^{jmz}f(z)\mathrm{d}z{\to}0 \quad \text{as} \quad R{\to}\infty\ .$$

The proof of this lemma is as follows:
By (ii), if R is large enough, $|f(z)| < \varepsilon$ for all points of S. Also,

$$|e^{jmz}| = |e^{jmR(\cos\theta + j\sin\theta)}| = e^{-mR\sin\theta}$$

and so

$$\left| \int_S e^{jmz} f(z)dz \right| = \left| \int_0^\pi f(z)e^{jmz} Rje^{j\theta}d\theta \right|$$

$$< \varepsilon \int_0^\pi e^{-mR\sin\theta}Rd\theta = 2\varepsilon R \int_0^{\pi/2} e^{-mR\sin\theta}d\theta \ .$$

However, as θ increases from 0 to $\pi/2$, it may be shown that $\sin\theta/\theta$ decreases from 1 to $2/\pi$ and so, if $0 \leqslant \theta \leqslant \pi/2$, $(\sin\theta/\theta) \geqslant (2/\pi)$. Hence,

$$\int_S e^{jmz} f(z)dz \leqslant 2\varepsilon R \int_0^{\pi/2} e^{-2mR\theta/\pi}d\theta < \pi\varepsilon/m \ .$$

The result of the lemma follows immediately.

We now return to integrals of the form $\int_{-\infty}^{\infty} e^{jmx} f(x)dx$. Such integrals are covered in the main by the previous section but, using Jordan's Lemma, it may be seen that, if $f(z)$ is the ratio of two polynomials $n(z)$ and $d(z)$ and $d(z)$ has no real roots then, if the degree of $d(z)$ exceeds that of $n(z)$ by at least *one*, and if m is positive,

$$\int_{-\infty}^{\infty} e^{jmx} f(x)dx = 2\pi j\Sigma R^+$$

The integrand is seen to satisfy the conditions of Jordan's Lemma, and so $\int_S e^{jmz} f(z)dz \to 0$ as $R \to \infty$. If the same contour is used as in the previous section, it follows, on letting $R \to \infty$, that

$$\int_{-\infty}^{\infty} e^{jmx} f(x)dx = 2\pi j\Sigma R^+ \ .$$

Again, if the integrand possesses first-order poles on the real axis, the result is modified, as in the previous section, to

$$P \int_{-\infty}^{\infty} e^{jmx} f(x)dx = 2\pi j\Sigma R^+ + \pi j\Sigma R^\circ \ .$$

One of the great uses of being able to evaluate integrals of the form discussed here is that, on taking real and imaginary parts of the result, it is seen that integrals of the forms

$$\int_{-\infty}^{\infty} f(x) \cos mx \, dx \quad \text{and} \quad \int_{-\infty}^{\infty} f(x) \sin mx \, dx$$

may be evaluated.

Examples

(i) Evaluate $\quad I = \int_{-\infty}^{\infty} \dfrac{xe^{jmx}}{x^2 + a^2} dx \ , \quad$ where $a > 0$ and $m > 0$.

The integrand is seen to satisfy the conditions laid down above, and the only singularity it possesses in the upper half-plane is a pole at $z = ja$ with residue

$$\lim_{z \to ja} \left[(z - ja) \frac{z\, e^{jmz}}{(z^2 + a^2)} \right] = \frac{1}{2} e^{-ma}.$$

Then, by the above argument

$$I = 2\pi j\, \tfrac{1}{2} e^{-ma} = \pi j e^{-ma}.$$

On taking real and imaginary parts of the integral I, it follows that

$$\int_{-\infty}^{\infty} \frac{x \cos mx}{(x^2 + a^2)}\, dx = 0 \;;\; \int_{-\infty}^{\infty} \frac{x \sin mx}{(x^2 + a^2)}\, dx = \pi e^{-ma}.$$

(ii) Show that $\displaystyle\int_0^{\infty} \frac{\sin mx}{x}\, dx = \frac{\pi}{2}$, where $m > 0$.

Since $\sin x/x$ does not behave suitably at infinity, it is not considered. The function e^{jmz}/z is considered instead. This latter function has no poles in the upper half-plane but does possess a simple pole at $z = 0$, that is on the real axis. The residue at this pole is seen to be unity and so, by the argument presented above,

$$P \int_{-\infty}^{\infty} \frac{e^{jmx}}{x}\, dx = \pi j.$$

On equating real and imaginary parts, it is seen that

$$P \int_{-\infty}^{\infty} \frac{\cos mx}{x}\, dx = 0 \;;\; \int_{-\infty}^{\infty} \frac{\sin mx}{x}\, dx = \pi.$$

Since $\sin mx/x \to m$ as $x \to 0$, there is no need to take the principal value in the second of these integrals. Also, since the second integral has an even function as integrand,

$$\int_0^{\infty} \frac{\sin mx}{x}\, dx = \frac{\pi}{2}.$$

In the discussion of the evaluation of integrals of the form $\int_{-\infty}^{\infty} f(x)dx$ and of the form $\int_{-\infty}^{\infty} e^{jmx} f(x)dx$ by contour integration, the contour used has consisted of a large semicircle, centre the origin and radius R, in the upper half-plane, together with the range $(-R,R)$ of the real axis. However, there is no special merit in a semicircle. All that is needed is a curve, joining the points $+R$ and $-R$, which tends to the point at infinity as $R \to \infty$. The rectangle with vertices $\pm R$, $\pm R + jR$ could have been used equally well and, indeed, in some cases may prove more convenient.

The use of this contour will be illustrated by the following example:

Evaluate $\qquad \int_0^\infty \frac{x \sin x}{x^2 + a^2} dx$, where $a > 0$.

This integral will be evaluated by considering the contour integral

$$\int_C \frac{z e^{jz} dz}{z^2 + a^2},$$

where C is the rectangular contour with vertices $\pm R$, $\pm R + jR$. The integrand is seen to satisfy the conditions necessary for the residue theorem to be applied, and the only singularity it possesses in the upper half-plane is a pole at $z = ja$ with residue

$$\lim_{z \to ja} \left[(z - ja) \frac{z e^{jz}}{(z^2 + a^2)} \right] = \frac{1}{2} e^{-a}.$$

Hence, the residue theorem yields

$$\int_C \frac{z e^{jz} dz}{z^2 + a^2} = \int_{-R}^R \frac{x e^{jx} dx}{x^2 + a^2} + \int_0^R \frac{(R + jy) e^{jR-y}}{(R + jy)^2 + a^2} j dy$$

$$- \int_{-R}^R \frac{(x + jR) e^{jx-R}}{(x + jR)^2 + a^2} dx - \int_0^R \frac{(-R + jy) e^{-jR-y}}{(-R + jy)^2 + a^2} j dy$$

$$= \pi j e^{-a}$$

It is seen that the contour integral divides up into four line integrals; the first along the real axis from $-R$ to R, and for all of this integration $y = 0$; the second from $+R$ to $+R + jR$ and for this integration only y varies, x remains constant and equal to $+R$; the third from $+R + jR$ to $-R + jR$, and for this integration only x varies, y remains constant and equal to jR; the fourth and final integral is from $-R + jR$ to $-R$, and for this integration only y varies, x remains constant and equal to $-R$.

Now $\qquad \left| \int_0^R \frac{(R + jy) e^{jR-y}}{(R + jy)^2 + a^2} j dy \right| \le \int_0^R \frac{(y^2 + R^2)^{1/2} e^{-y}}{(y^2 + R^2 - a^2)} dy$

$$\leq \frac{R\sqrt{2}}{R^2 - a^2} \int_0^R e^{-y} dy = \frac{R\sqrt{2}\,(1 - e^{-R})}{(R^2 - a^2)}$$

so that, as $R \to \infty$, both line integrals over the range 0 to R are seen to tend to zero.

Also,

$$\left| \int_{-R}^R \frac{(x + jR)e^{jx+R}}{(x + jR)^2 + a^2} dx \right| \leq \int_{-R}^R \frac{(x^2 + R^2)^{1/2} e^{-R}}{(x^2 + R^2 - a^2)} dx$$

$$\leq \frac{R\sqrt{2}}{R^2 - a^2} e^{-R} \int_{-R}^R dx = \frac{2\sqrt{2}\,R^2 e^{-R}}{R^2 - a^2}$$

which tends to zero as $R \to \infty$.

Using these three results, it follows that

$$\int_{-\infty}^{\infty} \frac{xe^{jx} dx}{x^2 + a^2} = \pi j e^{-a}\,.$$

On taking imaginary parts of this result,

$$\int_{-\infty}^{\infty} \frac{x \sin x\, dx}{x^2 + a^2} = \pi e^{-a}\,.$$

This conforms to the earlier result obtained using a semicircular contour. However, the method used in the earlier evaluation made use of Jordan's Lemma. Using the rectangular contour, it may be noted that Jordan's Lemma is not needed in the evaluation.

14.11 MANY-VALUED FUNCTIONS

So far it has been assumed, even if not stated explicitly, that the complex functions under discussion have been such that, for each value of the independent variable, the value of the function is unique. In other words, only single-valued functions have been considered. For example, Cauchy's theorem relies on the assumption that the function may be defined uniquely in the domain under consideration. However, many of the elementary functions are *not* single-valued, typical examples being $\sqrt[n]{z}$, z^α (where α is not an integer) and $\log z$.

To illustrate the idea of many-valuedness consider the case of the inverse $w = \sqrt{z}$ of the function $z = w^2$. To each value of z, two possible solutions, w and $-w$, of the equation $z = w^2$ correspond. If z is put equal to $re^{j\theta}$ then, for given r and θ ($\theta < 2\pi$), the two solutions are

$$w_1 = |\sqrt{r}|\, e^{j\theta/2} \quad \text{and} \quad w_2 = |\sqrt{r}|\, e^{j(\theta + 2\pi)/2} = -|\sqrt{r}|\, e^{j\theta/2}\,,$$

and these are the only continuous solutions for fixed θ. In the special case of a positive real z, θ is zero and the solutions are $w_1 = |\sqrt{r}|$ and $w_2 = -|\sqrt{r}|$. Here w_1 and w_2 are single-valued functions of z and are defined for all z. However, as z describes a circle of radius r about the origin, w_1 will vary continuously but its final value after completing one revolution will be $|\sqrt{r}|e^{j\pi} = -|\sqrt{r}| = w_2$. However, the function is seen to return to its original value, w_1, after two revolutions. Nevertheless, the situation after one revolution would make it appear that w_1 is discontinuous along the positive real axis. This conclusion is drawn since the values on either side of the real axis differ in sign and, except at the origin, are not zero.

Thus $w^2 = z$ defines a two-valued function of z. The two functions w_1 and w_2 are called the two **branches** of this two-valued function. It is not intended to discuss many-valuedness in any detail here, but it should be noted that each branch of the above two-valued function is a single-valued function in the z-plane provided a cut is made extending from the origin to infinity along the positive real axis. It is also important to distinguish between values of the function at points on the upper and lower edges of the cut. The cut prevents a complete circuit about the origin being made, and so, if the starting point is the value belonging to the branch w_1, it is no longer possible to change to the branch w_2. Hence w_1 and w_2 are single-valued on the cut plane.

In general, the uniqueness of the values of a function may be ensured theoretically by making cuts along appropriate lines in the z-plane. The path traced by z is not allowed to cross such a cut, and the cuts are arranged so that closed paths in the plane which lead to many-valuedness are no longer possible.

For the example considered above, it might be noticed also that the values of the two branches are exchanged only when z describes a closed path about the origin. For this reason, the point $z = 0$ is termed a **branch point** of the function $w = \sqrt{z}$.

The function $\sqrt[n]{z}$, where n is an integer, exhibits exactly the same behavior as $\sqrt{z}$ except that, in this case, each revolution multiplies the value of the function by $e^{2\pi j/n}$, and the function returns to its original value after n revolutions. The point $z = 0$ is a branch point of this function also.

Again, the function z^α, where α is not an integer, is multiplied by $e^{2\pi j\alpha}$ after each revolution, and it has $z = 0$ as a branch point. As far as the function $\log z$ is concerned, its value is increased by $2\pi j$ after each revolution around the origin. Once again the point $z = 0$ is a branch point and $\log z$ may be made single-valued by making a cut in the z-plane along the positive real axis.

In order to evaluate integrals where the integrand is a many-valued function, by contour integration, it becomes necessary to use the plane cut in the appropriate way and to indent the contour so as to bypass any branch points. This will be illustrated by the following example.

Consider an integral of the form $\int_0^x x^{\alpha-1} f(x) dx$, where α is not an integer. Since $z^{\alpha-1}$ is a many-valued function, the cut plane must be used when attempting to evaluate integrals of this type by contour integration. Also, in general, the function to be integrated has a branch point at the origin. Integrals of this type may be dealt with by taking as contour the large circle S, centre the origin and radius R; but with the plane cut along the real axis from 0 to ∞ and with the branch point at $z = 0$ enclosed by a small circle σ, centre the origin and radius τ. Now suppose $f(x)$ to be a rational function of x with no poles on the real axis. Let $\phi(z) = z^{\alpha-1} f(z)$, then if $z\phi(z) \to 0$ uniformly as $|z| \to 0$ and as $|z| \to \infty$, it is seen that
(i) on S, for large enough R, $|z\phi(z)| < \varepsilon$ and so $|\phi(z)| < \varepsilon/R$. Hence,

$$\left| \int_S \phi(z) dz \right| < \frac{\varepsilon}{R} 2\pi R = 2\pi\varepsilon$$

and the integral around S is seen to tend to zero as $R \to \infty$.
(ii) on σ, for small enough τ, $|z\phi(z)| < \varepsilon$ and so $|\phi(z)| < \varepsilon/\tau$. Hence,

$$\left| \int_\sigma \phi(z) dz \right| < \frac{\varepsilon}{\tau} 2\pi\tau = 2\pi\varepsilon$$

and the integral around σ is seen to tend to zero as $\tau \to 0$.

Thus, letter $R \to \infty$ and $\tau \to 0$ leads to

$$\int_0^\infty x^{\alpha-1} f(x) dx + \int_\infty^0 (xe^{2\pi j})^{\alpha-1} f(x) dx = 2\pi j \Sigma R^*$$

where ΣR^* denotes the sum of the residues of $f(z)$ at its poles within the contour. It is important to note that the values of $x^{\alpha-1}$ are not the same for points on the upper and lower edges of the cut. This is seen most easily by writing $z = re^{j\theta}$ so that $z^{\alpha-1} = r^{\alpha-1} e^{j\theta(\alpha-1)}$. For values of z on the upper edge of the cut, $|z| = r$ and $\theta = 0$ but, on the lower edge, $|z| = r$ once again but $\theta = 2\pi$. Hence the above result, which has been arrived at by using the residue theorem. Finally, since $e^{2\pi j(\alpha-1)} = e^{2\pi j\alpha}$, the result may be written

$$\int_0^\infty x^{\alpha-1} f(x) dx = \frac{2\pi j \Sigma R^*}{1 - e^{2\pi j\alpha}}$$

It might be noted that this integral might have been evaluated by integrating the function $z^{\alpha-1} f(-z)$ around a contour consisting of a large semicircle in the upper half-plane and the real axis indented at any branch points and poles that may occur. In this case, the cut plane is unnecessary. However, the contribution of the real axis to this contour integral is

$$\int_\tau^R x^{\alpha-1} f(-x) dx + \int_R^\tau (re^{\pi j})^{\alpha-1} f(-re^{\pi j}) e^{\pi j} dr$$

$$= \int_\tau^R x^{\alpha-1} f(-x)dx - e^{\pi j \alpha} \int_\tau^R r^{\alpha-1} f(r)dr \,,$$

since, when z reaches the negative part of the real axis in traversing the specified contour, arg z has increased to π.

To take a specific example, suppose it is required to show that, for $0 < \alpha < 1$,

$$\int_0^\infty \frac{x^{\alpha-1}dx}{1+x} = \frac{\pi}{\sin\alpha\pi} \,.$$

To evaluate this integral by the method outlined above, consider

$$\int \frac{z^{\alpha-1}dz}{1+z}$$

taken around the contour consisting of the large circle S but with the plane cut along the real axis from 0 to ∞ and with the branch point at $z = 0$ enclosed by the small circle σ. All the conditions of the above theory are satisfied, and the integrand has only one pole inside the contour, at $z = -1$, with residue $(-1)^{\alpha-1} = -e^{\pi j \alpha}$.

Hence

$$\int_0^\infty \frac{x^{\alpha-1}dx}{1+x} = -2\pi j \left\{ \frac{e^{\pi j \alpha}}{1 - e^{2\pi j \alpha}} \right\} = \frac{\pi}{\sin\alpha\pi} \,.$$

As indicated above, this integral may be evaluated also by considering

$$\int \frac{z^{\alpha-1}dz}{1-z}$$

taken around the contour consisting of a large semicircle S in the upper half-plane and the real axis indented at the branch point $z = 0$ and the pole $z = 1$. Since the integrand is analytic within and on this contour the residue theorem may be applied. The integrals around both the large semicircle S and the indentation enclosing the branch point are seen to be zero, but the integral around the indentation at $z = 1$ is seen to have the value πj in the limit of zero radius for the indentation. Hence, the residue theorem yields

$$P\int_0^\infty \frac{x^{\alpha-1}dx}{1-x} - e^{\pi j \alpha} \int_0^\infty \frac{x^{\alpha-1}dx}{1+x} + \pi j = 0 \,,$$

the first integral being a principal value with respect to the singularity at $x = 1$. Equating real and imaginary parts leads to

$$\sin\alpha\pi \int_0^\infty \frac{x^{\alpha-1}dx}{1+x} = \pi$$

as before, and

$$P\int_0^\infty \frac{x^{\alpha-1}dx}{1-x} = \cos\alpha\pi \int_0^\infty \frac{x^{\alpha-1}dx}{1+x} = \pi\cot\alpha\pi .$$

EXERCISES 14

(1) Determine the residues of the following functions at their poles:

$$\frac{4}{1-z}, \quad \frac{z}{(z-a)(z-b)(z-c)}, \quad \frac{3e^z}{z^4}, \quad \frac{4z-1}{z^2+3z+2},$$

$$\frac{1}{z^2(z-1)}, \quad \cot z, \quad \frac{e^{\frac{1}{2}}}{z^2}, \quad \frac{e^z}{(z^2+2z+2)^3}.$$

(2) If C is the unit circle, evaluate the following integrals using the residue theorem:

$$\int_C \frac{dz}{1+4z^2}, \quad \int_C \tan\pi z \, dz, \quad \int_C \frac{e^z}{\cos\pi z} \, dz, \quad \int_C \frac{(z+4)^3 dz}{z^4+5z^3+6z^2}.$$

(3) Using contour integration, evaluate the following integrals:

$$\int_0^{2\pi} \frac{d\theta}{1-2p\cos\theta+p^2}, \quad \text{where } 0<p<1 ; \quad \int_0^{2\pi} \frac{d\theta}{5+3\sin\theta} ;$$

$$\int_{-\infty}^\infty \frac{x^2 dx}{(x^2+1)^2(x^2+2x+2)} \quad ; \quad \int_0^\infty \frac{dx}{1+x^4} ;$$

$$\int_{-\infty}^\infty \frac{\cos ax}{(x^2+b^2)} \, dx, \quad \text{where } a>0, b>0 ; \quad \int_0^\infty \frac{\cos mx}{x^2+1} \, dx, \quad \text{where } m>0 .$$

(4) Show that
$$\int_{-\infty}^\infty \frac{\cos x \, dx}{(x^2+a^2)(x^2+b^2)} = \frac{\pi}{(a^2-b^2)} \left\{ \frac{e^{-b}}{b} - \frac{e^{-a}}{a} \right\} .$$

(5) By evaluating $\displaystyle\int_C \frac{z dz}{\cosh z - \cos\alpha}$, where C is the contour con-

sisting of the rectangle with vertices $\pm R$ and $\pm R + 2\pi j$, show that, if $0 < \alpha < \pi/2$,

$$\int_{-\infty}^{\infty} \frac{dx}{\cosh x - \cos \alpha} = \frac{2(\pi - \alpha)}{\sin \alpha}.$$

(6) Show that

$$\int_{-\infty}^{\infty} \frac{x^6 dx}{(x^4 + a^4)^2} = \frac{3\sqrt{2}\pi}{8a}, \quad \text{where } a > 0.$$

(7) Show that

$$\int_{-\infty}^{\infty} \frac{x^2 - x + 2}{x^4 + 10x^2 + 9} dx = \frac{5\pi}{12}.$$

(8) Show that

$$P \int_{-\infty}^{\infty} \frac{dx}{(x + 1)(x^2 + 2)} = \frac{\pi\sqrt{2}}{6}.$$

(9) By integrating $e^{jz} z^{\alpha - 1}$ around a quadrant of a circle of radius R, prove that

$$\int_0^{\infty} x^{\alpha - 1} \cos x \, dx = \Gamma(\alpha) \cos(\pi\alpha/2) \,; \int_0^{\infty} x^{\alpha - 1} \sin x \, dx = \Gamma(\alpha) \sin(\pi\alpha/2)$$

where $0 < \alpha < 1$.

(10) By evaluating

$$\int_C \frac{e^{az}}{\cosh \pi z} dz, \quad \text{where C is the rectangular}$$

contour with vertices $\pm R$ and $\pm R + j$, show that, if $-\pi < a < \pi$,

$$\int_0^{\infty} \frac{\cosh ax}{\cosh \pi x} dx = \frac{1}{2} \sec \left(\frac{a}{2} \right).$$

(11) Show that

$$\int_0^{\infty} \frac{\log x}{(1 + x^2)^2} dx = -\frac{\pi}{4} \quad \text{and} \quad \int_0^{\infty} \frac{dx}{(1 + x^2)^2} = \frac{\pi}{4}.$$

Chapter 15
Tensors

15.1 BASIC CONCEPTS

The concept of a tensor originated in developments in differential geometry due to Gauss, Riemann, and Christoffel. However, it has proved an extremely important tool for modern theoretical physics and emerged as ideal for the presentation of Einstein's General Theory of Relativity. The somewhat specialised Cartesian tensors are found useful in various branches of continuum mechanics. For these reasons, a brief introduction to tensors will be given in this chapter with special mention of Cartesian tensors at the end.

Consider an n-dimensional space and suppose $(x^1, x^2, \ldots, x^n)$ are the coordinates of a point in the space. Suppose also that coordinate systems are defined so that the coordinates of one system (say $x^{i'}$, $i = 1, 2, \ldots, n$) are continuous functions of the coordinates of any other system (say x^i, $i = 1, 2, \ldots, n$) with the partial derivatives, $\partial x^{i'}/\partial x^j$ $(i,j = 1, \ldots, n)$ continuous and the Jacobian determinant formed from those partial derivatives non-zero. Then, in an obvious notion

$$x^{i'} = x^{i'}(x^1, x^2, \ldots, x^n) \quad , \quad i = 1, 2, \ldots, n \, .$$

The non-vanishing of the Jacobian implies that the transformation of coordinates is invertible, and so

$$x^i = x^i(x^{1'}, x^{2'}, \ldots, x^{n'}) \quad , \quad i = 1, 2, \ldots, n \, .$$

Again

$$\mathrm{d}x^{i'} = \sum_{r=1}^{n} \frac{\partial x^{i'}}{\partial x^r} \mathrm{d}x^r \quad , \quad 1 \leq i \leq n$$

or, using summation and range conventions analogous to those introduced in Chapter 6,

$$\mathrm{d}x^{i'} = \frac{\partial x^{i'}}{\partial x^r} \mathrm{d}x^r \, ,$$

where the free index i may take the values $1, 2, \ldots, n$ and the dummy index r is summed from 1 to n.

15.2 CONTRAVARIANT VECTORS AND TENSORS

Consider the points P and Q with coordinates x^r and $x^r + dx^r$ respectively. These points define an infinitesimal displacement vector $\overrightarrow{PQ}$ with the components dx^r. As has been seen already, in another coordinate system

$$dx^{r'} = \frac{\partial x^{r'}}{\partial x^s} dx^s ,$$

where $(\partial x^{r'} / \partial x^s)$ is evaluated at the point P.

The components of the displacement vector will be different in different coordinate systems, but $\overrightarrow{PQ}$ has an absolute meaning. This displacement vector is the prototype for a class of geometrical objects called **contravariant vectors**.

A set of quantities T^r, associated with a point P, is said to be the components of a contravariant vector if each of the quantities transforms on change of the coordinate system according to

$$T^{r'} = \frac{\partial x^{r'}}{\partial x^s} T^s . \tag{15.1}$$

Now introduce the Kronecker delta defined by

$$\delta^k_{\ j} = \begin{cases} 1 & \text{if } k = j \\ 0 & \text{if } k \neq j . \end{cases}$$

An obvious property of the Kronecker delta is that $\delta^k_{\ j} A^j = A^k$, since the only surviving term on the left-hand side of this equation is the one for which $k = j$. Also, since the coordinates x^i are independent, $\partial x^k / \partial x^j = \delta^k_{\ j}$. Again, it may be shown that

$$\delta^i_{\ j} \delta^j_{\ k} = \delta^i_{\ k} , \ \delta^i_{\ i} = n , \ \frac{\partial x^k}{\partial x^{i'}} \frac{\partial x^{i'}}{\partial x^j} = \delta^k_{\ j} .$$

Returning to equation (15.1) and multiplying throughout by $\partial x^k / \partial x^{r'}$ gives

$$\frac{\partial x^k}{\partial x^{r'}} T^{r'} = \frac{\partial x^k}{\partial x^{r'}} \frac{\partial x^{r'}}{\partial x^s} T^s = \delta^k_{\ s} T^s = T^k$$

and so, the solution of (15.1) is

$$T^k = \frac{\partial x^k}{\partial x^{r'}} T^{r'} .$$

Furthermore, the quantities T^{rs} are the components of a contravariant second-order tensor if they transform, according to

$$T^{rs'} = \frac{\partial x^{r'}}{\partial x^m} \frac{\partial x^{s'}}{\partial x^n} T^{mn} .$$

It follows that a contravariant vector might be termed a contravariant first order tensor.

A quantity ϕ, defined at some point of the space, is called an **invariant** (or a **scalar**) if it has the same value in all coordinate systems; that is, it remains unchanged on transformation so that $\phi' = \phi$.

15.3 COVARIANT VECTORS AND TENSORS; MIXED TENSORS
Consider the invariant ϕ, then

$$\frac{\partial \phi}{\partial x^{r'}} = \frac{\partial x^s}{\partial x^{r'}} \frac{\partial \phi}{\partial x^s} .$$

The gradient of the scalar field ϕ, $(\partial \phi/\partial x^s)$, is then the prototype of the **covariant vectors**.

A set of quantities T_r is the components of a covariant vector if each transforms according to

$$T_r{}' = \frac{\partial x^s}{\partial x^{r'}} T_s .$$

Similarly, the quantities T_{rs} are the components of a covariant second-order tensor if they transform according to

$$T_{rs}{}' = \frac{\partial x^m}{\partial x^{r'}} \frac{\partial x^n}{\partial x^{s'}} T_{mn} .$$

Furthermore, consider the n^2 functions $T^r{}_s$ whose transformation law is

$$T^r{}_s{}' = \frac{\partial x^{r'}}{\partial x^m} \frac{\partial x^n}{\partial x^{s'}} T^m{}_n .$$

In this case, the quantities $T^r{}_s$ are the components of a mixed tensor of second order.

It may be noted that the indices are placed on tensors as superscripts when they denote contravariance and as subscripts when they denote covariance. However, the notation used so far proves cumbersome for higher-order tensors. This may be overcome by denoting only the number of indices appearing on the tensor, and this is achieved by introducing a collective index. Thus, $T^{i_1 \ldots i_p}{}_{j_1 \ldots j_q}$ is denoted by $T^{(p)}{}_{(q)}$ and the tensor transformation law may be written symbolically as

$$T^{(p)}{}_{(q)}{}' = \frac{\partial x^{(p)}{}'}{\partial x^{(r)}} \frac{\partial x^{(s)}}{\partial x^{(q)}{}'} T^{(r)}{}_{(s)} \, . \tag{15.2}$$

Using the transformation law in this form, it is straightforward to show that:
(i) the sum of two tensors of equal rank, defined by adding corresponding components, is itself a tensor. (Here the rank of a tensor, $T^{(p)}{}_{(q)}$ is denoted by p/q);
(ii) the product of two tensors of ranks p/q and m/n, defined by multiplying component by component, is a tensor of rank $(p + m)/(q + n)$.

15.4 FURTHER PROPERTIES OF TENSORS

The order of indices on a tensor is important; T^{ij} is not necessarily the same as T^{ji}. However, if $T^{ij} = T^{ji}$ that tensor is said to be **symmetric**. If, on the other hand, $T^{ij} = -T^{ji}$ that tensor is said to be **skew-symmetric** or **anti-symmetric**. The identity

$$T^{ij} = \tfrac{1}{2}(T^{ij} + T^{ji}) + \tfrac{1}{2}(T^{ij} - T^{ji})$$

shows that any contravariant second-order tensor may be written as the sum of two tensors, one of which is symmetric and the other skew-symmetric.

For a symmetric second-order tensor, there are $\tfrac{1}{2}n(n + 1)$ independent components; whereas, for a skew-symmetric second-order tensor, there are $\tfrac{1}{2}n(n - 1)$ independent components. The second result follows since all the quantities T^{ii} (no summation here) must be zero to satisfy the property $T^{ii} = -T^{ii}$.

Now consider the mixed tensor $T^{m}{}_{nrs}$ and form the sum $T^{m}{}_{mrs}$. Using (15.2) gives

$$T^{m}{}_{mrs}{}' = \frac{\partial x^{m}{}'}{\partial x^{p}} \frac{\partial x^{q}}{\partial x^{m}{}'} \frac{\partial x^{t}}{\partial x^{r}{}'} \frac{\partial x^{u}}{\partial x^{s}{}'} T^{p}{}_{qtu}$$

$$= \delta^{q}{}_{p} \frac{\partial x^{t}}{\partial x^{r}{}'} \frac{\partial x^{u}}{\partial x^{s}{}'} T^{p}{}_{qtu}$$

$$= \frac{\partial x^{t}}{\partial x^{r}{}'} \frac{\partial x^{u}}{\partial x^{s}{}'} T^{q}{}_{qtu} \, .$$

Thus, $T^{m}{}_{mrs}$ is seen to be a tensor of type A_{rs}; that is, a covariant second-order tensor. It is reasonable to write $T^{m}{}_{mrs} = T_{rs}$.

This process of summing over two indices (one a superscript, the other a subscript) of a tensor is called **contraction**. Note that, if $T^{i}{}_{j}$ is a tensor, $T^{i}{}_{i}$ is an invariant called the **trace** of $T^{i}{}_{j}$.

Using the results concerning the sum and product of two tensors, together with the idea of contraction, allows new tensors to be formed from given ones. Also, once the concept of the zero tensor has been established, tensor equations may be written.

A tensor is defined to be zero (that is, the **zero tensor**) if all its components are zero. Also, it is seen from equation (15.2) that the components of a tensor in one coordinate system are homogeneous linear combinations of the components in any other system. It follows that, if all the components are zero in one system, they will be zero in any other system. Hence, if a tensor is zero in one coordinate system, it is zero in all coordinate systems. It follows that any physical law which may be written by equating the components of a given tensor to zero is independent of the coordinate sytem. This is, quite obviously, an extremely important result.

Three points concerning tensor indices should be noted:

(i) a free index appearing in one term of a sum of tensors must appear in the same position in every other term of the sum,

(ii) only indices of different type may be contracted,

(iii) no index may appear more than twice in a product of terms.

15.5 TENSOR DETECTION

On occasions it is necessary to decide whether or not a set of functions forms the components of a tensor. The direct method is to see if they satisfy the tensor transformation equation (15.2). In practice a simpler test is provided by the **quotient law** which states that n^p functions of x^i form the components of a tensor of order p (whose contravariant and covariant character may be determined readily), provided that an inner product of these functions with an arbitrary tensor is itself a tensor. It will be sufficient to give the proof for the following particular case.

The set of n^3 functions T^{ijk} forms the components of a tensor of the type indicated by its indices if

$$T^{ijk} \, S^p_{\ ij} = R^{pk} \, ,$$

provided $S^p_{\ ij}$ is an arbitrary tensor and R^{pk} is a tensor.

Referred to a system of coordinates $x^{i'}$, the transformed quantities, satisfy

$$T^{ijk'} \, S^p_{\ ij}{}' = R^{pk'} \quad .$$

Using (15.2) gives

$$T^{ijk'} \, \frac{\partial x^{p'}}{\partial x^l} \frac{\partial x^m}{\partial x^{i'}} \frac{\partial x^n}{\partial x^{j'}} S^l_{\ mn} = \frac{\partial x^{p'}}{\partial x^q} \frac{\partial x^{k'}}{\partial x^r} R^{qr}$$

$$= \frac{\partial x^{p'}}{\partial x^q} \frac{\partial x^{k'}}{\partial x^r} T^{ijr} \, S^q_{\ ij} \, .$$

With a change of dummy indices, this leads to

$$\frac{\partial x^{p'}}{\partial x^l} \left\{ T^{ijk'} \, \frac{\partial x^m}{\partial x^{i'}} \frac{\partial x^n}{\partial x^{j'}} - T^{mnr} \frac{\partial x^{k'}}{\partial x^r} \right\} S^l_{\ mn} = 0 \, .$$

On multiplying by $\partial x^t/\partial x^{p'}$ and summing over p' from 1 to n (that is, on inner multiplication by $\partial x^t/\partial x^{p'}$), this becomes

$$\left\{ T^{ijk'} \frac{\partial x^m}{\partial x^{i'}} \frac{\partial x^n}{\partial x^{j'}} - T^{mnr} \frac{\partial x^{k'}}{\partial x^r} \right\} S^t_{mn} = 0 \ . \tag{15.3}$$

However, S^t_{mn} is an arbitrary tensor, and so the quantity in brackets must be identically zero, that is

$$T^{ijk'} \frac{\partial x^m}{\partial x^{i'}} \frac{\partial x^n}{\partial x^{j'}} = T^{mnr} \frac{\partial x^{k'}}{\partial x^r} \ .$$

Inner multiplication by $\dfrac{\partial x^{t'}}{\partial x^m} \dfrac{\partial x^{u'}}{\partial x^n}$ yields

$$T^{tuk'} = \frac{\partial x^{t'}}{\partial x^m} \frac{\partial x^{u'}}{\partial x^n} \frac{\partial x^{k'}}{\partial x^r} T^{mnr} \ ,$$

and so T^{mnr} is a third-order tensor and is contravariant in all its indices.

In this proof, it is vital that the tensor S^t_{mn} be arbitrary and not possess any symmetric or skew-symmetric properties. If this is the case, it may be arranged for only one of its components to differ from zero. In fact, each component may be selected in turn as the one that does not vanish. Hence, the expression in brackets in (15.3) must be identically zero. However, if S^t_{mn} is symmetric in m and n, the deduction does not follow as above. In this case, the deduction from (15.3) is

$$T^{ijk'} \frac{\partial x^m}{\partial x^{i'}} \frac{\partial x^n}{\partial x^{j'}} + T^{ijk'} \frac{\partial x^n}{\partial x^{i'}} \frac{\partial x^m}{\partial x^{j'}} = T^{mnr} \frac{\partial x^{k'}}{\partial x^r} + T^{nmr} \frac{\partial x^{k'}}{\partial x^r}$$

or

$$(T^{ijk'} + T^{jik'}) \frac{\partial x^m}{\partial x^{i'}} \frac{\partial x^n}{\partial x^{j'}} = (T^{mnr} + T^{nmr}) \frac{\partial x^{k'}}{\partial x^r}$$

where some dummy indices have been changed. Inner multiplication by

$$\frac{\partial x^{t'}}{\partial x^m} \frac{\partial x^{u'}}{\partial x^n}$$

then shows that $(T^{mnr} + T^{nmr})$ is a contravariant tensor of the third order.

It is apparent, therefore, that great care must be exercised when applying this test.

15.6 SOME RESULTS IN TENSOR CALCULUS

Firstly, the concept of distance will be introduced into the n-dimensional space. If the distance $\mathrm{d}s$ between the neighbouring points with coordinates x^i and $x^i + \mathrm{d}x^i$ is given by the quadratic differential form

$$\mathrm{d}s^2 = g_{ij} \, \mathrm{d}x^i \, \mathrm{d}x^j$$

where the g_{ij} are functions of x^i subject to the restriction

$$g = |g_{ij}| \neq 0$$

the space is termed a **Riemann space**. It is postulated also that the distance between two neighbouring points is independent of the coordinate system so that ds is an invariant. Application of the quotient law shows that $(g_{ij} + g_{ji})$ is a second-order covariant tensor. Also

$$g_{ij} = \tfrac{1}{2}(g_{ij} + g_{ji}) + \tfrac{1}{2}(g_{ij} - g_{ji}) \, .$$

However, the term $\tfrac{1}{2}(g_{ij} - g_{ji})\mathrm{d}x^i\mathrm{d}x^j$ is seen to make no contribution to ds^2 and so there is no loss of generality in assuming g_{ij} to be symmetric. Thus g_{ij} is a second-order covariant symmetric tensor called the **metric** (or **fundamental**) **tensor** of the Riemann space. The quadratic form $g_{ij}\,\mathrm{d}x^i\mathrm{d}x^j$ is called the **metric**.

In a three-dimensional Euclidean space referred to a system of rectangular Cartesian axes, the line element is

$$\mathrm{d}s^2 = (\mathrm{d}x^1)^2 + (\mathrm{d}x^2)^2 + (\mathrm{d}x^3)^2 = \delta_{ij}\mathrm{d}x^i\mathrm{d}x^j$$

where $i,j = 1,2,3$. Hence, in this case, the metric tensor is

$$g_{ij} = \delta_{ij} \, .$$

Now, if $|g_{ij}| = g$ once again and Δ^{ij} denotes the cofactor of g_{ij}, then

$$g_{ik}\,\Delta^{kj} = \delta^j_{\ i}\, g \, ,$$

and so Δ^{ij}/g is the inverse of g_{ij} and will be denoted by g^{ij} so that

$$g_{ik}\,g^{kj} = \delta^j_{\ i} \, .$$

The inner product of the metric tensor g_{ij} and the contravariant vector A^j is the covariant vector $g_{ij}\,A^j$ which is said to be **associate** to A^j. Hence, define

$$A_i = g_{ij}\,A^j$$

then

$$g^{ij}A_j = g^{ij}g_{jk}A^k = \delta^i_{\ k}A^k = A^i \, .$$

This process of association is often termed 'raising the subscript' or 'lowering the superscript.' A free index may be raised or lowered throughout a tensor equation by mutliplying throughout and contracting with the appropriate metric tensor.

So far in this short discussion of tensors, no mention has been made of differentiation of tensors. Consider the contravariant vector v^i and its transformation law

$$v^{i'} = \frac{\partial x^{i'}}{\partial x^j}\,v^j \, .$$

Differentiating with respect to $x^{k'}$ yields

$$\frac{\partial v^{i'}}{\partial x^{k'}} = \frac{\partial v^j}{\partial x^l}\frac{\partial x^l}{\partial x^{k'}}\frac{\partial x^{i'}}{\partial x^j} + v^j\frac{\partial^2 x^{i'}}{\partial x^l \partial x^j}\frac{\partial x^l}{\partial x^{k'}},$$

and so it is seen that the partial derivative $\partial v^j/\partial x^l$ does not transform as a tensor under all transformations. However, under linear transformations it would transform as a tensor since, under such transformations, $\partial^2 x^{i'}/\partial x^l \partial x^j$ would be zero.

It would seem desirable if expressions could be evolved which involve the derivatives of a tensor but which are the components of a tensor also. To do this, it is necessary to introduce two functions formed from the metric tensor g_{ij}. These are the **Christoffel symbols** of the first and second kinds and are defined by

$$[i\,j,k] = \frac{1}{2}\left(\frac{\partial g_{ik}}{\partial x^j} + \frac{\partial g_{jk}}{\partial x^i} - \frac{\partial g_{ij}}{\partial x^k}\right)$$

and

$$\Gamma^p_{\ ij} = g^{pk}\,[i\,j,k]$$

respectively.

In order to find the transformation laws for these two functions note that, since it is covariant, the metric tensor transforms according to

$$g_{ij}{}' = \frac{\partial x^r}{\partial x^{i'}}\frac{\partial x^s}{\partial x^{j'}}g_{rs}.$$

Differentiating this equation with respect to $x^{k'}$ gives

$$g_{ij,k}' = \frac{\partial g_{ij}{}'}{\partial x^{k'}} = \left(\frac{\partial^2 x^r}{\partial x^{k'}\partial x^{i'}}\frac{\partial x^s}{\partial x^{j'}} + \frac{\partial x^s}{\partial x^{i'}}\frac{\partial^2 x^r}{\partial x^{k'}\partial x^{j'}}\right)g_{rs}$$

$$+ \frac{\partial x^r}{\partial x^{i'}}\frac{\partial x^s}{\partial x^{j'}}\frac{\partial x^t}{\partial x^{k'}}g_{rs,t}$$

where a comma has been used to denote a partial derivative as shown and where the fact that $g_{rs} = g_{sr}$ has been used.

Two similar equations for $g_{jk,i}$ and $g_{ki,j}$ are obtained by cyclic interchange of the indices i, j and k, then

$$[i\,j,k]' = \frac{1}{2}(g_{jk,i}' + g_{ki,j}' - g_{ij,k}')$$

$$= [r\,s,t]\frac{\partial x^r}{\partial x^{i'}}\frac{\partial x^s}{\partial x^{j'}}\frac{\partial x^t}{\partial x^{k'}} + \frac{\partial^2 x^r}{\partial x^{i'}\partial x^{j'}}\frac{\partial x^s}{\partial x^{k'}}g_{rs}.$$

Also, the contravariant metric tensor transforms according to

$$g^{pk'} = \frac{\partial x^{p'}}{\partial x^u}\frac{\partial x^{k'}}{\partial x^v}g^{uv}$$

and so, $\quad \Gamma^p{}_{ij}' = g^{pk'}[i\,j,k]'$

$$= \Gamma^u{}_{rs}\frac{\partial x^{p'}}{\partial x^u}\frac{\partial x^r}{\partial x^{i'}}\frac{\partial x^s}{\partial x^{j'}} + \frac{\partial x^{p'}}{\partial x^r}\frac{\partial^2 x^r}{\partial x^{i'}\partial x^{j'}}\;.$$

Clearly, the Christoffel symbols do not transform as tensors except in the special case of linear transformations of coordinates. Inner multiplication of the final equation above by $\partial x^a/\partial x^{p'}$ yields

$$\frac{\partial^2 x^a}{\partial x^{i'}\partial x^{j'}} = \Gamma^p{}_{ij}'\frac{\partial x^a}{\partial x^{p'}} - \Gamma^a{}_{rs}\frac{\partial x^r}{\partial x^{i'}}\frac{\partial x^s}{\partial x^{j'}} \tag{15.4}$$

Now consider the transformation law for a covariant vector:

$$v_i' = v_a\frac{\partial x^a}{\partial x^{i'}}\;.$$

Differentiating this with respect to $x^{j'}$ gives

$$v_{i,j}' = v_{a,b}\frac{\partial x^a}{\partial x^{i'}}\frac{\partial x^b}{\partial x^{j'}} + v_a\frac{\partial^2 x^a}{\partial x^{j'}\partial x^{i'}}\;.$$

Using (15.4) to eliminate the second-order partial derivative, it is found that

$$v_{i,j}' = v_{a,b}\frac{\partial x^a}{\partial x^{i'}}\frac{\partial x^b}{\partial x^{j'}} + v_a\Gamma^p{}_{ij}'\frac{\partial x^a}{\partial x^{p'}} - v_a\Gamma^a{}_{rs}\frac{\partial x^r}{\partial x^{i'}}\frac{\partial x^s}{\partial x^{j'}}$$

which, after some relabelling of dummy indices, may be rearranged to give

$$v_{i,j}' - \Gamma^p{}_{ij}'v_p' = (v_{a,b} - \Gamma^q{}_{ab}v_q)\frac{\partial x^a}{\partial x^{i'}}\frac{\partial x^b}{\partial x^{j'}}\;.$$

Defining

$$v_{a;b} = v_{a,b} - \Gamma^q{}_{ab}v_q$$

it follows that the above equation may be written

$$v_{i;j}' = v_{a;b}\frac{\partial x^a}{\partial x^{i'}}\frac{\partial x^b}{\partial x^{j'}}$$

and $v_{a;b}$ is a second-order covariant tensor called the **covariant derivative** of v_a with respect to x^b.

In a similar manner, the covariant derivative of the contravariant vector v^i is seen to be given by

$$v^i{}_{;j} = v^i{}_{,j} + \Gamma^i{}_{pj}v^p\;,$$

and the covariant derivatives of higher-order tensors may be found in an analogous manner; for example

$$v_{ij;k} = v_{ij,k} - \Gamma^p_{jk} v_{ip} - \Gamma^p_{ik} v_{jp}$$

$$v^i_{j;k} = v^i_{j,k} - \Gamma^p_{jk} v^i_p + \Gamma^i_{pk} v^p_j$$

and so on.

Hence, it has proved possible to build up expressions which involve the derivatives of a tensor but which transform like tensors.

15.7 CARTESIAN TENSORS

Suppose attention is restricted now to a three-dimensional Euclidean space in which a right-handed system of rectangular Cartesian coordinates x_i ($i = 1,2,3$) has been chosen. As has been shown already, in this case,

$$ds^2 = \delta_{ij}\, dx_i\, dx_j\, .$$

The linear equations

$$x_i' = a_{ij} x_j + b_i\, , \, (i,j = 1,2,3) \tag{15.5}$$

define a transformation to a new coordinate system x_i'. If $\mathbf{A} = (a_{ij})$ is a third-order square matrix and $\mathbf{x}'$, $\mathbf{x}$ and $\mathbf{b}$ are column matrices with elements x_i', x_i and b_i ($i = 1,2,3$) respectively, these equations could be written in matrix form as

$$\mathbf{x}' = \mathbf{A}\mathbf{x} + \mathbf{b}\, .$$

The necessary and sufficient condition for the x_i' to form a rectangular Cartesian coordinate system is

$$ds^2 = dx_i'\, dx_i' = a_{ij}\, a_{ik}\, dx_j\, dx_k = \delta_{jk}\, dx_j\, dx_k\, ,$$

that is

$$(a_{ij}\, a_{ik} - \delta_{jk}) dx_j\, dx_k = 0$$

for all dx_j, and so

$$a_{ij}\, a_{ik} = \delta_{jk}\, . \tag{15.6}$$

In terms of matrices, this condition may be written

$$\mathbf{A}^T \mathbf{A} = \mathbf{I}$$

where $\mathbf{I}$ is the third-order unit matrix.

Hence, $\mathbf{A} = (a_{ij})$ is an orthogonal matrix, and the above transformation is seen to be a combination of two transformations:

(i) $x_i' = x_i + b_i$, which defines a translation to new parallel axes.
and
(ii) $x_i^* = a_{ij}\, x_j$, which since it is subject to the condition (15.6), defines an orthogonal transformation.

Inner multiplication of (15.5) by a_{ik} gives

$$x_k = a_{ik} x_i' - a_{ik} b_i$$

and so

$$\frac{\partial x_i'}{\partial x_j} = \frac{\partial x_j}{\partial x_i'} = a_{ij}. \tag{15.7}$$

Hence, if Cartesian coordinates are used in a Euclidean space, the distinction between contravariance and covariance is seen to disappear. This result has been anticipated in this section by writing all indices as subscripts.

A **Cartesian tensor** of order n in a three-dimensional Euclidean space may be defined as a set of 3^n quantities which transform according to equation (15.2) when the coordinates undergo a positive ($|\mathbf{A}| = 1$) orthogonal transformation. This is a less stringent condition than that imposed on a tensor, and it may be noted that all tensors are Cartesian tensors, but Cartesian tensors are not necessarily tensors in the normal sense. By using equations (15.2) and (15.7), it follows that $C_{i_1 i_2 \dots i_n}$ is a Cartesian tensor of order n if the transformed quantities satisfy

$$C'_{i_1 i_2 \dots i_n} = a_{i_1 j_1} a_{i_2 j_2} \dots a_{i_n j_n} C_{j_1 j_2 \dots j_n}$$

on change of the coordinates by the positive orthogonal transformation $x_i' = a_{ij} x_j$.

The use of this latter equation, instead of (15.2), shows that, as might be expected, the quotient law applies to Cartesian tensors. Also for a Euclidean space referred to a system of rectangular Cartesian axes, the metric tensor is the Kronecker delta δ_{ij} and so, for this case, all the Christoffel symbols are zero. Hence, for Cartesian tensors, the covariant derivatives reduce to the more familiar partial derivatives. It should be noted that not all the Christoffel symbols vanish in a Euclidean space referred, for example, to spherical polar coordinates.

As stated at the beginning of the chapter, tensors proved to be the ideal tool for the mathematical formulation of the General Theory of Relativity, while the simple Cartesian tensors occur in continuum mechanics, particularly in the theory of elasticity. Hence, tensors deserved to be mentioned in a text on mathematical methods. However, the present chapter is but a brief introduction to the subject and, for more details of both tensor algebra and tensor calculus, the interested reader should consult the specialist books on tensors.

EXERCISES 15

(1) If δ^i_j is the Kronecker delta, show that

(i) $\qquad \delta^i_j \delta^j_k = \delta^i_k$,

(ii) $\delta^i{}_i = n$,

(iii) $\dfrac{\partial x^k}{\partial x^{i'}} \dfrac{\partial x^{i'}}{\partial x^j} = \delta^k{}_j$,

(iv) $\delta^i{}_j$ is a mixed tensor of the second order.

(2) If A^i is an arbitrary contravariant vector and $C_{ij} A^i A^j$ is an invariant, show that $(C_{ij} + C_{ji})$ is a second-order covariant tensor.

(3) Show that $g_{ik,j} = [ij,k] + [kj,i]$. Using this result, together with the equation

$$g_{ij} g^{ik} = \delta^k{}_j ,$$

show that

$$\Gamma^i{}_{ij} = \frac{\partial}{\partial x^j} \{\log \sqrt{g}\}$$

where g is positive.

(4) Prove that $g^{rs}{}_{;t} = 0$.

(5) Suppose $ds^2 = (dx^1)^2 + (dx^2)^2 + dx^3)^2$. Take x^1 and x^2 as coordinates in the subspace $x^3 = f(x^1, x^2)$ and show that, in this subspace,

$$g_{rs} = \delta_{rs} + f_r f_s$$

where $f_r = \partial f/\partial x^r$ and $r,s = 1,2$.
    Also show that

$$g^{rs} = \delta_{rs} - \frac{f_r f_s}{1 + f_t f_t} \quad \text{and} \quad \Gamma^r{}_{st} = \frac{f_r f_{st}}{1 + f_u f_u} .$$

Answers to Exercises

EXERCISES 1

(1) $5(x - 3)^4$, $2x(1 - x)(1 - 2x)$, $-\frac{1}{2}(4 + x^2)/\sqrt{\{x^3(4 - x^2)\}}$

(2) $-\tan^2 x$, $(\cos\sqrt{x})/2\sqrt{x}$, $(\sin\sqrt{x} - \frac{1}{2}\sqrt{x}\cos\sqrt{x})/\sin^2\sqrt{x}$

(3) $3\sin^2 x\cos 4x$, $3\cos 2x/\cos^4 x$, $3\tan^2 3x(1 + 2\cos^3 3x)$

(4) $nx^{n-1}(a^2 - x^2)^{n-1}(a^2 - 3x^2)$, $n(a - b)(a - x)^{n-1}/(b - x)^{n+1}$,

$$2x(3 - 5x + 3x^2)/\sqrt{(3 - 4x + 2x^2)}$$

(5) $(-a)^n\, 2^{1/2}\, e^{-ax}\cos(ax - \frac{1}{4}n\pi)$

(6) $e^x(x^2 + 20x + 90)$

(10) 1 , $-\frac{1}{2}$

(11) 0 , $\frac{3}{5}$

(12) (a)   maximum $(0,9)$, minima $(\pm\sqrt{5}\,, -16)$, points of inflexion

$$\left(\pm\sqrt{\frac{5}{3}}\,, -\frac{44}{9}\right)\text{ , concave up if } |x| > \sqrt{\frac{5}{3}}\text{ ; down if } |x| < \sqrt{\frac{5}{3}}\text{ ;}$$

(b)   maximum $(0,1)$, minima $(\pm 1,0)$, points of inflexion

$$\left(\pm\sqrt{\frac{1}{3}},\frac{4}{9}\right)\text{ , concave up if } x > \sqrt{\frac{1}{3}}\text{ ; down if } x < \sqrt{\frac{1}{3}}\text{ .}$$

EXERCISES 2

(1) $10 + 3j$, $2 + 2j$, $-1 + j$, $5 - 5j$.

(3) $-j$, $(33 - 13j)/37$, j .

(5) $(8 + 16j)/5$.

(6) 1 .

(7) (a) $x = 1$,   (b) $4x + 10y = 21$,

(c)   circle centre a , radius k ,

(d)   circle centre $-p/3$, radius $2|p|/3$.

(8) $\frac{1}{2}(\pm\sqrt{3}\pm j)$, $\pm j$.

(9) $\frac{1}{2}, -\frac{1}{4}, -(1 \pm 3j)/10$.

(10) -8 .

(11) $\sin 3\theta = 3\sin\theta - 4\sin^3\theta$,

   $\cos 3\theta = 4\cos^3\theta - 3\cos\theta$.

EXERCISES 3

(1) $\frac{1}{4}x^2 + \frac{3}{4}x + \frac{9}{8}\log(2x - 3)$, $2x + 11 \log(x - 4)$,

$$-\frac{1}{6}x^3 - \frac{1}{8}ax^2 - \frac{1}{8}a^2x - \frac{1}{16}a^3 \log(a - 2x) .$$

(2) $\frac{1}{2}\log(x^2 - 1)$, $\frac{7}{3}\log[(3 + x)/(3 - x)] - x$,

$$\frac{1}{3}x^3 + 5x + \frac{5\sqrt{5}}{2} \log [(x - \sqrt{5})/(x + \sqrt{5})]$$

(3) $\frac{1}{3}\tan^{-1}\frac{1}{3}(x + 1)$, $\dfrac{1}{2\sqrt{2}} \log [(x - 1 - \sqrt{2})/(x - 1 + \sqrt{2})]$,

   $x - 2\tan^{-1}(x + 1)$, $\frac{1}{3}x^3 - 7x + 7\sqrt{7} \tan^{-1} (x/\sqrt{7})$.

(4) $-\frac{1}{4}\log(a^4 - x^4)$, $\frac{1}{6}\log(1 + 3 \sin^2 x)$,

   $\log \cosh x$, $\log(\log x)$.

(5) $\frac{1}{2}\log(x^2 + 9) + \frac{1}{3}\tan^{-1}\frac{1}{3}x$,

   $3\log(x^2 + 4x + 13) - 3\tan^{-1}\frac{1}{3}(x + 2)$,

$$x - \log(x^2 + x + 1) + \frac{2}{\sqrt{3}} \tan^{-1}\left(\frac{2x + 1}{\sqrt{3}}\right) .$$

(6) $\log(x - 1) - \log x + \dfrac{1}{x}$.

   $\frac{1}{6}\log(x - 1) + \frac{1}{2}\log(x + 1) - \frac{1}{6}\log(2x + 1)$,

   $\frac{1}{6}\log\{(x^2 - 1)/(x^2 + 2)\}$,

   $\frac{1}{4}\log\{(1 + x)/(1 - x)\} - \frac{1}{2}\tan^{-1}x$.

(7) $\sinh^{-1}\frac{1}{3}(x + 1)$, $\cosh^{-1}(2x + 1)$, $\dfrac{1}{\sqrt{2}} \sin^{-1}\frac{1}{3}(4x - 3)$.

(8) $(x^2 + 5)^{1/2}$, $-(4 - 3x - x^2)^{1/2} - \dfrac{3}{2} \sin^{-1}\left(\dfrac{2x + 3}{5}\right)$,

$$(x^2 + 2x)^{1/2} + \cosh^{-1}(x + 1) .$$

(9) $-\frac{1}{3}\operatorname{cosec}^3x$, $-\frac{1}{3}\log(a^3 - x^3)$, $\frac{1}{3}(1 + \log x)^3$, $-[b(a - b\cos x)]^{-1}$.

(10) $-\frac{2}{3}(x + 2)(1 - x)^{\frac{1}{2}}$,

$\dfrac{2}{105}(ax + b)^{\frac{3}{2}}(15a^2x^2 - 12abx + 8b^2)/a^3$,

$\sec^{-1}x$, $\frac{1}{6}\log\{x^2/(2x^2 + 3)\}$.

(11) $-\frac{1}{2}\log\cos 2x$, $\sin x - \frac{1}{3}\sin^3 x$,

$\dfrac{1}{3}\tan^3 x - \tan x + x$, $\dfrac{1}{8}x - \dfrac{1}{32}\sin 4x$,

$\log\tan(\frac{1}{4}\pi + \frac{1}{2}x) - \operatorname{cosec} x$, $-\frac{1}{2}\log\cos x$,

$\frac{2}{3}\sqrt{3}\tan^{-1}\{(2\tan\frac{1}{2}x + 1)/\sqrt{3}\}$.

(12) $\frac{1}{2}x(9 - x^2)^{\frac{1}{2}} + \frac{9}{2}\sin^{-1}\frac{1}{3}x$, $\frac{1}{2}x(9 + x^2)^{\frac{1}{2}} - \frac{9}{2}\sinh^{-1}\frac{1}{3}x$,

$\sin^{-1}(x - 1)^{\frac{1}{2}} - (3x - 2 - x^2)^{\frac{1}{2}}$,

$\frac{1}{2}\tan^{-1}(x + 2) + \frac{1}{2}(x + 2)/(x^2 + 4x + 5)$.

(13) $\frac{1}{5}x^5(\log x - \frac{1}{5})$, $\frac{1}{4}(x^4 - 1)\tan^{-1}x + \frac{1}{4}x - \frac{1}{12}x^3$,

$ax\sinh(x/a) - a^2\cosh(x/a)$, $-(x^2 + 2x + 2)e^{-x}$.

(14) $\frac{1}{2}x(32 + 2x^2)^{\frac{1}{2}} + 8\sqrt{2}\sinh^{-1}\frac{1}{4}x$,

$\dfrac{1}{13}e^{3x}(2\sin 2x + 3\cos 2x)$,

$\frac{1}{2}(\sinh x\sin x - \cosh x\cos x)$,

$Le^{-Rt/L}\{pL\sin(pt + \varepsilon) - R\cos(pt + \varepsilon)\}/(R^2 + p^2L^2)$.

(15) $e^{ax}(x^3a^3 - 3x^2a^2 + 6xa - 6)/a^4$,

$\frac{1}{6}x(3 - 2x^2)\cos 2x + \frac{1}{4}(2x^2 - 1)\sin 2x$,

$\dfrac{1}{27}x^3\{9(\log x)^2 - 6\log x + 2\}$,

$(x^2 + 2)\sinh x - 2x\cosh x$.

(16) $204\frac{3}{5}$, 2 , $a^{n+1}(2^{n+1} - 1)/(n + 1)$.

(17) 1 , $\pi/2$, $\pi/4$.

(18) $\frac{1}{5}(e^{2\pi} + 1)$, $e - 2$.

(19) $a(1 - \pi/2)$, $\dfrac{10}{3} - 8\log\dfrac{3}{2}$.

(20) $\alpha/2\sin\alpha$, $\frac{1}{8}\pi - \frac{1}{2}\tan^{-1}\frac{1}{2}$.

(21) $4/35$, $128\sqrt{2}/105$.

(22) 0 , 0 .

(23) $\frac{1}{2}$, does not exist , $\pi/2$.

(24) $\frac{1}{2}$, a , does not exist.

(25)   log2 , does not exist , π .

(26) $3\pi/256$, $63\pi/512$, $5\pi/64$.

(27) $2a^5/15$, $(12a^4)^{-1}$, $a^7/140$.

(28) $9\pi/8$, $a\pi$, π .

EXERCISES 4

(1) $\dfrac{1}{4} - \dfrac{(n+3)}{2(n+1)(n+2)}$.

(2)   convergent ; divergent ; convergent .

(6)   (a) $|x| > \frac{1}{2}(3 + \sqrt{5})$ and $|x| < \frac{1}{2}(3 - \sqrt{5})$,

   (b) $\frac{1}{2}(3 - \sqrt{5}) < |x| < \frac{1}{2}(3 + \sqrt{5})$.

EXERCISES 5

(1) $\begin{pmatrix} 5 & -8 & 1 \\ 4 & 0 & 0 \end{pmatrix}, \begin{pmatrix} 1 & 6 & 1 \\ -2 & 6 & -10 \end{pmatrix}, \begin{pmatrix} 5 & 4 \\ -8 & 0 \\ 1 & 0 \end{pmatrix}, A$.

(2) $\begin{pmatrix} 1 & 2\frac{1}{2} & 5\frac{1}{2} \\ 2\frac{1}{2} & 4 & 7\frac{1}{2} \\ 5\frac{1}{2} & 7\frac{1}{2} & 9 \end{pmatrix} + \begin{pmatrix} 0 & -\frac{1}{2} & \frac{1}{2} \\ \frac{1}{2} & 0 & -\frac{1}{2} \\ -\frac{1}{2} & \frac{1}{2} & 0 \end{pmatrix}$.

(3) $\begin{pmatrix} 10 & 13 \\ 11 & 14 \end{pmatrix}, \begin{pmatrix} 7 & 3 & 8 \\ 11 & 4 & 9 \\ 12 & 5 & 13 \end{pmatrix}$.

(4) $\begin{pmatrix} 9 & 20 \\ 4 & 16 \\ -3 & 12 \end{pmatrix}$, not defined, $\begin{pmatrix} 9 & 4 & -3 \\ 20 & 16 & 12 \end{pmatrix} = (AB)^{\mathrm{T}}$.

(5) -32 , 180 , -468 .

(7) $x_1 = -1$, $x_2 = -3$, $x_3 = 2$.

(8) $x_1 = 230/43$, $x_2 = 150/43$, $x_3 = 140/43$.

(9) $\begin{pmatrix} -2 & 0 & 1 \\ -5 & -1 & 0 \\ 0 & -1 & -3 \end{pmatrix}$, $\begin{pmatrix} \frac{1}{2} & -\frac{1}{10} & \frac{1}{2} \\ 0 & \frac{1}{5} & 0 \\ -\frac{1}{2} & \frac{3}{10} & -\frac{3}{2} \end{pmatrix}$, $\frac{1}{4}\begin{pmatrix} -16 & 4 & 4 & 0 \\ -31 & 8 & 6 & 1 \\ 34 & -8 & -8 & 2 \\ -14 & 4 & 4 & -2 \end{pmatrix}$

(10) $x_1 = -3$, $x_2 = 2$, $x_3 = 1$.

(11) $x_1 = 26\frac{1}{2}$, $x_2 = 23$, $x_3 = -3$.

(12) $x_1 = 3$, $x_2 = 1$, $x_3 = 2$.

(13) (i) $\lambda_1 = 1$, $x_1 = \begin{pmatrix} 2 \\ -1 \end{pmatrix}$; $\lambda_2 = 4$, $x_2 = \begin{pmatrix} 1 \\ 1 \end{pmatrix}$,

(ii) $\lambda_1 = 3$, $x_1 = \begin{pmatrix} 2 \\ 1 \end{pmatrix}$; $\lambda_2 = 2$, $x_2 = \begin{pmatrix} 1 \\ 1 \end{pmatrix}$,

(iii) $\lambda_1 = 2$, $x_1 = \begin{pmatrix} 3 \\ -2 \end{pmatrix}$; $\lambda_2 = 7 + 5j$, $x_2 = \begin{pmatrix} 1 \\ 1 \end{pmatrix}$,

(iv) $\lambda_1 = 1$, $x_1 = \begin{pmatrix} 1 \\ 0 \\ 0 \end{pmatrix}$; $\lambda_2 = 2$, $x_2 = \begin{pmatrix} 4 \\ 1 \\ 0 \end{pmatrix}$;

$$\lambda_3 = 3 , x_3 = \begin{pmatrix} 29 \\ 12 \\ 2 \end{pmatrix} .$$

(14) $\begin{pmatrix} a - b & 0 & 0 \\ 0 & a - b & 0 \\ 0 & 0 & a + 2b \end{pmatrix}$.

(15) $\begin{pmatrix} 0 & 0 & 0 \\ 0 & 3 & 0 \\ 0 & 0 & -6 \end{pmatrix}$.

(16) Equation referred to its principal axes is

$$3y_1{}^2 + 2y_2{}^2 = 1$$

which is the equation of an ellipse.

(17) Equation referred to its principal axes is

$$2y_1{}^2 + y_2{}^2 - y_3{}^2 = 1$$

which is the equation of an hyperboloid of one sheet.

EXERCISES 6

(4)   The required perpendicular distance is

$$|\mathbf{r} - \mathbf{a}| = p - \mathbf{a} \cdot \hat{\mathbf{u}}$$

(9)   (i) (2,4,8) ;   (ii) $(-8,-24,14)$;

(iii), (iv) 19 ;   (v) 1 .

(10)   10° 40′

(11) $\lambda\mathbf{k}$,   where λ is an arbitrary constant.

(12)   (i) 41 ;   (ii) -36 ;   (iii) $(0,-15,-10)$;

(iv) $(195,-10,15)$;   (v) 0 .

Angle between $\mathbf{a}$ and $\mathbf{b}$ is $\cos^{-1}(-7/\sqrt{17.22})$,

Angle between $\mathbf{a}$ and $\mathbf{b} \times \mathbf{c}$ is $\pi/2$.

(13) $\frac{1}{2}\sqrt{82}$.

(14)   4/3 .

(17) mv_i ; $u_i v_i$; $\varepsilon_{ijk}\, u_i v_j w_k$.

(18)   (i) $(\mathbf{a} \cdot \mathbf{b})(\mathbf{c} \cdot \mathbf{d})$;   (ii) 0 ;   (iii) $(\mathbf{b} \times \mathbf{a})_m$;

(iv) $2(\mathbf{c} \cdot \mathbf{d})(\mathbf{a} \times \mathbf{b})_i$

(21) $(1,0,0)$, $\left(0, -\dfrac{5}{\sqrt{29}}, -\dfrac{2}{\sqrt{29}}\right)$, $\left(0, \dfrac{2}{\sqrt{29}}, -\dfrac{5}{\sqrt{29}}\right)$.

(23) $\mathbf{v} \cdot \left(\dfrac{d\mathbf{v}}{dt} \times \dfrac{d^3\mathbf{v}}{dt^3}\right)$.

EXERCISES 7

(1) $4t^3$.

(2)   (a) -1 ,   (b) $(y^2 x^2 + y^2 + 2xy^2 - 3x^3 + 4x^3 y)/x^2 y^2$.

(3)   (a) $\partial u/\partial x = y^{-1}\sec^2(x/y)$, $\partial u/\partial y = -\dfrac{x}{y^2}\sec^2(x/y)$,

(b) $\partial f/\partial r = 2r\sin^2\theta + 3r^2$, $\dfrac{\partial f}{\partial \theta} = 2r^2\sin\theta\cos\theta$,

(c) $\partial u/\partial r = 3r^2 + t - 1$, $\partial u/\partial s = 2st$, $\partial u/\partial t = s^2 + r - 3$,

(d) $\partial\phi/\partial p = 2p\log q\exp(p^2\log q)$, $\dfrac{\partial\phi}{\partial q} = p^2 q^{-1}\exp(p^2\log q)$.

(8)　$\partial u/\partial t = 4t^3(\sin^2\theta + 2\cos^2\theta\sin\theta + \cos^4\theta)$,

　　　$\partial u/\partial\theta = 2t^4(\cos\theta\sin\theta + \cos^3\theta - 2\sin\theta\cos^3\theta - 2\sin^2\theta\cos\theta)$.

(9)　$\dfrac{1}{16}\left(3\dfrac{\partial^2 u}{\partial r^2} - \dfrac{\partial^2 u}{\partial s^2} + 2\dfrac{\partial^2 u}{\partial s\partial r}\right)$.

(12)　$\pi^2 y + \frac{1}{2}4\pi (x - \pi)y + \cdots$

(13)　$9 + 6(x + 1) - 5(y + 3) - 3(x + 1)^2 + (y + 3)^2$

　　　　　$-2(x + 1)(y + 3) + (x + 1)^2(y + 3)$.

(14)　$87 + (54h_1 + 81h_2) + \dfrac{1}{2!}(90h_1{}^2 - 36h_1h_2 + 108h_2{}^2)$

　　　　$+ \dfrac{1}{3!}(72h_1{}^3 - 18h_1{}^2h_2 + 72h_2{}^3) + \dfrac{1}{4!}(24h_1{}^4 + 24h_2{}^4)$

(15)　$(0,0)$; $(-1,-1)$.

(16)　$(0,0)$; $(2\sqrt{2},4)$; $(-2\sqrt{2},4)$.

(17)　(a,a) , $(0,0)$.

(19)　$c^6/27$.

(20)　$x = y = z = 2s/3$.

(21)　$(\pm a,0)$; $(a/\sqrt{5} , -4a/\sqrt{5})$; $(-a/\sqrt{5} , 4a/\sqrt{5})$.

EXERCISES 8

(1)　(i)　$ye^{3x} - x^2 = $ const.

　　(ii)　$\sin x \cos y = $ const.

　　(iii)　$x^{-4}y^{-3}e^y = $ const.

　　(iv)　$y(x - 2)^{-1} = (x - 2)^2 + $ const.

　　(v)　$(y^{-3} + 1 + 2x)e^{-x} = $ const.

　　(vi)　$xy^2(y - x)^{-2} = $ const.

(2)　(i)　$Ae^{-2x} + Be^x + Ce^{-x}$

　　(ii)　$e^{-2x}(A\cos 3x + B\sin 3x)$

　　(iii)　$Ae^{2x} + Be^{-2x} + (C + Dx)e^{-3x}$

(3)　(i)　$e^x(A\cos 2x + B\sin 2x) + 5x^2 + 4x + 2$

　　(ii)　$(A + Bx + 7x^2)e^{-5x}$

　　(iii)　$A\cos 2x + B\sin 2x - \frac{1}{4}\cos 2x\log[\tan(x + \pi/4)]$

    (iv) $(A + Bx)e^{-x} + (\frac{1}{2}x^2\log x - \frac{3}{4}x^2)e^{-x}$

(4)   (i) $u = 1 + 3x^2 + \frac{3}{5}x^4 - \frac{1}{15}x^6 + \cdots$

             $v = x^{3/2}(1 + \frac{3}{8}x^2 - \frac{1.3}{8.16}x^4 + \cdots)$

    (ii) $u = 1 + 2^2x + 3^2x^2 + 4^2x^3 + \cdots$

             $v = u\log x - 2(2x + 2.3x^2 + 3.4x^3 + \cdots)$

    (iii) $u = x + 2x^2 + 3x^3 + \cdots$

             $v = u\log x + 1 + x + x^2 + \cdots$

    (iv) $a_0(1 - \frac{1}{4}x^2 - \frac{1}{12}x^3 + \cdots) + a_1(x - \frac{1}{6}x^3 - \frac{1}{24}x^4 + \cdots)$

(5)   (a) $(p - 3)^{-1}$; $2p^{-4}(3 + 2p^2 + p^3)$;

             $(p^2 + a_1p + a_2)\mathscr{L}[f] - (p + a_1)f(0) - f'(0)$.

    (b) $(1 - \cos 3x)/9$; $(3x - \sin 3x)/27$; $\dfrac{a\sin bx - b\sin ax}{ab(a^2 - b^2)}$.

(6) $(1 + y_0)e^{3x} - e^x$.

(7) $\dfrac{25}{4}e^{2x} - 40e^x + 3x^3 + \dfrac{27}{2}x^2 + \dfrac{63}{2}x + \dfrac{135}{4}$.

(8) $[(b - c)e^{bx}\sin ax + a(e^{cx} - e^{bx}\cos ax)]/[(b - c)^2 + a^2]$.

(9) $\dfrac{1}{26}(3e^x \sin 2x + 2e^{-2x} - 2e^x \cos 2x) + 2e^x(2\cos 2x - \sin 2x)$.

(10) $A(11\sin x - 11x\cos x - x^2\sin x)/8$.

EXERCISES 9

(1)   (a) 5 ,   (b) 23/3 ,   (c) 13/3 .

(2)   303 .

(3) $(2 - \pi/4 , \pi - \frac{1}{2} , 0)$.

(4) 18π .

(5) 320π .

(6)   80/3 .

EXERCISES 10

(1) $69/\sqrt{14}$; in the direction of $\nabla\phi$.

(2) $\left(\dfrac{1}{a},\dfrac{1}{b},\dfrac{1}{c}\right)\Big/\left(\dfrac{1}{a^2}+\dfrac{1}{b^2}+\dfrac{1}{c^2}\right)^{1/2}$.

(5) $7xz$; $(2y-3xy,\,2x^2,\,3yz)$.

(6)   (i) $3r\mathbf{r}$;   (ii) r^{-2} ;   (iii) $n(n+1)r^{n-2}$;   (iv) $6r^3$.

(9) $2r^{-4}$.

(10) $-(y^2\sin x + z^3x - 4y + 2z)$; $15 + 4\pi$.

(11)   (i) -8π ;   (ii) 12π .

(12) $6\pi^2 - 4\pi$.

(13) -6 .

EXERCISES 11

(1)   (a)   (i) $\dfrac{4\pi^2}{3} + 4\sum\limits_{n=1}^{\infty}\left(\dfrac{1}{n^2}\cos nx - \dfrac{\pi}{n}\sin nx\right)$

         (ii) $\dfrac{\pi^2}{3} + 4\sum\limits_{n=1}^{\infty}\dfrac{(-1)^n}{n^2}\cos nx$

    (b)   (i) $\dfrac{a(1-\cos 2\pi a)}{\pi}\left\{\dfrac{1}{2a^2} - \sum\limits_{n=1}^{\infty}\dfrac{\cos nx}{(n^2-a^2)}\right\} - \dfrac{\sin 2\pi a}{\pi}\sum\limits_{n=1}^{\infty}\dfrac{n\sin nx}{(n^2-a^2)}$

         (ii) $\dfrac{2\sin\pi a}{\pi}\sum\limits_{n=1}^{\infty}\dfrac{n(-1)^{n-1}\sin nx}{(n^2-a^2)}$

(2) $\dfrac{\pi}{2} - \sum\limits_{n=1}^{\infty}\dfrac{[1-(-1)^n]}{n}\sin nx$

(3) $\dfrac{2\pi^2}{3} + 2\sum\limits_{n=1}^{\infty}\left\{\dfrac{\cos nx}{n^2} + \left[\dfrac{(-1)^n\pi}{2n} - \dfrac{1}{\pi n^3}(1-[-1]^n)\right]\sin nx\right\}$

EXERCISES 12

(1) $\sum\limits_{r=1}^{\infty}\left[\dfrac{2}{a}\int\limits_{0}^{a}f(z)\sin\dfrac{r\pi z}{a}\,dz\right]\dfrac{\sin\dfrac{r\pi x}{a}\sinh\dfrac{r\pi(b-y)}{a}}{\sinh\dfrac{r\pi b}{a}}$

(2) $\dfrac{4l}{\pi^2}\sum\limits_{n=1}^{\infty}\dfrac{1}{n^2}\sin\left(\dfrac{n\pi}{2}\right)\sin\left(\dfrac{n\pi x}{l}\right)e^{-n\pi y/l}$

(3) $\dfrac{2u_0}{3} + \dfrac{4u_0}{\pi^2}\sum\limits_{n=1}^{\infty}\dfrac{(-1)^{n+1}}{n^2}\cos\left(\dfrac{n\pi x}{c}\right)\exp(-n^2\pi^2kt/c^2)$.

EXERCISES 13

(1) (a) $f(x) = 6P_0 - 4P_1(x) + P_2(x)$,

   (b) $f(x) = 4P_3(x) - 2P_2(x) + P_1(x) - 2P_0$.

(2) (a) $f(x) = \frac{1}{2}P_0 + \frac{3}{4}P_1(x) - \frac{7}{16}P_3(x) + \cdots$

   (b) $f(x) = \frac{1}{2}P_0 + \frac{5}{8}P_2(x) + \cdots$

(3) $f(x) = \sum\limits_{r=1}^{\infty} c_r J_0(\lambda_r x)$ where

   (a) $c_r = 2/a\lambda_r J_1(a\lambda_r)$;   (b) $c_r = \dfrac{2a}{\lambda_r J_1(a\lambda_r)}\left\{1 - \dfrac{2J_2(a\lambda_r)}{a\lambda_r J_1(a\lambda_r)}\right\}$

EXERCISES 14

(1) -4 at $z = 1$;

   $\dfrac{a}{(a-b)(a-c)}, \dfrac{b}{(b-a)(b-c)}, \dfrac{c}{(c-a)(c-b)}$ at $z = a, b, c$;

   $\frac{1}{2}$ at $z = 0$; -5 , 9 at $z = -1$, -2 ;

   $1, -1$ at $z = 1,0$; 1 at $z = n\pi$, $(n = 0,\pm 1, \ldots)$;

   0 at $z = 0$; $-\dfrac{1}{16}e^{-1\pm j}(3 \pm 2j)$ at $z = -1 \pm j$.

(2) 0 ; $-4j$; $-4j \sinh\frac{1}{2}$; $-16\pi j/9$.

(3) $2\pi/(1 - p^2)$, $\pi/2$; $7\pi/50$;

   $\pi/2\sqrt{2}$; $\pi e^{-ab}/b$; $\pi e^{-m}/2$.

Bibliography and References

Chisholm, J. S. R. and Morris, Rosa M., *Mathematical Methods in Physics*, North-Holland.

Chorlton, F., (1976), *Vector and Tensor Methods*, Ellis Horwood.

Collinson, C. D., *Introductory Vector Analysis*, Arnold.

Graham, A., (1979), *Matrix Theory and Applications for Engineers and Mathematicians*, Ellis Horwood.

Kreyszig, E., *Advanced Engineering Mathematics*, John Wiley.

Lawden, D. F., *Tensor Calculus and Relativity*, Methuen.

Phillips, E. G., *Analysis*, Cambridge.

Piaggio, H. T. H., *Differential Equations*, Bell.

Rudin, W., *Principles of Mathematical Analysis*, McGraw-Hill.

Stephenson, G., (1961), *Mathematical Methods for Science Students*, Longman.

Tall, D. O., *Functions of a Complex Variable*, Routledge and Kegan Paul.

Index